Handbook of Operations Research

MODELS AND APPLICATIONS

Handbook of Operations Research

MODELS AND APPLICATIONS

Edited by

Joseph J. Moder, Ph. D.
Department of Management Science
University of Miami

and

Salah E. Elmaghraby, Ph. D.
Graduate Program in Operations Research
North Carolina State University

VNR **VAN NOSTRAND REINHOLD COMPANY**
NEW YORK   CINCINNATI   ATLANTA   DALLAS   SAN FRANCISCO
LONDON   TORONTO   MELBOURNE

Van Nostrand Reinhold Company Regional Offices:
New York Cincinnati Atlanta Dallas San Francisco

Van Nostrand Reinhold Company International Offices:
London Toronto Melbourne

Library of Congress Catalog Card Number: 77-13402
ISBN: 0-442-24596-3

Manufactured in the United States of America

Published by Van Nostrand Reinhold Company
135 West 50th Street, New York, N.Y. 10020

Published simultaneously in Canada by Van Nostrand Reinhold Ltd.

15 14 13 12 11 10 9 8 7 6 5 4 3 2

Library of Congress Cataloging in Publication Data

Main entry under title:

Handbook of operations research.

  Includes index.
  1. Operations research. I. Moder, Joseph John, 1924–
II. Elmaghraby, Salah Eldin, 1927–
T57.6.H36   001.4′24   77-13402
ISBN 0-442-24596-3

CONTRIBUTORS

Gary E. Blau, Ph.D.
Senior Research Specialist in Mathematical Applications, Central Research at Dow Chemical Co. in Midland, Michigan.

Robert G. Brown
Consultant in Materials Management Systems, Box 332, Norwich, Vermont.

John M. Burnham, Ph.D.
Professor of Business Administration in the Division of MBA Studies at Tennessee Technological University in Cookeville, Tennessee.

Anthony J. Cantanese, Ph.D.
Dean of the School of Architecture and Urban Planning at the University of Wisconsin-Milwaukee.

Robert B. Fetter, Ph.D.
Professor in the Center for the Study of Health Services, Institution for Social and Policy Studies at Yale University, New Haven, Connecticut.

Eric G. Flamholtz, Ph.D.
Associate Professor of Accounting and Information Systems in the Graduate School of Management at the University of California, Los Angeles, California.

Richard L. Francis, Ph.D.
Professor of Industrial and Systems Engineering at the University of Florida in Gainesville, Florida.

Leonard L. Garver, Ph.D.
Senior Application Engineer in Advanced System Planning, Electric Utility Systems Engineering Department of The General Electric Co., Schenectady, New York.

Charles E. Gearing, Ph.D.
Professor and Acting Dean of Management at the State University of New York at Binghamton, New York.

Gus W. Grammas, Ph.D.
Assistant Professor of Management Science in the Graduate School of Business at Columbia University in New York, New York.

Arnoldo C. Hax, Ph.D.
Professor of Management in the Alfred P. Sloan School of Management at the Massachusetts Institute of Technology, Cambridge, Massachusetts.

David H. Hinds
Chief of Programming and Planning Support in the Office of Transportation Administration of Metropolitan Dade County, Miami, Florida.

Andrew K. S. Jardine, Ph.D.
Associate Professor, Faculty of Business Administration at the University of Windsor in Windsor, Ontario, Canada.

Richard R. Klimpel, Ph.D.
Research Manager of Mathematical Applications, Central Research at Dow Chemical Co. in Midland, Michigan.

Philip Kotler, Ph.D.
Professor of Economics (Harold T. Martin Chair) in the Graduate School of Management at Northwestern University, Evanston, Illinois.

Richard O. Mason, Ph.D.
Associate Professor of Management and Information Systems, and Assistant Dean of the Graduate School of Management at the University of California, Los Angeles, California.

Alan G. Merten, Ph.D.
Associate Professor of Management Science in the School of Business Administration at the University of Michigan in Ann Arbor, Michigan.

Alex M. Mood, Ph.D.
Professor Emeritus of Administration, Public Policy Research Organization, at the University of California in Irvine, California.

Brian F. O'Neil, Ph.D.
Associate Professor of Management and Logistics in the School of Business Administration at the University of Miami, Coral Gables, Florida.

Edward S. Quade, Ph.D.
Head (Retired) of the Mathematics Department at the Rand Corporation in Los Angeles, California. (1127 Las Pulgas Place, Pacific Palisades, California.)

Michael S. Salvador, Ph.D.

Manager, Ernst & Ernst in Charlotte, North Carolina.

E. S. Savas, Ph.D.

Professor of Public Systems Management in the Graduate School of Business at Columbia University in New York, New York.

Ernest M. Scheuer, Ph.D.

Professor of Management Science in the School of Business Administration and Economics at the California State University at Northridge.

William E. Souder, Ph.D.

Associate Professor of Industrial Engineering, Systems Management Engineering and Operations Research at the University of Pittsburgh, in Pittsburgh, Pennsylvania.

William W. Swart, Ph.D.

Professor of Management Science and Associate Dean of the School of Business Administration and Economics at the California State University at Northridge.

Turgut Var, Ph.D.

Professor of Economics and Commerce at the Simon Fraser University in Burnaby, British Columbia, Canada.

John A. White, Ph.D.

Professor of Industrial and Systems Engineering at the Georgia Institute of Technology in Atlanta, Georgia.

PREFACE

Operations Research, OR, was officially "born" in the United States as an organized activity in 1952 when the Operations Research Society of America was formed, though the activity had been going on for a number of years prior to that date, starting in Great Britain just before the outbreak of World War II. Interestingly enough, only one pamphlet and one book on the subject were available at that time (in 1948 the pamphlet "Operational Research" was published by P.M.S. Blackett, and in 1952 the book *Methods of Operations Research* by Philip M. Morse and George E. Kimball), but no scientific journals were devoted primarily to it. The next few years witnessed a number of publications on OR, which were either Proceedings of Conferences on OR (in 1954 and 1957), or booklets sponsored by various institutes and associations such as the Midwest Research Institute (1954), the Railway Systems and Procedures Association (1954), the American Management Association (1956), and the National Industrial Conference Board (1957). In the same period there appeared the book edited by McCloskey and Trefethen, *Operations Research for Management* (1956) and two bibliographies: one by the OR Group of the Case Institute of Technology (1956, with supplement for 1957) and the other by Riley (1953). The next book of note bearing the title OR appeared in 1957 and was edited by three prominent researchers (C. West Churchman, Russell L. Ackoff, and E. Leonard Arnoff) and authored by no less than 14 contributors. It represented, in fact, the most up-to-date thinking in the field as viewed by the specialists and the originators of the ideas. The next five years passed with only a trickle of contributions—between the years 1957 and 1962, the books on OR can be counted on the fingers of one hand!

Then came the flood: since 1962, the number of books on OR runs in the hundreds. There are introductory books, specialized books in every facet of OR, progress review books and bibliographies, "reading" books, and so forth. Nor was the burst of activity confined only to books; the technical journals multiplied, the professional societies proliferated, and most important, the literature on the subject increased at a high rate. The contributions varied from the totally theoretical—some of which appearing in highly specialized mathematical journals—to the totally applied, some of which appeared in trade journals. We know of at least three abstracting services in OR.

In this maze of the relevant and the speculative, theoretical and applied, introductory and advanced, there seems to be a definite place for a handbook—an authoritative, concise, complete and up-to-date survey of the field that is equally useful to the specialist to "look up" an area outside his expertise, as well as to the practitioner who is interested in knowing what is useful in a particular situation without getting too involved in the theoretical derivation of the results.

Perhaps the best way to introduce this two-volume *Handbook* is to contrast what it is and what it is not. This *Handbook* is not a "textbook" because it sacrifices the most distinguishing aspect of the latter: it does not explain in a thorough and understandable fashion the derivations of the results. It is content with the statement of the premises and the results based on them. On the other hand, this *Handbook* is not a "survey" book, though it does attempt to cover the waterfront, because a survey must be critical, giving detailed patterns of advancement as well as avenues of future research. Finally, this *Handbook* is not a "catalog," though it does provide, as much as possible, a complete listing of the significant results in the field. But it goes beyond the mere listing, and establishes the connection between theory and practice.

This *Handbook* is intended to serve as a reference book that should appeal to the expert, the practitioner and the novice alike. It is divided into two volumes; the first one carried the subtitle, "Foundations and Fundamentals," while this one carries the subtitle, "Models and Applications." This division, while easing the physical packaging problem, serves also to segregate the theory and other philosophical and historical considerations from the practice of OR in either its modeling of common processes or in its application to several fields of human endeavor.

The volume on Foundations and Fundamentals is a concise and definitive reference book on the fundamental concepts and methodologies of OR. It is divided into three Sections, written by 21 leading authorities in their fields, and offers a panoramic and up-to-date view of OR.

The *first section* (4 chapters) serves as a general introduction to the field. It covers the origin and subsequent development of OR, tracing its growth to its current international status. This is perhaps the most comprehensive exposition of this aspect of OR. This section also covers the professional education of the practitioners, and the general approach to the conduct of OR studies. These two topics are usually ignored or glossed over lightly in other publications in OR.

The *second section* (8 chapters) and the *third section* (9 chapters) classify and summarize the theory and methodology of OR. They survey the salient contributions in the various methodologies, giving the most significant theoretical results in clear and concise form. The first classification of methodology appears in the selection of the subjects in each section; with Section 2 dealing with deterministic theory and Section 3 with stochastic or probabilistic theory. The two sections combined cover the various facets of mathematical programming (linear, integer, nonlinear, large scale, geometric, and dynamic), stochastic processes and the theory of queues, graphs and networks, optimal control, value theory and decision analysis, game theory and gaming, search theory, and simulation. To the nonexpert in theory, these two sections offer an introduction and a road map if the reader wishes to gain expertise in a particular methodology. To the expert, on the other hand, the two sections offer a convenient summary and, in many instances, the future areas of research in unsolved problems. The list of references at the end of each chapter should be of valuable service to both types of readers.

This volume of the *Handbook* on Models and Applications is directed to answer the question of where has the theory of OR been applied? The answer is written by 27 competent authors who have themselves been associated with the different fields of application. Apart from documenting these applications, this volume, which is divided into two sections, provides a perspective and a view of future movement in the applications of OR.

The *first section* (12 chapters) documents the applications to various functional processes that are common to most operational systems, and the degree of success obtained in these applications. The coverage ranges from the standard topics, such as forecasting and project selection, planning and control, to more uncommon topics in OR literature such as accounting, finance, and human resources management.

The *second section* (8 chapters) concentrates on illustrations of OR applications to human enterprises. It presents a concise and illuminating discussion of the tools that were used, the problems encountered, and the utility derived from them in eight broad areas: the military, health services, education, transportation, urban systems, leisure industries, electric utilities and process industries.

Despite their comprehensive posture the two volumes still miss a number of topics in both theory and application. For instance, the first volume carries no mention of the theory of "fuzzy systems," though it may prove to be one of the most innovative and stimulating ideas that has come forth within the past ten years. On the other hand, this volume on Models and Applications has no discussion of OR models and application in a variety of fields, such as management information systems, agriculture, and the railroads, among others.

We have an apology and an explanation to make. The apology is to the readers of this *Handbook* who may have wished to consult it on any, or all, of these topics. The explanation is simply the following: working under the usual constraints of time and space, we had to make choices and these (as well as many other) topics were excluded from the final product. We trust that we have made the correct choices or at least reached a satisficing solution.

The time is now ripe for us to define the audience to whom this *Handbook* is addressed. It is primarily addressed to operations researchers, management scientists, systems analysts, industrial engineers, managers, and others who use quantitative methods in resolving systems-type problems in operational systems. The two volumes are intended to serve as reference books to the expert, novice, and practitioner alike, although each would use it in different ways and for different purposes. The first volume is useful to the specialist from two points of view: first, as a handy resumé of the areas of his expertise and, second, as a place to "look up" an area outside his expertise and discover its essential features and the most important and current references on it. It is useful to the practitioner who is interested in finding out what is useful in a particular situation. And it is useful to the novice since each chapter includes an easy-to-read introductory section on the subject matter of the chapter, from which the reader can gain quick and easy familiarity with its more advanced studies. The typical novice is defined as one who has studied the following subjects or their equivalent: a standard college undergraduate course in calculus and matrix algebra, a one-year course in probability and statistics, an elementary course in computers and their programming, and a one-year course in the methodology and techniques of OR.

On the other hand, this volume on Models and Applications, being an authoritative exposition of the applications of OR methodology in a variety of contexts and operational systems, should have wide appeal to all people engaged in OR, either in theory or practice. It is also accessible to all since the emphasis shifts from theory to utility.

We also believe that this *Handbook* will have appeal to persons other than those mentioned above. In particular, the first volume should be appealing to applied mathematicians, statisticians, computer scientists, and engineers whose interests veer towards the analysis and synthesis of complex systems. With the current emphasis on "applicable" mathematics, more and more mathematicians are finding OR a fertile field of application of their mathematical expertise and acumen. On the other hand, the optimization of engineering design is gaining a strong foothold in traditional disciplines such as mechanical and civil engineering. A select few, and to date they are only a small minority that is growing, will find the first volume of the *Handbook* almost indispensable. As to this second volume, various functional area specialists (professionals in accounting, finance, personnel management, production and inventory, information systems, and project management) and staff specialists in various operational systems (urban systems, health services, transportation, military, electric utilities, process industries, and leisure industries) will have interest in it, wherein the use of OR in their specific areas is described.

Two college classroom uses for the handbooks are as follows: Both volumes will find use as a supplement or reference book for undergraduate and graduate students taking the typical one-year professional course in OR methodology and techniques; these courses are taught in Departments of Industrial and Systems Engineering or Operations Research, and to a lesser extent in Management Science (School of Business Administration), Applied Mathematics and Computer Science. The main reason for this type of adoption of the *Handbook* is that it presents a concise and comprehensive coverage of the foundations and methodology of OR, and in the case of this second volume, it indicates to the students the rich array of applications of OR theory that may not be adequately covered in their textbook. This second volume will also find use as a supplement in courses in quantitative methods or operations management offered in most business school MBA programs. The primary objective of these courses is to show how OR is (or can be) used in solving "business" problems, which is consonant with the objective of this volume of the *Handbook*.

This *Handbook* was written by a total of 48 authors who are recognized authorities in their respective fields. It is a distillation of their expertise, deep knowledge, and insight into the theory and practice of OR as it stands in the mid-70's. It is also a reflection of their individual biases and subjective preferences. We believe that this is how it should be: the reader is presented not with a bland and colorless collection of surveys, but with forceful, and oftentimes provocative, panoramic views of the various topics discussed. The reader may not agree with a particular interpretation or classification—in fact, we hope the reader will not agree with all of the views expressed in this *Handbook*—but if he is stimulated and informed we would feel that the mission of the *Handbook* has been accomplished.

Individual differences among authors manifest themselves in several ways. For instance, some chapters contain references to general textbooks in which the topics are discussed in more detail, while others provide almost complete bibliographies. Some authors sketched in a heuristic manner the rationale of their conclusions, while others followed a more formal path. Some authors refrained from passing judgement on the "worthiness" of a particular method in a particular application; while others went ahead and expressed their views freely. And so on. We, as editors, did not attempt any "homogenization" of styles or views, and we firmly believe that this "hands off" policy adds strength and color to the *Handbook*.

Without attempting a formal definition of OR—the reader will find more than one definition in Section I of the first volume of this *Handbook*—one can safely state that OR is primarily concerned with the study of operational systems, where these latter are defined as systems that are subject to human decision (as contrasted to, say stellar systems which lie outside the sphere of human decision-making, albeit they obey logical laws of nature). One may ask, then, if OR is synonymous with systems theory? In our view, answer is no; there are differences between the two disciplines. Sometimes the difference is a matter of degree, and sometimes it is in basic outlook. As always, the content of either is highly conditioned by its historical development.

Traditionally, systems theory has been closely related to "hardware" systems (the first "systems engineering," as such, was in the field of telephony), while OR is identified with the "software." OR tends to be concerned with problems which can be represented by mathematical models, which, in turn, can be analytically studied and optimized. Systems theory, on the other hand, although formal in nature, is concerned with problems of greater complexity, and is more global and abstract in its approach. Its components may consist of mathematical models, but may also incorporate social and biological factors which have not been successfully quantified. OR tends to be mostly concerned with smaller scale problems of existing systems, as contrasted with systems theory which usually connotes a larger and more encompassing perspective of new systems.

A system is any cohesive collection of items that are dynamically related. Every system does something, and what it does can be regarded as its purpose. Systems theory is primarily concerned with the discovery of the mechanisms by which such purpose is achieved and by which equilibrium or self-regulation is maintained. OR is one of the most important inputs to such a theory, providing the quantitative models of the mechanisms that are amenable to such treatment. Thus OR may be legitimately viewed as one among several disciplines that contribute to the general theory of systems.

A handbook of this size is evidently the outcome of the cooperative effort of a large number of people. In closing, it is our pleasure to acknowledge our indebtedness to them. The editorial advisory committee composed of Drs. R. E. Fetter and David B. Hertz helped guide the formulation of the broad outlines of the structure of this *Handbook*, the scope of its coverage, and its general thrust and orientation. Theirs was a key input at the time of conception of the idea of a handbook. To the 48 authors go our thanks, individually and collectively, for their valuable inputs, and for their patience and understanding in the face of sometimes impatient and sometimes seemingly over-critical editors. Our special thanks go to our colleagues who unselfishly gave of their time and effort reviewing some of the chapters in this *Handbook*. In particular, we wish to mention the names of Drs. Jacques Vander Eecken and Willy Gochet, both of the Catholic University of Leuven, and Professors Marianne Gardner and Henry L. W. Nuttle, both of North Carolina State University at Raleigh.

JOSEPH J. MODER
Miami, Florida

SALAH E. ELMAGHRABY
Raleigh, North Carolina

CONTENTS

Handbook of Operations Research

MODELS AND APPLICATIONS

Applications of Operations Research to Common Functional Processes

I-1

FORECASTING

Robert G. Brown
Consultant

1. INTRODUCTION

A decision involves (a) a choice among alternatives and (b) a commitment of resources (Howard [1966]). Much of operations research (OR) is concerned with models that demonstrate the consequences of these alternatives, before the decision is taken, based on current information about the significant factors involved. While some of the pertinent information is observable and measurable, there is usually a time lag between the time when a decision is taken and the time when its consequences become apparent. During that time lag some of the information may change. Thus, the decision is based, not on observable information, but on a forecast.

Any OR model itself is in a way a forecast of several possible futures. This chapter takes the narrower view of techniques that have been developed for repetitive estimates of the parameters of the distribution of some factor taken into account in the model of decision alternatives. Forecasts made once only are usually based on a special study of the circumstances involved. We shall be concerned with forecasts that are revised over and over again as new information becomes available, in order to modify the values of the parameters, and hence the choice among the alternatives available. The revisions may be at regular intervals (every week or every quarter) or at intervals of unequal length. For example, analog fire-control systems that track targets have their own special techniques for continual revision of the forecast of the location of the aiming point.

3

1.1 Sampled Time Series

There are two different kinds of time series that may be forecast, which can be contrasted as "rate" versus "state" variables (Forrester [1961]). A *state variable* is sampled periodically, but the value observed does not depend directly on when it is observed during a short interval of time. A *rate variable* is also sampled periodically, but the value observed tends to be proportional to the length of the interval since the previous observation.

Examples of state variables would be: temperature, the number of subscribers to a magazine, speed, and cost. Examples of rate variables include: rainfall, number of copies sold, position, and demand. The dimensions of state variables are often numbers (think of speed as knots, rather than miles per hour), while the dimensions of rate variables are number/unit time.

There are three consequences of the distinction between rate and state variables in the design of a forecasting process: (a) If the observations are sampled at irregular intervals, then the actual length of the interval must be taken into account in estimating rates, though it is not important in estimating states. (b) Forecasts are computed for each of the next several intervals of time, out to some lead time, when the consequences of the current decision become important. The relevant forecast of a state variable is the value *at* the end of the lead time. The forecast of a rate variable is the sum of the forecasts *through* the lead time. (c) The form of the distribution of the errors in forecasting a state variable will be similar to the form of the distribution of the residual noise in the observed data. The form of the distribution of errors in forecasting a rate variable tends to become normal, whatever the distribution of the noise, since the relevant errors are the sums of the errors in forecasting individual time periods.

1.2 Sampling Interval

The length of the interval between sampling the current data for purposes of revising the forecast depends largely on: (a) the length of the lead time over which the forecast is required; and (b) the highest frequency of cyclic variation that must be represented by the model. Within these broad limits, the interval can be chosen as any convenient clock or calendar time. The interval ought to be long enough that there is a good chance that the observed event will have occurred.

There is seldom any reason for revising a forecast more than about ten times within a decision lead time, and usually the forecast is revised at least once during the lead time. Planning the acquisition of timber land for pulp wood, where it takes 80 years for trees to mature, can be revised about once a decade. Local effects of weather on requirements for generating electricity might be observed every hour.

When there are repetitive cyclic variations, as in monthly temperature variances, or in measurements of the volume of mail received by day of the week, then it is necessary to observe the series at least twice within the cycle of the highest frequency that is to be represented (Nyquist [1928]). Monthly observations won't tell you how to staff the mailroom on Mondays versus Thursdays, and daily observations won't distinguish between first and second shift workloads.

If the unpredictable (random) noise in the data is high compared with the predictable signal, then it is wise to increase the length of the sampling interval for rate variables, thus averaging out some of the noise. With state variables that have a low signal-to-noise ratio, it may be better to observe often and use the appropriate filtering techniques to recover the signal (Sittler [1957]).

1.3 Forecasting Processes

The techniques of forecasting can be grouped broadly into three categories: (a) descriptive, (b) explanatory, and (c) derived.

A process can be observed periodically giving values X_t with additional data as time goes on. These data can be described by a model, and the coefficients in the model can be estimated by some process of fitting the model to the data. Often the fitting process assigns different weights to different observations. This model, which describes history to date, can be evaluated for some future point in time to produce a forecast. We shall discuss the data in Section 2, alternative forecasting models in 3, weighting schemes in 4 and forecast errors in 5. In Section 6 it will be noted that, while it is desirable to have an accurate forecast, the variance of the forecast errors is not always the sole, or even the main, criterion for choice among alternative statistical descriptions of the time series.

When it is possible to build a model of the environment, the causes of change can be made explicit, and the forecast resulting from such a model explains what is going on. These methods range from the formal models of economics (Leontieff [1966]; Evans [1969]), through special models, e.g. a model of the reasons why people buy more product during a sale (Brown [1967]), to the very subjective marketing intelligence discussed in Section 7. Although descriptive forecasts can at best make probability statements about the likelihood, timing, and magnitude of turning points in a series, there are some very powerful ways of detecting turning points quickly after they have happened (Harrison, Stevens [1971]; Brown [1971]). On the other hand explanatory forecasts have as a primary objective the prediction of the timing and magnitudes of turning points.

Life-cycle curves (Bass [1969]) have an appeal as an explanatory forecast. Every product does have a period of initial growth, a mature period, and a declining period as it disappears from the market. While such models accurately describe the history of demand for every product, they do not appear to predict in advance the change from one phase to another.

Technological forecasting (Ayres [1969]) is becoming increasingly popular and useful in an attempt to foresee the major factors that influence the environment. Unfortunately, no one has yet developed a good sociological forecast that would foresee the clash between the environmentalists and the Nixon economists that has caused worldwide shortages.

Given that a production schedule has been set, with definite quantities of products with known specifications, it is possible to "explode" that schedule to compute the timing and quantity of requirements for all subassemblies, components, parts, and raw materials that make up the product. (See Chapters I-6 on inventory control and I-5 on production planning.) There may also be a causal relationship between the data to be forecast and some leading indicator. For example, variation in the rate of growth in the numbers of applications for College Entrance Examination Boards is clearly related to variation in the birth rate 17 years earlier. There is a reason for the relationship, and the leading indicator is available with sufficient lead time to be useful in the forecast.

Yule [1926] pointed out that there is always a statistical correlation between any two time series that themselves are autocorrelated. Thus there is a grave danger in the promiscuous use of multiple regression to seek a "good r^2" between series to be forecast and various potential leading indicators. The history available is only a sample of the total time series, and if one hunts long enough an apparent relationship will be found. However, if the coefficients in the model disappear or change sign with additional information, the model is not reliable for decision making—the "leading indicators" cease to lead just at the critical juncture.

2. DATA

The principal focus of the remainder of this chapter is the statistical, descriptive, forecasts used in making short-range decisions (usually out to about 10 times the interval between forecast revisions) repetitively. OR has been concerned with the techniques of finding appropriate models, and of revising the forecasts with new observations. The best results are obtained by a suitable blend of these descriptive forecasts with explanations from marketing intelligence, as discussed in Section 7.

2.1 Sampled Observations

The data represent sample observations from either a rate variable, such as demand for a product, or a state variable, such as its cost. Decisions are to be made now that will affect a lead time in the future. The length of that lead time might itself be a variable to be forecast.

2.2 Outliers

There are many sources of error in observations. The process itself may have stochastic variation. There are errors in observing and recording the actual data. The observations may include spurious effects, such as abnormally low demand during a strike, or abnormally high room temperatures when there is a draft on the thermostat. It is sometimes advisable to distinguish between the actual data recorded historically and a time series that represents a good base from which to project future observations.

An historical series should be screened for outliers—observations that don't represent the process to be forecast—before fitting a model to the data. A simple and robust screening process is illustrated in Figure 1. Since the highest or lowest observation could be an outlier, these two observations are temporarily excluded from the set. The range between the extremes of the remaining observations is a quick estimate of the normal variability of the data. The distance from the maximum to the next-to-largest (or from the minimum to the next-to-smallest) is an indication of the likelihood that the extreme observations are representative. For historical series of from 20 to 100 observations, if this distance exceeds about 0.4 times the range, then it is worthwhile to examine the data more carefully. Obviously this simple test will not detect two outliers if they are both too high, nor will it detect anomalies in data that have a clear repetitive cyclic pattern or a significant secular trend. A more thorough screening would detect residual differences between the raw data and a descriptive model fit to it where the difference exceeds, say, 4σ.

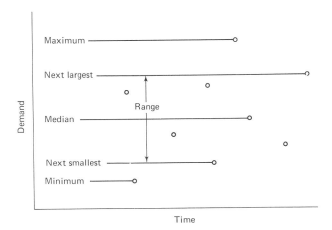

Fig. 1. Editing history for outliers.

2.3   Transformations

Economic data often show a basic exponential growth. It is easier to represent the logarithms by a forecast model than to represent the observations themselves.

While decisions to replenish stock are based on net total demand, it may be appropriate to forecast, with separate techniques and separate series, new orders, returns of merchandise, requirements imposed by an assembly schedule, government and export orders, demand caused by a special promotion, and so on. The total demand is hard to represent by a forecast model, so it is transformed by breaking it up into constituent series, each of which can easily be described.

2.4   Noise, Residuals and Errors

There are three separate expressions for the stochastic elements of a time series and its forecast. *Noise* is used to refer to the inherent variability of the process and of the uncertainty introduced by the way that the process is observed. Noise is thus one component of the data to be used. *Residuals* refer to the differences between the observed data and some calculated value based on a forecast model that has been fit to those data. Thus residuals refer to historical data and a model evaluated in the past. Forecast *errors* are the differences between a forecast developed now and what is later observed at the corresponding future point in time.

2.5   Stationarity

The process underlying the series of observations can, at least conceptually, be described by some set of difference equations (if discrete) or differential equations (if continuous). We don't know what those equations are, of course, and probably couldn't solve them if we did. If the coefficients in those equations are independent of time, the process is said to be *stationary*. If the coefficients change stochastically with time, the series is *non-stationary*. Clearly, if there is a systematic variation of the coefficients with time, that variation could be represented by additional equations in the system.

Most series to be forecast are non-stationary in the long run, but can be considered to be esentially stationary for the forecast computed as of any one point in time.

3. MODELS

At the current time T we have available a sequence of observations X_t for some dense set of integers, $t \leqslant T$. The forecast model can be $\hat{X}_{T+\tau}$ where in general the times τ are positive, and may be a vector of values. A general expression for the model is

$$\hat{X}_{T+\tau} = \mathbf{a}_T \mathbf{F}(\tau),$$

where the vector **a** represents coefficients in the model estimated from observations up to and including time T, and the matrix **F** is some set of fitting functions, in which the rows correspond to terms in the model and the columns to points in time. In most practical applications **F** measures time relative to the most recent observation, and the origin of time on an external scale is reflected in the values of the coefficients **a**.

3.1 Polynomial Models of a Time Series

One common class of models is the real polynomials, where $F(1, t) = 1$; $F(2, t) = t$; $F(3, t) = \frac{1}{2}t(t - 1)$ and so on. In some techniques of forecasting the model may appear to be quite different, as for example in the differences and sums in the Box-Jenkins [1970] methods. However, since the solution of a linear difference equation can be a real polynomial, the difference is one of convenience in analysis rather than a real difference in the mathematical properties of the model.

A first-order polynomial (straight line) is frequently a good model of the local changes in the observed data. Note that a constant (a zero-order polynomial) is a special case in which the coefficient of the linear term is zero. A fit of a straight line to any set of data will result in some value for the second coefficient, representing the secular trend. If the value is small, one might prefer to eliminate that term from the model. However, values of that coefficient that are small enough to be rejected by a statistical test are so small that they have no effect on the short-term forecast. The cost of the statistical test itself may be greater than the cost of using the term in the forecast, even where it might be unnecessary. Of course, if the forecast is to be projected over lead times that are more than about 10 times as long as the interval between forecast revisions, then it is more important to eliminate spurious trends from the model.

Mathematical techniques are available (Brown [1963]) for forecasting with any order of polynomial. Unless there is a reason for using higher order polynomials (such as tracking the path of a ballistic missile) quadratics and higher orders are usually spurious as descriptions of the kinds of series that are commonly forecast.

3.2 Seasonal Models

Tides go through a cycle from high to low twice a day. Temperature in the higher latitudes goes through a cycle from high to low once a year. Demand for electrical power goes through a cycle, with a complex shape, repeated every week (with exceptions for major holidays and an overriding annual cycle). Demand for stocked products may go through a cycle that is repeated for each selling season.

The usefulness of the forecast for decision making can be improved by including a representation of these cyclic variations that anticipates when the high and low values will occur in the future.

Not all series that have high and low values are cyclic in this sense. Business and economic "cycles" do not repeat with sufficient reproducibility to make it practical to infer future high and low points from an analysis of history.

There are two quite different approaches, each with many variations, for representing seasonal cycles.

If there are N observations per cycle ($N = 12$ months in a year, or $N = 7$ days in a week, for example) one can have a record of N indices that either add a quantity (positive or negative) to the forecast, or multiply it by a quantity greater than or less than one.

The values of these indices can be inferred from the data observed in corresponding times in the cycles in the past. In some naive techniques the index for September, say, is inferred from data only about past Septembers. In more sophisticated techniques, such as the Census II and Census X-11 (Shishkin [1957]) there is some averaging of adjacent observations as well.

In retail marketing of consumer products the seasonal indices are often cumulative, representing the percent of the total season done to date.

In any of these approaches the whole set of indices can be called a "profile." In many situations there is a small family of relevant profiles, and the forecasts for individual series can be developed by selecting the best representative from that family for each individual series.

Profiles have a decided merit in forecasting in that the concept is easy to explain to the user, and any thoughtful person can see how it works. However, they have a decided disadvantage in that they are unstable. If a random variable x has variance σ^2, then its reciprocal $y = 1/x$ has a variance of the order of σ^4. Most of the methods using seasonal or cyclic profiles require division, at some step of the computation, by a stochastic variable (or by the estimate of its mean, which also has a nonzero variance). If the denominator in that division is of the order of the noise in the observations, then relatively small variations can have very great leverage in modifying the forecasts. Unfortunately, this instability usually comes just at the time when the decisions to be made have the greatest consequence (looking forward to the next peak).

In the Bayesian method of Harrison and Stevens [1971], this instability is minimized by the assumption that the noise variance is a function only of the deseasonalized average underlying the observations at all points in the cycle. The effect is to increase the sensitivity to change at high points in the cycle, and reduce it at the low points.

For example, consider the "percent-done" forecast of a consumer product. Early in the selling season, it is necessary to commit to a total quantity to be produced, and at least have a position in the raw materials, if not a good fraction of the actual production. Suppose that 10% of the season's sales are booked, on the average, within the first three weeks when it is necessary to make the final commitment for expensive raw materials. If some large customer who traditionally orders later, places his order early this year, then a serious overstatement of the total season requirements might occur. This actually happened in retail merchandising in the United States for the first few years that Christmas promotions were started the first of November, after they had traditionally started with the Macy's Thanksgiving Day parade.

An alternative approach is to represent cyclic variation by a Fourier series

$$\hat{X}_t = \sum c_k \cos \omega kt + \sum s_k \sin \omega kt,$$

where c_k and s_k are coefficients estimated from past data by a suitable regression. $k = 1, 2, \ldots, N$ is the index of summation over all frequencies up to the Nyquist frequency (the highest frequency that can be represented in a sampled series goes through half a cycle in the interval between observations). $\omega = $ the fundamental frequency $(2\pi/f)$, where f is the number of observations in one seasonal cycle. t is the time when the forecast is to be evaluated, and is often a vector of integer values.

This sort of model (Brown [1963]) has the advantage of being stable, even at the low points of the cycle, because the coefficients are estimated in a generalized average process over the whole set of data available, not just the relative observation within each cycle. It has the disadvantage in practice of being much harder for the lay user to comprehend. There are existing computer packages (Brown [1973]) that involve the user in editing input and interpreting output in a meaningful form so that most users don't feel a need to understand the inner workings of the process.

If only the first pair of terms in the Fourier series is used, the seasonal profile is a simple sine wave with any amplitude and phase angle, governed by the two coefficients c_1 and s_1. As additional pairs of terms are added to the series, the shape of the profile can be changed. Fourier's theorem shows that if a discrete series repeats exactly every f observations, then the points can be represented exactly by f terms in this series.

The amplitude of the jth frequency included in the model is $A_j = \sqrt{c_j^2 + s_j^2}$. The square of the amplitude is sometimes called the *power* at that frequency. Let σ_j^2 be the variance of the residual differences between the data and a model with all frequencies up to and including the jth. Then, if the model is fit (usually by least squares) to a history that spans about 3 to 8 past cycles, the jth frequency should be included if the amplitude $A_j \geq \frac{1}{2}\sigma_j$. Note that in computing

σ^2 one must take account of the degrees of freedom lost by the number of terms in the model. Hence it is possible for the minimum variance to be achieved for some model with less than f terms. That model itself, however, would be spurious if the power at the highest frequency included is not large compared with the residual variance.

3.3   Time Series Analysis

Suppose that a series X_t has been reduced to a series with zero mean $Y_t = X_t - \hat{X}_t$, where the model $\hat{X}_t$ provides for consistent polynomial trends and cyclic variations. The autocovariance σ_τ^2 is the expected value of the product $Y_t Y_{t-\tau}$, where τ is the *lag*. When the model $\hat{X}_t$ represents all the systematic variation in the data, the autocovariance will be essentially zero for all positive lags. Large values (positive or negative) of the autocovariance indicate that there is predictable information in the series Y_t that could be incorporated into a model. Spectral analysis (Jenkins and Watts [1969]; Rosenblatt [1963]) is the specialized branch of statistics dealing with the mathematical methods of finding the necessary and sufficient model to represent such a series adequately.

3.4   Probability Models

Time-series models represent a collection of observations by a model which takes the point of view that any observation is a sample from some distribution whose parameters can be estimated and projected forward in time. From these parameters (usually the mean and variance in practice, although one could develop the entire characteristic function) one can generate the probability distribution as of the time when the consequences of the decision become relevant.

An alternative representation is to model the data by a frequency distribution with parameters p_j for the relative frequency of observations falling in the jth class interval. Then, if the distribution is not expected to change in a predictable way during the decision lead time, decisions can be taken with respect to the current empirical frequency distribution.

4. SMOOTHING WEIGHTS

In virtually all techniques of forecasting in use today, the coefficients (referred to in general as a vector **a**, and in special cases above as $[c_k, s_k]$ or p_j) in the model are determined initially by fitting the model to some historical data and then revising the values of the coefficients as new observations become available. Usually, the choice of coefficients is made to minimize the sum of squares of the residual differences between data and the model, with provision for assigning different weights to the residuals at different points in time. That is, in general, the coefficients a are chosen to minimize $S = \sum w_j (X_{T-j} - \hat{X}_{T-j})^2$, where the summation is taken over all available j up to the most recent observation at time T. The relative advantages of different weighting schemes w_j can be judged both in terms of the accuracy of the resulting forecasts and the ease of carrying out the computations.

4.1 Uniform Weights

The simplest set of weights gives equal importance to all the history used: $w_j = 1$ for $0 \leqslant j \leqslant T$. Even when the coefficients are revised with some different weighting scheme, often the initial values are obtained by a simple least-square fit which implies equal weights.

A moving average is a uniformly weighted least-squares estimate of a single constant to represent the data; the fitting function being the trivial value $F(t) = 1$ for all t. The weights are $w_j = 1$ for the most recent N observations $0 \leqslant j \leqslant N - 1$, and $w_k = 0$ for $k \geqslant N$. Some forecast coefficients are estimated in higher order polynomials by fitting the model to the most recent N observations each time a new value is obtained. The values of the coefficients can be expressed in terms of: (a) their previous values, (b) the error in the most recent one-ahead forecast, (c) the order of the polynomial, and of course (d) the number N of observations to be used.

4.2 Optimum Weights

Wiener [1949] showed that if the time series is stationary, then there exists an optimum set of weights in the sense of minimizing the variance of the forecast errors (ordinary least squares minimizes the variance of the residuals). These weights can be expressed as functions of the properties of the autocovariance function.

Winters [1960] proposed a method for computing the weighting functions for a level, a trend, and seasonal indices. In each case the weights are exponentially declining of the form α^j. Separate values of α are found for the level, for the trend, and for seasonal indices by systematically exploring the accuracy of the forecasts obtained by combinations of the weighting functions.

Box and Jenkins [1970] developed the theme for quite a wide class of potential models, combining calculations from the autocovariance function with the systematic exploration of a space in which it is known in advance that the optimum weights (by term and time lag) must lie. The Box-Jenkins technique is particularly powerful when (a) there is a great deal of data to work with and (b) something is known about the underlying mechanism of the process that generates the observations. For example, the initial impetus of this work was for on-line process control systems in the chemical industry where the results have been used with great success.

4.3 Exponential Discounting

There is an intuitive appeal to a process ($w_j = \alpha^j$, $\alpha < 1$) that gives greater weight to more recent information, and the computational simplicity of revising estimates of the values of the coefficients in even quite elaborate models (with polynomials and Fourier representations of seasonal cycles, which could be thought of as complex polynomials). These properties of exponential smoothing (Brown 1959, etc.) have made it quite popular. This is particularly true in applications where it is necessary to recompute a great many forecasts, and the costs of computation must be considered against the costs of decisions that may be based on less than the most accurate forecasts.

Van Dobben de Bruyn [1969] and Trigg and Leach [1967] have proposed ways in which the discount rate α, in an exponentially weighted moving average, can be increased in periods when the forecast has been unbiased for greater stability, and reduced when a significant bias develops in the forecast errors to "forget" older information more rapidly.

The forecast revision process itself is a feedback loop, correcting future forecasts on the basis of errors in recent forecasts. When the weighting scheme in the forecast computations is also a feedback loop, it becomes virtually impossible to do a rigorous analysis of the regions of instability for the system, if any. It is not sufficient to demonstrate any number of cases where the method appears to work. One also requires a demonstration that identifies the areas in which it will not work, if there are any.

Many of the techniques, both proposed and used, attempt to find the best value of the discount rate by repetitive simulations over some available set of data, to pick that value which gives the most accurate forecasts (minimum error variance). There are several dangers to these simulations. First, if there are significant differences in the mean error (which should be zero), then these differences are more likely to have been caused by the way the initial values of the coefficients are set than by differences in the discount rate or the smoothing constant.

Second, a more important fallacy is pointed up by the following experiment. Generate a very long series of numbers by any process that introduces some serial correlation. Now divide the series (which is guaranteed to be stationary and homogeneous by the way that it was obtained) into short segments of the length over which the simulation is normally alleged to find the best value of the discount rate. Carry out the simulations in each of these segments. Note that, although all segments are finite samples from the same process, there is quite a distribution of values of the recommended discount rates. Note further that one "knows" the value of the discount rate for any segment only after that segment has become history, and that the value is quite likely to be different from the one for the following segment, which won't be known until it is past and therefore useless as a forecast.

The difference between the accuracy obtained by uniformly using some standard discount rate, say $\alpha = 0.9$, (for which there is beginning to be some theoretical justification) and the accuracy that could be achieved if one knew *in advance* the optimum value, is small compared to the sampling error in estimating the best value of the discount rate from relatively short (50 observations) segments of a long series.

4.4 Bayesian Forecasts

Harrison and Stevens [1971] have developed a new and rigorous approach to forecasting time series that includes most of the others as special cases. Before each observation one has a set of prior probabilities of the values for each of the coefficients in the model. Although one could start from a state of fairly complete ignorance, usually there are good grounds for stating these probabilities with reasonable accuracy, if not precision.

After the observation has been obtained, Bayes rule is invoked to determine posterior probabilities that the observation came from each possible combination of model coefficients, and the forecast is computed as a probability distribution based on those posterior distributions. In particular, this method makes it possible to ignore a transient pulse, while responding quickly to changes such as steps and ramps in the underlying process. The computational scheme continually condenses the number of posterior distributions back to the number of states assumed in the process. The states usually include a default state where none of the elements of the process has changed, and a state corresponding to each coefficient and to the noise in which the variance of the distribution is much larger than in the default case, indicating a perturbance to that coefficient. The condensation of the number of states is important; otherwise the number of distributions would grow as the square of the number of observations.

5. FORECAST ERRORS

In any of the techniques of forecasting a time series, "the" forecast is essentially an estimate of the mean of the distribution of observations at a future time. For most decisions one also needs to have the entire distribution. If the distribution has a known form that can be described by a standard function, then an estimate of one or two parameters is sufficient to estimate the probabilities of possible values of future observations.

5.1 Form of the Distribution

Although for purposes of formal analysis it is often convenient to assume that the noise in the input data is normally distributed, there is no assurance that this assumption is justified for real observations. The distribution of noise is often quite skewed, and may have two or more modes. Even when the distribution is symmetrical about a single mode, the kurtosis may be quite different from 3.

Forecasts into the future are distributed, and the variance of the distribution of forecasts depends on the variance of the noise in the data observed. However, since the forecasts result from many past observations, the form of the distribution is usually normal, regardless of the form of the distribution that describes the noise in the observations.

The distribution of errors in forecasting a state variable will be the result of convolving the distribution of the forecasts with the distribution of future noise, which is usually considered to be independent of the distribution of past noise.

The distribution of errors in forecasting the sum of a rate variable over a lead time which is much longer than the interval between observations is the distribution of the sum of samples from several such distributions, which tends to become more and more normal as the lead time increases.

5.2 Dispersion

In most distributions of practical interest the entire distribution can be reproduced from the forecast of the mean and one other parameter, usually the standard deviation.

When there is a collection of series to be forecast, it will usually be found that from series to series there is a consistent relationship between the variance of the forecast errors and the level of the forecast. For example, while the number of bushels of wheat a_w can be quite different from the number of bushels of rye a_r forecast for a given year, it will be found that over all grain forecasts, there is a strong central tendency for $\sigma^2 \propto \mu a^\lambda$, where the parameters μ and λ are characteristic of the whole family of grain forecasts. This result is especially true for forecasts of demand for the various items stocked in the same inventory.

Thus, one can use evidence from the entire family of forecasts to estimate μ and λ and use the relationship to establish the standard deviation of the distribution of errors for any particular series.

An alternative law $\sigma^2 = \mu a + \lambda a^2$ was suggested by Burgin and Wild [1967]. Stevens [1974] provides the basis for an analysis of the kind of generating process that could give rise to laws of either kind.

The mean absolute deviation (MAD) is an estimate of the dispersion that would be appropriate if the forecasts where designed to minimize the sum of the absolute values of the residual differences between the data and the median—rather than the more common objective of the sum of squares of residual differences from the mean. In the early days of OR, when data processing capacity was severely limited, the MAD was used in lieu of the standard deviation simply because the computations took less time and space. Its use is widespread [Brown 1959] especially in computer applications for forecasting demand for stocked items. However, with the speed and capacity of present-day computers there is little justification for the use of MAD.

If the distribution is normal, then MAD = 0.8σ (actually the constant is $\sqrt{2/\pi}$ = 0.7979). However, for other distributions, the actual ratio may have virtually any value.

Since the mean of the distribution of forecast errors should be zero, the variance is the mean square error. Thus one can establish a suitable model (as a constant, with linear and seasonal terms, or from a variance law related to the forecast) and revise the coefficients in that model of the mean square error each time the forecast error is measured after the forecast has been revised with new information.

If there is negligible autocorrelation in the noise in the observations, then the variance of the error in forecasting the total of a rate variable over the lead time would be the sum of the variances of the errors in forecasts for each period during that lead time L. Hence, the standard deviation to be used in making decisions is approximately $\sigma\sqrt{L}$. Where there is serial correlation, the relationship is often approximately $\sigma_L = L^\delta \sigma_1$, where σ_1 is the standard deviation of one-ahead forecast errors, the lead time is L (measured in intervals between forecast revisions), and δ is a constant characteristic of the whole family of series to be forecast.

5.3 Tracking Signals

The accuracy that can be achieved for a forecast is limited by the noise in the input data. However, it is reasonable to expect that the forecasts are unbiased—the mean of the forecast errors should be zero. So long as the process continues to be consistent with the forecast model the forecast errors should vary around zero. If the forecast model is wrong, or if the process itself changes so that the previous model is wrong, then there will be a sequence of positive (or of negative) errors, so that the average error is no longer zero.

The tracking signal is a technique for determining whether the average error is currently reasonably close to zero. If the average error exceeds some control limit, then a notice can be triggered to advise the user so that he can take appropriate action.

The best action to take is to find the assignable cause of the bias in the forecasts and make such changes as are reasonable to correct the cause: change one or more coefficients in the model, change the form of the model itself, or change some or all of the weighting factors used in revising the forecast. There is one school of thought that seeks to have a computer system automatically compensate for tracking signals, because there might be too many for people to deal with. Another school of thought holds that an occasional very long report, with many tracking signal trips, is itself highly useful information for management. The fact that many individual forecasts are out of control may indicate the necessity for intervention throughout the planning and control system to short-cut the response time of programmed decision rules to changes in the forecasts.

Cumulative Sums.   There are three types of control limits for tripping the tracking signal.

Brown [1959] proposed a cumulative sum of the forecast errors $Y_t = Y_{t-1} + e_t$, with $Y_0 = 0$. This fluctuates around zero if the forecasts are unbiased, but grows rapidly if there is a sequence of forecast errors all of the same sign. For a discount rate β and a polynomial forecast model of degree $n - 1$, the variance of the cumulative sum is

$$\sigma_Y^2 = ((1 + \beta)/2(1 - \beta^{2n}))\sigma_e^2,$$

where σ_e^2 is the variance of the forecast errors. Whenever $|Y| \geqslant 3\sigma_Y$ a report is triggered. Obviously, the constant 3 could be made larger to reduce the number of false detections, or could be made smaller if it is vital to cut the risk of failing to detect real changes.

Smoothed Errors versus MAD.   Trigg [1964] proposed the use of single exponential smoothing on the algebraic forecast errors $Y_t = \beta Y_{t-1} + (1 - \beta)e_t$. If at any time $|Y| \geqslant 0.4$ MAD (or any other constant), the exception report is triggered. MAD is revised by $\text{MAD}_t = \beta \text{MAD}_{t-1} + (1 - \beta)|e_t|$.

This approach has a decided advantage over the first in two respects. (a) Suppose that there were a single large error, but not quite large enough to trip the tracking signal. From that point on the first method would have the (unweighted) cumulative sum fluctuate around the level set by that single large error, and a quite reasonable forecast error might trip the tracking signal much later. (b) Suppose that the tracking signal were almost ready to trip (the cumulative sum close to one limit) and we get a perfect forecast. In the first method the unweighted cumulative sum would not change but the estimate of the standard deviation σ_e would decrease and cause the control limits to shrink, tripping the tracking signal. The smoothed error overcomes both difficulties.

The variance of the smoothed forecast errors is approximately

$$\sigma_Y^2 = ((1 - \beta)/(1 + \beta)^2)\sigma_e^2.$$

V-Masks.   Barnard [1959] extended Wald's sequential analysis techniques to develop a V-mask which could be centered over the most recent value of the (unweighted) cumulative sum of forecast errors, pointing backwards. If any previous value of the cumulative sum series lies outside the mask, that is a sign of significant bias in the forecasts. The slope and intercept of the two arms of the V are computed from the variance of the errors and the risks: (a) of failing to detect a significant change; and (b) of detecting a change when there really isn't one. Brown [1971] extended this logic to produce a parabolic envelope of all V-masks over all possible levels of bias that might be considered "significant." This approach has been used with considerable success in detecting turning points in the prices of shares on the stock exchange.

5.4   Filtering the Input Data

Just as there may be extraneous phenomena and recording errors in the historical series used to initialize the forecast, current input may be inappropriate as a basis for revising the forecast. If the current observation is more than about 4σ from the forecast, then it is wise to provide for review and possible correction of the input before it is processed in the forecast system.

6. CRITERIA FOR CHOICE

There are many alternative techniques of forecasting available. Provided any of them is used properly with full understanding of the essential assumptions, methods of initializing the process, and the use of available controls, they will all provide very much the same forecast in the sense of either: (a) choice among the alternative decision opportunities; or (b) the economic consequences of the alternative chosen (Chambers [1971]). There are three techniques in widespread use for repetitively revising the forecasts for large families of series, such as the demand for stocked items or the prices of shares and commodities. There is also an extensive literature of refinements and extensions of these three techniques. In this section we can give the highlights of each approach, but the interested reader is urged to consult the original source material cited to get full details for possible implementation.

6.1   Adaptive Smoothing

The original foundations stem from exponential smoothing (Brown [1959]), and were extended to include Fourier models of seasonal patterns (Brown [1963, 1967]). Adaptive smoothing is widely used in demand forecasting for inventory control, and is available in a variety of computer program packages. It is most appropriate in situations where demand patterns are described reasonably well by level, trend, and seasonal patterns, which for most of the series don't change abruptly. It produces good results quickly for very large inventories, which in some cases may be more important than a more accurate or responsive forecast which would take considerable time and effort to develop.

The forecast model for any series is $\hat{X} = aF$ where a is a vector of m coefficients computed separately for each time series, F is a $(m \times T)$ matrix of fitting functions with a row for each of the m terms in the model and a column for each of the T time periods to be forecast, so that $\hat{\mathbf{X}}$ is a vector of the next T forecasts. If there are 12 observations during an annual cycle, the fundamental frequency is $\omega = 2\pi/12$, and there are only seven possible forms of the model. The simplest model has only a level and trend, while the most complex includes terms in the Fourier series up to $\cos 6\omega t$. The rows of the matrix $\mathbf{F}$ are shown below.

	Used in Model						
Fitting Function	1	2	3	4	5	6	7
$f_1(t) = 1;\ \ f_2(t) = t$	x	x	x	x	x	x	x
$f_3(t) = \cos \omega t;\ \ f_4(t) = \sin \omega t$		x	x	x	x	x	x
$f_5(t) = \cos 2\omega t;\ \ f_6(t) = \sin 2\omega t$			x	x	x	x	x
$f_7(t) = \cos 3\omega t;\ \ f_8(t) = \sin 3\omega t$				x	x	x	x
$f_9(t) = \cos 4\omega t;\ \ f_{10}(t) = \sin 4\omega t$					x	x	x
$f_{11}(t) = \cos 5\omega t;\ \ f_{12}(t) = \sin 5\omega t$						x	x
$f_{13}(t) = \cos 6\omega t$							x

Of course with other fundamental frequencies, other models are possible.

The coefficients a are initially computed by a least squares fit of N observations of history to the $(m \times N)$ matrix $\mathbf{F}$, evaluated at corresponding points in time. Terms are included in the model up to that frequency where the power (square of the amplitude) is at least 0.25 times the variance of the residuals from fitting that model, taking account of the degrees of freedom available for error.

With each new observation the vector a is revised by

$$\mathbf{a}_T = \mathbf{L}'\mathbf{a}_{T-1} + \mathbf{h}e,$$

where $\mathbf{L}$ is an $(m \times m)$ transition matrix defined by $\mathbf{f}(t) = \mathbf{L}\mathbf{f}(t - 1)$ which carries the value of the fitting functions at one time period into the next. The t-th column of the $\mathbf{F}$ matrix is denoted by $\mathbf{f}(t)$, and e is the (scalar) error in the most recent one period ahead forecast, $e = x_T - \hat{X}_{T-1}$. The vector $\mathbf{h}$ of m smoothing constants is determined by the following procedure.

Through the use of z-transforms and some elementary trigonometry (see Brown [1963 or 1967]) one can derive a closed form for the matrix $\mathbf{H} = \sum \beta^j \mathbf{f}(-j)\mathbf{f}'(-j)$, summed over $j = (0, \infty)$, where $\beta < 1$ discounts the importance of older data, or increases the weight given to more current data. Then the smoothing vector is $\mathbf{h} = \mathbf{H}^{-1}\mathbf{f}(0)$. Both $\mathbf{L}$ and $\mathbf{h}$ are program constants that need to be computed only once and stored for use in revising all forecasts.

If the forecasts are for a rate variable (such as demand on an inventory) and the observations are taken at irregular intervals of time, then the actual observed demand is transformed by a calendar into a rate for a standardized interval of time. The resulting forecasts can be transformed by the same calendar to correspond to future interval lengths. Note that this use of a "profile" common to all series is not subject to the same variance amplification as would be the case where the profile is inferred from historical data, rather than known absolutely.

6.2 Box-Jenkins

The primary reference is Box, Jenkins [1970] although the fundamental concepts were published much earlier [1962]. The forecasts are based on an extensive analysis of the statistical properties of the series. To gain the benefit of the full power of this approach, one needs quite a long series (at least 100 observations) and it helps considerably to understand the basic process being observed to have prior judgement as to the kinds of observations expected. The range of models is much more general than in Section 6.1, and the approach is valuable where the more accurate forecasts are worth the effort to develop them.

The first step in the analysis is to difference the historical data available and compute partial autocorrelation functions ϕ of the differenced series $w_t = \nabla^d z_t$, in which the input data z_t may have been transformed.

The second step is to express the differenced series in terms of a model with a suitable number of autoregressive and moving average terms

$$w_t = \phi_1 w_{t-1} + \cdots + \phi_p w_{t-p} + a_t - \theta_1 a_{t-1} - \cdots - \theta_q a_{t-q},$$

where the ϕ_p are the partial autocorrelation functions. There are least-squares techniques for estimating the coefficients in this sort of model, and for computing the variance of the noise in the data.

The difference and moving-average operators can be unscrambled to produce a forecast model in terms of the original observations

$$z_t = \Phi_1 z_{t-1} + \cdots + \Phi_p z_{t-p} + \Theta_0 + a_t - \Theta_1 a_{t-1} - \cdots - \Theta_q a_{t-q}.$$

If the input data were transformed, the forecast would be generated in transformed terms and then put through the inverse process to get the forecast in observed terms.

If there are seasonal cycles the contributions are computed by differencing over the length of the cycle, so that the September effect, for example, is based on data for all previous Septembers.

One of the major applications for this technique is to control processes in the chemical industry where: (a) there are series of temperatures, pressures, flow rates, etc., with a great many observations available; (b) one knows quite a bit about the probable dynamics of the system being controlled; (c) the objective of the control is to change the stream of observed temperatures, pressures, and flow rates; and (d) the economics of improved yields on each of relatively few processes warrant considerable effort to develop highly precise forecasts of the state of the system over the control response time.

6.3 Bayesian Forecasts

Harrison and Stevens [1971] have developed a practical forecasting scheme which includes the essentials of the previous two as special cases. A rigorous treatment of the mathematical foundations and practical guides to use is in preparation. So long as the data observed continue to be consistent with the forecasts, the forecasts are stable and the projected distribution of errors approaches the minimum limits consistent with the noise in the observations. A single large excursion increases the sensitivity of the process. If successive observations confirm a step or ramp change, the forecasts quickly settle down with a new forecast model. But if the excursion was a transient pulse, the forecasts stay where they were previously.

The computations are relatively much more expensive than those required by the method given in Section 6.1 so that the power is warranted in cases where there are significant and unpredictable changes in the underlying process, such as forecasts of consumer products demand, especially where there is an element of style or irregular market promotions. The user's prior probabilities about what might happen can be taken into account so that the system can start producing useful forecasts with little or no available history. Alternatively, where there is history available one can start at the beginning of the series with an arbitrary state of "ignorance" and let the computations learn the appropriate priors through simulation.

A typical basic model for the current observation is $d_t = \mu_t + \epsilon_t$, where μ is the level of the underlying process and ϵ is the noise in the current observation. The current level is related to the slope by $\mu_t = \mu_{t-1} + \beta_t + \gamma_t$, where the trend itself changes by $\beta_t = \beta_{t-1} + \delta_t$. The step change γ and the ramp change δ, as well as the noise ϵ, are assumed to be samples from independent and normal distributions with zero means and known (but not necessarily constant) variances V_ϵ, V_γ, and V_δ.

In the multi-state model there are generally two states for each possible perturbance, each with different variances V^j. In the no-change state the variances are small; in the change state, the variance is quite large. There are also prior probabilities π_j that the state was j previously and is in j now. An example of four states, the associated probabilities, and variance ratios used by the authors as standard starting conditions is shown below. The noise variance V_0 is specified by a variance-law relationship to the current forecast (section 5.2), and the ratios $R^{(j)} = V^{(j)}/V_0$.

State	j	π_j	R_ϵ	R_γ	R_δ
No change	1	0.900	1	0	0
Step	2	0.003	1	100	0
Ramp	3	0.003	1	0	1
Transient	4	0.094	101	0	0

Let the vector ϕ have five elements for, respectively, (a) the expected value of the level, (b) the expected value of the slope, (c) the variance (second moment about the mean) of the level, (d) the covariance of the slope and level, and (e) the variance of the slope. Then, if the joint distribution of the level and slope at time $t - 1$ is a bivariate normal with parameters ϕ_{t-1}, then the posterior distribution after the observation d_t is also bivariate normal with revised parameters ϕ_t.

The five elements of the revised parameter vector are given on the left in each equation below—if the value appears on the right it is understood to be the value as of the previous iteration.

$$m = m + b + A_1 e$$

$$b = b + A_2 e$$

$$v_{\mu\mu} = r_{11} - A_1^2 V_e$$

$$v_{\mu\beta} = r_{12} - A_1 A_2 V_e$$

$$v_{\beta\beta} = r_{22} - A_2^2 V_e$$

The five "smoothing" constants are defined as follows, where e is the error in the current observation compared with the most recent forecast:

$$r_{11} = v_{\mu\mu} + 2v_{\mu\beta} + v_{\beta\beta} + V_\gamma + V_\delta$$

$$r_{12} = v_{\mu\beta} + v_{\beta\beta} + V_\delta$$

$$r_{22} = v_{\beta\beta} + V_\epsilon$$

$$V_e = r_{11} + V_\epsilon$$

$$A_1 = r_{11}/V_e$$

$$A_2 = r_{12}/V_e$$

(There are also expressions for seasonal profile indices, which have been omitted here.)

If there were N possible states initially, this process generates N^2 possible combinations of having been in state i ($i = 1, N$) prior to the current observation, and of now being in state j ($j = 1, N$). These N^2 possibilities are condensed into N bivariate normal distributions with the same (weighted) first and second moments, so that the revision procedure can be carried on indefinitely.

7. MARKETING INTELLIGENCE

None of the statistical descriptive forecasts can anticipate a change in the model of the process being forecast. As noted above, there are some elegant techniques for detecting the change quickly and for making the appropriate response. When there is an economic advantage to do so, and as one gains a greater insight into the mechanism underlying the observations, then the forecast model can be made more and more elaborate.

In many instances there are changes in the process which can be foreseen, but which are not incorporated in the forecast model. For example, an intensive direct mail campaign may increase the number of subscribers to a periodical; the introduction of value-added tax (VAT) in Britain caused a wave of buying just before it went into effect; the massive promotion to introduce a new product like Tange or the Polaroid SX-10 not only sells that product, but creates an awareness of generically similar products, and displaces demand for old products; directives from Washington radically change the patterns of purchase and consumption of petroleum products.

The consequences of these changes in products, in marketing, in the economy, and in government regulation often cannot be computed with any precision, but experienced managers who give careful thought to the possibilities are more likely to indicate the direction of the change than if the issue isn't even raised, since there are no formal methods of dealing with the problem. As Forrester [1961] has remarked, the only forecast of such an effect that is guaranteed to be wrong is zero.

Therefore it is advisable to have competent managers review the forecasts produced by the statistical, descriptive, system and make whatever changes seem appropriate to account for new products, promotions, competition, government action, weather, shortage of materials, and so on.

Part of the implementation of a forecasting system should provide reports for selected items of the statistical forecasts and any previous changes that have been introduced by marketing intelligence. These reports can be aggregated for related products, markets and time period, to make them easy for experienced and knowledgable people to review. Often a corporation will have total sales goals, or forecasts of the available market, which don't match the sum of the individual product sales forecasts.

When there is a disparity between the top-down goals and the bottom-up forecasts, management should review the reasons why there is a difference, and what factors were considered in each. Then if the individual product sales forecasts are to be changed to meet the goals or potentials, not only is there a question of how to spread the aggregate change among items, but also what specific actions must be taken to assure that the resulting forecast will materialize.

If production and distribution decisions are taken on a good forecast, and then marketing action is taken to assure that the actual sales match the forecast, the costs of having the wrong forecast are minimized. Marketing the forecast may be a more economical avenue toward accurate decisions than elaborate attempts to forecast the market.

Of course, anyone with experience in subjective sales forecasting will immediately recognize that input from marketing is "no good." In organizations where the people responsible for such forecasts feel sure that the results will be modified, second-guessed and ignored, it is not surprising to find that the effort devoted to their preparation is insufficient to do a good job. A practical device that is sometimes used is to provide feedback to encourage learning about what is effective intelligence to modify the forecast. Suppose that the statistical forecast of sales for March is 1000 units. The net subjective forecast for March, frozen earlier to assure that ample material is available, was 1500. In April the actual sales reported for March are known to be 1375. If material had been provided on the basis of the statistical model, there would have been a potential shortage of 375 (mitigated, of course, by safety stock—See Chapter I-6). On the basis of the net subjective forecast there was a potential overstock of 125. If the shortage is considered twice as serious as extra inventory, the net improvement due to the subjective intelligence is $(2 \times 375) - 125 = 625$. This could be expressed in dollars, or as a normalizing factor, a multiple of the standard deviation of forecast errors.

In any one particular period there are likely to be several forecast series where there was some sort of change from the raw descriptive forecast. A report back to the people who introduced the marketing intelligence, ranked from high to low in order of the figure of merit for the change, acts as positive feedback to encourage further significant and meaningful changes. It also has the effect of minimizing the amount of time spent in making changes that are of little value and actively discourages those changes which turn out to have been wrong. Whether the reaction is to discontinue the wrong changes or to take more pertinent action to market the resulting forecast, the result is greater profit, efficiency and pleasure for the organization.

REFERENCES

Ayres, R. U., *Technological Forecasting and Long Range Planning*, McGraw-Hill, New York (1969).

Barnard, G. A., "Control Charts and Stochastic Processes," *J. Roy. Stat. Soc.* 21 Series B: 239–271 (1959).

Bass, F. M., "A New Product Growth for Model Consumer Durables," *Management Sci.* 15, No. 5: 215–227 (January 1969).

Box, G. E. P. and G. M. Jenkins, "Some Statistical Aspects of Adaptive Optimization and Control," *J. Roy. Stat. Soc.* 24, Series B: 297ff (1962).

—— and ——, *Time Series Analysis Forecasting and Control*, Holden-Day, San Francisco (1970).

Brown, R. G., *Statistical Forecasting for Inventory Control*, McGraw-Hill, New York (1959).

——, *Smoothing, Forecasting and Prediction of Discrete Time Series*, Prentice-Hall, Englewood Cliffs, N.J. (1963).

——, *Decision Rules for Inventory Management*, Holt, Rinehart and Winston, New York (1967).

——, "Detection of Turning Points in a Time Series," *Decision Sci.* **2**, No. 4: 383–403 (October 1971).

——, *APL*Plus 747 Forecast User's Guide*, Scientific Time Sharing Corp, Washington, D.C. (1973).

Burgin, T. A. and A. R. Wild, "Stock Control–Experience and Usable Theory," *Operational Res. Quart.* **18**, No. 1: 35–52 (1967).

Chambers, C. C., S. K. Mullick, and D. D. Smith, "How To Choose the Right Forecasting Technique," *Harvard Bus. Rev.* **65**, 45–74 (July–August 1971).

Evans, M., *Macro-economic Activity: Theory, Forecasting and Control*, Harper & Row, New York (1969).

Forrester, J. W., *Industrial Dynamics*, MIT Technology Press, Cambridge, Mass. (1961).

Harrison, P. J. and C. F. Stevens, "A Bayesian Approach to Short-term Forecasting," *Operational Res. Quart.* **22**, No. 4: 341–362 (December 1971).

Howard, R. A., *Decision Analysis, Applied Decision Theory*, Proceedings of the Fourth International Conference on Operational Research, John Wiley & Sons, New York, pp 55–71 (1966).

Jenkins, G. M. and D. G. Watts, *Spectral Analysis and its Applications*, Holden-Day, San Franicisco (1969).

Kalman, R. E., "New Methods in Wiener Filtering Theory," Proceedings of the first symposium on engineering application of random function theory and probability, John Wiley & Sons, New York (1963).

Leontief, W., *Input-Output Economics*, Oxford University Press, New York (1966).

Nyquist, H., "Certain Topics in Telegraph Transmission Theory," *AIEE Trans.* **41**, 614–644 (April 1928).

Rosenblatt, M., (ed) *Time Series Analysis*, John Wiley & Sons, New York (1963).

Shishkin, J., "Electronic Computers and Business Indicators," National Bureau of Economic Research Occasional Paper 57 (1957).

Sittler, R. W., "Lectures on Sampled Data Systems Analysis," MIT Lincoln Laboratory Memorandum 2M-0671 **22**, chapters 10–12 (August 1957).

Stevens, C. F., "On the variability of demand for families of items," *Operational Res. Quart.* **25**, No. 3: 411 (1974).

Stevens, C. F. and P. J., Harrison, *Bayesian Forecasting*, a series of reports issued jointly by the Statistics Departments of University College London and the University of Warwick.

Trigg, D. W., "Monitoring a Forecast System," *Operational Res. Quart.* **15**, No. 3: 271–274 (September 1964).

Trigg, D. W., and A. G. Leach, "Exponential smoothing with an adaptive response rate," *Operational Res. Quart.* **18**, No. 1: 53–60 (1967).

van Dobben de Bruyn, C. S., "Smoothing Sales Data by Progressive Correction," *Statistica Neerlandica* **17**, No. 3: 243–265 (1969).

Wiener, N., *Extrapolation, Interpolation and Smoothing of Stationary Time Series*, MIT Technology Press, Cambridge, Mass. (1949).

Winters, P. R. "Forecasting Sales by Exponentially Weighted Moving Averages," *Management Sci.* **6**, No. 3: 324–342 (April 1960).

Yule, G. U. "Why Do We Sometimes Get Nonsense Correlations Between Time Series," *J. Roy. Stat. Soc.* **89**, (new series) 1–64 (1926).

I-2

ACCOUNTING AND FINANCE

John M. Burnham
Tennessee Technological University

1. INTRODUCTION

Today, when dealing with firm-level problems of common concern, a rather broad interdisciplinary approach is being taken by (nominally) economics, accounting, or financial specialists. This orientation was claimed, years ago, to be a primary benefit of a professional operations research (OR) study (Churchman, et al. [1957]) and can, at least in part, be attributed to colleges demanding courses in quantitative methodology and research regardless of major business field. Both practitioners and academicians possess, in addition to particulars of their own area, a common foundation in statistics and OR, economic principles, and industrial management.

Although accounting, finance, and economics roles tend to be blurred by recognition of their interdependence, each individual's approach must, to some extent, reflect the viewpoint of his departmental specialization. The traditional role of accounting, for example, has been related to recording and analyzing economic events measured in dollar terms—a highly detailed and procedurally oriented activity. Managerial economics takes a rather aggregative approach to the firm, reflecting supply and demand schedules, material, labor and capital costs, product prices, production functions and technology, the nature of competition, and the firm's relationship to the economic, political, and social environment. The financial specialist sits squarely in the middle, making financial decisions based on estimates of demand. But finance is also responsible for investment, financing, and dividend decisions requiring the most detailed knowledge of their implications. The economist has always studied inventory as an indicator of economic activity; the accountant has accepted detailed responsibility for its valuation and security; and the financial specialist has recognized inventory as a dominant element in working capital management, a principal determinant of profitability.

This chapter offers a polarized approach to each area as a way of dealing with progressively higher levels of organizational activity. Studies dealing with firm-level interdependencies and extra-firm influences and factors are, however, difficult to assign uniquely. Therefore, any of the classifications of work which this chapter "assigns" to some specialist has been done for purposes of subject matter management rather than to imply boundaries.

1.1 Accounting

The raw material for business decision making results from a pattern: business events give rise to transactions which must first be expressed in dollar terms, then classified, recorded, summarized, and analyzed. Accounting, which carries out these tasks, is called *Financial* (external) or *Managerial* (internal).

Financial Accounting supplies periodic profit-and-loss and balance sheet statements, and other reports for outsiders: investors, creditors, regulatory bodies, and tax authorities, for example. The subclassification, *Tax Accounting*, provides expertise on tax regulations to guide the company in meeting its "minimum lawful tax" obligations, choosing inventory accounting procedures, depreciation schedules, and organization of its corporate and subsidiary structure for minimum tax purposes.

Managerial (Internal, Cost) Accounting provides a variety of continuous and intermittent reports to management for purposes of performance measurement, cost analysis and control, and budgeting. *Internal Auditing* is aimed at safeguarding cash, receivables and payables, physical assets, and their records—with control variables which include both systems design and audit. *Accounting System Design* integrates the recording and classification phases of accounting with the many and diverse user needs for summaries and interpretation.

A relatively clear division between timely and accurate historical description, and useful information for normative evaluation and adjustment, is confounded by the existence of a common training and data base and the need to "shift gears" from one to the other in the interest of overall company benefit. Managerial Accounting is, then, both a descriptive procedure and a goal-seeking activity engaged in performance measurement and control.

Specific activities of accounting groups include:

- management and control of current assets (cash, notes receivable, credit accounts, inventories), current liabilities (payables, notes, warranties, pension, retirement, and other employee compensation programs), long-lived, fixed assets and acquisition or replacement programs, of long-term liability accounting and measurement retirement programs for bonds and other long-term debt instruments;

- analysis and execution of short- and intermediate-term debt agreements in the context of liquidity maintenance;
- accounting for multi-unit, multi-company, and multi-national organizations, and their unique valuation, tax/import duty, transfer, and consumption problems;
- "patrolling" for compliance with legalities (e.g., wage/price controls);
- a variety of responsibilities in cost analysis, profit planning, performance measurement, and cash and performance budget programs.

Examples of statistical and mathematical programming applied to these accounting functions abound in the literature. Statistical decision theory is applied to optimal credit policy determination and probabilistic cost-volume-profit analysis. Emphasis will later be given to linear programming (LP) and its use for transfer pricing, joint cost allocation, and working capital management.

1.2 Finance

According to modern financial theory, the overall goal of the corporation is long-term maximization of its market value. This goal encourages good operating decisions: to invest in new product development, to strive for orderly and consistent earnings growth, to set and to achieve revenue and market-share targets, etc.—always reaching for the long-term, though possibly at the expense of some short-term profit reports. Financial management seeks to optimize the matching of sources and uses of funds in terms of their ability to enhance market value.

Fund *sources* are: increases in equity capital, increases in debt, or the liquidation of assets (sales revenue)—all providing cash or its equivalent.

Fund *uses* are: decreases in equity capital (share purchase or dividend distributions), reduction of debt, or investment in earning assets—all consuming cash or its equivalent. Dividends to shareholders provide a yield on their stock investment. Interest payment to a creditor is a before-taxes expense which goes to reduce an accrued liability. Each use of funds has some influence on the firm's market value, as does the structure of the firm's balance sheet.

Market value is measured by earnings and the price-to-earnings ratio accorded the common shares in the market-place. Earnings are added to the net worth or equity account, and thus a willingness to pay \$20 for a share earning \$2 accords a P/E ratio of 10. The required return on equity (reciprocal of the P/E ratio: 0.10 here) is the *cost of equity capital* (K_e). K_e taken together with K_d, the cost of debt capital, provides a means of estimating the *overall cost of capital*

(K_o). One of the important elements in the analysis of sources and uses of funds is to manage the firm's capital structure to achieve the lowest K_o—since after-tax returns on investments of capital must equal or exceed K_o in order to maintain the share price in the marketplace. K_o is thus an index of overall company performance.

Most financial situations/decisions are highly complex. Investment commitments are interdependent and their returns are often correlated. Correlated cash flows can lead, over time, to wide variances in total cash flows. This *business risk*, then, with its multi-project companion *portfolio risk*, can lead to so-called risk of ruin, or *financial risk:* the likelihood that unfavorable variances in net operating income, combined with creditor debt service requirements, could render the company illiquid and/or insolvent, and bring about either serious reduction in net worth—or bankruptcy. The combined treatment of investment, financing, working capital management, dividend payout, and liquidity planning—all of which are probabilistic, interdependent, and dynamic—leads to highly complex formulations and solutions. The greatest attention here will be given to the integrated models and their interpretation for management purposes.

2. ACCOUNTING

Underlying the uses of OR and/or statistics by the accounting profession are two differing themes. A more or less descriptive approach uses methodology to enhance the accuracy or efficiency of traditional accounting functions. The prediction of accurate bad debt allowances is an example, depending heavily on statistics for both description and control. Alternatively, and to an increasing extent, decision theory and mathematical programming are used to provide credit policy and planning guidance, or to enhance credit decision-making processes.

This section will consider both themes in dealing with elements of two areas of interest to the profession: working capital (credit and receivables, cash, payables, and inventory), and managerial accounting (budgeting, joint costs, and transfer pricing). Some brief references to other work will help readers locate reports of many aspects not covered here.

2.1 Working Capital Elements

Sales volume for most businesses is greatly enlarged by the decision to sell "on credit." The *wheel of retailing* is set in motion as assets (inventory) are converted to assets (cash). *Sales on credit* lead to *Accounts Receivable*. Each credit sale is converted, eventually, into either a Paid Account (cash) or a Doubtful Account (loss). The net proceeds (*Credit Sales* less *Uncollectible Accounts*) are then reinvested through *orders* and *payment* for *Inventory*—and the wheel begins another turn. Accounts receivable are frequently the largest current assets a firm possesses, and therefore of great interest to sales departments, credit managers, collection agencies, factors (who purchase accounts receivable), management, and stockholders. Cash and inventory management practices have substantial impact on return on investment.

Credit Sales—Statistical analysis and Markov transition matrices with absorbing states have been successfully used to deal with prediction of the rate of conversion of accounts receivable into cash, and bad debt loss; and through comparisons with these predictions, as a control device for credit department action.

Detailed statistical analysis is used to identify different *behavior* classes of customers, their buying volume, and their payment patterns. Where significant differences justify the increased complexity, the proportion of credit sales attributable to each group can be calculated for weighting the results of the overall analysis. Substantial variation in volume may result from seasonal fluctuations and promotional activities; this calls for ways of deseasonalizing sales experience and allowing for secular trending. In order to assure accurate transition matrix values, estimation procedures have been suggested ranging from a moving average or exponential smoothing to the more extensive treatments by regression analysis (Lewellen and Edmister [1973]).

The statistical analysis results in frequency distributions describing the probability that a dollar of credit sales will be paid at the end of successive time periods. The assembly of these data into a Markov matrix permits manipulation toward a number of ends. In a regular Markov matrix, the first two columns are the absorbing states, representing payment in full of a credit sale or movement into the bad debt category. The remainder of the matrix gives transition probabilities for the likelihood that a dollar of sales debt owed at the end of time period t will still be owed at the end of $t + 1, t + 2, \ldots$ and including $t = n$, the bad debt absorbing state. Since each credit sales dollar must ultimately be absorbed, either into "paid" or "bad debt," the matrix can yield a steady-state distribution of receivables probabilities by age, and their variances; the loss expectancy rate and its variance; and the dollar expectancies for each age account when the vector of current dollars of receivables by age is an input. The basic theory of Markov processes is described quite clearly by Kemeny, et al. [1972, pp. 113–17, 215–29, 237–50].

Through cyclic repetitive chain manipulation (Cyert, et al. [1962]), a vector of (past, or predicted future) sales can be premultiplied by the transition matrix, to yield the predicted dollar inflows and their variances as a function of time for cash management planning. The steady-state probabilities can be used, with actual sales experience, to provide a control function within the credit department. So long as the actual account payments are within ± an appropriate number of standard deviations of those expected, no action is required; otherwise, possible shifts in payment patterns should be investigated. The index of mean collection period to that expected has also been suggested as a control measure (Benishay [1965]).

The results of credit sales analysis have been extended into the realm of *credit-granting policy*. Many banks and most finance companies use *credit-scoring* models. Descriptively, a scoring model attempts to assign numerical weights to various personal and credit history items on a credit application form. High scores are then interpreted as high disposition to pay credit obligations promptly. In a study on secured loans made by a West Coast finance company (Cohen & Hammer [1966]), a large sample of credit experience histories was analyzed using score levels to "refuse" applicants, and the actual experience was tallied against the rule. For each successively higher score level, the percentage of *bad* (repossessions) accounts eliminated was compared with the percentage of *good* (paid-off) accounts also eliminated by the hurdle score. In its implementation, the volume of loans desired, probable proportion of losses, and probable number of satisfactory accounts refused were all considered in setting the hurdle score.

Mehta [1968] analyzes present credit policy as measured by bad debt ratios, receivables outstanding, the average collection periods, and volume of credit sales (aggregate of decisions to grant credit). The model is that of sequential decision making under risk, using the Bayes criterion of minimizing the expected opportunity losses associated with each action choice. (The chapter on decision analysis provides details of concepts and solution procedures.) At each stage there exist three alternatives with respect to an application: *accept* credit sales (opportunity cost is the likelihood of nonpayment plus expected credit collection costs), *refuse* credit sales (opportunity cost is the likelihood of payment times the contribution margin), or *investigate* further (opportunity cost is related to evaluating records, obtaining agency ratings, doing checks of other creditors, or, finally, doing a financial statement analysis—each step of which involves some further costs but also provides more data for credit decision making).

Based on response classifications, size of order, old or new customer, and other determinants of probability of payment or nonpayment, one of the three alternatives (accept, refuse, investigate) involves the least expected opportunity loss, and is used to provide operating decision rules to the credit personnel. Further work (Mehta [1970]) uses dynamic analysis and Markov chains *within* the normal collection period, when action choices are presented which involve *extension* of credit, granting *additional* credit, or a possible decision to *tighten* credit through intensifying current collection efforts.

Cash Management—The cash balance acts to "damp" maladjustments in timing between inflows and outflows of funds. According to a study by the National Industrial Conference Board (Pflomm [1961]), control of cash transactions is actually a variety of problems: predicting cash balance changes, financing cash requirements, investing excess cash, and improving collection procedures. Computer simulations have been run to describe (future) cash budgets under a variety of conditions of interest to management, while so-called optimal financing models have been developed using LP or dynamic programming (DP) (Elton and Gruber [1974]). The major stock brokerage houses have sought to improve the firm's earnings on excess cash through the services of institutional money market specialists. And extensive work has been done since the early 1950's (Horn [1964]; Leone [1964]) to improve collection procedures.

Pro forma cash budgets, cash simulation models, and more sophisticated statistical cash forecasting models include not only the "driving force" of cash and credit sales for the planning period, but the effect of longer term decisions such as capital investments, term loan or bond maturities. Also scheduled are shorter-term legal obligations such as tax dates, wages and salaries, and other contracts. The output of any cash forecasting model identifies the timing and amount of expected changes in cash balances.

Stochastic variation in the cash flows can be handled by maintaining a liquid *balance* whose level is determined by comparing the opportunity costs of shortages (borrowing, forced premature assets liquidation, discounts passed up) to the carrying cost of excess funds (longer-term, higher-yielding securities not invested in, or no yield at all!). Optimal *policies* may be defined for situations in which the expected holding and shortage cost is convex and in which decisions to adjust level of cash do not involve fixed cost (Girgis [1968]). Under somewhat more complex assumptions, and with fixed costs associated with increases or decreases, a convex bounding approach can be used to provide a simple, nonoptimal policy, when the true optimal policy is complex (Neave [1970]). Decision rules based on the policies will prescribe appropriate adjustments at each review stage. Just as in its inventory counterpart, this form of cash management model does not choose among alternative investment and financing possibilities to optimally manage excess or shortage situations. In recent years, LP has been frequently used for this purpose.

Several points must be mentioned here. First: because of the general availability of high-speed computers and good user-oriented mathematical programming software, the actual solution of a highly detailed yet comprehensive cash management problem with, perhaps, several thousands of decision variables and hundreds of important and realistic constraints, is completely feasible. Any difficulty lies in the conception of the problem, in its detailed formulation, and in the interpretation of results.

Second: the degree of detail and the frequency with which it must be run for decision purposes becomes a matter of economics. Unpublished studies using City of Miami, Florida, data indicate that weekly analyses are sufficient, with a fifty-two week rolling horizon for longer term. A portion of the model uses daily stages, and then a set of longer, unequal-length periods (months). More detail means more realism—and probably more frequent revision and higher run costs. Of course, less detail (or higher aggregation) means less accuracy, perhaps more managerial insight, and less run time.

Third: the trade-offs between detail and aggregation, and the *level* of decision guidance being sought, are most often a function of the quality and experience of the individuals operating the cash management system.

Fourth: many of the real constraints cannot be described accurately in symbols, and goal hierarchies exist which can only be approximated in terms of single-criterion objective functions.

A detailed description of a deterministic multistage LP cash management model follows. The purpose of the presentation is not prescriptive, but rather indicates some of the general, as well as the particular, elements of this, the heart of the working-capital management program.

The model (Orgler [1970]) includes all four classes of decision variables: the controllable payments schedule, debt financing, investment alternatives, and cash balance. Short-term financing variables include any allowed by policy or other financing agreements. Investments include maturity, transaction costs, and yields; and the model recommends which securities to sell short of maturity if this becomes necessary. Cash balance includes any minimum levels set by policy, or compensating balance agreements, and uses both average daily minimum balances over the horizon and absolute minimums maintained within each interval. All amounts of cash in excess of the minimum specified levels will be used in the most profitable way—for investment, reduction of loans, or partial liquidation and then reinvestment or loan reduction. Only if no opportunity can be found will excess cash be carried into the next interval. For a recent treatment of cash management as a transshipment problem under somewhat restricted conditions, see Srinivasan [1974].

The model maximizes net revenues from the cash budget with reinvestment in any interval in which any revenue occurs (or maturing investments provide cash). The objective function coefficients include: transaction costs, lost yield from premature securities sale, loan interest, penalties for early debt reduction; also, as revenues: discounts taken on accounts payable, interest saved on debt reduction, and earnings from securities. Yields are in absolute percentages adjusted for holding period, so all costs and gains are strictly comparable over the horizon (Orgler uses one year).

Constraints include: expressions for inflow and outflow timing, minimum cash balance requirements, representations of the payables schedule, financing alternatives, securities availabilities, "termination" constraints to prevent liabilities buildup toward the horizon of the model, and a variety of managerial constraints applying to quick and current financial ratios during financial reporting periods.

Required inputs to the model include: cost and revenue coefficients, future estimates of these same values within the planning horizon, the payments schedule, and estimated cash inflows over time. Upper or lower bounds for right-hand sides of various constraints must be input, all within the framework of the multistage technology matrix.

Much useful information can be gained from the dual solution. Values (costs) of minimum compensating balance agreements, worth (cost) of line-of-credit as compared with alternate spot financing schemes, value (cost) of balance-of-payments restrictions near horizon end, can be determined directly. Major proposed changes to credit or collection policies can be evaluated using parametric programming and "what if?" arguments. A year's model for a large company ($500 million annual sales) would contain some 3000 variables and 400 constraints, with perhaps 20-25 unequal periods. Initial solution of the "big" problem from fresh input will be rather expensive. With most third-generation computer codes, the entire solution can be stored and the program will *re*-solve modified problems beginning with the earlier optimal solution—a great saving in computer input and run time.

Orgler [1970] suggests benefits in the order of 1 percent of the average balance of the marketable securities account, and reduction in interest expense on short-term loans by 5 percent annually. For most firms, adopting the integrated approach to cash management would also have important behavioral benefits not measurable in dollars.

I directed graduate students in a series of studies of OR applications, using data and policy inputs from the cash management group at the City of Miami, Florida. Revenues from taxes are received in a relatively brief period each year; tax sharing from state and federal sources brings in money periodically, as do licenses, use fees, and local sales taxes. Principal outflows include: capital improvement projects, wages and salaries, and operating costs associated with city services. To test whether improved financial operation was possible, both deterministic and stochastic versions of a recursive DP model were developed. Restricting the model to choices among certificates of deposit, treasury bills, and time deposits, and using deterministic ex post procedures, an investment income improvement of over 20% was achieved on a test year. The model was also used to simulate cash flows, using budgetary planning data and regression data for variability of account balances. It was demonstrated that cash balance requirements could be reduced from $500,000 to about $230,000, based on the opportunity costs of borrowing as compared with the yields from long-term paper held from year's beginning. Even with the "curse of dimensionality" inherent in DP, the model consumed only $5 per run in computer time. The reports were never published, since no real gain in theory could be claimed. To date there is no indication that the results of the study have been implemented.

Inventory—Discussion here will be limited to the accounting point of view and to some of the implications of inventory management for working capital management.

Inventory is an element of current assets, subject to conversion through production and/or distribution and sale. It may suffer physical deterioration or pilferage, and can be mislaid or misdirected. Good inventory control can considerably improve return on investment by minimizing funds tied up in these assets. The two kinds of opportunity costs rising out of inventory—carrying cost of idle, excess inventory, and shortage or backlogging cost for items short—permit model construction aiming at optimal carrying levels and replenishment programs. These are still very much in evidence in the accounting practitioners' literature (Slaybaugh [1971]). Recent work in accounting firms' publications emphasizes the benefits of simulation in evaluating various policies which might be applied to inventory management (Shaw [1971]).

Computerized inventory systems management is very much in vogue today. Some readers will recognize "MRP," Materials Requirements Planning as a current example (Peterson [1975]). The system captures data from the normal paperwork flow accompanying purchasing, production, sales, and service activities. Such paperwork is all relevant to some portion of either accounting or production/marketing. It is *not* additional work, but rather another use of data/tasks accomplished for other purposes.

Conclusions—Each Working Capital item can be treated separately, as can each subproblem under every item. One of the objectives of financial management is to balance the risks and costs associated with small inventories, small cash balances, and small receivables, with the gains to return on investment that accrue by keeping current assets small. We have seen the varied roles of the accounting profession in detailed development of methodologies for managing working capital. The same elements, being part of aggregate financial management, will appear again in that context.

2.2 Managerial Accounting

Reports, studies, and comparisons generated for internal management use in planning, operating, and controlling the business firm have none of the restrictions imposed by the principles and standards of financial accounting and auditing. The normative elements of credit, cash, and inventory management all fall within managerial accounting. Most of the contributions of OR to this area are in planning.

Cost-Volume-Profit (*CVP*) *or Breakdown Analysis*—CVP uses the concept of contribution margin, or marginal income per unit of sales, as a principal tool for comparison. With the trend toward more realistic assumptions and more integrated approaches to product decisions, a variety of models has been developed. The original purpose of breakeven was to estimate the minimum required sales volume to recover the full costs of production. Its extensions (see Condition VII) have brought it fully into capital budgeting, a Finance function.

Condition I: Single Period, Single Independent Product, Certainty Conditions— In an existing plant with excess capacity, a decision to increase output will involve added material and energy costs proportional to output changes—and a fixed cost for the added labor input. This is a marked departure from traditional CVP analysis. The comparison is between revenues from the additional product $(P \cdot \Delta Q)$ and the sum of the added labor cost (L) (man-months, man-years) and the direct variable costs (VC) of the additional units produced $(L + VC\Delta Q)$. This situation can arise in considering temporary second-shift operation of an existing plant with all additional labor force being new-hires. There may be some minimum number of workers required to run the second shift.

Condition II: Multi-Period, Single Independent Product, Certainty Conditions—The known cost of increased fixed plant (F) and the variable labor, material, and energy costs (VC) associated with units of production are compared with sales revenues $(R = P \cdot Q)$. Volume greater than that at which the revenue curve crosses the cost curve $(F + VC \cdot Q)$ is profitable. Various assumptions about costs, price per unit, and volume relationships, and the net profits and BEP's associated with each, complete the traditional CVP analysis. Recent work (Manes [1966]) urges that cost of capital be included in the CVP calculations, since there are opportunity costs associated with making the present capital investment instead of others. If more than one (accounting) period is required to recover total costs (BEP), then the contribution margin should be discounted back to the present,

$$\text{Discounted Contribution Margin} = \left\{ \sum_t [P \cdot Q(t) - VC \cdot Q(t)]/(1 + K_o)^t \right\}$$

where K_o is the overall cost of capital.

Condition III: Multi-Period, Single Independent Product, Alternative Production Techniques, Certainty Conditions—The different combinations of $(F + VC(Q))_T$ yield BEP_T's which are portions of the short-run cost curves for the technologies (T) described. The linear portions of their respective curves lie approximately in the long-run total cost curve for the product. The range of demand must determine the technology chosen. For a *given* price per unit, the proper decision is to choose the technology with lowest total cost for the planning volume selected (Mitchell [1969]). Cost of capital should be included in the calculations according to present thinking.

Condition IV: Multi-Period, Single Independent Product, Alternative Production Techniques, Curvilinear Revenue and Cost Functions, Certainty Conditions— Elasticity of demand provides a price-volume relationship $(P(Q))$. Technology (T) provides a total cost-volume relationship $C(Q, T)$ for each alternative production method, including both fixed and variable costs without restriction to linear functions. The calculus derivative (dP/dQ) describes rate of change in profit $(R(Q) - C(Q))$ and determines the maximum profit point by solving for Q for zero slope (Goggans [1965], and Givens [1966]). The problem may also take the form of changes in volume, price, or quality (variable cost). This permits movement from one product-demand elasticity curve to another. Concurrent changes in volume and price which result in the same profit can be used to develop a profit indifference curve to assist in the measurement of profit risk when making price change analyses (Morrison & Kaczka [1969]).

Condition V: Single-Period, Multi-Product Certainty Decisions with Optimizing Objectives—When multiple products compete for the limited resources of the present fixed plant, constrained optimization using LP is more useful to management than independent CVP. This is the classical product mix problem (Jaedicke [1961]). Interpretation of the dual shadow prices shows the marginal value of each scarce resource (Charnes, et al., 1963).

Condition VI: Multi-Period, Single Independent Product, Uncertainty Conditions—Variations in cost with volume can be analyzed statistically using regression analysis. The result quantifies average relationships and provides a standard error of estimate $(S_{y.x})$ describing cost variance. Analysis can be indecisive from the strict CVP viewpoint, due to the size of $S_{y.x}$ (Raun [1964]). Decision theory and the utility of payoffs associated with alternative actions can be used to provide expected action values. The variations in price, cost structure, and sales volume, are analyzed together to present the probability of loss and its magnitude (Jaedicke & Robichek [1964]). Specific statistical analysis of profit variation through model sampling (Liao [1975]) offers further refinement, avoiding two restrictive assumptions: normal distributions, and independence of returns. Products can thus be compared by their relative risk, as well as by their expected profit. As a part of LP post-optimality analysis, sensitivity testing can provide some information on the effect of contribution margin variation as well as variations in upper-bounded demand constraints.

Condition VII: Multi-Period, Interdependent Multi-Product Decisions, Uncertainty Conditions—When new product additions are being evaluated, the correlation of sales volumes among products will require explicit inclusion of "portfolio risk" elements in the analysis in order to evaluate aggregate risk and returns. Full variance-covariance matrix generation and manipulation, as well as the simpler diagonal matrix approach, has been used for probabilistic CVP (Johnson & Simik [1971]).

A most interesting recent report of CVP analysis dealing with the Lockheed Tristar (Reinhardt [1973]) appeared in the *Journal of Finance*. Using data gleaned from the lengthy Congressional hearings resulting from Lockheed's severe liquidity crisis, this study is done under what corresponds closely with Condition VI (or VII, depending on interpretation). Three kinds of outlays are identified: costs of activities from initial design to prototype evaluation (RDTE—Research, Development, Testing, and Evaluation); construction of production facilities, machine tool, and other equipment manufacture or purchase (IIT—Initial Investment and Tooling); and the cost of airframe component purchase and assembly into the airframe. RDTE is a nonrecurring and largely intangible front-end investment in know-how. IIT is also nonrecurring and is analogous to fixed-plant investment (F) eventually chargeable against production on an absorption basis; and the last is the recurring direct cost of manufacture (VC). The nonrecurring costs totalled $850 million to $1 billion.

Two factors operate to make the model nonlinear: the learning curve in aircraft manufacture, which shows a consistent reduction in direct labor charges as a function of the number of units produced (Hartley [1971]); and the finite production rate (between three and five ships a month after delivery of the first). A large and long-term capital opportunity cost is involved in the nonrecurring costs of RDTE and IIT, as well as the stream of payments on delivered ships. To judge from the statements at the hearings, *Lockheed apparently ignored cost of capital in their breakeven calculations.* The nondiscounted cash flows and the direct cost of RDTE and IIT led Lockheed to predict breakeven at about 200 ships sold. Inclusion of the cost of capital at 10% for the four-year RDTE and IIT periods, and for the long delivery period, moves the breakeven point out to some 500 ships. Since the world market for wide-body, intermediate-range ships, assuming a 10% annual rate of growth in air travel, was estimated to be some 775 aircraft (an optimistic figure), and the Douglas DC-10 was a reality (leaving Lockheed a 35-40% market share—perhaps 300 ships in all), the result is no capital recovery on the opportunity costs of the billion-dollar nonrecurring elements. Reinhardt concludes that the presentation of an undiscounted CVP analysis by Lockheed, which induced the Government to guarantee a $250 million loan, may have consigned *both* airbus projects to languishing economic futures.

Profit Planning and Control—The *planning* (or fixed) *budget* of the firm describes its future programmed activities and their outcomes in dollar terms, for the budget period; e.g., the monthly pro forma cash budget provides details of funds flows by day/week, and their timing and amount. A planning budget reflecting goals, decisions, and profit plans, when coupled with an income statement, becomes a *performance budget*—a benchmark against which to measure progress; e.g., the monthly pro forma cash budget is coupled with investment opportunities for excess funds or costs of alternate sources of funds to meet cash deficiencies), and the revenue (net cost) of cash management operations is estimated for the period.

When the performance budgeting concept is applied after the fact, and the actual results are compared with those planned, the variances (favorable/unfavorable) are analyzed. The flexible budget provides programmed results allowing for the effect of uncontrollable factors, and generates new performance standards under the revised conditions. Profit planning and control is routinely applied within decentralized operating organizations, assigning profit center management responsibility and authority, and evaluating managerial performance based on the results.

However, the development of computer technology has led to major changes in both planning budget generation and after-the-fact flexible budgeting: the accounting data base can be manipulated statistically to provide the necessary empirical distributions for highly realistic and detailed simulations of budget behavior under a variety of "what if?" scenarios; and mathematical models can provide both the descriptive (flexible budget) and normative (feedback and control responses) extensions useful for divisional activity management.

The literature of accounting has described a variety of budget simulation models for both profit-making and non-profit-making enterprise; e.g., RAPID is a university budgetary simulation (Peat, Marwick and Mitchell [1967]). The development of various mathematical models to yield budget and performance evaluation details will be briefly traced here.

The product mix which maximizes expected contribution margin can be obtained by a straightforward application of mathematical programming, and is the logical input for a planning budget. Treatments providing insightful discussion of the mechanics and interpretation of the results have been reported: recognizing linear conditions and showing the usefulness of sensitivity analysis (Onsi [1966]; Dopuch, et al. [1967]; Demski [1967]); on the realistic effect of integer restrictions (Rappaport [1967, 1969]; Jensen [1968]; Glover [1969]); on the explicit recognition of random elements in both profit coefficients and resources/demand (Gonedes [1969]; Ferrara & Hayya [1970]). Ranging can help identify "strategic" resources and their values. The stability of the solution in adjusting to resource quantity changes can be examined effectively through post-optimality analysis rather than using traditional flexible budgeting. Identification and explanation of under utilized ("non-strategic") fixed resources which are slack at optimum, while avoiding performance penalty; and assessment of the impact of cost or productivity changes both directly and in terms of the contribution, technology, resources combination; all are demonstrated in the literature, and are identified with industrial applications. The decision to engage in wide-ranging parametric programming in order to trace a probabilistic profit profile (Ferrara & Hayya [1970]) is an analytical approach to earlier simulation procedures (Hertz [1964, 1968]) with essentially the same objectives.

Cost Accounting—"In the past ten to fifteen years considerable emphasis has been placed on 'proper' methods of planning and controlling a decentralized firm. If we postulate that the firm's objective is to maximize profits, the problem becomes one of the allocation of scarce resources. Decentralization is intended to combat the inefficiencies inherent in a large centrally planned and controlled organization . . . By making each division a profit center, thus responsible for its own planning and controlling, the informational flow is greatly reduced and decisions are more in keeping with the current state of affairs. If there were no dependencies between divisions, a simple division of the firm into smaller independent operating units would be highly advantageous" (Hass [1968]).

Most decision centers are, however, interdependent with respect to factors of production, particularly capital. Economy of scale suggests sharing of certain services (firm-level coordination, and more obvious technical service elements).

Divisions are frequently suppliers of product to other decision centers—where selling price, perceived as *revenue* to supplier-division, is a material *cost* to the buying division. Ideally, the method devised to assign overhead, joint costs, or transfer payments will have each decision center making decisions optimal for the whole firm, with a minimum of cost for coordination, information flow, and messages. Shubik [1964] suggests using game theory and the "Shapley Value" derived from the individual profit possibilities of each division operating alone, compared with their superadditive profits (synergism) when acting together guided by a corporate coordinating function.

There is general agreement that an effective way to accomplish goal-congruent behavior is through an administered price system. Decision center management acts to achieve optimal divisional operations in response to material, labor, and capital costs, and product prices—each, to some extent, a decision variable controllable by the firm (Gordon, in Bonini, et al. [1964]).

Inventory Valuation—shows the effect of differing cost systems. A *direct* cost accounting system accumulates all of the variable costs of manufacture and assigns them to finished units of production as inventory value—a current asset. In addition to direct costs, a *full absorption* cost system also prorates costs of factory and administrative overhead to units of production on a standard volume basis. Substantially all of the costs of operation are charged against inventory as it is created, thus increasing its book value. One of the results of this procedure is that reported profits increase as end-of-period inventory builds up. OR studies, one using analytical inventory models (Ijiri, et al. [1965]), and the other DP (Bailey [1973]), have compared the two costing methods to show that direct costing leads to production-inventory decisions favoring the firms's profitability.

Considerable challenge is offered by the need for allocation procedures which decision centers understand, and which will motivate decisions good for the firm. Statistical studies supplemented by calculus have developed two criteria consistent with firm goals, by which allocation schemes may be evaluated. Quite often indirect costs are allocated to profit centers on the basis of a product attribute; e.g., direct cost, value, size, weight. Brief and Owen [1968] recommend using a least-squares minimization to evaluate the choice of both the attribute and the weighting scheme; i.e., the most consistent and equitable scheme will have the smallest sum-of-squares. A second study (Brief & Owen [1970]) look at the purpose of overhead allocation to product; that of matching period costs with period revenues. The best allocation scheme is the one which yields an efficient estimator of the overall rate of return in each reporting period; i.e., a scheme which minimizes the least-squares deviations of return in period t from the overall return determined to have been achieved in the planning horizon. Moriarty [1975] suggests that joint costs are only incurred to avoid the higher cost of purchasing the needed services elsewhere—hence the allocation of the costs should be proportional to the savings, or costs avoided, by the groups sharing the services.

Once the attribute and weighting schemes have been decided, the accounting system must make the (proportional) indirect cost assignments to the divisions. One procedure used with some success is the technology matrix of input-output (I/O) analysis. I/O assumptions are fairly restrictive: product and divisional independence; fixed (unvarying) relationships between cost and profit centers; clearly defined prices for interdivisional transfer of intermediate products; and linearity. But, for certain process-type enterprises with substantial vertical integration (chemicals, textiles, basic metals) the procedures are fruitfully applied (Livingstone [1969, 1973]; Ijiri [1968; Farag [1968]. Since the I/O framework is descriptive and aggregative (not analytical and detailed), its proper uses in cost accounting require auxiliary calculations and analysis. For example, I/O strict linearity results in distortions when used for budgetary extrapolation (in the presence of the usual economy of scale). Bounds on both resources and demand are common characteristics of realistic optimization. But, I/O contains no provision for bounding, so I/O specifications based on the constant material balances may be operationally infeasible. For constructive criticism of these procedures, see Gambling and Nour [1970]. For an excellent detailed industrial implementation report, see Tuckett [1969].

Fixed Costs—The usual LP decision variables have profit coefficients representing contribution margin, so that plant (sunk) costs are not directly attributable to product. Government contractors on cost-plus-percentage work, and custom-product, monopolistic, and oligopolistic marketers have problems with this conventional scheme. Proper full-cost bid prices can only be developed by explicit inclusion of fixed costs in the functional. Colantoni, et al. [1969] describes the errors due to "standard-cost-standard-volume" fixed-cost allocations, as opposed to solving for full price. Treatments using general linear, nonlinear, and integrally constrained formulations are solved directly. Differential earning rates (cost of capital, variable percentage) and appropriate pricing and capacity allocation implications can also be analyzed through this full-cost optimization procedure. Inclusion of *fixed charges* in the objective function is reported in Groves, et al. [1970].[1]

Transfer Pricing—Issues surrounding proper interdivisional pricing for goal congruence have been debated for over twenty years. Accounting professionals currently state at least three different points of view:

1. *Negotiation:* an acceptance that market forces really do determine prices (Fremgen [1970]). Selling and buying division activities that include outside

---

[1]Fixed charges (e.g., capacity, out-of-pocket, caretaker and enabling costs) are incurred if particular product is built, but are not a direct function of the quantity of product, nor of competing products. See Shillinglaw [1967].

sources and customers are truly competitive under all conditions of the market when clearly defined firm goals guide all decision centers.

2. An *opportunity cost transfer price* can be developed under perfect competition and under the monopsonistic seller (or monopsonistic buyer) conditions often prevailing in the firm (Holstrum and Sauls [1973]). The opportunity cost is defined by evaluation of the next best alternative (purchase or sale) and of the benefits foregone by not accepting it. The analysis of detailed market conditions, and the careful application of marginal analysis to demand shifts in both intermediate and final product markets, are involved. The *firm* must set the proper price, and check against possible data misstatements by decision centers.

3. *Taxes or Subsidy Payments* should operate to equalize the true firm-level contributions of the decision centers (Hirschleifer, [1964]; Ronen & McKinney [1970]). The Central Office (firm) acts as a clearing house for data from supplying and purchasing divisions which describe their supply and demand schedules. Through the subsidy (tax), the division is credited (or charged) with its quantity-price decision's effect, including external-market elasticity, on profits at the firm level.

These three "philosophical" views of optimal transfer price development are not unquantitative. Rather, they point up the shortcomings of those pure mathematical programming approaches which, at the present state of the art, do not adequately handle the internal (division managers) and external (market) behavioral aspects of the situation.

Mathematically derived shadow prices (marginal worth of a resource) can be used to set selling prices on goods for which there is *no intermediate market* (Onsi [1970]). The solution chooses the volume that maximizes firm-level profits for a given demand schedule and a price equal to the shadow prices of resources used in production. This is only appropriate, however, when these same resources can be used for other products *having* outside market prices. The selling division then prices the intermediate product to maintain total contribution margin.

When a resource is underutilized, or when the shadow price associated with the outside product is very high, this approach will cause difficulties through high intermediate product pricing to buying divisions. Decomposition techniques can be used to achieve an optimal firm-level solution by centralized pricing ("negotiation") (Baumol & Fabian [1964]; Hass [1968]). There are many examples of the failure of pure economic shadow prices to assign proper transfer prices for *decentralized* operating divisions (e.g., Manes [1970]). Where centralized pricing can be justified on a behavioral basis the decomposition technique is effective.

Shulman [1969] discusses the added complexities of national instability, "joint" ownership, taxes, profits repatriation, and other elements of transfer pricing arising in the operation of overseas divisions and subsidiaries—the multinational firm—but makes no mathematical proposals.

2.3 Trends and Conclusions

Accounting professionals are thinking and acting at the firm level. Each of the topics covered in this fragmentary treatment ends with a consideration of broad implications of managerial action. A thrust in the professional consulting area—the *management services* offered by accounting firms outside the traditional auditing and accounting systems areas—includes such diverse activities as: management information systems design; merger valuation advice; obtaining local investment in overseas firms; reorganizations overseas; parochial school financial systems; improving market efficiency; PPBS; systems analysis for higher education; pastoral planning; and a variety of other profit- and non-profit-management applications with little "traditional accounting" relevance.

Implicit in the existence of a computerized accounting system, the great computational power in third- and fourth-generation functional mathematical programming codes, the many user-oriented statistical packages, the optical scanning devices used for bank check processing, and in the strong interest expressed by accounting practitioners in broad management topics, is the possibility that, at least *technically*, many of the compromises of decentralization may no longer be necessary. The increasingly complex formulations of recent years suggest that more centralized administered price systems may be nearly here. And, at the opposite pole, accountants are studying quantitatively the behavioral effects of information for both descriptive and normative purposes (Theil [1969]; Lev [1969]; Hinomoto [1971]; Demski [1972]).

3. FINANCE

"The principal role of the capital market is allocation of ownership of the economy's capital stock. In general terms, the ideal is a market in which prices provide accurate signals for resource allocation: that is, a market in which firms can make production-investment decisions, and investors can choose among the securities that represent ownership of firms' activities under the assumption that security prices at any time 'fully reflect' all available information [i.e., an "efficient" market]," (Fama [1970, p. 383]). The goal "long-term maximization of the market value of the firm" implies strategic and operating decisions involving many variables and constraints. "Price" is the best estimator of value. Some of the determinants of value are: earnings, growth of earnings, dividends, net worth, size, and leverage (Gordon, [1962]; Sloane & Reisman [1968]). These variables influence the cost of debt borrowing, the cost of equity capital, and the overall cost of capital, K_o, over time.

K_o prescribes the investment opportunities schedule which the firm may consider. The investments, their business and portfolio risk elements, and the method(s) by which they are financed influence the cash flow and working capital position of the firm and determine its solvency or financial risk of ruin. The net result of these decisions over time is a market price reflecting the investors' assessment of expected returns from holding, length of time required to achieve the returns, and the variance of returns (or risk) inherent in the investment.

This complex and interdependent set of relationships leads to a financial system model made up of many elements of micro- and intra-division decision problems and cash management variables, plus more aggregative elements of demand, price, factor costs, and environment.

It was not ever thus!

3.1 Finance—Historical

Principal financial concerns in the 1900's related to capital market and institutions, equity and debt financing, promotion, mergers, and consolidations. In the heyday of post-World War I prosperity, the investment banker's role, and securities and common stock financing principles, were added to financial thinking. During the Depression (1930's), urgent and continuing emphasis rested on liquidity management, lender protection, and the response of the firm to reorganizations and proceedings in bankruptcy. The regulatory requirements for more financial disclosure, and the great increase in emphasis on financial accounting systems, subsequently led to work on evaluation of firms through analysis, with much study of sound financial structure. During these decades, most financial thinking had empirical, experience-based origins.

By the 1950's, external financing and analysis, planning and projection of cash flows, and a rising interest in the efficient allocation of capital in the firm had been added. In the 1960's, the financial role expanded to include aggregate financial assets management on the basis of contribution to goals. Since then, the valuation of the firm both by investors and by creditors, and integrative theories of finance have led to an analytical field of study with a full complement of advanced mathematical and statistical methodology (Van Horne [1969]; Philippatos [1973]). The uncertainties of inflation, violent price changes, non-growth conditions, and floating exchange rates, are all explicitly represented in the complex analytical models of the mid-decade.

3.2 Elements of Financial Decision Making

Investments—A rational investor seeks the highest possible certain returns. If only risky investments are available and their variances of return are equal, the investor will choose to receive the highest expected return. If different return variances exist for equal expected return, the investment with the lowest variance will be chosen. Investor utility (risk aversion) will operate to select among investments with unequal expectations and unequal variances. Weighted average returns and variances guide independent investment selection. When investment returns are not independent, covariance as well as variance will be considered to assemble a portfolio of risky investments which lie along the efficient frontier (no set of investments exists which has greater expected return except with greater variance—and no set of investments exists with a lesser variance except with a lesser expected return) for the universe of investment alternatives being considered (Markowitz [1959] ; Sharpe [1963]). Risk and return expectations guide the investor in choosing the mix of risky assets to hold for the investment planning period (horizon) (Burnham [1970]). *Price* synthesizes these factors with supply and demand for securities, reflecting the entire capital market's assessment of each alternative investment.

Figure 1 is one way of representing the many dimensions of the real-world equities investment management process. This diagram, developed by Burnham [1970], identifies the elements and relationships in institutional investment management activities. For investors not restricted by regulation or policy, the analysis associated with "stock selection" will include real estate, commodities, options, equities, corporate bonds, money market instruments—all available as investment alternatives. The development of EDP systems in the secondary (stock) capital markets was a virtual necessity for handling the complex professional money investment management activities of brokers and institutions, even ignoring the volume of public transactions involved.

Indeed, the biggest change in investment strategies and tactics has resulted from the availability of accurate real-time data on secondary market transactions (price, volume), and the capability to manipulate these data statistically with relatively low cost and extremely high speed. Each element (block) in the diagram can be associated with various OR models and their outputs, with the frequency and volume of the activity a function of: the kinds of investments being considered, the goals of the manager, and the relation between the planning horizon and the dynamics of the (present or potential) portfolio components.

In FORECASTING, proprietary smoothing and filtering models are used together with more classical regression/econometric forms on parameters such as price, value, and market indices. Operationally, the investor's problem has a number of dimensions, from goals and choices of investment media and on through actions and control.

In STOCK SELECTION ANALYSIS multivariate, cluster, and ranking models (Falk and Heintz [1975]) were used to analyze the industry and economic effects of risk. Individual securities are evaluated fundamentally (assets, earnings, growth, variability of growth, price, dividends) and 'filtered' for above-average performance not yet recognized by the market. "Beta" compares percent price change with percent change of an appropriate market index, in order to measure the volatility of a stock. "Beta has been used as a relative measure of risk—but more frequently, to 'pick' stocks in an up-market. At the same time, this un-

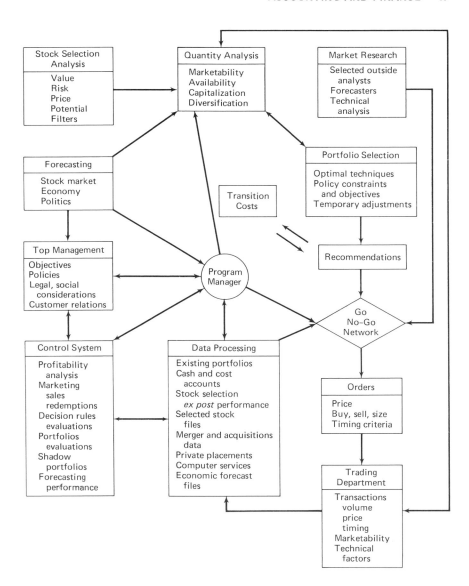

Fig. 1. The process of investment management. Source: Burnham, J. M. *Conditional Chance Constrained Programming Techniques in Portfolio Selection.* University of Texas at Austin, Graduate School of Business Administration (April, 1970) and on demand by University Microfilms, Ann Arbor, Michigan, with permission.

orthodox application of regression concepts is used to determine "Alpha"—the percentage change in stock price, with NO change in the level of the market index! In an even or rising market as determined by the forecasting techniques, selection will favor high positive Alpha and high positive Beta stocks, the maximum Beta values being constrained by risk tolerance.

Like most stock selection work the QUANTITY ANALYSIS activities are entirely computerized. Their key elements include: the amount of stock outstanding, that in 'public' hands, and the volume-behavior of the stock (price response to large purchases and sales). See the work of Computer Directions Advisors (Levy [1969]) for an example of proprietary services available. At this stage the various regulatory and policy constraints on portfolio proportions of individual stocks may be applied to the analysis.

PORTFOLIO SELECTION activities use various mathematical models to examine the expected behavior of the portfolio (bundle of risky assets) in terms of its reward and risk characteristics. Quadratic programming (Markowitz [1959]), Linear Programming (Sharpe [1963]), and geometric mean return criteria (Latané [1975]) have been applied to the portfolio problem. Satisficing (as contrasted with optimization) has been a guide to investment decisions, where risk of loss in individual holdings (Burnham [1970]) or across the portfolio as a whole (Barron, Burnham, and Joy [1973]) has required preemptive selling decision rules to protect the assets. Logically, the satisficing individual or funds manager wants to maximize the likelihood that a specified asset growth goal (the satisficing level) is, in fact, achieved. This objective function has been described as a conditional chance-constrained multi-stage problem (Burnham [1970]) and small test problems have been solved using SUMT (Fiacco and McCormick [1968]). Mathematical conversion of the probabilistic form to its deterministic equivalent leads to an expression with the measure of anticipated gain divided by the measure of anticipated risk—more or less equivalent to "Alpha divided by Beta"! This sort of reward/risk ratio has been institutionalized by the Value Line (Bernhold [1976]) advisory service in ranking stocks for year-ahead performance AND risk class, as well as for the longer three-to-five year horizon.

ORDERS and TRADING activities provide execution of decisions made by the Portfolio or Program Manager. Since large buying or selling activities can effect the trading prices obtainable, Quantity Analysis is a vital input to this activity. So block trading, Third Market activities, and trading through regional exchanges can be employed to obtain the highest average realization from a sale, or lowest average price on the buy side. Data on "float" or number of shares NOT closely held, *and* on Exchange floor activities, *and* on Third Market and block pricing, are nearly all computerized.

Perhaps the most vital and least publicized activity is CONTROL, in the many respects indicated in its block in Figure 1. As a management system, CONTROL can achieve substantial gains despite inadequacies or inexactness in other areas, such as FORECASTING, STOCK SELECTION, or PORTFOLIO SELECTION. Since *price* is a random variable, and *value* an inexactly estimated quantity, and estimates and decisions in each of the other areas is dependent on these quantities, a set of decision rules should, and can, be established and implemented to protect the portfolio assets from serious damage due to these inexact figures. Ongoing research by Burnham et al. [1971] has developed the "shadow" concept—using a simulation model of the ongoing portfolio of risky assets with all additions to the portfolio based on reward/risk and minimum anticipated gain criteria, and all deletions from the portfolio based on having realized most, or all, of the gains anticipated when buying, *or* on having experienced a decline in price greater than some predetermined magnitude *for the risk class involved.* Whitmire, et al. [1971] and Lindsley [1971] provide more detail in these areas. Lindsley also reports the results of test application to the portfolio of a pension fund managed by an insurance company. A number of doctoral dissertations have developed from these beginnings. The "shadow" idea is not to manage a portfolio, but rather to give the Program Manager a control measure against which to evaluate his own actions in the real portfolio. Thus, the mechanically-managed "shadow" is a benchmark and a means of evaluating the likelihood of meeting the management's goals by using the policy guidelines, regulations, and so forth which constrain the manager, AND the actual state of the market for the securities held in the portfolio. For access to much of this material consult the PROBE[2] office (Kozmetsky [1976]).

Recent federal pension reform legislation in the United States, especially with respect to liability of the company for the acts of its fiduciary officers, may give added impetus to more rapid development of the PROBE control concepts pioneered at the University of Texas. It seems certain that further developments in the fiduciary investments management area will continue to involve OR practitioners because of the required blend of statistical, decision-analytic, simulation design and evaluation, and optimization skills required to assist the new "prudent men" money managers in both performance and protection.

Capital Budgeting—is to the firm what security or portfolio choice is to the investor. *Capital rationing*—implies more acceptable projects than the available capital can undertake, requiring discrimination in selection. The interdependence of expected net cash flows variances, varying maturities or timing of flows, and differing levels of return expectations require a full range of mathematical methodology. The essence of the procedures is to maximize the expected return from a bundle of risky assets subject to some upper bound on risk, using integer linear or quadratic programming (Weingartner [1966a, 1966b]; Byrne, et al. [1967, 1969]; Carleton [1969]; Mao & Brewster [1970].

---

[2]PROBE means Portfolio Rational and Objective Beneficial Evaluation.

Business firms have generally been slow to adopt these sophisticated capital expenditures optimization techniques (Mao & Helliwell [1969]). Perhaps because the model framework is more understandable, simulation models have been widely used. Simulations treat the cash flows from projects as random variables, and use some combination(s) of Monte Carlo, sequential decision tree analysis, iterative parametric manipulation, or stochastic LP to develop heuristically a risk-return curve for multiple risky projects. For a stochastic returns, LP approach including a detailed formulation, see Lockett and Gear [1975]. An excellent summary of the various capital budgeting model classes appears in Sundem [1975]. The paper also provides simulation results to aid in evaluation of the usefulness of various models in particular environments. For the use of decomposition to establish the correct *transfer price* for the financial resource and a solution for capital mix, dividends, and new financing based on optimal allocation, see Morris [1975]. Integer restrictions are readily handled by simulation (Hertz [1964, 1968]; Salazar & Sen [1968]; Economos, 1969).

The principal distinction between investment portfolio analysis and multiproject capital budgeting is reversibility—the opportunity to convert the risky asset back into cash at a known transaction cost and approximate sale price, so that negative returns can be limited. There is no organized and orderly secondary market for capital equipment, and installation and removal expenses are substantial. Many capital budgeting decisions include heavy, nonrecurring, irreversible investments in technological know-how and in research, development, and prototype testing (Reinhardt [1973]).

Management is, in reality, engaged in sequential, incremental decision making based on the prospective returns and costs associated with a *continuation* of funding for current projects, as well as with new investments, many of which costs are also incremental. Those present projects (and capital equipment) that do not have future net returns meeting the criteria for new investments are cancelled (salvaged). Salvage becomes return of capital, available for reinvestment. Losses are applied to shelter current income from taxes. This sort of partial reversibility is called the *optimal abandonment decision*, and has been applied to venture capital, aerospace, and consumer, new product development (Van Horne [1969]), and to fixed capital (Robichek & Van Horne [1967]). The reversibility framework applies, in a somewhat modified form, to the determination of value of a call option (the contractual right to retire a bond before maturity by paying a "call premium"), and to the bond refunding decision itself. Solution techniques use DP, and depend on probabilistic forecasts of future interest rates over the horizon to bond maturity (Pye [1966]; Weingartner [1967]; Elton & Gruber [1971, 1972]).

Financial Structure—The leverage inherent in the after-tax cost of debt capital makes desirable some proportion of debt in the firm's permanent capital structure. The addition of debt capital implies the existence of investment opportunities which can meet the debt interest requirements and also provide incremental equity returns over the life of the project without lowering the market price of the stock. The firm seeks the lowest K_o possible, and calls the associated capital mix its "optimal structure."

Risk is implicit in all cash flow analysis of investment, capital additions, or dividends. The portfolio of investment returns and their variance, and the stream of interest payments and expected net operating income over time provide a measure of the risk of deficit (negative earnings). Tinsley [1970] calls this the risk of "runout" and disengages it from debt additions per se. Runout is, rather, an aggregate condition associated with cash flows of all types. When runout threatens, asset liquidation is required to assure that fixed payments to creditors can be made. The dollar loss of runout is the discount accompanying forced conversion of assets. The probability of runout, developed from the portfolio cash flow, combined with these distress liquidation losses, provides a quantitative measure of the expected loss associated with leveraged firms. Market value becomes, then, a function of the particular likelihood of runout, and is lowered when expected runout costs exceed expected income gains from debt. In this sense, precautionary liquidity is the analog of inventory safety stock.

Dividends—The disposition of after-tax earnings is a financing decision. Earnings not distributed increase the book value (net worth/share) and are a source of funds for investment. In theory at least, all earnings in excess of the firm's needs (i.e., that cannot be employed to earn at the rate K_o) should be returned to the shareholders as dividends, or else the market value of the shares will fall. However, firms behave as though there is a "target" payout proportion which may increase dividends in a time of earnings growth, in a discrete though sometimes regular manner—but which resists dollar reduction in payout despite unfavorable, temporary earnings performance. Some analysts suggest that dividends form a reasonable basis for market value (Walter [1963]; Bauman [1969]; Hakansson [1969]). By the use of marginal analysis and the "ex dividend" change in market price, dividend payout should be increased until the point at which the downward change in market price exceeds the amount of dividend paid—leading to the condition of maximizing shareholder "wealth"—the present value of the dividend stream *and* the maximum market price for the shares held. These arguments are usually incorporated into a "sources and uses" model, such as was described in Section 2.1 for cash management, or in the context of an aggregate financial planning model (Section 3.3). For self-financing firms (no debt), two formal models, using analytical techniques, provide some insight into the relations between growth, investment, and dividends. Manne [1968] demonstrates that: a) nonlinear marginal utility for cash withdrawals explains positive investment decisions and concurrent dividend distributions by the firm; b) optimal dual variable values permit recursive identification of the primal variables that may be operated at positive levels in capital investment, in time

t, in an optimal solution; c) the ratio of the dual variables (marginal worth of another unit of cash in period t compared with its worth at the planning horizon T) determines the optimal dividend policy for periods t/T.

The calculus of variations has been applied to dividend-type valuation models to quantify optimal dividend-growth-assets relations which maximize market price (Wallingford [1973]). For a chosen asset growth rate, optimal payout of dividends will vary directly with higher rates of return. For a chosen (anticipated) rate of return, dividend payout will vary inversely with increasing required growth rates. No dividends are paid if assets growth is equal to rate of return, and no earnings are retained if growth is not required (stationary assets).

3.3   Integrative Financial Decision Models

Large-scale LP models are now fairly commonplace in manufacturing, process industry, transportation, retailing, and nonprofit institutions. However, the sequential process (solve the finance problem—or marketing, or production, or inventory—taking other decision elements as *constants*, or *constraints* to the finance situation) is suboptimal. A welcome trend works *across* divisional/functional lines and provides solutions for larger and larger portions of the enterprise. Explicit time-stages permit segmented horizon planning. Updating and rerunning based on newer data seems routine. And, gradually, multiple objective functions are being treated using goal programming techniques. An integrative model which has been implemented, is described in Hamilton and Moses [1973].

Production—Dzeilinski and Gomory [1965] developed an operational computer code based on decomposition for the joint problem of optimal economic lot size, inventory, and work force decisions in a multi-production process—minimizing total costs with no stock-outs permitted. The decomposition uses the dual variable price vector for each submatrix element in much the same way that divisional production/price proposals are generated and reviewed by the firm in establishing proper transfer prices (Section 2.2—Cost Accounting).

Nonlinear programming and the sequential unconstrained minimization technique (SUMT: Fiacco & McCormick [1968]) has also been applied to the integrated materials-manufacturing-distribution problem (Damon & Schramm [1972]). A substantial improvement in the objective function results from simultaneous solution, rather than by the usual sequential process. The objective is to maximize the cash-equivalent position of the firm at the end of the planning horizon. The deterministic model is confined to short planning horizons—too short for adjustments to fixed plant, for example—so that production technology and demand can be taken as given functions. Model outputs are: production level, inventory stock, sales, revenue, and cash balance quantities. Solution (the formulation is both nonlinear and nonconvex) using SUMT gives convergence to a local optimum only, due to nonconvexity. The simultaneous solution profitability is 27 percent greater than that achieved by the best sequential model.

Vertically integrated, multi-plant, multi-product firms such as steel, petroleum, synthetic fibers and textiles, and automobile manufacture, have special problems in dealing with optimization of the entire system. Extraction, conversion, refining and fabrication/assembly operations take place in many different plants and locations. Each such facility may be independent technologically, have a marketable intermediate product, and (usually) is decentralized for accounting as well as management purposes. Overall optimization is not a simple matter.

To deal effectively with the various aspects of this problem in the English chemical industry, Tuckett [1969] found it necessary to solve for three distinct 'optimal' conditions: minimize input costs; maximize net profit; and maximize the throughput or turnover of products for each accounting entity in the firm. Outside purchase as well as sale possibilities for intermediate products, net balance-of-payments, quality, plant-to-process and plant-to-product relationships, and input/output technology imbedded in the product-in, product-out vectors of the various processes, are important elements of the constraint set. Once the three separate firm-level solutions are available, "super-standard" costs are generated by using the minimum-cost solutions in conjunction with the maximum-profit solutions. When volumes, costs, and marginal worth are all available from this adjusted optimum, any plant variances result in penalties at the level of the firm. A somewhat similar example for the English Coal Board appears in Harrison and Baker [1974].

An informal Working Paper (Gentry & Phyrr [1972]) suggests a long-run (8 years) simulation of the financial planning process. A target earnings-per-share (EPS) growth rate is substituted for the financial goal of market value maximization. The selected growth rate is "reasonably" stable and competitive, and will be sought over a definite planning period, e.g., 10 percent annual compounded EPS growth for the next four years. The program simulates management's selection among various new investment alternatives which, combined with the existing portfolio, will yield the firm's target EPS. Output relates the required rates of return distribution with the desired EPS rate of growth. Model reality is added by financial risk, debt/assets ratios, and cash flow stability constraints. Twenty-three variables are inputs for the simulation, permitting detailed evaluation of the feasibility of various target goals of the firm. This small model has been successfully used as a teaching device by the authors in their graduate finance classes. For a report on the use of full-scale models by several large corporations, see Grinyer and Batt [1974]. The discussion is nontechnical and includes costs, activities for which the models are used, and some of their shortcomings in practice and in development.

3.4 Banking

The above models have dealt with modern coporate finance. Banking institutions have similar issues to face: profitability, return on equity, liquidity, portfolio structure, demand for funds and interest rates, cash management, composition of secured and unsecured loan portfolios and criteria for granting loans in each category, portfolio management as trustees . . . the list seems endless. Cohen and Hammer [1966] give a reasonably current survey of analytical methods applied to the banking business. The bibliography accompanying Crane [1971] deals with LP approaches to bank bond portfolios. Crane applies two-stage LP under uncertainty, seeking to maximize expected return subject to an upper bound on permissible loss. When probabilistic cash outflows are involved, the solution provides a recommended mix of bonds of varying maturities. A paper covering cost of capital and dividend policies in commercial banks (Magen [1971]) shows the significant *differences* between banks and other corporate enterprises in these important relationships with stockholders.

3.5 Conclusions and Trends

To the extent that the conditions and assumptions surrounding the various financial planning models are valid (or do not distort reality significantly), existing mathematical programming techniques and computer codes can yield interpretable, even implementable, solutions. Progress has largely been conceptual— the recognition that many of the traditional elements of finance (and even of other functional areas!) are interdependent, stochastic, and dynamic. Recent work shows explicit nonlinearity, risk, and both long- and short-term horizons in the same framework. Cash management has become very sophisticated. The numerous examples of working, capital-oriented models shows increasing concern with return on this asset element. Willingness to use a wide variety of techniques to reach desired goals (analytically speaking), and to move to heuristics to trace probability distributions for analysis of outcome where single values are not sufficient, is healthy. Even healthier is the evidence that some of the models are in active use.

BIBLIOGRAPHY

Bailey Jr., A. D., "A Dynamic Programming Approach to the Analysis of Different Methods in Accounting for Inventories," *Acount. Rev.* **XLVIII**, No. 3: 560–74 (July 1973).

Barron, F. Hutton, John M. Burnham, and O. Maurice Joy, "A Pragmatic Portfolio Management Model" *Proceedings of the Fourth Annual Meeting of the American Institute for Decision Sciences, November 1972*, New Orleans, Louisiana (July–December 1973)

Bauman, W. Scott, "Investment Returns and Present Values," *Finan. Anal. J.* **25**, No. 6: 107–120 (1969).

Baumol, William J., and Tibor Fabian, "Decomposition, Pricing for Decentralization, and External Economies," *Management Sci.* **XI,** No. 1: 1–32 (1964).

Benishay, H., "Managerial Controls of Accounts Receivable: A Deterministic Approach," *J. Account. Res.* **3,** 114–133 (Spring 1965).

Bernhold, Arnold, *The Value Line Investment Survey*, Bernhold, New York, (1976, Weekly).

Brief, Richard P., and Joel Owen, "A Least Squares Allocation Model," *J. Account. Res.* **6,** 193–199 (Autumn 1968).

——, and ——, "The Estimation Problem in Financial Accounting," *J. Account. Res.* **8,** 167–177 (Autumn 1970).

Burnham, John, *Conditional Chance-Constrained Programming Techniques in Portfolio Selection*, University of Texas at Austin, Graduate School of Business (April 1970).

——, et al., "PROBE I: July–December 1970," Graduate School of Business Administration, The University of Texas at Austin (February 1971).

Byrne, R., A. Charnes, W. W. Cooper, and K. Kortanek, "A Chance-C, istrained Approach to Capital Budgeting With Portfolio Type Payback and Liquidity Constraints and Horizon Posture Controls," *J. Finan. and Quant. Anal.* **2,** No. 4: 339–364 (1967).

——, ——, ——, and ——, "A Discrete Probability Chance-Constrained Capital Budgeting Model - I," *Opsearch* **6,** No. 3: 172–198 (1969).

——, ——, ——, and ——, "A Discrete Probability Chance-Constrained Capital Budgeting Model - II," *Opsearch* **6,** No. 4: 226–261 (1969).

Carleton, Willard T., "Linear Programming and Capital Budgeting Models: A New Interpretation," *J. Finan.* **XXLV,** 825–833 (December 1969).

Charnes, A. and W. W. Cooper, "Deterministic Equivalents for Optimizing and Satisficing Under Chance Constraints," *Operations Res.* **11,** No. 1: 18–39 (1963).

Charnes, A., W. W. Cooper, and Y. Ijiri, "Breakeven Budgeting and Programming to Goals," *J. Account. Res.* **1,** 16–43 (Spring 1963).

Churchman, C. West, Russell Ackoff, and E. L. Arnoff, *Introduction to Operations Research*, John Wiley & Sons, New York (1957).

Cohen, K. J. and Frederick S. Hammer, *Analytical Methods in Banking*, Richard D. Irwin, Inc., Homewood (1966).

Colantoni, Claude S., Rene Manes, and Andrew Whiston, "Programming, Profit Rates, and Pricing Decisions," *Account. Rev.* **XLIV,** No. 3: 467–481 (1969).

Crane, D. B., "A Stochastic Programming Model for Commercial Bank Bond Portfolio Management," *J. Finan. and Quant. Anal.* **6,** No. 3: 955–976 (1971).

Cyert, R. M., H. J. Davidson, and G. L. Thompson, "Estimation of the Allowance for Doubtful Accounts by Markov Chains," *Management Sci.* **8,** No. 3: 287–303 (1962).

Damon, W. W. and R. Schramm, "A Simultaneous Decision Model for Production, Marketing and Finance," *Management Sci.* **19,** No. 2: 161–172 (1972).

Demski, Joel, "An Accounting System Structured on a Linear Programming Model," *Account. Rev.* **XLII,** No. 4: 701–712 (1967).

——, "Information Improvement Bounds," *J. Account. Res.* **10,** No. 1: 58–76 (1972).

Dopuch, Nicholas, J. G. Birnberg, and Joel Demski, "An Extension of Standard Cost Variance Analysis," *Account. Rev.* **XLII,** No. 3: 526–36 (1967).

Dzeilinski, B. P. and R. E. Gomory, "Optimal Programming of Lot Sizes, Inventory and Labor Allocations," *Management Sci.* **11,** No. 9: 874–890 (1965).

Economos, A. M., "A Financial Simulation for Risk Analysis of a Proposed Subsidiary," *Management Sci.* **15,** No. 12: B–675–682 (1969).

Elton, Edwin J. and Martin J. Gruber, "Dynamic Programming Applications in Finance," *J. Finan.* **26,** No. 2: 473–506 (1971).

——, and ——, "On the Cash Balance Problem," *Operational Res. Quart.* **25,** No. 4: 553–72 (1974).

——, and ——, "The Economic Value of the Call Option," *J. Finan.* **XXVII**, No. 4: 891–901 (1972).

Falk, Hiam and James A. Heintz, "Assessing Industry Risk by Ratio Analysis," *Account. Rev.* **50**, No. 4: 758–79 (1975).

Fama, E. F., "Efficient Capital Markets: A Review of Theory and Empirical Work," *J. Finan.* **25**, No. 2: 383–423 (1970).

Farag, S. M., "A Planning Model for the Divisionalized Enterprise," *Account. Rev.* **XLIII**, No. 2: 312–320 (April 1968).

Ferrara, William L. and Jack C. Hayya, "Toward Probabilistic Profit Budgets," *Management Account.* **52**, 23–26 (October 1970).

Fiacco, Anthony V. and Garth P. McCormick, *Non-Linear Programming: Sequential Unconstrained Minimization Techniques*, John Wiley & Sons, New York (1968).

Fremgen, James M., "Transfer Pricing and Management Goals," *Management Account.* **52**, 25–31 (December 1970).

Gambling, Trevor E., and Ahmed Nour, "A Note on Input-Output Analysis: Its Uses in Macroeconomics and Microeconomics," *Account. Rev.* **XLV**, No. 1: 98–102 (1970).

Gentry, James A., (Compiler) *Finance Workshop, Sixth National Meeting of the American Institute for Decision Sciences*, October 30, 1974, Atlanta, Georgia.

——, and Steven A. Pyhrr, "Simulation of the Financial Planning Process: An EPS Growth Model," Working Paper 73-2, Graduate School of Business, University of Texas at Austin (September 1972).

Girgis, N. M., "Optimal Cash Balance Levels," *Management Sci.* **15**, No. 3: 130–140 (1968).

Givens, Horace R., "An Application of Curvilinear Breakeven Analysis," *Account. Rev.* **XLI**, No. 2: 141–43 (1966).

Glover, Fred, "Management Decision and Integer Programming," Account. Rev., **XLIV**, No. 2 (June, 1969) 300–303.

Goggans, Travis P., "Breakeven Analysis with Curvilinear Functions," *Account. Rev.* **XL**, No. 4: 867–871 (1965).

Gonedes, N. J., "Accounting for Managerial Control: An Application of Chance-Constrained Programming," *J. Account. Res.* 1–20 (Spring 1969).

Gordon, Myron J., *The Investment, Financing, and Valuation of the Corporation*, Richard D. Irwin, Inc., Homewood, Ill. (1962).

——, "The Use of Administered Price Systems to Control Large Organizations," in *Management Controls: New Directions in Basic Research*, Bonini, et al. editors, McGraw-Hill, New York (1964).

Greer, C. C., "The Optimal Credit Acceptance Policy," *J. Finan. and Quant. Anal.* **2**, 399–415 (December 1967).

Grinyer, Peter H., and Christopher D. Batt, "Some Tentative Findings on Corporate Financial Simulation Models," *Operational Res. Quart.* **25**, No. 1: 149–68 (1974).

Groves, Roger, Rene Manes, and Robert Sorenson, "The Application of the Hinsch-Dantzig (Fixed Charge) Algorithm to Profit Planning: A Formal Statement of Product Profitability Analysis," *Account. Rev.* **XLV**, No. 5: 481–489 (July 1970).

Hakansson, Nils H., "On the Dividend Capitalization Model Under Uncertainty," *J. Finan. and Quant. Anal.* **4**, 65–87 (March 1969).

Hamilton, William F., and Michael A. Moses, "An Optimization Model for Corporate Financial Planning," *Operations Res.* **21**, No. 3: 677–92 (1973).

Harrison, F. B. and A. Baker, Accountants Test Models: Some Experience in National Coal Boards Products Division," *Operational Res. Quart.* **25**, No. 1: 3–18 (March 1974).

Hartley, Ronald V., "Decision Making When Joint Products Are Involved," *Account. Rev.* **XLVI**, No. 4: 746–755 (1971).

Hass, Jerome, "Transfer Pricing in a Decentralized Firm," *Management Sci.* **14,** No. 6: 310–331 (1968).

Hertz, David, "Risk Analysis in Capital Investment," *Harvard Business Rev.* **42,** 95–106 (January–February 1964).

———, "Investment Policies That Pay-Off," *Harvard Business Rev.* **46,** 95–106 (January–February 1968).

Hinomoto, H., "Optimum Strategics For Management Information Processing and Control," *J. Account. Res.* **9,** No. 2: 253–267 (Autumn 1971).

Hirshleifer, Jack, "Interval Pricing and Decentralized Decisions," in *Management Controls: New Directions in Basic Research*, Bonini, et al. editors, McGraw-Hill, New York (1964).

Holstrum, Gary L. and Eugene H. Sauls, "The Opportunity Cost Transfer Price," *Management Account.* **55,** 29–33 (May 1973).

Horn, Frederick E., "Managing Cash," *J. Account.* **CXII:** 56–62 (April 1964).

Ijiri, Y., *Management Goals and Accounting For Control*, North Holland Publishing Co., Amsterdam (1965).

Ijiri, Y., "An Application of Input-Output Analysis to Some Problems in Cost Accounting," *Management Account.* **49,** 49–61 (April 1968).

Jaedicke, R. K., "Improving B-E Analysis by Linear Programming Technique," *NAA Bull.* **42,** 5–12 (March 1961).

——— and Alexander A Robichek, "Cost-Volume-Profit Analysis Under Conditions of Uncertainty," *Accounting Rev.* **XXXIX,** No. 1: 17–34 (1964).

Jensen, R. E., "Sensitivity Analysis and Integer Linear Programming," *Accounting Rev.* **XLIII,** No. 3: 429–437 (1968).

Johnson, G. L. and S. S. Simik II, "Multi-product C-V-P Analysis Under Uncertainty," *J. Account. Res.* **9,** No. 2: 278–386 (Autumn 1971).

Kemeny, John G., Arthur Schleifer Jr., J. Laurie Snell, and Gerald L. Thompson, *Finite Mathematics With Business Applications.* 2nd ed., Prentice-Hall, Englewood Cliffs (1972).

Kozmetsky, George, "Project PROBE," Graduate School of Business, The University of Texas at Austin (1976).

Latané, Henry A., Donald L. Tuttle, and Charles P. Jones, *Security Analysis and Portfolio Management*, (2nd edition) Ronald Press Company, New York (1975).

Leone, Edmund, "Techniques for Improving Cash Turnover," *Finan. Exec.* **32,** 38–42 (January 1964).

Lev, B., "Testing a Prediction Method for Multivariate Budgets," *J. Account. Res.* Supplement to **7,** 182–197 (1969).

Levy, Robert A. "Computer Directions Advisors, Inc.," *Financial Services, Investment Research, Capital Management*, Silver Spring, Maryland (September 1969).

Lewellen, Wilbur G. and Robert O. Edmister, "A General Model For Accounts Receivable Analysis and Control," *J. Finan. and Quant. Anal.* **8,** No. 2: 195–206 (March 1973).

Liao, Mawson, "Model Sampling: A Stochastic Cost-Volume-Profit Analysis," *Account. Rev.* **50,** No. 4: 780–90 (October 1975).

Lindsley, Philip, III, "Formulation of a Portfolio Evaluation Model–Managerial Aspects," Unpublished Professional Report (MBA). Graduate School of Business, the University of Texas at Austin (May 1971).

Livingstone, J. L., "Input-Output Analysis for Cost Accounting, Planning, and Control," *Account. Rev.* **XLIV,** No. 2: 330–343 (April 1969).

Livingstone, J. L., "Input-Output for Cost Accounting, Planning and Control: A Reply," *Account. Rev.* **XLVIII,** No. 1: (1973) 381–382.

Lockett, A. Geoffrey and Anthony E. Gear, "Multistage Capital Budgeting Under Uncertainty," *J. Finan. and Quant. Anal.* **X,** No. 1: 21–36 (1975).

Magen, S. D., "Cost of Capital and Dividend Policies in Commercial Banks," *J. Finan. and Quant. Anal.* **6,** No. 2: 733–746 (1971).

Manes, Rene, "A New Dimension to Breakeven Analysis," *J. Account. Res.* **4,** 87–100 (Spring 1966).

———, "Birch Paper Company Revisited: An Exercise in Transfer Pricing," *Account. Rev.* **LXV,** No. 3: 565–572 (1970).

Manne, A. S., "Optimal Dividend and Investment Policies for a Self-Financing Business Enterprise," *Management Sci.* **15,** No. 3: 119–129 (1968).

Mao, James C. T. and John F. Brewster, "An E-S_n Model of Capital Budgeting," *Eng. Econ.* **15,** 103–131 (Winter 1970).

Mao, James C. T. and John F. Helliwell, "Investment Decision Under Uncertainty: Theory and Practice," *J. Finan.* **XXIV,** No. 2: 323–38 (1969).

Markowitz, Harry, *Portfolio Selection: Efficient Diversification of Investments,* John Wiley & Sons, New York (1959).

Mehta, Dileep, "The Formulation of Credit Policy Models," *Management Sci.* **15,** No. 2: B–30–50 (1968).

———, "Optimal Credit Policy Selection: A Dynamic Approach," *J. Finan. and Quant. Anal.* 421–444 (December 1970).

Mitchell, G. B., "Breakeven Analysis and Capital Budgeting," *J. Account. Res.* **7,** 332–338 (Autumn 1969).

Moriarty, Shane, "Another Approach to Allocating Joint Costs," *Account. Rev.* **L,** No. 4: 791–95 (1975).

Morris, James R., "An Application of the Decomposition Principle to Financial Decision Models," *J. Finan. and Quant. Anal.* **X,** No. 1: 37–66 (1975).

Morrison, Thomas A. and Kaczka, Eugene, "A New Application of Calculus and Risk Analysis to Cost-Volume Profit Changes, *Account. Rev.* **XLIV,** No. 2, (April 1969) 330–343.

Neave, E. H., "The Stochastic Cash Balance Problem With Fixed Costs For Increases and Decreases," *Management Sci.* **16,** No. 7: 472–490 (1970).

Onsi, Mohamed, "Linear Programming: An Accounting Information Model," *Management Account.* **45,** 46–52 (September 1966).

———, "A Transfer Pricing System Based on Opportunity Cost," *Account. Rev.* **XLV,** No. 2: 535–543 (1970).

Orgler, Yair E., *Cash Management Methods and Models,* Wadsworth Publishing Co., Belmont, California (1970).

Peat, Marwick and Mitchell, "Computer Assisted Planning for Colleges and Universities," *World,* (Autumn 1967) 7–13.

Peterson, Leroy D., "Design Consideration for Improving the Effectiveness of MRP," *Prod. and Inv. Management,* pp. 48–68 (September 1975).

Pflomm, Norman E., "Managing Company Cash, A Research Report," National Industrial Conference Board, New York (1961).

Philippatos, George C., *Financial Management–Theory and Techniques,* Holden-Day, San Francisco (1973).

Pye, Gordon, "The Value of the Call Option on a Bond," *J. Pol. Econ.* **LXXIV,** 200–205 (April 1966).

Rappaport, Alfred, "Sensitivity in Decision Making," *Account. Rev.* **XLII,** No. 3: 441–456 (1967).

———, "Integer Programming and Managerial Analysis," *Account. Rev.* **XLIV,** No. 2: 297–299 (1969).

Raun, D. L., "The Limitations of Profit Graphs Breakeven Analysis, and Budgets," *Account. Rev.* **XXXIX**, No. 4: 927–945 (1964).

Reinhardt, U. E., "Break-Even Analysis for Lockheed's Tri Star: An Application of Financial Theory," *J. Finan.* **XXVIII**, No. 4: 821–838 (1973).

Robichek, A. A. and James C. Van Horne, "Abandonment Value and Capital Budgeting," *J. Finan.*, pp. 577–589 (December 1967).

Robichek, A. A., D. Teichroew, and J. M. Jones, "Optimal Short Term Financing Decision," *Management Sci.* **12**, No. 1: 1–36 (1965).

Ronen, J. and G. McKinney, "Transfer Pricing for Divisional Autonomy," *J. Account. Res.* **8**, 99–112 (Spring 1970).

Salazar, R. C. and S. K. Sen, "A Stimulation Model of Capital Budgeting Under Uncertainty," *Management Sci.* **15**, No. 4: (1968), B–161–179.

Sharpe, William, F., "A Simplified Model for Portfolio Analysis," *Management Sci.* **9**, No. 2: (1963) 277–293.

Shaw, Robert J., "Simulation of Inventory Policies," *Management Cont.*, pp. 169–172. Peat, Marwick & Mitchell Co. (August, 1971).

Shillinglaw, Gordon, *Cost Accounting Analysis and Control Revised*, pp. 61–62 R. D. Irwin, Homewood, Illinois (1967).

Shubik, M., "Objective Functions and Models of Corporate Optimization," *Quart. J Econ.* **LXXV**, No. 3: 345–375 (1961).

———, "Incentives, Decentralized Control, the Assignment of Joint Costs and Internal Pricing," in *Management Controls: New Directions in Basic Research*, Bonini, et al. editors, McGraw-Hill, New York (1964).

Shulman, J. S. "Transfer Pricing in the Multi-National Firm," *European Bus.*, 46–54 (January 1969).

Sloane, William R. and Arnold Reisman, "Stock Evaluation Theory: Classification, Reconciliation, and General Model," *J. Finan. and Quant. Anal.* **3**, 171–203 (March 1968).

Slaybaugh, Charles J., "Inventory Management Program," *Management Account.* **53**, 13–16–22 (July 1971).

Srinivasan, V., "A Transshipment Model for Cash Management Decisions," *Management Sci.* **20**, No. 10: 1350–63 (1974).

Sundem, Gary L., "Evaluating Capital Budgeting Models in Simulated Environments," *J. Finan.* **XXX**, No. 4: 977–92 (1975).

Theil, H., "On the Use of Information Theory Concepts in the Analysis of Financial Statements," *Management Sci.* **15**, No. 9: 459–480 (1969).

Tinsley, P. A., "Capital Structure, Precautionary Balances, and Valuation of the Firm: The Problem of Financial Risk," *J. Finan. and Quant. Anal.* **5**, 33–62 (March 1970).

Tuckett, R. F. "Combined Cost and Linear Programming Models of Industrial Complexes," *Operational Res. Quart.* **20**, No. 2: 223–236 (1969).

Van Horne, James C., *Financial Management and Policy*, 2nd. ed., Prentice-Hall, Englewood Cliffs (1969).

Van Horne, J. C., "The Analysis of Uncertainty Resolution in Capital Budgeting for New Products," *Management Sci.*, **15**, No. 8: B376–B386 (April 1969).

Wallingford, B. A. II, "An Inter-temporal Approach to the Optimization of Dividend Policy with Predetermined Investments," *J. Finan.* **XXVII**, No. 3: 627–635 (1973).

Walter, James E., " 'Dividend Policy' Its Influence on the Value of the Enterprise," *J. Finan.* **XVIII**, No. 2: 280–292 (1963).

Weingartner, H. M., "Capital Budgeting of Interrelated Projects: Survey and Synthesis," *Management Sci.* **12**, No. 7: 483–516 (1966).

———, "Criteria For Programming Investment Project Selection," *J. Account. Res.* **4**, 65–76 (Autumn 1966).

———, "Optimal Timing of Bond Refunding," *Management Sci.* **13**, No. 7: 511–524 (1967).

Whitmire, Raymond E., et al. "Project PROBE II: A Progress Report," (January–June 1971) Graduate School of Business, The University of Texas at Austin (September 1971).

I-3

MARKETING

Philip Kotler
Northwestern University

INTRODUCTION

Although operations research (OR) is a relative latecomer in marketing, it has already yielded useful insights and decision models in such areas as new product development, competitive pricing, advertising budgeting and media selection, sales call time allocation, and marketing mix planning. Beginning in the late 1950's, marketing operations researchers have produced a rich harvest of models on almost every conceivable, quantifiable marketing problem or process. Unfortunately, usage has lagged substantially behind model development; in some cases due to the inappropriateness of the models, but in even a larger number of cases to marketing management's widespread lack of understanding and sympathy for quantitative approaches to marketing. Today, some models are fully established and running in some larger companies but constitute the exception rather than the rule. The vast majority of marketing decisions are still made intuitively despite the availability of more rigorous decision procedures borne out of years of patient OR work.

COMPLEX FACTORS IN THE MARKETING PROCESS

Although modern companies spend large sums of money collecting information about their customers, competitors, and the general environment, marketing executives still feel substantial uncertainty surrounding their marketing decisions. At least nine types of complexity can be identified.

Shape of Response Function

The shape of the market's response to additional marketing expenditure is typically unknown. If a firm doubles the scale of its marketing expenditures, will its sales double, more than double, or less than double? Adequate data to learn the answer are difficult to collect and analyze in any real situation.

Marketing Mix Interaction

Marketing effort, far from being a homogeneous input, is a composite of many different types of activities undertaken by the firm to improve its sales. Marketing effort includes (1) pricing; (2) promotional activities such as advertising, personal selling, sales promotion, and public relations; (3) distribution activities related to the availability of goods and servicing of orders; and (4) product development and improvement activities. The firm's marketing problem is to develop a sound mix of these activities in the face of great uncertainty as to the separate and joint effect of different activities. The market's response to variations in the level of any one marketing input is conditional on the level of the other activities. Furthermore, variation of two or more marketing activities at the same time can have joint effects that are greater or less than the sum of the separate effects. To model these interactive effects on a conceptual level, let alone to measure them on an empirical level, is an extremely challenging task.

Competitive Effects

Sales results are a function of the relative marketing efforts by the firm and its competitors, and the firm has no control over competitors' moves. At best, the firm imperfectly forecasts the behavior and reactions of competitors. The notion of optimal decision making means choosing the best decision that could be made in the light of forecasted competitors' behavior or response.

Delayed Response

The market's response to current marketing outlays is not immediate, but in many instances stretches out over several time periods beyond the occurrence of the outlays. A large firm such as Coca-Cola can stop all its advertising and yet continue to enjoy current and even increasing sales for a while, living off its "advertising capital." The delayed or carry-over effects of many marketing expenditures make the optimal timing of marketing expenditures particularly challenging.

Multiple Territories

The market's response to different levels of marketing expenditure will vary by territory, making it difficult for the firm to determine the best way to allocate its marketing funds. Should company funds be concentrated in the areas where the firm is already doing well or in the areas where it is doing poorly? In one form or another this question plagues most firms, and their present methods of resolving it leave much to be desired.

Multiple Products

Most companies produce more than one product and face a difficult problem of allocating scarce marketing funds among them. Marketing strategies cannot be evolved for each product separately because of the strong demand and cost interactions that generally prevail among different products in the company's line. The price on a particular company product cannot be raised without considering its effect on the sale of the other products. A new product cannot be added to the product line on its own merits if it might severely reduce the revenues of existing company products. Many organizations never grapple with these critical issues, and as a consequence they achieve substantially suboptimal results.

Marketing-Corporate Interactions

Marketing decisions cannot be optimized without simultaneous decision making in the production and financial areas. Whether a new advertising campaign will be profitable depends not only on the sales it produces but also on its effect on company employment, inventories, and cash flows. Marketing, production and financial decisions must be made in concert so that they produce the best excess of total sales over total costs. Unfortunately, most departments are guided by departmental instead of corporate utility criteria when they plan their respective actions.

Multiple Objectives

A company tends to pursue multiple and often contradictory objectives. Company presidents are often heard to say that they seek maximum sales at minimum cost. While this may be good rhetoric, it is terrible logic in that there is no marketing plan that simultaneously maximizes sales and minimizes costs. The firm must somehow state its multiple objectives in such a way that a clear objective function emerges to guide the choice of a marketing strategy from a potentially large number of strategies.

Uncertainty Effects

Marketing processes are full of uncertainties beyond those just isolated. Relations between marketing efforts and sales responses are subject to systematic and random disturbances through time and space which must be taken into account in the marketing planning process.

HOW COMPANIES COPE WITH THE COMPLEXITY OF MARKETING PROCESSES

Given the numerous complexities associated with marketing, how do marketing managers reach decisions in which they can place any confidence? Production managers in their decision making can turn to a body of engineering theory, and financial managers can turn to a body of financial theory. Can the marketing manager turn to a body of marketing theory?

The general answer to this question is "no." A systematic body of normative marketing theory is not fully available to marketing decision makers. They cope by turning to one or more of four sources of support.

Experience

Most marketing men believe that experience is the best teacher in the area of marketing. The marketing practitioner knows that inspired marketing ideas are not enough; that salespeople are unevenly endowed and motivated; that customers vary immensely in their perceptions of product and company attributes; and that production and financial managers in the company have different ideas on the right marketing move.

Yet experience is not enough, and herein lies the difference between the old marketing philosophy and the new. The great fault of experience is that it is unique in every man. Each man distills a message biased by his own experience and personality. It is not a random coincidence that sales managers attribute more power to personal selling and advertising managers attribute more power to advertising.

Standard Operating Procedures

With the passage of time, companies tend to evolve standard policies and procedures to guide their decision makers. Product managers are given advertising budgets that reflect safe historical ratios of advertising budgets to sales; salesmen are advised on how many calls to make to customers of varying importance; pricing executives abide by certain traditional markups on cost; and many other marketing activities become rule-bound over time. The unfortunate and disturbing characteristic of rules is that they typically start off as sound, but always continue past their relevance to the situation.

Facts

Many executives act as if the answers to most marketing problems lie in the collection of facts. They will say to marketing research: "Go and find out how many people like this flavor," or "How do people view our company?" or "How do customers and prospects view our competitors?" It is not that these requests are wrong, but rather that there is an erroneous implication that the facts talk for themselves and will resolve the issue. Facts take on meaning only in the context of a framework of assumptions and theory. The fact that more people report a preference for one flavor over another does not in itself mean that the first flavor is the one to produce. It is also important to understand the strength and stability of preference, and the relation of reported preference to actual behavior. Solutions to problems are often as sensitive to the models for analysis as they are to the bare facts themselves. Facts are important, but like experience, they are not enough.

Assorted Theories of Market Response

Companies occasionally make a special effort to build an explicit theory of market behavior. Outside experts are called in, marketing experiments may be designed, and mathematical models may be formulated. It is at this point that it is realized that there is no shortage of company theories about market behavior. One executive believes that small amounts of advertising do not do any good, another that higher prices improve confidence in the product, and another that buyers mainly want quality. All these have mathematical translations and could, if systematized in larger models, have important implications for the company's marketing programming. Yet one rarely sees a company where the executives venture to integrate their theories of marketing response into an explicit system for analysis and marketing decision making.

ENTER OPERATIONS RESEARCH

Early OR breakthroughs on problems of production, inventories, and physical distribution did not surprise marketing practitioners, because these business problems appeared to have a clear quantitative nature. Then, in the late fifties, OR began to be applied to such marketing problems as advertising budgeting, sales-force assignment, and pricing strategy. The first model building efforts attempted to fit the marketing problem to existing models and tools—calculus, linear programming, queuing theory, and Markov processes—rather than to develop fresh models for the unique problems. For example, consumer brand selection was modeled as a simple first order Markov process, even though this left out competitive marketing strategy, in-store purchase factors, mass communications, and word-of-mouth influence in the buying process. The problem of optimal advertising media was modeled in straightforward linear programming terms, although this meant overlooking media duplication and replication and the nonlinear discount structure. In time it was recognized that the simplified problems bore insufficient resemblance to the real problems facing marketing management. The very naivete of these early models inspired criticism and revision and led inevitably to more complex models embodying a higher degree of realism.

Today, the published literature includes several hundred marketing articles, books of readings, textbooks, and bibliographies. (See Selected Bibliography at the end of the article). New articles regularly appear in *Management Science, Operations Research, Operational Research Quarterly, Journal of Marketing Research*, and the *Journal of Advertising*.

One of the first companies to invest heavily in marketing OR was DuPont. The company placed over $1 million in the hands of a specific group of company operations researchers to discover and quantify how advertising works ("A Profit Yardstick . . . ," [1958]). Other DuPont operations researchers made some early applications of modern decision theory to problems in product pricing and new-product introduction (Green [1963]).

Other companies making early appearances in marketing OR were Scott Paper, which conducted sophisticated field advertising experiments; Monsanto, which developed a large number of computer programs to help its executives analyze a variety of marketing problems (Clark [1962]); General Electric, which has worked for many years on the construction of simulators of specific markets; and Anheuser-Busch, which carried out sophisticated advertising experiments.

These early companies were later joined by Pillsbury, Union Carbide, Lever Brothers, and Westinghouse Electric. Advertising agencies such as Batten, Barton, Durstine & Osborn, Young and Rubicam, and N. Y. Ayer, have reported the development of sophisticated models in the areas of media selection and new-product development. Short summer courses in marketing OR have been offered periodically by M.I.T., Wharton, and Stanford.

The Diebold Group, Inc., sent out in 1966 a questionnaire to companies and academics doing marketing OR in order to find out what was being done. Their summary report indicates, among other things, that the marketing areas of greatest application (in descending order) were internal profit analysis, market analysis, competitive strategy, sales effort effectiveness, and pricing. The most promising techniques (also in descending order) were simulation, modeling, Monte Carlo methods, linear programming, and critical path analysis.

Specific Applications

The most viable marketing OR models have been developed in the areas of
(1) new products; (2) pricing; (3) advertising; (4) sales-force management; and
(5) marketing mix planning. Substantial progress has also been made in physical
distribution models (these are reviewed in Chapters 6, 8 and 9 of this section of
this Handbook). Fewer results have been achieved to date in modeling the sales
promotion decision, although encouraging signs of progress are now appearing.

NEW PRODUCT MODELS

Many new product models have been developed bearing such acronyms as
SPRINTER, DEMON, NEWS, and STEAM. The company interested in finding a
model to aid in its new product decision making is confused by the abundance
of available models, which differ in their level of aggregation, data demands, and
purposes. The company often requires an independent consultant to help it
choose a relevant model from among those available.

Part of the confusion can be cleared up by distinguishing three types of new
product models: (a) models for identifying new product opportunities; (b)
models for estimating the potential sales and profits for new product concepts;
and (c) models for forecasting the future demand for recently launched products
on the basis of initial market results.

New Product Identification Models

Companies typically rely on market surveys, focused group interviews, internal
brainstorming, salesmen suggestions, and research laboratories for new product
ideas. A growing number of companies are turning to rigorous *market structure
studies* pioneered by Stefflre [1968] (Silk [1969]) to reveal attractive new
product opportunities. The first step in the study uses multidimensional scaling
(Green and Rao [1972]) to map buyers' perceptions of the dimensions making
up a familiar product space and the perceived location of existing brands in that
space. Management examines this space for areas lacking brands. Any interesting new brand possibility is turned into a product concept that is tested on a
sample of consumers. If consumer response is positive and the market looks
large enough, the new brand is designed carefully in terms of elements that will
position it exactly where it was seen in the space. Market structure studies are
also used to analyze possible repositionings of weak products through product
redesign and fresh marketing strategy.

In addition to having good demand potential, new product concepts must fit
the company's resources and constraints. The major device for quantitatively
appraising the company-product fit is some version of a weighted factor score

device (Kline [1955]; O'Meara [1961]; Richman [1962]). It requires listing important company and marketing factors, assigning weights reflecting their relative importance in product success, and scoring the product on each factor according to the degree to which it is favorable. By multiplying the factor scores by the factor weights, a single number is derived which reflects the desirability of developing the product.

New Product Profit Potential Models (Pre-Launch)

If a firm finds it can logically undertake development of a new product concept in terms of company objectives and resources, it must determine whether it would in fact be worthwhile to do so. The question is answered by evaluating long run profit potential.

This essentially calls for projecting expected revenues and costs over a given time horizon and then applying some decision criterion to the data. The future revenue stream calls for estimating total market volume and growth, future prices, and company share of market. Total market volume is a function of population size, per capita consumption, effective purchasing power, and the availability of substitutes. Market share is a function of the relative attractiveness and force of the company's marketing mix (product quality, price, promotion, distribution) in relation to competitors' marketing mixes (Kotler [1971], Chapter 4). The future cost stream is estimated on the basis of the opportunity value of the funds invested in the product and required to meet the expected demand levels.

Different decision criteria can be applied to the estimates of future revenue and costs to make the final decision. Many firms rely heavily on *breakeven analysis* or *payout period analysis*. They judge a new product opportunity favorably if the breakeven sales level seems easily attainable or the payout period seems reasonably short. Unfortunately, neither analysis provides an estimate of return on investment (ROI) nor handles uncertainty in a quantitative way.

An increasing number of companies are applying *discounted cash flow analysis* to decide whether to launch a new product. Specifically, future net income is discounted by the company's cost of capital to yield the present value of the opportunity. If this figure exceeds the present value of the required investment, the firm can make a GO-decision. Alternatively, the company can look for that rate of discount of the future income stream which would bring its present value into equivalence with the present value of investment, and use this ROI as the sign of the attractiveness of the opportunity.

Further refinements are possible. Management can examine how alternative marketing mix plans would effect estimated revenue and costs and therefore ROI. Or management can adopt one of several methods for quantifying uncertainty as part of the estimation process. For example, Disman [1962] recommended scaling down the present value estimate by management's subjective probability of the product actually achieving technical and commercial success. Other possibilities include modeling the problem in terms of decision tree analysis and deriving expected values, getting measures of both return and risk, or deriving the full probability distribution of expected ROI through Monte Carlo simulation (Pessemier [1966]).

Two specific pre-launch models deserve special attention. DEMON (*De*cision *M*apping via *O*ptimum Go-No *N*etworks) (Learner [1968]) was developed by operations researchers and the advertising agency of Batten, Barton, Durstine, and Osborn, Inc. (BBD&O). The model is set up to indicate whether to go national (Go), drop the product (No), or collect further information on the product's chance of success (On). The decision is made on the basis of which alternatives promise the highest expected return, given the latest data. If the answer is "On," the model indicates which new marketing research study is the best to carry out—that is, best in the sense that it would probably do the most to reduce the uncertainty clouding the Go-No alternatives. After this study is made, the results lead to a revision in the proposed marketing strategy, and a new evaluation is then made of the Go-No-On alternatives. This approach requires that top management state its constraints regarding the planning period, payout period, minimal acceptable profits, profits required to go national, marketing research budget, and the degree of confidence needed. Furthermore, management must state its marketing program for introducing the product. The proposed advertising, sales promotion, distribution, and pricing plans are critical in making an estimate of product sales. A distinctive feature of the sales forecasting model is the utilization of recursive links between levels of advertising expenditure, audience exposure, awareness, market trial, and market usage. These links have been functionally estimated on the basis of least squares regression using past data from 200 packaged goods in sixteen product categories. DEMON has been used on some products, but its cost of implementation prevented widespread adoption. More recently it was revised and renamed NEWS (Light and Pringle [1970]).

The N. W. Ayer new product model (Claycamp and Liddy [1969]) also attempts to predict product performance before market introduction. It utilizes three equations, with three dependent variables and twelve independent variables. The first equation is designed to predict the level of advertising recall, to be expected 13 weeks after launch, as a function of product positioning, media impressions, copy execution, consumer promotion, and product category interest. The second equation is designed to predict the expected level of initial purchases at the end of 13 weeks as a function of the estimated advertising recall from the first equation plus distribution, packaging, family brand, consumer promotion, product satisfaction, and category usage. The third equation is designed to predict repeat purchase levels after 13 weeks on the basis of advertising recall and initial purchase estimated from the first two equations plus relative price, product satisfaction, and purchase frequency. Values for the independent variables are estimated from commercial data and expert judgment. Parameter estimation and model validation utilized a data base of 60 new consumer products introduced in the Philadelphia area during the late sixties. The model structure allows the firm to estimate initial and repeat sales on the basis of planned and/or expected values of the independent variables. These results help the firm decide on whether to launch the product.

New Product Sales Forecasting Models (Post-Launch)

After a new product has been introduced into the market, the company must carefully analyze early sales to make sure that it has a winner. It turns out that early sales alone are an insufficient basis for making a confident forecast of future sales. Initial sales do not reveal how satisfied the market is with the product and what users are saying to nonusers. High initial sales may reflect an effective promotion campaign designed to get high trial; if the product fails to meet expectations, sales may shortly turn down. For this reason, disaggregate sales and other data are required by most models. We will review the better known models here.

Fourt and Woodlock Model. Fourt and Woodlock [1960] proposed a simple data-based model for forecasting future sales of consumer packaged goods based on early sales returns. Their model consisted of submodels for predicting first-time purchases and repeat purchases, respectively. They realized that reliable sales forecasting required disaggregating total sales into the amount of purchases occurring for the first time and the amount of repeat purchases (first-repeats, second-repeats, etc.). If trial and repeat purchase rates were low, the product was in serious trouble; if trials were high and repeats low, the product was apparently not delivering the expected satisfaction to the consumer and this called for product or message redesign or market retargeting; if trials were low and repeats high, the product needed better promotion to stimulate first purchases; and if trial and repeat purchase rates were high, the product's future looked assured. To get data for first time and repeat purchase, the company had to obtain consumer panel data. Store audit data and warehouse receipts data were not adequate.

The first time purchase model was given by:

$$Q_t = r\overline{Q}(1 - r)^{t-1}, \tag{1}$$

where

Q_t = sales at time t;
r = rate of penetration of untapped potential;
$\bar{Q}$ = potential sales;
t = time period.

This is a one parameter model requiring estimating r from the latest sales data. The repeat purchase model consisted of projecting measured repeat ratios by depth-of-repeat class into future total purchases, on the assumption that these repeat ratios would hold constant.

The basic type of model has been refined in subsequent work. Parfitt and Collins [1968] published a model which estimates ultimate brand share as the product of three factors:

$$s = p\,r\,b, \tag{2}$$

where

s = ultimate brand share;
p = ultimate penetration rate of brand (percent of new buyers of this product class who try this brand);
r = ultimate repeat purchase rate of brand (percent of repurchases of this brand to all repurchases by persons who once purchased this brand);
b = buying rate index of repeat purchase of this brand (average buyer = 1.00).

This model is fitted to early sales results and updated. Massy [1969] significantly extended the basic Fourt and Woodlock approach in his sophisticated model called STEAM (*St*ochastic *E*volutionary *A*doption *M*odel). STEAM is designed to predict the probability that a household will make its first or next purchase at or before a particular time, given that its last purchase occurred at a given time. It predicts the time paths of the cumulative proportions of one-time buyers, two-time buyers, and so on, and therefore future demand. It combines several sub-models, probability distributions, parameter estimation techniques, and simulation to produce the forecast.

Sprinter. Urban developed several models which go under the name of SPRINTER (*S*pecification of *Pr*ofits with *In*teraction under *T*rial and *E*rror *R*esponse). His original SPRINTER (1968) consisted of demand, cost, profit, and uncertainty submodels. The demand submodel considered life cycle, industry, competitive and product interdependency effects. SPRINTER allowed the manager to estimate the differential company profit and uncertainty that would be obtained by including the new product in the line. The manager could also use the model to find the marketing strategy that would optimize profits subject to risk constraints. The model was primarily designed for prelaunch Go-No decision making and tested on a set of chemical products.

Subsequently, Urban introduced SPRINTER MOD III (1970) which is oriented to frequently purchased consumer products and which uses test market results to forecast future sales. It employs a more behavioral conception of demand by postulating buyers as being in several states such as potential trial, preference, loyalty I, and loyalty II, with different probabilities of inter-state transition, depending on advertising, specific product appeals, and word-of-mouth. The model requires early national sales and micro-level behavioral data to forecast future sales as a function of alternative marketing strategies and provides a method for finding the optimal marketing strategy. The model is available on a conversational on-line basis and has been applied with impressive success to a number of new consumer product entries.

Bass Model. Bass [1969] developed a model differing from the previous ones in (1) addressing itself to consumer durables rather than nondurables and (2) using an epidemiological model as a basis. Bass applied his model to eleven major appliance innovations, including room air conditioners, electric refrigerators, home freezers, and black and white television. He used the first few years of actual sales, when these products were first introduced, to estimate the parameters p, r, and $\bar{Q}$ of the following equation:

$$Q_t = \left(p + r\,\frac{Q_T}{\bar{Q}}\right)(\bar{Q} - Q_T), \tag{3}$$

where

Q_t = the number of new adopters in the current period;

p = coefficient of innovation; i.e., the individual conversion rate in the absence of the adopters' influence;

r = coefficient of imitation; i.e., the effect of each adopter on each non-adopter;

Q_T = the cumulative number of adopters to date;

$\bar{Q}$ = the total number of potential adopters.

With the equation fitted, Bass estimated future sales including the time when annual sales would reach a peak and the magnitude of sales in the peak year. All of these appliances were not expected to have replacement sales for some years, at which point his forecast stopped. He obtained excellent fits to actual sales data in several product cases: for example, an $R^2 = .92$ for fifteen years of room air conditioner sales, based on using the first three years of sales to fit the equation.

PRICING MODELS

Although there is much talk about the growing role of non-price factors in the marketing process, pricing remains a very complex issue for many firms. Pricing is a problem when a new product is being introduced or an old product phased out, when a price change is contemplated in the face of uncertain customer and competitor reactions, and when a company must react to a competitor who has just changed his price. Pricing is also a problem in industries when companies submit sealed bids for jobs. And it is a problem when the company's product line is characterized by substantial demand and cost interdependencies.

The Price Modification Decision

An increasing number of companies are using Bayesian decision theory for formal analyses of the likely response of customers and competitors to a contemplated change. Green [1963] described a specific application by a large chemical manufacturer. The company had been selling a plastic substance to industrial users for several years, and had captured 40 per cent of that market. Top management became concerned as to whether or not its current price of $1 per pound could be maintained much longer because of a developing oversupply. Management saw that the solution to its problem lay in penetrating a certain market segment which was closely held by a substitute plastic product produced by six companies. Therefore, it was decided to evaluate the following four alternatives: maintaining the price at $1, or reducing the price to 93 cents, 85 cents, or 80 cents.

Among the chief uncertainties top management considered were:

1. How much penetration in the key segment would take place without a price reduction?
2. How would the six companies producing the substitute plastic react to each possible price reduction?
3. How much penetration in the key segment would take place for every possible price reaction by the suppliers of the substitute plastic?
4. How much would penetration into the key segment speed up penetration in other segments?
5. If the key segment was not penetrated, what would be the probability that the company's competitors would initiate price reductions soon?
6. What would be the impact of a price reduction on the decision of existing competitors to expand their capacity and/or potential competitors to enter the industry?

The data gathering phase consisted mainly in asking key sales personnel to place subjective probabilities on the various possible states of the key uncertainties.

The next step was to estimate the likely payoffs of different courses of action. A decision-tree analysis revealed that there were over four hundred possible outcomes. For this reason, the estimation of expected payoffs was programmed on a computer. The results indicated that in all cases a price reduction had a higher expected payoff than status quo pricing; in fact, a price reduction to 80 cents had the highest expected payoff.

Finally, to check the sensitivity of these results to the original assumptions, the results were recomputed for alternative assumptions on the rate of market growth and on the appropriate cost of capital. It was found that the ranking of the strategies was unaffected by the change in the assumptions.

The Bidding Decision

The theory of competitive bidding has received considerable refinement in the hands of applied mathematicians. The objective of a company in a bidding situation is to get the contract, and this means setting a lower price than the competition. The lower the company sets its bid, the lower its potential profits but the higher its probability of getting the contract award. The chief hurdle is to estimate the probability of getting the contract at various bidding levels. This requires estimating the bids of various competitors, and also judging the influence of nonprice factors on the buyer's final choice (Simmonds [1968]).

The Product Line Pricing Problem

When a company's products have demand and cost interdependencies, none of its products can be priced in isolation. Total sales and profits on the line must be expressed as a function of the simultaneous prices set for the individual products. Urban [1969] advanced a model for the case of a class of frequently purchased consumer products. Hess [1967] analyzed a complex problem dealing with the optimal pricing of two related chemicals, one being an improved version of the other it was gradually replacing.

ADVERTISING MODELS

A number of thorny problems confront companies in connection with the wise use of advertising monies. They would like to have better ways to analyze whether they are spending too little or too much on advertising; whether they are timing their advertising expenditures optimally through the year; and whether their agency is choosing the best media.

The Spending Level Decision

One of the earliest and still most interesting spending level studies on advertising was developed by Vidale and Wolfe [1957]. In their model, the change in the rate of sales at time t is a function of four factors: the advertising budget, the sales response constant, the saturation level of sales, and the sales decay constant. Their basic equation is:

$$\frac{dS}{dt} = rA\,\frac{M - S}{M} - \lambda S,$$

where

S = rate of sales at time t;

$\frac{dS}{dt}$ = change in the rate of sales at time t;

A = rate of advertising expenditure at time t;

r = sales response constant (defined as the sales generated per advertising dollar when $S = 0$);

M = saturation level of sales;

λ = sales decay constant (defined as the fraction of sales lost per time unit when $A = 0$).

The task of the company is to estimate the three parameters of the model and then use the equation to determine the advertising budget that would produce the desired or optimum levels of sales and profits.

Kuehn [1961] developed and tested an elaborate advertising model in which sales are a function of:

1. The percentage of customers with brand loyalty and the rate of decay in this brand loyalty.
2. The percentage of customers not committed to this firm or its main competitors.
3. The size and rate of growth of the total market.
4. The relative influence of price and distribution in the marketing process.
5. The relative influence of the interaction of product characteristics and advertising in the marketing process.
6. The relative share and effectiveness of this company's advertising expenditure.

Given the variables and the information required as inputs to this model, it is possible to derive a theoretically optimal advertising expenditure level.

Subsequent advertising budget models introduced the desirability of estimating sales/advertising response functions through the use of planned experiments. In the early sixties, Ackoff and his associates planned experiments to measure the effect of different levels of advertising expenditures on beer sales for the Anheuser-Busch Company (Rao [1970]). The analytical use of these results allowed Anheuser-Busch to achieve substantial increases in sales and market share for their brand while bringing down per case expenditures on advertising.

The theory of using experiments for deriving optimal advertising expenditures was carried to its ultimate form by Little [1966] who developed an adaptive control framework requiring periodic experimentation. Little conjectured that the sales advertising response function was probably neither very stable nor very unstable from period to period but drifted and had to be tracked. The latest measured results would be used to set the next advertising budget. Specifically, suppose a company set a budget for the coming period on the basis of applying profit maximization criteria to its most recent information on the sales function. It would plan to spend this rate in all markets except a subset of $2n$ of them randomly drawn. In n of the test markets the company would spend a deliberately low amount of dollars, and in the other n it would spend a deliberately high amount of dollars. This experiment would yield information on the average sales created by the low, medium, and high rates of advertising, and this would provide the best estimate of the current sales reponse function. In turn, this estimate is used to determine the best promotional rate for the next period. If this procedure is carried out each period, Little showed that actual advertising expenditures will track closely to the optimal advertising expenditures. A number of companies have tried or are using this adaptive control method of setting their advertising expenditures.

Little [1970] subsequently developed an alternative approach called ADBUDG that departed radically from the scientific control framework of his first model. He found a considerable number of managers who did not want to or were not able to carry out periodic experiments and who resisted leaving budget setting to the mercy of the results of experiments. This led him to adopt an *evolutionary approach* to model building characterized by asking a manager how he thought advertising worked and developing a very simple quantitative version of the manager's mental model. This model would go through subsequent refinements as the manager showed a readiness and wish to add further variables. Much of the data was also drawn subjectively from the manager, such as his estimates of what would happen to sales if advertising were cut in half, or reduced to zero, or increased by 50 percent over the normal rate. ADBUDG was introduced into several companies with good management response and in fact has evolved into a more total approach to setting the marketing mix called BRANDAID (Little [1975]).

The Advertising Timing Decision

Kuehn's model (1961) permits a determination to be made of the optimal timing pattern of advertising expenditures through the year. Given seasonal sales movements, Kuehn shows that the appropriate timing pattern depends on many factors, of which two important ones are the degree of advertising carry-over and the amount of habitual brand choice. Thus, under specific assumptions, the greater the amount of the advertising carry-over effect, the greater the lead time should be; and the smaller the amount of habitual purchasing behavior, the more the advertising curve should vary in amplitude than the sales curve (Kuehn [1962]).

A somewhat different approach to the timing question has been developed by Forrester of MIT. In one of his company applications of "industrial dynamics" Forrester [1959] showed how the poor timing of advertising expenditures was responsible for accentuation of production and inventory fluctuations. This stemmed from the fact that advertising has a lagged impact on customer behavior; customer buying decisions at retail have a lagged impact on factory sales; and factory sales have a lagged impact on production scheduling and new advertising scheduling.

The Media Selection Decision

On October 1, 1962, *Advertising Age* carried the headline "Y&R, BBD&O Unleash Media Computerization." Later, BBD&O sponsored full-page newspaper and magazine advertisements reading "Linear Programming showed one BBD&O client how to get $1.67 worth of effective advertising for every dollar in his budget."

The model developed at BBD&O used a linear programming approach (Buzzell [1964]). The problem is stated as one of selecting the media mix which would maximize the number of effective exposures subject to (1) the size of the total advertising budget, (2) minimum and maximum usage rates of various media, and (3) specified exposure rates to different market segments.

In the meantime, the Young and Rubicam (Y&R) agency developed a different approach that they called the "high assay model" (Moran [1963]). The Y&R model uses a sequential rather than a simultaneous decision process. The basic idea is to start with the media available in the first week and select the single "best buy." After this selection is made, all the remaining media choices are reevaluated to take into account duplication and potential media discounts. Then, if the achieved exposure for the week is below the optimal rate, a second selection is made for the same week. The optimal rate is a complex function of several marketing and media variables. The cycling process continues until the optimal exposure rate for the week is reached, at which point new media choices are considered for the following week. The cycling process is continued until the entire budget is spent.

A simulation model has been developed by the Simulmatics Corporation, which does not profess to find the "best" media plan but rather to estimate the exposure value of any given plan (Simulmatics [1962]). The model consists of a sample universe of 2,944 make-believe media users representing a cross-section of the United States population by sex, age, type of community, employment status, and education. Each individual's media choices are determined probabilistically as a function of his social-economic characteristics and location in one of ninety-eight American communities. A proposed media schedule is exposed to all the persons in this hypothetical population. As the simulation of the year's schedule progresses, the computer tabulates the number and types of people being exposed. Summary graphs and tables are automatically prepared at the end of the hypothetical year's run, and they supply a multidimensional picture of the schedule's probable impact. The advertiser examines these tabulations and then decides whether the audience profile and the reach and frequency characteristics of the proposed media schedule are satisfactory.

Gensch [1969] developed an improved simulation model that uses the following inputs: (1) the proposed media plan and schedule; (2) weights for the effectiveness of different media; (3) weights for the effectiveness of alternative size and color advertising forms; (4) weights showing the value of different patterns of exposure frequency; (5) media costs and volume discounts; (6) weights showing the value of an exposure to different types of persons in the target population; and (7) Brand Rating Research Corporation data showing the reading and viewing patterns over time of a real sample of individuals. From these inputs, the computer program generates weekly and cumulative output on (1) the number and percentage of people in the target population reached by the proposed media schedule and its cost; (2) the number of persons reached zero, one, two, etc., times during the period by the proposed media schedule; and (3) an adjusted exposure number representing the overall impact of the proposed media schedule, taking into account all of the objective and subjective evaluations of the media and the value of exposures to different members of the target audience. Gensch's program also includes a heuristic procedure that leads to improved schedules, though not necessarily the optimal schedule.

A model which has attracted great interest and usage is the one developed by Little and Lodish [1969] called MEDIAC (Media Evaluation using Dynamic and Interactive Applications of Computers). The model is available on a conversational on-line basis and handles in an analytical fashion a large number of marketing and advertising facets of the real media problem, such as market segments, sales potentials, exposure probabilities, diminishing marginal response rates, forgetting, seasonality, and cost discounts. The model states the media problem as one of maximizing total sales subject to current exposure value constraints, media usage constraints, and budget constraints. The model is solved either through piecewise linear programming, dynamic programming, or heuristic techniques depending on the size of the problem and the complexity of the functions.

Much remains to be done in the media selection field. Many advertising agencies still use no or very simple models for media selection, arguing that they cannot get the client to pay for the development or use of these models. Clients in turn are too lenient in accepting exposure data from their agency rather than insisting on post measures of attitudinal and sales changes caused by the advertising program. Finally, most of the models need to incorporate improved behavioral underpinnings about the effects of learning, forgetting, and competitive exposure so that more meaningful solutions to the scheduling problem can be obtained.

SALES-FORCE MODELS

In spite of the great cost and importance of personal selling in the marketing mix, less OR has been reported in this area than in the advertising area, which in many ways is a less tangible problem. Nevertheless, the studies that have been conducted have significance for sales-force management.

The Salesman Routing Decision

In situations where salesmen have many calls to make through large territories, the traveling salesmen algorithms can be used to find the optimal routing for the salesmen (Little, et al. [1963]; Karg and Thompson [1964]). Often the problem is not simply the optimal routing of salesmen through a set of cities but also the choice of cities or accounts to call on. The cost interactions between the two problems call for a joint solution to calling and routing. Cloonan [1966] has formulated a model for this problem and has investigated the power of different heuristics to achieve the highest profit call routing solution.

The Sales Manpower Requirements Decision

Markov process analysis has been used by a large insurance company to aid in the analysis of its sales-force manpower needs (Midler [1961]). Each year the company loses a fraction of its sales force through resignation, retirement, and death. The existing salesmen have different levels of experience, education, and ability. The company has to hire new men to replace those who leave and additional men to meet the company's growth requirements. Top management's problem is to estimate future manpower needs by class of service and age in the light of the turnover characteristics and planned sales growth.

The first step is to calculate "survival" rates for agents in various service and age classes. These estimated rates are then used in a Markov analysis to project future characteristics of the sales force if no new men are hired. Different alternative recruitment patterns are analyzed for their effect on the composition of the future sales force and probable level of sales.

The Optimal Allocation of Sales-Call Time

The best level and allocation of sales effort depends on the correct assessment of customer response to variations in the number of sales calls.

An early investigation was made by the Operations Research Group at Case Institute for the General Electric Company (Waid [1956]). Customers were sorted into classes on the basis of similar characteristics. The accounts in each class were sorted again into subclasses on the basis of the call time spent with each customer. Then the average dollar volume was computed for each subclass. Finally, a curve was drawn through the scatter of points to show the relationship between average dollar volume and sales-call time.

The scatter for each class of account lay in a basically positive direction but unfortunately was too diffused to permit the fitting of a statistically significant curve. The operations researchers, after trying other approaches that fared no better, tentatively accepted the hypothesis that salesmen typically spent more time with accounts than was necessary. On the basis of this hypothesis, the research group recommended that the number of calls be cut back. They strongly felt that some diversion of calls from present accounts to new accounts was warranted and would also result in a substantial net increase in business. This recommendation was followed, and company sales remained high.

In another early effort, Magee [1958] described an experiment where salesmen were asked to vary their call pattern in a particular way to determine what effect this would have on sales. His experiment called for first sorting accounts into major classes. Each account class was then randomly split into three sets. The respective salesmen were asked to spend less than five hours a month with accounts in the first set, five to nine hours a month with the second set, and a minimum of ten hours a month with the third set for a specified period of time. The results indicated that call time had a definite effect on sales volume, with the most profitable call norm in this particular situation appearing to be five to nine hours a month.

More recent work on the problem of optimal sales-call patterns has produced a number of useful interactive computer models to aid salesmen or sales management in planning call allocation time more efficiently. Lodish [1971] designed a model called CALLPLAN. Salesmen input their best estimates of expected sales in response to several alternative call levels on each account and prospect. The computer fits a curve through the salesmen's estimates to develop a sales response function for each account. The response functions, costs, and constraints are then solved mathematically to produce the best time allocation to maximize contribution. The solution reflects such factors as travel time and costs to get to geographical areas within the territory, amount of time required per call on an account within an area, account profitability, and minimum and maximum account call frequency limitations. CALLPLAN is being tried or used in several companies ("Computers Route . . . , " [1972]) and producing sales increases of between five and twenty-five percent in the majority of applications.

A more specialized call plan model was designed by Montgomery, Silk, and Zaragoza [1971] to handle the allocation of salesmen's time to products as well as accounts and time periods. Called DETAILER, the model has been used in the pharmaceutical industry to help detailmen (salesmen) know which company products they should promote on each trip to each account. The model requires the estimation of sales response functions to call effort for the various products in the line and an allocation heuristic.

The Sales Territory Design Decision

Sales territories are usually designed on an intuitive or a loose workload basis. They have to be periodically revised because the territories undergo different growth rates in potential and workload. Hess [1967] has formulated a computer program for this problem based on an earlier program using linear programming to create optimal size congressional districts. The program builds sales territories that are equal either in sales potential or workload, and as compact as possible to minimize traveling time. Hess and Samuels [1971] reported the results of seven applications (primarily in the pharmaceutical industry) and the demonstrated effectiveness of the new alignments produced by the computer program.

MARKETING MIX MODELS

A final area of marketing OR is the development of interactive computer-based models to help marketing executives, particularly product and brand managers, develop short-run and long-run marketing plans. Increasingly, companies are requiring their product managers to submit a detailed marketing plan that is quantified in terms of expected sales, costs, and profits. To help them in this task, several companies have developed their own version of a conversational computer program for marketing planning. Early marketing planning simulators were highly aggregate and financial in character. Subsequent simulators allowed product managers to test the effect of alternative marketing mixes on sales and profits.

A model ("Concorn Kitchens," [1971]) used by a large consumer packaged goods company provides a good example. The product manager seats himself at a computer terminal, activates the program, and types in the product's name. The computer prints out historical data for the last five years on the product's total market volume, company sales, company market share, price, gross margin, overhead, advertising, promotion, and net operating profits. The computer also proceeds to print out a projection of each of these variables over the next five years, using the most plausible extrapolation rule in each case. The manager scans the extrapolated values of these variables and modifies any which appear unreasonable in the light of new developments. The computer then summarizes the revised extrapolation (called the planning base). In the next phase, the manager tries out various marketing mixes which might produce an improved picture of future profits. This exercise requires his supplying estimates of elasticities for price, advertising, and promotion over the next five years. He tries different marketing mixes until he is satisfied with the forecasted profit flow. He can also modify the assumed elasticities to test the sensitivity of the forecasted profit flow to other estimates.

Additional refinements can be introduced, such as getting away from the assumption of constant elasticities. Little [1975] developed BRANDAID as a more flexible and elaborate decision calculus for marketing mix planning. BRANDAID uses an aggregate response function and has a modular structure which permits adding or deleting a marketing activity, adding detail within an activity, adding market segments or time periods, and inserting a customerized treatment of a particular area. It handles, either through direct indices or response submodels, such manufacturer decision and competitor variables as product characteristics, price, advertising, consumer promotion, trade promotion, salesman effort, pack assortment, package graphics and function, and production capacity; retailer variables such as availability, price, promotion, and advertising; and environmental influences such as seasonality and trend. The model is calibrated through judgment, analysis of historical data, tracking, field measurement, and adaptive control. It has undergone two years of development in one company and is in trial use in some other companies.

Although the parameters for marketing mix response functions are often supplied through executive estimation, some analysts have been able to estimate response parameters statistically with encouragingly high R^2's. Montgomery and Silk [1972] report an equation showing the sales of a pharmaceutical firm as a function of current and lagged direct mail expenditures, samples and literature expenditures, and journal advertising expenditures, with an $R^2 = .93$. Lambin [1972] reports an equation showing the market share of an oil company as a function of service station share and advertising share with an $R^2 = .96$. Urban [1969] reports an equation showing the sales of a consumer packaged product as a function of the prices and number of shelf facings of this brand and substitute brands. The evolution of improved data gathering methods and statistical techniques will make it possible to derive more hard-data based marketing mix equations to use in computerized marketing planning models.

CURRENT ISSUES IN MARKETING OPERATIONS RESEARCH

Elegant or Evolutionary Model Building

The original orientation of operations researchers in marketing was to create the best possible model for each type of problem, one that would include all the relevant variables, the best data estimation techniques, and produce optimal and not just satisficing results. This orientation worked in the areas of production and inventory control where the clients were technically oriented and where the tangible superiority of the model can be demonstrated. In marketing however, such models meet with great resistance from hostile managers who are largely unexposed to higher mathematics. They see marketing processes—with their nonlinearities, lags, and interactions—as too complex to be wrapped up in a small set of equations, and they know that hard data are rarely available for an accurate fitting of these equations. As a result, elegant marketing models found little reception in executive suites. Many operations researchers soon adopted a more *evolutionary strategy* of model building (Montgomery and Urban [1969]), calling for developing a simple model out of the manager's own statements about how he thinks the market works and getting the manager to use it. The model would be refined in stages as the manager himself calls for or agrees to the desirability of additional features, all the time with his full understanding of how the model works. This gives him a proprietary feeling for the model and he is not afraid to use it. Schultz and Slevin [1972] have gone further and called for *behavioral model building*; that is choosing model features that will maximize the likelihood of the model's implementation because these features take into account the attitudes and behavioral tendencies of the ultimate users.

The evolutionary model building approach is winning increasing support among marketing operations researchers. This is occurring at some price, however, in that few elegant models have appeared since 1970 because of the belief that they would not find practical acceptance by management.

Aggregate, Flow, or Disaggregate Models

Early marketing decision models employed an aggregate sales response function in the tradition of economic demand functions. In 1967, Amstutz [1967] went to the other extreme in creating a micro-behavioral model in which hypothetical individual buyers making up a market went through experiences of being exposed to products, ads, word-of-mouth, and retailers; and individually making buying and brand choices as a stochastic function of their demographics, product ownership, and other characteristics. Although Amstutz's microsimulation was impressive in its detail, many operations researchers felt that it was too detailed, complex, and costly to use as a normal strategy for model building in the marketing area. Urban [1968] advocated an intermediate microanalytic level of aggregation that modeled flows of population groups from state to state over time and their average characteristics (SPRINTER MOD III). Current model builders still seem to favor aggregate response functions, although those who would incorporate more behavioral processes and underpinnings will continue to press for microanalytic or microbehavioral models.

Hard Versus Soft Data

Model builders and marketing managers have a strong preference for hard-data (objective)* based models, although for possibly different reasons. Model builders feel more scientific and objective. Managers feel more confident and, furthermore, hard data saves them from having to furnish numbers which might be difficult or embarrassing to supply. Hard-data analysts believe in the ultimate possibility of accurately measuring and estimating most processes, given adequate time and financial support; and they continue to improve econometric and experimental techniques for producing objective data. They favor the growth of data utilities containing media data, consumer panel data, store audit data, buying power data, and so on that can be accessed by different users. Soft-data (subjective) analysts have nothing against hard data, but are impressed by its scarcity and cost. They do not believe that models should be in limbo because hard data is not available, or that important variables should be left out of a model for the same reason. They have a positive feeling that every company has some experienced managers who have an uncanny judgment about the true magnitudes and parameters that are needed. The task is to draw out these estimates through the best available expert query techniques. They believe that inadequate data is no justification of inadequate reasoning, and that an organized quantitative analysis should be preferred to a disorganized, nonquantitative analysis. Lodish has suggested that the inclusion of soft data and variables often has an advantage of leading to results that are "vaguely right instead of precisely wrong." The trend seems to be in favor of increased acceptance of soft-data when necessary and obtained through careful expert query techniques.

Batch or Interactive On-line Models

Early models were on a batch processing basis, which meant that the manager supplied the needed numbers on a form which would be keypunched into a data deck that would be added to a program deck and loaded on a computer, with some time elapsing before he saw the results of his first round of analysis. This

---

*Hard-data describes objective data based on survey or experimental methods, as opposed to soft-data which describes subjective data based on expert estimates.

added another obstacle to management's interest in models. With the advent of on-line terminals, marketing operations researchers began to cast their models into conversational on-line form. Managers could sit down comfortably at a computer terminal, type in answers to questions posed by the computer, and get immediate solutions. They could change any input on the spot to see what changes it would produce in the solution. This has been an immense boon to furthering managerial interest and usage in models, and most marketing operations researchers are putting their models on an interactive on-line basis.

Narrow or Comprehensive Models

Early models focused on one marketing variable such as advertising, sales force, or price, and sought to set, optimally, that variable independently of the levels of the other variables. In marketing this is likely to lead to suboptimization because of the strong interactions between the elements of the marketing mix in influencing consumer response. Marketing managers rarely change one marketing variable without making compatible adjustments in some others; for example, a price increase may require some advertising to inform the buyers and some repackaging to support a higher demand image. Furthermore, marketing variables cannot be optimized without simultaneous and fuller consideration of production and financial variables. Although a narrow focus permits exploring the detailed links between sales and a particular control variable, the practicalities of developing marketing plans favor more comprehensive model building, and this trend is taking place.

Nonadaptive or Adaptive Modeling

Early models were developed on the assumption that the response parameters, once measured, would hold true for a long time. Little [1966] has questioned the stability of response parameters and has advocated that parameters be regularly updated through systematic and periodic field experimentation. This principle is widely accepted today, although most companies have not formally implemented it.

Deterministic or Stochastic Modeling

Early models were deterministic in their formulation. While most of the leading models are still deterministic, model builders increasingly favor some way of explicitly introducing and handling uncertainty.

Single Variable or Multiple Variable Objective Function

Most marketing decision models are formulated to maximize short-run profits or, at best, a discounted cash flow. Few have grappled with the fact that management normally seeks to satisfy several objectives through its marketing strategy and that the problem formulation should reflect this. A few models introduce the other objectives in the form of constraints on profit maximization. Other ways of handling multiple objectives, such as goal programming or weighted multiple variable objective functions, have yet to make a strong appearance in marketing models.

INTRODUCING MARKETING OPERATIONS RESEARCH INTO THE COMPANY

An increasing number of companies will take a close look at their marketing problems through the eyes of OR. This is inevitable because marketing budgets are among the largest and fastest growing company budgets. Marketing accounts for approximately 40 cents of every retail dollar and 30 per cent of the gainfully employed persons in the United States (Cox [1965]). Competition continues to grow keener, customers continue to grow more discriminating, and products, as a result, become less secure. Company prosperity requires the best possible judgment about marketing expenditures and strategy.

Operations Research Personnel

Large companies are likely to have OR departments that undertake scientific studies of company problems in the areas of production scheduling, inventory control, and physical distribution. Typically their personnel have not worked on marketing problems, and this is a proper cause for concern. Operations researchers have a tendency to be technique centered; they tend to force their tools onto marketing problems and in the process often oversimplify the problems. They may come up with a good answer to a wrong statement of the problem because of their concern with mathematical solvability. They can avoid many pitfalls by reviewing the now extensive literature on marketing OR.

The best arrangement is for one of the company's operations researchers to specialize in this area and read the relevant literature. In time, his experience with several marketing problems in the company will make him very effective. As an alternative, the large company can directly hire a person who has specialized in marketing OR.

The marketing OR can be located either in the OR department or in the marketing research department. It is clear that his effectiveness requires that he be in frequent contact with line and staff marketing personnel so that he senses their problems, their types of information, and their current procedures for problem-solving. At the same time, marketing personnel will grow more familiar with him and the OR approach.

The small company usually does not have the option of employing a full-time operations researcher, let alone a specialist in marketing OR. Yet there is every reason to believe that the small company would benefit as much as the large company from the scientific study of its marketing problems. The small company's recourse is to hire a marketing OR consultant.

Top Management Support and Understanding

Marketing OR is particularly vulnerable to suspicion by the rank and file because mathematics seems alien to marketing problems and poses a serious language barrier. For marketing OR to succeed, it needs the cooperation and understanding of marketing managers who will be asked for data and ideas. For their cooperation to be positive, it is necessary for top management to establish at the beginning that marketing OR is a high-priority activity and must be supported by all managers.

Some top managers have enthusiastically recognized that their companies are in the computer age and that nothing less than a crash program of in-house management education would prepare management to take up the challenge of the computer. This happened at Pillsbury when the president, Robert Keith, recognized the great potential of the new decision-making techniques and personally sponsored and participated in a several-day company seminar on decision theory, mathematical models, statistical techniques and computers. This seminar was repeated at several levels of management.

Problem Selection

Marketing OR also gains respect in a company to the extent that it achieves early successes. It is therefore important to select appropriate problems. Three types of marketing situations generally pose a good opportunity for marketing OR.

Evaluation of Nonrecurrent Major Policy Changes. When a company faces a major marketing decision, such as a shift from one type of marketing channel to another or a price reduction in an oligopoly situation, the thinking of management can be considerably aided by simple decision-tree analysis or simulation models, both of which are easy for management to understand.

Improvement of Marketing Systems and Procedures. Most companies can benefit from studies of their current procedures for sales forecasting, marketing mix planning, and allocation of budgets to products and territories. Studies of the current procedures yield clues as to alternative decision procedures that would lead to important gains in performance.

Developing Better Information and Analytical Facilities. Operations researchers can render a service by installing time-sharing equipment and showing marketing managers how to call in various useful stored computer programs. Executives become very involved with time sharing when they try it, and this helps considerably in whetting their appetite for computer methods in marketing. The problem, if any, is that they may become too enthusiastic about accepting the computer printouts. The point must be driven home to each executive that the computer models are tools to aid judgment, not replace it. The executive must understand the basics of each model he uses, or else he is apt to make serious mistakes.

CONCLUSION

The increasing application of OR in the marketing area promises to make a substantial contribution toward the improvement of company efficiency. Although still in its infancy, marketing OR has already produced useful insights and decision procedures in the areas of new-product strategy, pricing, advertising, salesforce management, and marketing mix planning, and can be expected to produce new types of models and refinements in the future.

REFERENCES

"A Profit Yardstick for Advertising," *Business Week* (November 22, 1958).

Amstutz, A. E., *Computer Simulation of Competitive Market Response*, MIT, Cambridge, Mass. (1967).

Bass, F. M., "A New Product Growth Model for Consumer Durables," *Management Sci.* **15**, No. 5: 215–227 (1969).

Bass, F. M., C. W. King, and E. A. Pessemier, eds., *Applications of the Sciences in Marketing Management*, John Wiley & Sons, Inc., New York (1968).

Buzzell, R. D., "Batten, Barton, Durstine & Osborn, Inc.: Use of Linear Programming Methods in the Selection of Advertising Media," *Mathematical Models and Marketing Management*, Division of Research, Graduate School of Business Administration, Harvard University, Ch. 5 (1964).

Clark, W. A., "Monsanto Chemical Company: A Total Systems Approach to Marketing," in D. Meacham and V. B. Thompson (eds.), *Total Systems*, American Data Processing, Inc., Detroit (1962).

Claycamp, H. J., and L. E. Liddy, "Prediction of New Product Performance: An Analytical Approach," *J. Marketing Res.* **6**, No. 4: 414–420 (1969).

Cloonan, J. B., "A Heuristic Approach to Some Sales Territory Problems," in J. D. C. Little, ed., *Proceedings of the Fourth International Conference on Operations Research*, M.I.T., Cambridge, Mass. pp. 81–84 (1966).

"Computers Route the Salesmen," *Business Week* (July 1, 1972).

"Concorn Kitchens," in Boyd, H. W., and R. T. Davis, *Marketing Management Casebook*, Irwin, Homewood, Ill., pp. 125–136, (1971).

Cox, R., *Distribution in a High-level Economy*, Prentice-Hall, Englewood Cliffs, N.J. (1965).

Disman, S., "Selecting R&D Projects for Profit," *Chem. Eng.* (December 24, 1962) 87–90.

"EDP Keys New Era in Planning at Pillsbury," *Grocery Manufacturer* (January 1967); and "Involvement Helps at Pillsbury," *ibid.* (February 1967).

Forrester, J. W., "Advertising: A Problem in Industrial Dynamics," *Harvard Bus. Rev.* **37**, No. 2: 100–110 (1959).

Fourt, L. A., and J. W. Woodlock, "Early Prediction of Market Success for New Grocery Products," *J. Marketing* **24**, No. 4: 31–38 (1960).

Gensch, D., "A Computer Simulation Model for Selecting Advertising Schedules," *J. Marketing Res.* **6**, No. 2: 203–214 (1969).

Green, P. E., "Bayesian Decision Theory in Pricing Strategy," *J. Marketing*, **27**, No. 1: 5–14 (1963).

———, and V. R. Rao, *Applied Multidimensional Scaling*, Holt, Rinehart & Winston, New York (1972).

Hess, S. W., "The Use of Models in Marketing Timing Decisions," *Operations Res.* **15**, No. 4: 720–737 (1967).

———, and S. A. Samuels, "Experiences with a Sales Districting Model: Criteria and Implementation," *Management Sci.* **18**, No. 4, Part 2: 41–54 (1971).

Karg, R. L., and G. L. Thompson, "A Heuristic Approach to Solving Traveling Salesmen Problems," *Management Sci.* **10**, No. 5: 225–248 (1964).

Kline, C. H., "The Strategy of Product Policy," *Harvard Bus. Rev.* **36**, No. 4: 91–100 (1955).

Kotler, P., *Marketing Decision Making: A Model-Building Approach*, Holt, Rinehart & Winston, New York (1971).

Kuehn, A. A., "A Model for Budgeting Advertising," in F. M. Bass, *et al.* (eds.), *Mathematical Models and Methods in Marketing*, Irwin, Homewood, Ill. (1961).

———, "How Advertising Performance Depends on Other Marketing Factors," *J. Advertising Res.* **2**, No. 1: 2–10 (1962).

Lambin, J., "A Computer On-Line Marketing Mix Model," *J. Marketing Res.* **9**, No. 2: 119–126 (1972).

Learner, David B., "Profit Maximization Through New-Product Marketing Planning and Control," in Bass, Chapter 6 (1968).

Light, L., and L. Pringle, "New Product Forecasting Using Recursive Regression," in D. T. Kollat, R. D. Blackwell, and J. F. Engel (eds.), *Research in Consumer Behavior*, Holt, Rinehart & Winston, New York (1970).

Little, J. D. C., "A Model of Adaptive Control of Promotional Spending," *Operations Res.* **14**, No. 6: 1075–1097 (1966).

———, K. G. Murty, D. W. Sweeney, and C. Karel, "An Algorithm for the Traveling Salesman Problem," *Operations Res.* **2**, No. 6, (1963).

———, and L. M. Lodish, "A Media Planning Calculus," *Operations Res.* **17**, No. 1: 1–35 (1969).

———, "Models and Managers: The Concept of a Decision Calculus," *Management Sci.* **16**, No. 8: 466–485 (1970).

———, "BRANDAID: A Marketing Mix Model," *Operations Res.* **23**, No. 4: 628–673 (July–August 1975).

Lodish, L. M., "CALLPLAN: An Interactive Salesman's Call Planning System," *Management Sci.* **18**, No. 4, Part II: P-25–P-40 (1971).

Magee, J. F., "Determining the Optimum Allocation of Expenditures for Promotional Effort with Operations Research Methods," in F. M. Bass (ed.), *The Frontiers of Marketing Thought and Science*, American Marketing Association, Chicago (1958).

Massy, W. F., "Forecasting the Demand for New Convenience Products," *J. Marketing Res.* **6**, No. 4: 405–413 (1969).

Midler, J., "A Simulation Model of Sales Force Development with Application to Manpower Replacement, Sales Forecasting, and Corporate Growth," an unpublished paper (1961).

Montgomery, D. B. and A. J. Silk, "Estimating Dynamic Effects of Market Communications Expenditures," *Management Sci.* **18,** No. 10: 485–501 (1972).

——, and C. E. Zaragoza, "A Multiple-Product Sales Force Allocation Model," *Management Sci.* **18,** No. 4. Part 2: P-3 to P-24 (1971).

—— and G. L. Urban, *Management Science Marketing*, Prentice-Hall, Englewood Cliffs, N.J., p. 358 (1969).

Moran, W. T., "Practical Media Decisions and the Computer," *J. Marketing* **27,** No. 3: 26–30 (1963).

O'Meara, Jr., J. T., "Selecting Profitable Products," *Harvard Bus. Rev.* **39,** No. 1: 83–89 (1961).

Parfitt, J. H., and B. J. K. Collins, "The Use of Consumer Panels for Brand-Share Prediction," *J. Marketing Res.* **5,** No. 2: 131–146 (1968).

Pessemier, E. A., *New Product Decisions: An Analytical Approach*, McGraw-Hill, New York Ch. 4 (1966).

Rao, A. G., *Quantitative Theories in Advertising*, John Wiley & Sons, Inc., New York (1970).

Richman, B., "A Rating Scale for Product Innovation," *Bus. Horizons*, 37–44 (Summer 1962).

Schultz, R. L., and D. P. Slevin, "Behavioral Model Building," #8, Graduate School of Business, University of Pittsburgh (May 1972).

Silk, A. J., "Preferences and Perception Measures in New Product Development: An Exposition and Review," *Ind. Management Rev.* **2,** No. 1: 21–40 (1969).

Simmonds, K., "Competitive Bidding: Deciding the Best Combination of Non-Price Features," *Operational Res. Quart.* **19:** 5–14 (1968).

Simulmatics Media-Mix: Technical Description, The Simulmatics Corporation New York (October 1962).

Stefflre, V., "Market Structure Studies: New Products for Old Markets and New Markets (Foreign) for Old Products," in Bass (1968).

Urban, G. L., "Market Response Models for the Analysis of New Products," in R. L. King, *Marketing and the New Science of Planning*, 1968 Fall Conference Proceedings, American Marketing Association, Chicago, pp. 105–111.

——, "A New Product Analysis and Decision Model," *Management Sci.* **14,** No. 8: B-490–B-519 (1968).

——, "A Mathematical Modeling Approach to Product Line Decisions," *J. Marketing Res.* **6,** No. 1: 40–47 (1969).

——, "SPRINTER MOD III: A Model for the Analysis of New Frequently Purchased Consumer Products," *Operations Res.* **18,** No. 5: 805–854 (1970).

Vidale, M. L. and H. B. Wolfe, "An Operations-Research Study of Sales Response to Advertising," *Operations Res.* **5,** No. 3: 370–381 (1957).

Waid, C., D. F. Clark, and R. L. Ackoff, "Allocation of Sales Effort in the Lamp Division of the General Electric Company," *Operations Res.* **4,** No. 6: 629–647 (1956).

SELECTED REFERENCES

Texts on Marketing Models

Kotler, Philip, *Marketing Decision Making: A Model-Building Approach* (New York: Holt, Rinehart & Winston, 1971).

Montgomery, David B., and Urban, Glen L., *Management Science in Marketing* (Englewood Cliffs, N.J.: Prentice-Hall, Inc., 1969).

Simon, Leonard S., and Freimer, Marshall, *Analytical Marketing* (New York: Harcourt, Brace & World, 1970).

Texts on Quantitative Techniques

Clark, William A., and Sexton, Donald E., *Marketing and Management Science: A Synergism* (Homewood, Ill.: Richard D. Irwin, 1970).

Donnelly, James H., Jr., and Ivanevich, John M., *Analysis for Marketing Decisions* (Homewood, Ill.: Richard D. Irwin, 1970).

Frank, Ronald E., and Green, Paul E., *Quantitative Methods in Marketing* (Englewood Cliffs, N.J.: Prentice-Hall, Inc., 1967).

King, William R. *Quantitative Analysis for Marketing Management* (New York: McGraw-Hill, 1967).

Case Studies

Buzzell, Robert D., *Mathematical Models and Marketing Management* (Boston: Division of Research, Graduate School of Business Administration, Harvard University, 1964).

Original Monographs

Amstutz, Arnold E., *Computer Simulation of Competitive Market Response* (Cambridge, Mass.: MIT Press, 1967).

Pessemier, Edgar A., *New Product Decisions* (New York: McGraw-Hill, 1966).

Reprints of Major Readings

Bass, Frank M., *et al.*, eds., *Mathematical Models and Methods in Marketing* (Homewood, Ill.: Richard D. Irwin, Inc., 1961).

Frank, Ronald E., Kuehn, Alfred A., and Massy, William F., eds., *Quantitative Techniques in Marketing Analysis: Text and Readings* (Homewood, Ill.: Richard D. Irwin, 1962).

Montgomery, David B., and Urban, Glen L., *Applications of Management Science in Marketing* (Englewood Cliffs, N.J.: Prentice-Hall, 1970).

Murdick, Robert C., *Mathematical Models in Marketing* (Scranton, Pa.: Intext Educational Publishers, 1971).

Essays

Alderson, Wroe, and Shapiro, Stanley J., eds., *Marketing and the Computer* (Englewood Cliffs, N.J.: Prentice-Hall, Inc., 1963).

Langhoff, Peter, ed., *Models, Measurement and Marketing* (Englewood Cliffs, N.J.: Prentice-Hall, Inc., 1965).

Bibliography

Sheparovych, Zenon B., *et al.*, *A Selected Annotated Bibliography in Quantitative Methods in Marketing*, Bibliography Series No. 15 (Chicago: American Marketing Association, 1968).

I-4

HUMAN RESOURCE MANAGEMENT

Richard O. Mason
Eric G. Flamholtz
University of California, Los Angeles

1. INTRODUCTION

The use of operations research (OR) and management science (MS) methods to aid in managing human resources is, perhaps, the least developed area in the field. It is also, undoubtedly, the most difficult to develop. This is because so many diverse and value-laden factors impinge on the human resource management problem. Many factors influence the proper employment of human resources. These influencing factors stem from four basic forces or demands which the mangement scientist must keep in mind in performing analysis and in deriving recommendations. These are:

1) The organization's demand to have an effective job and role structure that is adequate to produce its goods and services in appropriate quantities and qualities, and on time.
2) The organization's demand for the efficient use of its resources.
3) The individual's demand to satisfy basic and self-actualization needs.
4) Society's demand for the production and appropriate distribution of goods and services consistent with an ethical stance with regard to the rights, duties and privileges of its citizens.

The first demand is addressed by organization and management theory, and concerns the optimal determination of an organization's role structure and the design of jobs. The second is addressed by industrial engineering and operations management, and is concerned with time and motion study, task definition and allocation, and the design of incentive systems which maximize productivity. The third is addressed by the behavioral sciences, and is concerned with methods for satisfying individual needs, studying individual and group attitudes, assessing the psychological properties of jobs and understanding group interrelationships and sentiments. The fourth is addressed by the social sciences and by ethics. It is concerned with the larger social, political, and legal forces that impact on the organization's use of its human resources. The management scientist must draw from all of these sources in formulating a human resource management problem. Each materially affects the objective functions specified, the constraints employed, the manner in which the study is conducted and, of course, the potential implementation of recommendations.

Despite the magnitude of the applications problem, its intention is clear. The purpose of applying OR and MS to management of human resources is to secure improvement in some social system by means of the scientific method. From the social system's or organization's point of view, improvement is probably best expressed in terms of maximizing the present worth of the present and future services of its participants. From the individual's point of view, improvement means maximizing the satisfaction of personal needs including physiological, security, social, status, and self-realization or fulfillment needs. Frequently these objectives are in conflict and the management scientist must find some "trade-off's" among them. Sometimes, however, these two objectives can be mutually supportive in the sense that decisions which lead to improvement on one side also lead to improvement on the other. Finding these kinds of "goal congruent" solutions is a primary objective of MS in the field, and is the goal of most of the research in the areas of socio-technical systems, the design of jobs, and of human resource management.

The means of securing improvement in social systems is through decision making. Accordingly, we believe that an appropriate way to review the use and application of OR in the field of human resource management is to specify the human resource management decision space. This approach provides a method for classifying the OR tools and techniques that have been used or might be used in each decision area. Human resource management generally involves six basic functions. These will serve to define the primary dimensions of the decision space.

I. *Acquisition*—providing for the recruitment, selection, and socialization of personnel.

II. *Development*—providing for the education, training, and development of the personnel.

III. *Allocation*—assigning personnel to jobs and roles (assuming that the jobs and roles are *given* how best to assign personnel to them).

IV. *Utilization*—determining the organizational structure, information and communication flow pattern, leadership style, and motivation scheme (assuming the personnel complement is *given* or adequate assumptions can be made about it—how best to design jobs and roles).

V. *Evaluation*—measuring an individual's contribution to the organization.

VI. *Maintenance and compensation*—determining the appropriate economic and noneconomic rewards necessary to maintain each individual's contribution to the organization, and to properly reward him for it. This conservation function includes salaries and wages, benefits, promotions, job conditions, status, recognition, and social incentives.

The remainder of the chapter is organized around these decision processes.

1.1 Acquisition-Recruitment

Recruitment is the process by which an organization develops a pool of applicants. The essential problem in recruiting human resources is to determine the source of the pool, the quantities required, their qualifications, and the timing of acquisition. Selection, then, is the decision to hire from the pool. Most applications of OR techniques assume the existence of a human resource pool comprised of a relatively large number of people who are rather homogeneous in capabilities and who are to be employed in a relatively few and quite similar tasks. The development of the recruitment pool depends on an understanding of the role of human resources in the productive aspects of the organization. Consequently, a good place to start a study is by determining the organization's "personnel response functions."

An organization's personnel response function relates its output to the levels of personnel input which are employed. The approach can be used in order to minimize either the cost or the number of personnel.

The decision problem can be stated as follows:

$$\text{Minimize } N \text{ or } C(N),$$

subject to the constraint

$$R(N) \geqslant G.$$

where N = the level of personnel input expressed in number of people, hours, number of sales calls, etc.; C = personnel cost as a function of N, in the case of linear costs this is simply: $c_1 + c_2 N$; G = a goal or a demand level of output; $R(N)$ = the personnel response function which converts inputs to outputs.

This decision is trivial when $R(N)$ is linear; however, this is seldom the case. Most likely $R(N)$ will approximate the familiar S-shaped sigmoid curve shown in Figure 1.

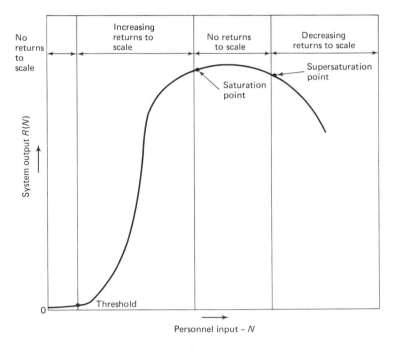

Fig. 1. Personnel response function.

The first portion of the curve reflects the situation where some limited amount of effort is required before any output is realized. Then, after a "threshold" point is reached, the system produces additional outputs for each additional increment of input. Frequently, this portion of the curve can be approximated by a linear function. The system continues to respond incrementally to personnel inputs until a "saturation" point is reached. Beyond this point additional inputs result in very little, if any, additional output. Finally, a "supersaturation" point is reached beyond which additional inputs actually result in negative outputs. This latter condition is obtained in typical situations where congestion, communication overloads, interpersonal problems and the like increase rapidly with additional personnel. The net effect is to restrict productivity. In sales and other personal service situations for example, supersaturation can result from the condition where additional sales effort serves as a disfunctional nuisance to prospective clients.

Scientifically based attempts to establish the quantities of personnel to be recruited, the size of the workforce, number of hours of work required, or other levels of input effort should be based on the management scientist's best estimate of the response function. This estimate can be obtained in two ways—by curve fitting procedures and by controlled experimentation. The first method is useful when there is a range of data available which shows the different levels of output that have been achieved when different levels of input were employed in a task or a class of similar tasks. Graphic techniques or curvilinear regression can be used to estimate the function using, for example, the logistic Pearl-Reed curve or the Grompertz curve as a model. Often, however, the available data is limited to a very narrow range of activity, and the full extent of the function can only be determined by some form of experimentation. In any event, care must be taken to insure that no significant technological or organizational changes take place during the period covered.

Once the objective and response functions have been estimated, the question of how many people must be hired can generally be answered using calculus, mathematical programming, or graphic techniques. Ackoff and his associates have applied this approach in the context of a long range planning effort to determine how many salesmen should be employed in a territory, and the average number of accounts that should be assigned to salesmen. In one case they found that the firm was generally operating beyond the saturation point and recommended that the salesforce be reduced rather than augmented. "The annual saving obtained by *not* acquiring the additional salesmen originally recommended was approximately twenty-five times the cost of these studies." (Ackoff [1970] ; Waid, Clark and Ackoff [1956]).

Although determining the response function is fundamental to any kind of human resource management, frequently simplifying assumptions are made about it, such as assuming a homogeneous labor pool which has a linear response function.

All problem solving methods have a basic conceptualization or metaphor underlying them. The one most frequently used in modelling human resource management problems is the notion of multi-period, feed forward flow model with people as the primary flow variables. Using this perspective the organization's current and perspective personnel are classified into a discrete set of "pools." The pools are specified for each given time period, t, according to attributes which are important to the analysis such as skills, age, education, pay level and organizational status. Collectively, these pools describe the state of the system at time t. Transitions are made from one state to another at time $t + \Upsilon$ on the basis of the structural properties of the human resource system and the decisions made. During any time period, t, people enter and exit the organization, acquire new skills, grow older, change their pay status, get promoted, etc., thereby changing the composition of the pools. Depending on the nature of these transitions, whether certain or probabilistic, state-descriptive flow models can either be deterministic or stochastic.

Deterministic flow models have been used frequently in multi-period manpower or workforce planning. Linear programming (LP) is the method most frequently used to provide solutions to this problem formulation. Dynamic programming, Linear Decision Rules, The Maximum Principle, and Search Methods have also been employed. These are covered in detail in Chapter I-5 "Aggregate Production Planning."*

Another approach to the problem of determing the quantities of personnel required for acquisition involves the use of stochastic models to predict the movements of people throughout organizational roles or positions. Stochastic models of an organization's manpower mobility are based upon the notion that people move among organizational roles in accordance with probabilistic laws. The models are best applied to organizations with (1) well defined hierarchical structures and (2) annual (or fixed period) promotion and hiring policies. Military organizations, educational institutions, and some industrial firms are good examples.

Stochastic models can be employed to analyze both individual and collective behavior in the system. One application is to use the model to estimate the probability that a given person will either remain in a specific organizational position, salary grade, service category, longevity category, etc., or will move to some other state. These probabilities are derived from knowledge of the probabilities of transition within the system between two specific time periods. They can be used to estimate the value of an individual to the organization (as discussed in the section on evaluation) and to predict his or her career pattern. Since an individual's history and experience can play a role in his future mobility, the probabilities employed in this application often must be conditioned by all or many of the prior states occupied by the individual.

Stochastic models may also be used to trace the expected movements of people collectively throughout the organization and, in turn, to project the number of people that will occupy each state at a specified future time period. Thus, they can be used to forecast manpower supply and to guide personnel policy.

In analyzing collective behavior it is frequently useful to assume that the organization's structure meets the requirements for Markov chain analysis. To use a Markov model properly the analyst must be satisfied that (1) there are a finite number of identifiable states in the system, (2) the conditional probability of moving from one state to another is *independent* of any past "events" and depends only on the present state (the Markovian property), (3) the transition

*References include Holt et.al. ([1960] 389–404); McCloskey and Hanssman [1957]; Arabayre et al. [1969]; Wagner [1970]; Hanssman and Hess [1960]; Nemhauser and Nutthe [1965]; Bishop and Rockwell [1958]; Bergstrom and Smith [1970]; Fan [1964, 1966]; Hwang and Fan [1966, 1967]; Nelson [1966]; Jones [1967]; Taubert [1968]; Sikes [1970]; Dill et al. [1966]; Lippman et al. [1967]; Silver [1967]; Conrath and Hamilton [1971]; and Walker [1969].

probabilities do not change with time (stationary probabilities) and that (4) a set of initial probabilities can be determined.

The problem may then be formulated as a special case of the general linear dynamic propagation model:

$$X(t + 1) = X(t) P + y(t) G + z(t) H,$$

where

$X(t)$ = a set of endogenous state variables assumed to be outside of the control of the decision-maker and subject to a transition matrix P;

$y(t)$ = a set of control variables which the decision-maker can directly influence but are subject to a structural matrix G;

$z(t)$ = a set of exogenous variables which impinge on the system from the outside but are subject to a structural matrix H.

A Markov personnel mobility model is based on a matrix of transition probabilities derived from historical data or from judgment. The matrix form, P, is illustrated in Figure 2. Adopting the convention that P_{ij} refers to the probability of a transition from state i to state j, it is possible to represent the probability of movement from any state to any other state after a specified number of time intervals.

In strictly hierarchical systems, it is conventional to order the matrix in the sequence of jobs of increasing importance. The P_{ii} is the probability of remaining in the same state (persistence) and P_{ij} is the probability of promotion for $j > i$, or the probability of demotion for $j < i$. Furthermore, one of the states (usually the nth) represents the "exit" state.

The matrix of transition probabilities has the following characteristics: 1) It is a square matrix having n dimensions, where n = the number of states; 2) $0 \leqslant P_{ij} \leqslant 1$, and 3) the sum of the probabilities of occupying the collectively exhaus-

X(1970)		P			
		A	B	C	Exit
100	A	.80	.10	0	.10
50	B	0	.90	.05	.05
10	C	0	0	.90	.10
0	Exit	0	0	0	1.00

expected distribution $\longrightarrow$ | 80   55   12*   14* = X(1971)
of personnel in 1971

*Results are rounded up from 11.5 and 13.5, respectively.

Fig. 2. Transition probabilities for personnel among positions from 1970 to 1971 with n = 4 states.

tive, mutually exclusive states is 1.0. If the transition matrix is raised to the second power, $\mathbf{P}^2$, it will describe the probabilities that each state will be occupied during the second consecutive time interval. If it is raised to the t-th power, it will describe the probabilities that each state will be occupied during the t-th time interval.

The basic model is formulated as follows:*

$$X(t + 1) = X(t)\, \mathbf{P},$$

where

$X(t) =$ an n-dimensional vector of the number of employees in each state i
$(i = 1, 2, \ldots n)$ during time period t;
$X(0) =$ the initial distributor vector of employees;
$\mathbf{P} =$ the Markov transition matrix.

Figure 2 shows the calculation of transition probabilities for a hypothetical system during a two year period.

The model can be expanded to include other dimensions such as new recruitment and lay-offs as well. Consider, for example, the formulation:

$$X(t + 1) = X(t)\mathbf{P} + \mathbf{R}_t$$

where

$\mathbf{R}_t =$ an n-dimensional vector containing the number of employees recruited or hired (positive coefficients) or laid-off or fired (negative coefficients) in each state i ($i = 1, 2, \ldots n$) during time period t.

Over a planning horizon of T periods a multi-stage planning model can be formulated as follows:

$$X(T) = X(0)\, \mathbf{P}^T + \sum_{t=1}^{T} \mathbf{R}_t \mathbf{P}^{T-t}$$

Generally speaking the decision-maker controls the conduct of the system through time by the recruitment and lay-off policy $(\mathbf{R}_t)$ or by changing the rates of promotion, persistence, demotion and exit contained in the matrix $\mathbf{P}$. Thus the model can be used to explore the implications of various policies by projecting their effects over some planning horizon. Alternatively, if a particular end or "target" state $X(T)$ is desired and $X(0)$ is known, the model may be used to identify the various recruitment policies $(\mathbf{R}_0, \mathbf{R}_1 \ldots \mathbf{R}_{T-1})$ which meet the objective. In this latter case, additional choice or optimization methods must be employed in order to select the "best" policy (expressed in terms of an $n \times T$ matrix of additions and deletions) from among those which achieve the target.

*In this simplified version of the model $y(t)$ and $z(t)$ are considered irrelevant.

The model can be used in planning personnel acquisitions to project the number of people expected to occupy each position at specified future times under certain policies or to solve for recruitment policies, R_f. These supplies of human resources can then be compared with anticipated needs for various roles. Gaps, if any, denote recruitment needs. Surpluses, if any, denote possible transfers, layoffs, etc.

Examples of the application of stochastic models in planning personnel requirements can be found in Bartholomew [1967], Vroom and MacCrimmon [1968], and Rowland and Sovereign [1969]. The approach has been applied to the University of California by Bartholomew [1969] and by Rowe, Wagner, and Weatherly [1970]. Recent theoretical development has been provided by Davies [1973].

The methods described above stress the use of models as a means of determining future personnel needs and guiding acquisition decision. Most of these models rely on historical data as a basis of projecting future needs. Regression models using various indices as predictors are frequently used for this purpose. This approach is, of course, inappropriate in situations where some form of structural change can be expected, since it assumes that relationships of the past will carry forward to the future. One way of coping with structural change forecasts is to draw on expert judgements in the making of human resource requirements forecasts. The Delphi Method is a systematic means of incorporating expert opinion to generate a forecast.

In the Delphi Methods, (Helmer [1968], Dalkey [1967]), a group of experts is selected and is asked anonymously to estimate future needs and to provide reasons for their estimates. The estimates and reasons are collected and fed back to all participants who in turn provide new estimates and reasons. This process is repeated for several rounds in an effort to obtain a reliable concensus of of opinion among the group of experts.

Milkovich, et al. [1972] have applied the Delphi Method to forecast professional manpower requirements in a large national retail organization. Using seven company managers as the panel of experts—and five rounds of information exchange—they found that the Delphi procedure came much closer to the firm's subsequent actual behavior than each of three regression models based on projected number of retail outlets, gross retail sales, and current number of retail outlets.

1.2 Acquisition-Selection

The essential problem involved in selecting human resources from an organizational perspective is to satisfy role and task requirements. Typically, personnel hiring decisions are oriented to selecting people who seem most likely to satisfy current needs. Attempts are also made to assess a person's "potential" or promotability. In some cases, trade-offs may exist between the selection of people with greatest current productivity and those with the highest future potential.

The traditional approach to personnel selection aims at "categorical prediction," by means of straight forward correlation analysis. For example, Dunnette [1966] states, "This model has sought to link *predictors* (that is, various measures of individual differences) directly with so-called *criteria*, (that is, various measures of organizational consequences of job 'success') through a simple index of relationship, the correlation coefficient." (p. 104). Once the model is estimated, prospective employees may be classified into potential successes and failures (in terms of performance on the job) by their scores on the predictor variable. Scores on two or more predictors can be combined in a multiple correlation coefficient to yield a linear combination of these predictor variables. Both linear and curvilinear methods of estimation may be employed.

Inskeep [1970] has employed this approach to study the labor turnover problem. Job tenure was correlated with various employee attributes. He found that home ownership, prior working experience, age when hired, and level of education (an inverse relationship) were the best predictors of job tenure.

As with all types of correlation analysis, there are important caveats to which the analyst should adhere. First, of course, correlation is not explanation nor does it alone establish cause and effect relationships. Consequently there should be a reason, based either on theory or experience, which explains why the predictors used should be responsible for the performance observed. Second, correlation analysis presupposes a random sample and, therefore, the analyst should scrutinize the data for possible bias. Frequently, strong cultural and sociological forces affect the selection of personnel which constitute the available labor pool at any point in time. Recruitment methods also influence the composition of the pool. Third, one should be careful that the structural assumptions used in estimation are still applicable when the selection decision is made. In periods of rapid technological, organizational, or social change this can be an important factor. Finally, one should always test the hypothesis that the correlation coefficient is zero. A non-zero coefficient does not always imply that the "real" coefficient is not zero.

Psychological testing has proven to be a useful method of estimating some of the "predictors" used in correlation models. Many organizations augment the typical application form with a battery of tests for this purpose. Some organizations report reasonably good success with the approach. It should be pointed out, however, that most test selection procedures serve to benefit the organization rather than the individual, even in cases of rejection. (Taylor and Nevis [1961]).

Although seldom used in practice, it is theoretically possible to use a decision theoretic approach in personnel selection. This approach measures the ability of a set of candidates for a specified job in terms of the conditional payoff of each person to the job for which he or she was selected. In addition, the probabilities of successful performance on these jobs are measured. The optimal selection strategy is then based on choosing the individuals with the greatest expected ability. Dunnette [1966] has developed an illustration of optimal personnel selection using this approach.

One variation of the decision-theoretic model, which is based on the use of measures of the monetary value contributed by people to a firm, shows some promise. It is an outgrowth on work to develop "human resource accounting" and "human resource valuation." (Flamholtz [1971, 1972, 1974]; Lev and Schwartz [1971]).

Using this approach, the value contributed by a person occupying a specified organizational position is measured in monetary terms. For example, in a professional service organization the monetary value contributed by an individual might be measured in terms of expected net contribution to profits (sales revenues less salary and other costs).

There are two basic dimensions or measures of a person's monetary value to an organization: 1) expected conditional value and 2) expected realizable value (Flamholtz [1972]). An individual's expected conditional value is the amount of benefit (contribution) the organization could potentially derive from a person's services if the individual remains in the organization during his or her expected service life. It is the potential value to be received on the condition that the person maintains organizational membership, and is therefore analogous to any conditional value. A person's expected realizable value is the value actually expected to be derived (realized) from a person's potential services, taking into account the probability of turnover. The difference between these two dimensions of a person's value is thus the opportunity cost of turnover.

At present, many personnel managers seem to base selection decisions on a criterion of expected conditional rather than expected realizable value. That is, they choose people who seem to possess the maximum conditional value to the firm. This may be appropriate in cases where there are very few alternative sources for employment open for employees. However, in situations where other employment options are open and few legal, moral, or cultural inhibitors to leaving an organization prevail there is some likelihood that an employee will seek other employment. This eventuality should be included in an estimate of his value to the organization and hence, realizable value is a more appropriate measure.

For example, consider a situation in which a personnel manager is faced with the choice of two candidates for a given position. Candidate A has a conditional value in the desired entry role of $30,000 and B has a conditional value of $25,000. Using a criterion of maximizing conditional value, the rational decision-maker would select A. However, suppose further that the probabilities of A and B quitting the firm are .30 and .10, respectively. If the selection decision is based on maximizing realizable value one should choose B since the realizable expected values for A and B are \$21,000 and \$22,500 respectively.

The above example is, of course, highly simplified since in practice one should estimate the probability of exiting at each stage in the stochastic process. The expected realizable value would be calculated accordingly rather than by using a single turnover rate. However, the example does demonstrate the potential criticality of employing estimates of the probability of exiting or quitting in making the personnel selection decision.

2. DEVELOPMENT

The essential question in the employee development decision is whether to provide education and training (including "on-the-job training") to the employee and if so, what kind, when, and for what duration. Relatively little active work has been done in applying OR to these problems. Balinsky and Reisman [1972] have developed a framework for modelling the problem which should prove useful. It is based on the dynamic feed forward flow models discussed earlier.

The simplest version of their approach is a single educational program, multi-period cost minimization model which assumes a planning horizon of N periods of equal time duration. The educational program can be completed in one time period. Formally the model is:

Minimize:
$X_1, \ldots, X_N$
$$\sum_{t=1}^{N} \theta^{t-1} \, [C_t(X_t) + g_{1,t}(S_{1,t+1}) + g_{2,t}(S_{2,t+1})]$$

subject to:

$0 \leqslant X_t \leqslant P_t; \quad t = 1, 2, \ldots, N$

(The number of people educated cannot exceed the total eligible population);

$S_{1,t+1} = S_{1,t} + (P_t - X_t) + \lambda(X_t) - d_{1,t}; \quad t = 1, 2, \ldots, N$

(conservation of labor pool level 1);

$S_{2,t+1} = S_{2,t} + [X_t - \lambda(X_t)] - d_{2,t}; \quad t = 1, 2, \ldots, N$

(conservation of labor pool level 2);

where,

X_t = the decision variable, the number of eligible people trained each period t; people who complete the educational program move from level 1 to level 2;

P_t = the available eligible population for training (given);

$S_{1,t}$ = the available labor pool on level 1 at the beginning of period t;

$S_{2,t}$ = the available labor pool on level 2 at the beginning of period t;

$\lambda(X_t)$ = the attrition or dropout rate, a function of the number of people admitted to the program in time period t;

$d_{1,t}$ = the outside demand or manpower requirements for personnel with level 1 training during period t (given);

$d_{2,t}$ = the outside demand or manpower requirement for personnel with level 2 training during period t (given);

θ = a discount rate;

$C_t(X_t)$ = the cost of providing education;

$g_{1,t}(S_{1,t+1})$ = penalty cost for manpower shortages or surpluses at level 1;

$g_{2,t}(S_{2,t+1})$ = penalty cost for manpower shortages or surpluses at level 2.

The single program model is solved using dynamic programming techniques, assuming a piecewise, linear, discontinuous objective function. Furthermore, the approach may be extended to develop a multi-echelon, multiperiod educational model, and to include variations such as modification in program duration, compulsory educational levels, and 4-level "college type" systems. LP methods are used to solve these extended versions and the general multi-echelon multiperiod model.

The modelling approach used above was explicitly designed to study formal educational systems, such as the college and university system. So, while it is instructive, it does not deal directly with the development decisions which most organizations must make. Some of its deficiencies in this regard are revealed by the constraint parameters it takes as given. For example, the pool of available eligible people, P_t, is, as we have seen above, a function of the recruitment and selection decisions and thus can in part be brought under the decision-makers' control. Also, the requirements, d, for personnel at various levels can be very much the product of decisions made by the organization.

Organizations engage in education, training, and development programs in order to increase the employee's productivity on the current job, to augment the range of activities in which the employee engages, to shift the employee to a new job, to promote him or her, or to improve the employee's morale and well being. Adequate models of the development decision therefore should include a set of alternative educational or training programs in which the individuals might participate, the cost of the programs both in terms of delivery (direct) and of lost production (opportunity), and finally the benefits gained from each program. The latter is the most difficult. Little is known about the full impact of educational and training programs on people and on their productivity on the job.

3. ALLOCATION

The basic allocation decision problem is how best to allocate an organization's human resources to the task or jobs it has to perform. In this sense allocation and utilization problems are "mirror images" of each other. Allocation problems take the task or job structure as given and seek to assign individuals to it; whereas, utilization problems take the individuals and their capabilities and characteristics as given or predictable and seek to develop task structures which best utilize their potential. Most management situations involve both problems simultaneously; however, it is useful to review each separately. OR techniques have been applied most frequently to allocation decisions.

Human Resource allocation problems exist at two levels in an organization. One is at the top management level where aggregate manpower planning takes place. Its purpose is to determine the broad assignment of manpower to organizational units, often expressed in terms of budgets for personnel and labor.

The second level of allocation problems is at the line supervisor level. It results in the actual assignment of a specific individual to a specific job. This decision problem, sometimes referred to as the optimal personnel assignment problem, concerns how best to assign n individuals $(I_1, I_2, \ldots, I_n)$ to n jobs $(J_1, J_2, \ldots, J_n)$ so as to maximize the total value of the assignment. Four basic approaches have been employed in analyzing allocation problems—transportation or assignment models, goal programming models, sequential assignment models, and simulations.

3.1 Transportation Models

The basic transportation or personnel assignment model has the following mathematical expression:

$$\underset{\{X_{ij}\}}{\text{maximize}}\ z \equiv \sum_{i=1}^{n} \sum_{j=i}^{n} r_{ij} X_{ij},$$

subject to

$$\sum_{i=1}^{n} X_{ij} = 1,$$

$$\sum_{j=1}^{n} X_{ij} = 1,$$

$$X_{ij} \in \{0, 1\} \quad \text{for all} \quad i\, j,$$

where

$X_{ij} = 1$ means that I_i was assigned to job J_j,

and

r_{ij}'s represent the ratings, scores or relative efficiencies of each individual for each job and form an $n \times n$ matrix R.

This formulation requires that each individual be assigned to one (and only one) job and that each job have one (and only one) individual assigned to it. The problem can be solved by the standard assignment or transportation LP method. See, for example, Hillier and Lieberman [1967] Chapter 6.

The most difficult problem for the analyst to cope with in applying this formulation to real personnel assignment situations is that of determining the appropriate objective function and, accordingly, the appropriate measure to employ in estimating the r_{ij}'s. Here several approaches are available.

1. Criterion: Maximize the sum of the rates of the assignment

$$\text{Functional: } \underset{\{X_{ij}\}}{\text{maximize}} \; z \equiv \sum_{i=1}^{n} \sum_{j=1}^{n} r_{ij} X_{ij}$$

When this approach is used an effort is made to measure the r_{ij}'s directly in terms of important organizational value such as performance times, cost, output per time unit, etc. Such measures are often difficult to obtain. As King [1967] points out, there are also several conceptual problems to deal with. Any such r_{ij} is a point estimate which has an error factor distribution associated with it. Furthermore it represents a *prediction* about the individual's expected performance in the job. Consequently, it is subject to the errors and uncertainties of predictive techniques. Conceivably, *actual* performance could be quite different from that suggested by the r_{ij}'s.

2. Criterion: Maximize the joint probability that each individual will be successful in the assigned job.

$$\text{Functional: } \underset{\{X_{ij}\}}{\text{Maximize}} \; z \equiv \sum_{i=1}^{n} \sum_{j=1}^{n} \log (P_{ij}) X_{ij}$$

In this approach, also suggested by King [1967], P_{ij} represents the probability that I_i will be successful in job J_j. Discriminant techniques can be used with historical data in order to estimate the probability that an individual with certain attributes will perform satisfactorily in each job. The joint probability of a successful assignment then is maximized by choosing one individual for each job in a manner which maximizes the *product* of their probabilities for success. Due to the properties of logarithms, the functional is expressed as indicated above.

Once the notion of the probability of success or failure is introduced, several methods of measuring and interpreting the criterion are available. Weil [1967] suggests the following additions to criterion 2 above:

3. Criterion: Minimize the joint probability of unsuccessful assignments to all jobs.

$$\text{Functional: } \underset{\{X_{ij}\}}{\text{Minimize}} \; Z \equiv \sum_{i=j}^{n} \sum_{j=1}^{n} \log (1 - P_{ij}) X_{ij}$$

4. Criterion: Maximize the expected number of successful assignments.

   Functional: $\underset{\{X_{ij}\}}{\text{Maximize}} Z \equiv \sum_{i=1}^{n} \sum_{j=1}^{n} P_{ij} X_{ij}$

5. Criterion: Minimize the expected number of unsuccessful assignments.

   Functional: $\text{Minimize } Z \equiv \sum_{i=1}^{n} \sum_{j=1}^{n} (1 - P_{ij}) X_{ij}$

6. Criterion: Maximize the (geometric) average odds $\left(\dfrac{P}{1 - P}\right)$ of success on all assignments.

   Functional: $\underset{\{X_{ij}\}}{\text{Maximize}} Z \equiv \sum_{i=1}^{n} \sum_{j=1}^{n} \log (P_{ij}/(1 - P_{ij})) X_{ij} \text{ for } 0 < P_{ij} < 1$

7. Criterion: Minimize the (geometric) average odds $\left(\dfrac{1 - P}{P}\right)$ of failure on all assignments.

   Functional: $\underset{\{X_{ij}\}}{\text{Minimize}} Z \equiv \sum_{i=1}^{n} \sum_{j=1}^{n} \log ((1 - P_{ij})/P_{ij}) X_{ij} \text{ for } 0 < P_{ij} < 1.$

The last two criteria are referred to as *logit* criteria. Weil [1967] argues that criteria 6 and 7 should be used because they favor a more equal distribution of probabilities than the one for mid-ranges. They also tend to favor making assignments as close to one as possible whenever the sum of the probabilities is greater than one, thus taking into account the "certainty" attached to successful (or unsuccessful) performance. In using these criteria care should be taken about the accuracy of the estimate, especially if large probabilities ($>.95$) or small probabilities ($<.05$) are present.

3.2 Goal Programming Models

Charnes, Cooper, et al. [1969] suggest that the ratings of individuals in jobs should be broken into component parts and that goal programming notions might be employed. This method uses the following definitions:

r_{ij} = the "amount" of the jth attribute required by job i.
a_{sj} = the "amount" of the jth attribute *possessed* by individual s.
V_{ij}^{-} = the "amount" of underfulfillment, a slack variable.
V_{ij}^{+} = the "amount" of overfulfillment, a slack variable.
n = the number of individuals and jobs
m = the number of relevant attributes.

The program may be formulated as:

$$\text{Minimize } Z \equiv \sum_{i=1}^{n} \sum_{j=1}^{m} V_{ij}^{-}$$
$$\{V_{ij}^{-}\}$$

subject to

$$\sum_{s=1}^{n} X_{is} a_{sj} - V_{ij}^{+} + V_{ij}^{-} = r_{ij} \qquad j = 1, 2, \ldots, m$$

$$\sum_{i=1}^{n} X_{is} = 1$$

$$\sum_{s=1}^{n} X_{is} = 1$$

$$X_{is} = \{0, 1\}$$

$$V_{ij}^{-}, V_{ij}^{+} \geqslant 0.$$

The criterion assigns a weight of zero to all overfulfillments, and a weight of unity to all underfulfillments, and seeks to minimize the amount of underfulfillment.

There are several obvious extensions to this model that might be employed, depending on the situation. In R and D management and other professional service situations, Childs and Wolfe [1972] argue that it is important to obtain skill categories that are appropriate for rating personnel in each professional group, and that these skills be weighted by the requirements of the project of job and by the priority of the project within the organization as a whole. They propose that an individual's effectiveness on a project, r_{ij}, is equal to the sum of his relative ability in each skill category times the importance of that category to the successful completion of the project weighted by the priority of the project to the system as a whole. Delphi techniques and Human Resource Accounting methods might also be employed to estimate r_{ij}'s. An application of this procedure to player selection in team sports is discussed in Chapter II-8 of this Handbook.

3.3 Sequential Assignment Models

The above formulations assume that all individuals are assigned to all jobs simultaneously. In practice this seldom happens. Instead, jobs open up and individuals must be assigned to them on a sequential basis.

This sequential aspect of the problem is relatively unexplored. Derman, Lieberman, and Ross [1972] however, have provided the first steps in an analysis of this type of sequential assignment problem. Simply stated, their result is as follows. Suppose that there are n people to perform n jobs, but that the jobs occur and people must be assigned to them in a random order. This situation, incidentally, is not unlike that which obtains in accounting and legal offices, welfare offices, computer software firms, and other enterprises where a "pool" of personal services are assigned to "cases" or "projects" as they appear. After an individual is assigned to a job, he or she is unavailable for future assignments. Each job, j, has a reward or payoff associated with it, X_j, which takes on the value x_j. Furthermore, each individual, i, has a performance measure, p_i, (assumed in this model to be intrinsic in the individual and not dependent upon the job to which he is assigned). A simplifying, but not constraining, assumption is that p_i satisfied the condition $0 \leqslant p_i \leqslant 1$ so that, for example, a lawyer rated "1.0" always wins the case, a "0.0" lawyer always loses, and a "0.5" has a 50/50 chance.

Under this condition the organization would like to maximize the total expected reward given by the functional:

$$\text{Maximize } Z \equiv E\left[\sum_{j=1}^{n} p_{ij} x_j\right]$$
$$\{X_j\}$$

where, $p_{ij} = p_i$ for the individual assigned to job j.

Drawing on Hardy's Theorem [1934], the authors show that if one has three basic pieces of information, namely the cumulative distribution function of X, the number n of jobs and people yet to be assigned, and an ordinal ranking on the individuals $p_1 \leqslant p_2 \leqslant \ldots \leqslant p_n$, an optimal assignment can be made by assigning the person corresponding to p_i to the next job if its reward, x, falls in the ith interval on the real line. The latter intervals depend on n and the distribution of X, but not on the p_i's. In essence, the result gives some analytical horsepower to a time honored managerial maxim: Assign the individual most likely to succeed to the jobs with the highest payoff and assign the one least likely to succeed to the lowest payoff jobs.

There is another deep assumption in the job assignment literature about which the management scientist must be extremely careful. The assumption is that payoffs received from assigning a person to a job are independent of the other assignments made. Seldom, if ever, does this lack of interaction and dependency exist.

Indeed, most roles and jobs are derived directly from the basic core technology and structure of the organization and are dictated by the flow of information, energy, and materials necessary to produce its goods and services. This is especially true in manufacturing and process industries. Socio-technical studies in these industries (see, for example, Engelstad [1972]) demonstrate quite clearly that important dependence relationships exist among the various jobs and tasks which comprise most process systems. These dependencies result in uncontrolled variations being transmitted to subsequent stages in the assembly line or production process.   This means, for example, that if a relatively ineffective employee is assigned to a particular job in the process, his errors will affect not only the direct performance on that job but also be propagated to subsequent jobs where the variance created must either be absorbed or passed on again.

A method for identifying these dependency relationships, called the "variance matrix," exists, and has been successfully employed in studying problems in process control (Engelstad [1972]).   Variance matrices are created by identifying the stages in a process and the qualities and attributes of system performance that are important within each stage.   A precedence matrix of interdependency is then formed.   Its elements represent the impact of performance with respect to an attribute at one stage in the process on attributes in subsequent stages.   The purpose is to ascertain the places in the system where the uncontrolled variations that are produced in one stage must be dealt with by the technology, organization or people at subsequent stages.

3.4 Simulations

Algorithmic techniques tend to break down in complex environments such as the labor assignment area, where the interaction of many variables affects the outcome.   This suggests that simulation methods may be appropriate.   Some preliminary research has been done in this area.

Nelson [1967], for example, has constructed and experimented with a general model which permits experimentation to take place in both machine and labor limited systems by manipulating such variables as queue discipline rule, labor assignment procedure, size of work force, degree of centralized control of labor assignment, the job routing characteristics of the network, and the labor efficiency matrix (i.e., the response function for each laborer on each machine or job).   Nelson's simulation experiments are based on simplified systems, and are geared to test structural relationships and to provide insights as to effective policy heuristics, rather than to simulate a particular real system; however, they do provide insight into useful manpower allocation rules.   This and other methods are discussed more thoroughly in Chapter I-9, "Scheduling and Sequencing."

4. UTILIZATION

The problem of utilization as defined here is analogous to the problem of optimal organizational design.   The issue is: Given a set of tasks the organization must perform, how best are they combined and organized so that jobs and roles may be defined which are both organizationally effective and individually satisfying.   The subject is too extensive to cover in the chapter; however, a few notes of perspective should be useful.

There are basically three schools of thought on the question of utilization. The "scientific management" school, founded by Frederick W. Taylor, would seek "rigid rules for each motion of every man, and the perfection and standardization of all implements and working conditions" (Taylor [1911], p. 85). The approach is based on the view that "Each man must learn how to give up his own particular way of doing things, adapt his methods to the many new standards and grow accustomed to receiving and obeying directions covering details, large and small, which in the past have been left to his individual judgment." (Taylor [1919])—a view summarized by McGregor's Theory X [1960]. Time and motion study and the detailed modelling of work activities are the results of applying their philosophy.

The human relations movement can be thought of as a reaction to this emphasis on the physical, physiological, and economic side of work, in that it placed a new emphasis on the psychological, social, and organizational aspects of work. Its basic assumption is that improvements in the organization can best be achieved through improvements in interpersonal relations and in the psychological well being of the organization's members (Drucker [1952]). It too has a view of man—summarized by McGregor's Theory Y—and an ethic which states that job satisfaction, job enrichment and the pursuit of "self actualization" and other needs are legitimate organizational goals in their own right.

The third school of thought might best be called the "socio-technical systems" school. It seeks to integrate the important developments of each of the previous schools into a coherent whole in which the organization is considered to be an open, social system, which has important relations with its external environment and in which technology plays a critical role.

Socio-technical analysis begins with the assumption that more than one work relationship structure exists for accomplishing a given set of tasks. Each such structure has different social and psychological characteristics and a different technology. These factors collectively influence the total performance of the system. For example, in their original long wall coal mining studies, Trist and his colleagues [1948, 1951] found that a variety of structures where possible ranging on the one hand from the conventional one with a complex formal structure and simple work roles (a'la "scientific management"), to on the other hand a work structure with a simple formal structure with complex work roles. In the latter structure each member worked with many different task groups on many main tasks during several shifts without a rigid division of labor. This "composite" structure was found to be superior in this situation in terms of both productivity and costs because it had the flexibility necessary to cope adequately with changing underground conditions. Moreover psychological stress was reduced and absenteeism due to accidents, sickness, or without reason declined. Rice's [1958] study of the textile mills in Ahmedabad, India had the same result. Rice's work further suggests that supervisory roles are subject to the same kind of analysis and that the same general results obtained.

The basic framework of the socio-technical approach can be summarized by the following equation:

$$O = T(\mathbf{I}, \mathbf{E})$$

where

O = the system's output
$\mathbf{I}$ = the inputs
$\mathbf{E}$ = the environmental influence on the system;

and

T = a transformation function that consists of a sequence of unit operations or tasks that are organized together by a work relationship structure.

Simply put, the utilization problem is to find the best T from among the alternative available structures. This involves collecting tasks together to form jobs and roles (roles being the set of rules and expectations that direct a worker's organizational working behavior). The suggested method involves scanning the environment to determine important environmental influences; indentifying the task and unit operations necessary to achieve the required output; identifying the key variances or deviations from standard that can emerge in the system and, via a matrix of variances, determining their interrelationships; analyzing the social system to determine its character and its method of dealing with variance (including employee's perception of their roles) and systematically tracking the impacts of these factors on the whole system (Van Beinum [1968]).

The transformation function T represents the *structure* of the organization, and is influenced by its technological requirements. The central elements of T which are least affected by environmental influences form the "technological core" of the organization (Thompson [1967]). Analysis of the technological core in order to improve utilization does seem to be amenable to existing OR techniques. Basically two different approaches are available for studying the technological core—a "bottom up" or synthetic approach and a "top down" or analytic approach.

Using the bottom up approach, Gerwin [1974] has recently applied list processing techniques, using McCarthy's LISP Language (Weissman [1967]) in order to replicate existing structures and, given a set of norms and criteria, to formulate new structures. The method assumes that work flow can be represented as a directed graph. The elemental tasks form a basic list and are represented by the nodes of the graph. The arcs indicate the direction of work flow. Each task interdependency is identified, typed as reciprocal, sequential, or pooled, and measured as to intensity. A heuristic procedure then groups tasks on the basis of connectedness, type of interdependency (reciprocal receives the highest priority), and degree of intensity. The resulting list structure is interpreted as the organizational structure. Gerwin has duplicated Thompson's [1967] bomber wing study using the method and also applied it to an industrial organization.

The list structure approach is inductive and synthetic in that it works from elements to structure. It's obverse is the decomposition approach. For some time now organization theorists have been intrigued with the decomposition principle of LP as it might apply to organizational design. The notion is that if an organization and all of its task and roles can be modelled by a large scale linear program, then the matrix of coefficients may give clues to organization form. To the extent that the problem is decomposible into several almost independent subproblems, it may suggest a form for decentralized organization. This would include assignments of people and tasks to organizational subunits.

The decomposition model permits other organizational interpretations to be made. For example, the shadow prices used to communicate between the master problem and the subproblem can be viewed as transfer prices for the system. The authors are aware of several companies who have applied this method. The approach was insightful but computationally expensive, and only moderate improvements in the objective function resulted. The decomposition technique was originally developed by Dantzig and Wolfe [1960], and has been interpreted in this context by Baumol and Fabian [1964].

5. EVALUATION OF HUMAN RESOURCES

Evaluation is the process of measuring a person's contribution to the organization. It involves measuring future as well as past contribution.

Traditionally, personnel evaluation methods have emphasized ratings. The principal instruments used are scales for rating a person's traits and skills. These ratings are made by supervisors and are used as inputs in compensation, allocation, and promotion decisions.

Another method of evaluation is psychometric measurement. The principal instruments used are tests of a person's mental abilities and personality traits. The validity of these measurements is typically assessed by comparing scores of a "known" group of people with some criterion of successful organizational performance; i.e., pay, organizational rank, supervisory judgments, etc. These measurements are used in employee selection and promotion.

There has been very little application of OR to the problem of human resource evaluation. A recent attempt has been made by Flamholtz [1971], who has developed a "stochastic model" for human resource valuation. His model is based on Howard's notion of a stochastic process with service rewards (Howard [1960]). The basic concept is that people move from one organizational role or position to another and render services to the organization. This movement can be considered a stochastic process in which the "rewards" are the benefits derived by the system as people occupy specified service states for given periods.

The Stochastic Rewards Valuation Model involves two basic dimensions of a person's value to an enterprise: (1) expected conditional value and (2) expected realizable value. A four-step procedure is used to measure them.

1) Define the set of mutually exclusive, exhaustive states a person may occupy in an organization.
2) Determine the value of each state to the enterprise.
3) Estimate a person's expected tenure, and
4) Estimate the probabilities that a person will occupy each possible state at specified future times (as noted previously, we can use a stochastic mobility model to predict the states to be occupied at specified future times).

Symbolically, a set of m service states, i, are defined, where $i = 1, 2, \ldots, m$, and m is the state of exit. The value, V_i, of each service state to the organization is determined. Then, the probabilities that a person will occupy each possible state at specified times and, in turn, derive the rewards associated with each state are estimated. $P(V_{i,t})$ denotes the probability of deriving value V_i at time t, where t is the valuation period.

Drawing upon the model, expected conditional value is:

$$E(CV) = \sum_{t=1}^{n} \sum_{i=1}^{m-1} [V_i \cdot P(V_{i,t})/(1+r)^t],$$

where $E(CV)$ is expected conditional value, r is a discount factor for the present value of money, and the other symbols have the meanings defined as above.

To obtain the expected realizable value $E(RV)$, the above summation is extended from $m - 1$ to m, to include the exit state m.

This model is intended for use in a variety of personnel decisions and is currently being applied in a medium-sized C.P.A. firm, Lester Witte & Company (Flamholtz [1974]).

6. MAINTENANCE AND COMPENSATION

The decision problem associated with maintenance and compensation is essentially who gets what and why. In formulating this problem two underlying considerations should be taken into account. First, in order to survive, every organization must guarantee the continued active and productive participation of its members. Secondly, an organization should discharge its ethical responsibility to insure that its accumulation of wealth is fairly and appropriately distributed among its members. The methods used to accomplish these two purposes are socialization, rewards, penalties, and sanctions.

In most organizations the question of who gets what and why focuses primarily on decisions with respect to compensation (wage and salary), recognition, and promotion; but it also includes such psychological considerations as participation in decision-making, degree of challenge of the job, ability to learn, the ability to relate work to one's social life and, of course, hope—the belief that the job leads to some desirable future. Although there is some contemporary research under way to improve the social and psychological dimensions of jobs dealing with such notions as design of jobs (Davis and Taylor [1972]), job enrichment and enlargement (Herzberg [1968]), and in theories of motivation (Maslow [1965, 1971]), most organizations in industrial nations are still primarily concerned with establishing appropriate pay systems. The application of OR has followed this concern and has been directed primarily towards establishing levels of monetary compensation.

The basic approach can be summarized in the following equation:

$$Pay = f(A, O, E)$$

The equation states that an individual's pay, including benefits, is a function of (1) a set, A, of individual attributes such as productivity, skills, age, seniority, education, potential, etc. (2) a set, O, of Organizational variables such as general level of pay for comparable work, the pay structure vis-a-vis the organizational role hierarchy, the organization's need for particular skills to achieve its goals, its total income level, etc. and (3) a set, E, of environmental variables such as labor and employment laws, union influence, etc. In formulating models, O and E, frequently come in as constraints rather than variables.

One technique for determining pay, using the above formulation, is to employ a linear regression model. In using this empirical or inductive approach, past data would be used to determine a formula of the form:

$$Pay_j = \sum_{i=1}^{n} w_{ij}\, a_{ij}$$

where

Pay_j = the salary, points or other measure of compensation for the jth job classification.

a_{ij} = the amount of attribute i possessed by a person in the jth job classification, whose salary is to be determined or the amount of attribute i required to properly execute job j.

w_{ij} = weight to be assigned to the ith attribute in the jth job classification.*

*If the weights are common to all jobs, then a simplified form w_i can be used. This form also has the advantage of not requiring replication of the data points for each of the job classifications, which would be necessary to obtain least squares estimates of all of the w_{ij} parameters.

Using this approach, data could be collected on individual attributes such as age, years of service, productivity, supervisory ability, responsibilities, and other relevant attributes. The a_{ij}'s for each position serve as the independent variables. Compensation levels become the dependent variables. Then, for example, using the method of least squares and multiple linear regression techniques, the w_{ij}'s can be estimated. (See Gilmore [1956], for a comprehensive treatment of multiple correlation and regression analysis for this purpose).

In critiquing this statistical approach for devising a compensation formula, however, Charnes, Cooper, and Ferguson [1955] list five desiderata which they believe any such formula must satisfy. They are:

1. Yield a linear formula.
2. Be consistent on an organization-wise basis, in the sense that it does not violate the ranked position-hierarchy of the organization; e.g., "The office boy (or star salesman) must not receive more compensation than the president."
3. Meet competitive conditions, but on a consistent basis, i.e., "overall" the organization desires to avoid losing valuable executive talent to competitors without creating inconsistencies within its own organization.
4. Avoid negative weights for any factor, e.g., clustering of older persons in certain positions of lower rank should not result in a penalty for age.
5. Avoid being prejudiced by current organizational salaries.

They point out that linear regression models are not particularly suitable for this kind of analysis, especially with regard to item 5. It is extremely difficult to obtain compensation and personnel data from other organizations (especially competitors), and even if it is available item 5 cannot be fully satisfied. Consequently, Charnes and Cooper [1955] propose a LP model. Using an early variant of goal programming, they propose the following formulation:

Let:

(i) X_{ij} be the known amount of attribute i (as rated) required on job level j. $j = 1, 2, \ldots, L$.

(ii) The jobs are ranked in descending (weak) order, $1, 2, \ldots, L$, so that the jth subscript indicates the position of the job in the hierarchy. That is, Pay 1 $\geqslant$ Pay 2, etc.

(iii) A salary ceiling Pay_M and a salary floor Pay_m are established in advance. Also intermediate level targets, Pay_j, may be used.

It is assumed that the organization's intention is to meet these prescribed levels "as closely as possible."

Level and consistency requirements (desiderata 2 and 3 above) are satisfied by employing a series of constraint inequalities which insure that each higher ranked position in the organization hierarchy received at least as high a salary as the one immediately below it, and that minimum (floor) and maximum (ceiling) salary conditions are maintained. The objective becomes to minimize the deviation or discrepancy (d_i^+, d_i^-) between the derived salary scale and the ceiling, floor, and intermediate "target" scale amounts.

The general form of the model is to find the w_i's that will:

$$\text{Minimize} \quad Z \equiv d_1^+ + d_L^- + \sum_{k=2}^{L-1} (d_k^+ + d_k^-),$$

subject to

$$\sum_{i=1}^{n} w_i X_{i1} + d_1^+ = \text{Pay}_M$$

$$\sum_{i=1}^{n} w_i X_{i1} - \sum_{i=1}^{n} w_i X_{iL} \geqslant 0$$

$$\ldots \text{etc.} \ldots$$

$$\sum_{i=1}^{n} w_i X_{i(L-1)} - \sum_{i=1}^{n} w_i X_{iL} \geqslant 0$$

$$\sum_{i=1}^{n} w_i X_{iL} - d_L^- = \text{Pay}_m$$

and

$$\sum w_i X_{ik} + d_k^+ - d_k^- = \text{Pay}_k \text{ for } k \in K$$

where

Pay$_k$ = any intermediate "target" level from out of a set K of externally given compensation level "bench marks" which it is desirable to approximate. Legal requirements, industry practices or competition for example, may give rise to the set K.

and,

$d_k^+ - d_k^-$ = slack variables from the set K which represent positive or negative deviations from the kth target.

Application of this approach assumes that the jobs are well defined and described in a manner which is consistent with the accomplishment of the functions necessary to achieve the goals and objectives of the organization. Once this is satisfactorily completed, compensation analysis can begin. This involves the following steps:

1. Determine the attributes or factors to be included. This involves answering the question, "What attributes should affect one's compensation on the job?"
2. Develop a rating scheme for each attribute. Typically ordinal rankings are to rate levels of importance for each attribute. (Although they have interval implications in an LP model). For example, the factor education might be assigned ratings such as

   5 = Ph.D.,
   4 = Master's degree,
   3 = Bachelor's degree,
   2 = A.A. or some college,
   1 = high school graduate.

The preceding, rather objective, rating can often be done by the analyst alone; however, more subjective factors such as "Degree of responsibility for personnel" or "Degree of judgment involved in the job" may require cooperative efforts.

Care should be taken to employ a sufficient number of rates for a particular attribute to discriminate among jobs, but not so many as to lose clarity and meaning. In practice, 5 or 6 different values usually meet the requirements; although binary rankings and rankings with as many as 18 different levels have been used.

3. Formulate a model which applies the rankings to the factors and takes into account the hierarchy of organization and other constraints and requirements.

   A supposition of salary schedules is that there exists a well defined hierarchy within the organization. The analyst must define this hierarchy and assure that the model takes it into account. (There are some deep managerial questions involved in this). Questions of competition for talent, value to the firm; etc., must also be taken into account.
4. Solve the model to obtain a suggested compensation schedule. If there are many jobs to be evaluated, a well selected sample can be used.
5. Use the results together with other inputs to decide on compensation. Metzger [1958] has additional suggestions on applying the method.

Rehumus and Wagner [1963] have overcome some of the measurement problems inherent in estimating ratings (Step 2 above) by building them into the model. After the number of rankings for a particular attribute are determined, a separate variable is specified for each (e.g., for the factor "knowledge" 14 rates, $K_{14} > K_{13} > \cdots > K_1$ are specified). For any given job, its compensation equation is specified by selecting just one rating variable for each attribute and summing them up together with a discrepancy variable. Constraints are invoked to insure that (1) no attribute contributes more than a prescribed percentage to the total compensation, (2) each rating is positive and (3) that a minimum acceptable difference between weights for successive attribute degrees is achieved (e.g., $K_2 - K_1 \geq .007$). Compensation in the model is expressed in terms of percentage of the highest salary, instead of in monetary terms. The authors have applied the technique successfully to a sample of administrative and clerical positions in a major oil company and to twenty-one executive positions in a public utility.

Recently, Bruno [1971] has augmented this LP approach and applied it to a school district, in order to derive salary schedules which (1) consider the resources of the organization in determining the final salary structure, (2) permit the flexibility of overlaps in salary between the various levels of the organizational salary hierarchy and (3), by means of employing a variety of objective functions, allow the salary schedule to reflect established school district priorities and objectives.

An interesting feature of Bruno's application of the model is that he employs a variety of objective functions and determines their differing implications. By maximizing various individual factors and by minimizing costs, he obtained realistic salary schedules under each of the different assumptions. These were used as an aid in the design of salary schedules or in collective bargaining negotiations. Another approach to the problem is given in Welch and Florian [1970].

7. LARGE SCALE MODELS OF THE HUMAN RESOURCE MANAGEMENT SYSTEM

The previous sections have described applications of OR to various functions of human resource management. Although it is also possible to study whole human resource management systems by means of a large scale model of the system, very few attempts have been made. One possible approach involves modelling the system and using computer simulations to evaluate the effects of various personnel policies and methods.

Weber [1971], for example, has developed a complex system model as a tool for corporate manpower planning. His model represents the human resources subsystem of a hierarchical organization, and focuses upon the behavior of individuals, management decisions, and aspects of the organization's environment. The model is based on theory rather than practice. That is, following the simulation approach used by Bonini [1963], the hypotheses underlying the model are drawn from behavioral science literature rather than from experience or analysis of the organization. The model is intended as a tool for evaluating the effects of alternative personnel policies on organizational performance criteria.

Weber's model is shown schematically in Figure 3. The arrows indicate causal relations among factors. The model consists of four major components: 1) individual's attributes, 2) organization policies, 3) organizational decisions, and 4) job market behavior. These factors are varied experimentally in the model to explore responses.

The model can be used to examine the effects of a variety of personnel policies. For example, Weber used it to examine promotion and salary increase policy (new and policy). In this experiment, he varied the weights assigned to job performance and aptitude in determining rewards.

An increased emphasis on rewards for performance lead to an increase in job satisfaction and a general improvement in performance. However, contrary to popular belief (Humbel [1965]), this policy resulted in *reduced* individual and managerial aptitude and ability, and, therefore, raises some questions about the long term effectiveness of basing rewards primarily on performance alone.

A recruiting policy, which emphasized individual aptitude levels which were higher on the average than the aptitude levels required by all jobs, was compared to a policy which attempted to match aptitude with the requirements of the job. As expected, the "high" aptitude policy resulted in increased average aptitude for the organization as a whole. However, job satisfaction decreased and no improvement in performance resulted. Moreover, the expected increase in resignations did not materialize.

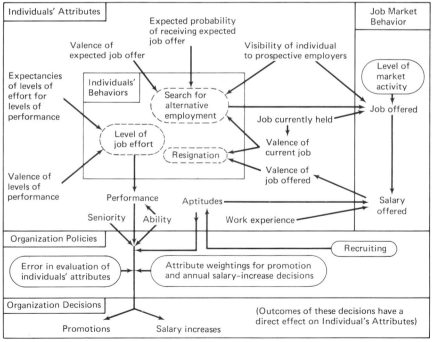

Fig. 3.

Errors were introduced into the personnel evaluation function with the expected results: lower job satisfaction, higher turnover, and poorer performance.

The effects of environmental variation were investigated by inducing fluctuations in the demand for labor which effected the visibility and search behavior of employees and, accordingly, their probability of leaving the organization. The high fluctuation run resulted in both an employee and management cadre with greater aptitude and ability and a higher measure of performance. Salary costs went down. Meanwhile, resignations and vacancies increased along with an increase in employee search for new jobs and a decrease in job satisfaction.

Although still in their embryonic states, it appears that simulation models of this type may prove to be useful in understanding the dynamics of large scale social systems and the effect of various human resource policies on them. Further, they may aid us in learning more about the consequences and implications of the assumption frequently made about human and organizational behavior, whether these assumptions derive from theory, practice, belief, or dogma.

8. CONCLUSION

This review of the application of OR to problems of human resource management reveals certain tendencies. For example, most of the applications to date have been in the areas of planning models and stochastic mobility models to guide acquisition decision, assignment models to guide allocation decisions, and LP pay scale models to guide compensation decisions. Very few applications have emerged which serve to guide development, utilization, or evaluation decisions. What accounts for this choice?

The reason most likely lies in the basic flow model metaphor which underlies most of these applications. This conceptualization works best when there is a finite set of well defined, mutually exclusive job roles or positions which are joined together in a hierarchial, graded structure, where the structure is relatively stable and the rules of transition are relatively constant through time. In most cases people, like water, are assumed to be homogenous and can be collected into "pools." The people then are assumed to flow from one pool to another throughout the hierarchy in certain patterns and at certain rates.

This approach works reasonably well in well ordered social systems such as the military, educational institutions, and some corporations where strong traditions and social forces serve to maintain the structure. When the work structure is not susceptible to severe environmental or social change, it is reasonable to assume that acquisition, allocation, and compensation decisions can be aided by these models.

Some development decisions might also be aided through more use of the flow model concept. For example, one interpretation of training and education is that it is a decision which alters the pattern and rate of flow of personnel throughout the system. This interpretation, of course, ignores the richer notion of human development which includes adding to the personal well being of the individual or adding to the social welfare of the community through new education and experience. And, this leads us to another point.

The objective functions employed in most applications to date have been formulated in terms of increased productivity of the organization. We know of no cases where the individual's intrinsic worth to his or her self or to society have been included. Even though the focus of this summary of application has been the organization, it is still likely that the organization may have objectives over and above those captured by this narrow concept of productivity. Little is know about measuring these other objectives. Using current solution methods these multi-stage, multi-value decision-models are difficult to deal with. But the matter seems worth pursuing.

Applications of OR to guide decisions in the evaluation and utilization area also suffer from a lack of proper conceptual development. The contemporary research under way in human resource accounting should prove useful in applying OR methods to problems of evaluation. Work currently being done in the area of organization theory and in socio-technical systems should also provide a better foundation for applying OR to utilization problems.

In summary, the vast field of human resource management has barely been touched by management scientists. There is much that he or she can still do, but it will require that they extend beyond the limiting notions of flow models and of productivity. Other objective functions and other structures will require new concepts. So, there is much work left to be done. But then, no management scientist worthy of his salt has ever shied away from such a challenge.

REFERENCES

1. Ackoff, Russell, *A Concept of Corporate Planning*, Wiley, New York (1970).
2. Arabayre, R. P., J. Fearnly, F. C. Steiger and W. Teather, "The Airline Crew Scheduling Problem: A Survey," *Transport. Sci.* **3**, No. 2,: 140–163 (May 1969).
3. Balinsky, Warren and Arnold Reisman, "Some Manpower Planning Models Based on Levels of Educational Attainment," *Management Sci.* **18**, No. 12: B–691–B–705 (August 1972).
4. Baumol, William J. and Tibor Fabian, "Decomposition, Pricing for Decentralization and External Economics," *Management Sci.* **11**, No. 1: 1–32 (September 1964).
5. Bartholomew, D. J., *Stochastic Models for Social Processes*, Wiley, New York (1967).
6. ——, "Decision-Making in Manpower Planning," *Operational Res. Quart.* **19** (Session Report) (April 1968) 129–132.
7. ——, "A Mathematical Analysis of Structural Control in a Graded Manpower System." Berkeley, California: University of California Research Program in University Administration, Office of the Vice President-Planning and Analysis, Paper P-3 (1969).

8. Bergstrom, G. L. and B. E. Smith, "Multi-Item Production Planning–An Extension of the HMMS Rules," *Management Sci.* **16,** No. 10: 614–629 (June 1970).

9. Bishop, A. B. and T. H. Rockwell, "A Dynamic Programming Computational Procedure for Optimal Manpower Loading in a Large Aircraft Company," *Operations Res.* **6:** 835–848 (1958).

10. Bonini, Charles P., *Simulation of Information and Decision Systems in the Firm*, Prentice-Hall, Englewood Cliffs, N.J. (1963).

11. Bruno, James E., "Compensation of School District Personnel," *Management Sci.* **17,** No. 10: B–569–587 (June 1971).

12. Charnes, A., W. W. Cooper, and R. O. Ferguson, "Optimal Estimation of Executive Compensation by Linear Programming," *Management Sci.* **1,** No. 2: 138–151 (January 1955).

13. ——, and R. J. Niehaus, "A Goal Programming Model for Manpower Planning," Carnegie-Mellon University - G.S.I.A., Management Sciences Research Report No. 115 (December 5, 1967).

14. ——, and D. Sholtz, "An Extended Goal Programming Model for Manpower Planning," Carnegie-Mellon University, G.S.I.A., Management Science Research Report No. 156 (December 23, 1968).

15. ——, and A. Stedry, "Static and Dynamic Assignment Models with Multiple Objectives and Some Remarks on Organization Design," Mangement Sci. **15, No. 8** (April 1969) B–365–B–375.

16. Childs, Martin and Harvey Wolfe, "A Decision and Value Approach to Research Personnel Allocation," *Management Sci.* **18,** No. 6: B269–B278 (February 1972).

17. Conrath, David W. and William F. Hamilton, "The Economics of Manpower Pooling," *Management Sci.* **18,** No. 2: B–19 - B–29 (October 1971).

18. Dalkey, Norman C., *Delphi*, Santa Monica, Cal: Rand Corporation, P-3704 (October 1967).

19. Davies, G. S., "Structural Control in a Graded Manpower System," *Management Sci.* **20,** No. 1: 76–84 (September 1973).

20. Davis, Louis E. and James C. Taylor, *Design of Jobs*, Baltimore-Penguin Books, Inc., 1972).

21. Dantzig, George B. and Philip Wolfe, "Decomposition Principles for Linear Programs," *Operations Res.* 8 (February 1960).

22. Derman, Cyrus, Gerald J. Lieberman, and Sheldon M. Ross, "A Sequential Stochastic Assignment Problem," *Management Sci.* **18,** No. 7: 349–355 (March 1972).

23. Dill, W. R., D. P. Garver, and Wesley L. Weber, "Models and Modelling for Manpower Planning," *Management Sci.* **13,** No. 4: 142–167 (December 1966).

24. Drucker, Peter F., "The Employee Society," *Am. Soc. Rev.* **58:** 358–363 (1952).

25. Duffett, R. H. E., "A Quantitative Approach to Company Manpower Planning," *Manpower and Appl. Psy.* **3,** No.'s 1 and 2: 11–22 (Winter 1969).

26. Dunnette, M. D, *Personnel Selection and Placement*, Wadsworth Publishing Company, Inc. Belmont, Ca. (1966).

27. Emery, Fred E., "The Democratization of the Workplace," *Manpower and Appl. Psychol.* **1:** 118–129 (1967).

28. ——, and E. L. Trist, "Socio-Technical Systems," in Emery, F.E. (Ed.) *Systems Thinking*, Penguin Harmondsworth, England, 281–296 (1969).

29. Engelstad, Per H., "Socio-Technical Approach to Problems of Process Control," in Davis and Taylor, *Design of Jobs*, 328–356 (1972).

30. Fan, L. T., and C. Wang, *The Discrete Maximum Principle*, John Wiley & Sons, New York (1964).

31. ———, and ———, *The Continuous Maximum Principle*, John Wiley & Sons, New York (1966).
32. Fisher, Franklin M. and Anton S. Morton, "The Costs and Effectiveness of Reenlistment Incentives in the Navy," *Operations Res.* **15, No. 3**: 373–387 (May–June 1967).
33. Flamholtz, Eric, "A Model for Human Resource Valuation: A Stochastic Process with Service Rewards," *Account. Rev.* **46**, 253–267 (April 1971).
34. ———, *Human Resource Accounting*, Dickenson Publishing Co., Encino, California (1974), Ch. 6.
35. ———, "Toward a Theory of Human Resource Value in Formal Organizations," *Account. Rev.* **47**: 666–678 (October 1972).
36. Gerwin, Donald and W. Christoffel, "Organizational Structure and Technology: A Computer Model Approach," *Management Sci.* **20**, No. 12: 1531–1542 (Aug. 1974).
37. Gilmore, Robert W., *Industrial Wage and Salary Control*, John Wiley & Sons, Inc. New York (1956).
38. Glover, W. S., and R. L. Ackoff, "Five-Year Planning for an Integrated Operation," in *Proceedings of the Conference on Case Studies in Operations Research*, Case Institute of Technology, Cleveland 38–47 (1936).
39. Gilford, J. P., *Psychometric Methods*, Second Edition, McGraw-Hill Book Co., New York (1954).
40. Hanssman, F. and S. W. Hess, "A Linear Programming Approach to Production and Employment Scheduling," *Management Tech.* **1**, No. 1: 46–51 (January 1960).
41. Hardy, G. H., J. E. Littlewood, and G. Polya, *Inequalities*, Cambridge University Press (1934).
42. Helmer, Olaf, *Social Technology*, Basic Books, New York (1968).
43. Herzberg, Frederick, "One More Time: How do you Motivate Employees?" *Harvard Bus. Res.* **46**: 53–62 (1968).
44. Hillier, Frederick S. and Gerald J. Lieberman, *Introduction to Operations Research*, Holden-Day, Inc., San Francisco (1967).
45. Holstein, William K. and William L. Berry, "The Labor Assignment Decision: An Application of Work Flow Structure Information," *Management Sci.* **18**, No. 7: 390–400 (March 1972).
46. Holt, C. C., F. Modigliani, T. Muth and H. A. Simon, *Planning Production Inventories and Work Force*, Prentice-Hall, Englewood Cliffs, N.J. (1960).
47. Howard, R., *Dynamic Programming and Markov Processes*, The M.I.T. Press (1960).
48. Humbel, J. W., "Improving Management Performance," *Person. Management*, **47**, 136–142 (March 1965).
49. Hwang, C. L. and L. T. Fan, "The Application of the Maximum Principle to Industrial and Management Systems," *J. Indust. Eng.* **XVIII**, No. 11: 589–593 (November 1966).
50. ———, "Optimum Production Planning by the Maximum Principle," *Management Sci.* **13**, No. 9: 751–755 (May 1967).
51. Inskeep, Gordon C., "Statistically Guided Employee Selection: An Approach to the Labor Turnover Problem," *Person. J.* **49**, No. 1: 15–24 (January 1970).
52. Jewett, Roger F., "A Minimum Risk Manpower Scheduling Technique," *Management Sci.* **13**, No. 10: B–578–B–592 (June 1967).
53. Jones, C. G., "Parametric Production Planning," *Management Sci.* **13**, No. 11: 843–866 (July 1967).
54. Kao, Richard C. and Thomas C. Rowan, "A Model for Personnel Recruiting and Selection," *Management Sci.* **5**, No. 2: 192–203 (January 1959).
55. Karush, W. and A. Vazsonyi, "Mathematical Programming and Employment Scheduling," *Nav. Res. Log. Quart.* **4**, No. 4: 297–320 (December 1957).

56. King, William, "A Stochastic Personnel-Assignment Model," *Operations Res.* **13**, No. 1: 67–81 (January–February 1967).

57. Lev, B. and A. Schwartz, "On the Use of the Economic Concept of Human Capital in Financial Statements," *Account. Rev.*, **46**: 103–112 (January 1971).

58. Lippman, Steven, Alan J. Rolfe, Harvey M. Wagner and John S. C. Yuan, "Optimal Production Scheduling and Employment Smoothing with Deterministic Demands," *Management Sci.* **14**, No. 3: 127–158 (November 1967).

59. Maslow, Abraham H., *Eupsychian Management: A Journal*, Irwin-Dorsey, Homewood, Ill. (1965).

60. ———, *The Farther Reaches of Human Nature*, The Viking Press, New York (1971).

61. ———, *Motivation and Personality*, Harper & Row, New York (1954).

62. McCloskey, Joseph F. and Fred Hanssman, "An Analysis of Stewardess Requirements and Scheduling for a Major Domestic Airline," *Nav. Res. Log. Quart.* **4**, No. 3: 183–202 (September 1957).

63. McGregor, Douglas, *The Human Side of Enterprise*, McGraw-Hill, New York (1960).

64. Metzger, Robert W., *Elementary Mathematical Programming*, John Wiley & Sons, New York (1958).

65. Milkovich, George T., Anthony T. Annoni, and Thomas S. Mahoney, "The Use of Delphi Procedures in Manpower Forecasting," *Management Sci.* **19**, No. 4: 381–388 (December 1972).

66. Nelson, Rosser T., "Labor Assignment as a Dynamic Control Problem," *Operations Res.* **14**, No. 3: 369–376 (May–June 1966).

67. ———, "Labor and Machine Limited Production Systems," *Management Sci.* **13**, No. 9: 648–671 (May 1967).

68. ———, "A Simulation of Labor Efficiency and Centralized Assignment in a Production Model," *Management Sci.* **17**, No. 2: B97–B106 (October 1970).

69. Nemhauser, G. L. and H. L. Nuttle, "A Quantitative Approach to Employment Planning," *Management Sci.* **11**, No. 8, 155–165 (June 1965).

70. Pappas, Ioannis, "Dynamic Job Assignment for Railway Personnel," *Management Sci.* **13**, No. 12: B809–B816 (August 1967).

71. Rau, John C., "A Model for Manpower Productivity During Organization Growth," *Nav. Res. Log. Quart.* **18**, No. 4: 543–559 (December 1971).

72. Rehmus, Frederick P. and Harvey M. Wagner, "Applying Linear Programming to Your Pay Structure," *Bus. Horizons* **6**, No. 4: 89–98 (Winter 1963).

73. Rice, A. R., *Productivity and Social Organization: The Ahmedabad Experiment*, Tavistock, London (1958).

74. Rowe, Stephen M. W. Gary Wagner and George B. Weathersby, "A Control Theory Solution to Optimal Faculty Staffing," Berkeley, Calif.: University of California: Research Program in University Administration, Office of the Vice President-Planning and Analysis, Paper P-11 (November 1970).

75. Rowland, Kendrith M. and Michael G. Sovereign, "Markov-Chain Analysis of Internal Manpower Supply," *Ind. Rel.* **9**, No. 1: 88–99 (October 1969).

76. Root, James G., "An Application of Symbolic Logic to a Selection Problem," *Operations Res.*, 519–526 (July–August 1964).

77. Sikes, T. W., "The Search Decision Rule Applied to Aggregate Planning: Improved Efficiency and Stochastic Extensions," Unpublished Ph.D. Dissertation, University of California, Los Angeles (1970).

78. Silver, E. A., "A Tutorial on Production Smoothing and Work Force Balancing," *Operations Res.* **15**: 983–1010 (1967).

79. Sinha, Negeshwar, P., *Manpower Planning: A Research Bibliography*, Minneapolis: Industrial Relations Center, University of Minnesota, Bulletin 52 (January 1970).

80. Smith, Robert D. and Paul S. Greenlaw, "Simulation of a Psychological Decision Process in Personnel Selection," *Management Sci.* **13**, No. 8: B409–B419 (April 1967).

81. Taylor, E. R. and Nevis, E. C., "Personnel Selection," *Ann. Rev. Psy.* **12**: 389–412 (1961).

82. Taylor, Frederick W., *The Principle of Scientific Management*, Harper Brothers, New York (1911).

83. ———, *Shop Management*, Harper Brothers, New York (1919).

84. Taubert, W. H., "Search Decision Rule for the Aggregate Scheduling Problem," *Management Sci.* **14**, No. 6: 343–359 (February 1968).

85. ———, "The Search Decision Rule Approach to Operations Planning," Unpublished Ph.D. Dissertation, University of California, Los Angeles, California (1968).

86. Thompson, James D., *Organization in Action*, McGraw-Hill Book Company New York (1967).

87. Trist, Eric L. and K. W. Bamforth, "Some Social and Psychological Consequences of the Longwall Method of Coal-getting," *Human Rel.* **4**, No. 1: 3–38 (1951).

88. Trist, Eric L. and H. Murray, "Work Organization at the Coal Face: A Comparative Study of Mining Systems," *Tavistock Institute of Human Relations*, Doc. 506 (1948).

89. ———, G. W. Higgin, H. Murray, and A. B. Pollack, *Organizational Choice*, Tavistock, London (1963).

90. Van Beinum, H. J. J., "The Design of the New Radial Tyre Factory as an Open Socio-Technical System," *Tavistock Institute of Human Relations, Human Resources Centre*, Doc. HRC 150 (October 28, 1968).

91. Vroom, Victor H. and Kenneth R. MacCrimmon, "Toward a Stochastic Model of Managerial Careers," *Admin. Sci. Quart.* **13**, No. 1: 26–46 (June 1968).

92. Waid, C., D. F. Clark and R. L. Ackoff, "Allocation of Sales Effort in the Lamp Division of the General Electric Company," *Operations Res.* **4**: 629–647 (1956).

93. Wagner, Harvey M., *Principles of Management Science*, Prentice-Hall, Englewood Cliffs, Inc., N.J. (1970).

94. Walker, James W., "Forecasting Manpower Needs," *Harvard Bus. Rev.* **27**, No. 2: 132–164 (March–April 1969).

95. Warner, Michael D. and Juan Prawda, "A Mathematical Programming Model for Scheduling Nursing Personnel in a Hospital," *Management Sci.* **19**, No. 4: 411–422 (December 1972).

96. Weber, Wesley L., "Manpower Planning in Hierarchical Organizations: A Computer Simulation Approach," *Management Sci.* **18**, No. 3: 119–144 (November 1971).

97. Weil, Roman L., "Functional Selection for the Stochastic Assignment Model, *Operations Res.* **15**, No. 6: 1063–1067 (November/December 1967).

98. Weissman, Clark, *LISP 1.5 Primer*, Dickenson Publishing Co., Belmont, California (1967).

99. Welch, N. and M. Florian, "An Application of Linear Programming to Wage Analysis," *Canadian Operational Research Society* **8**, No. 1: 28–37 (November 1970).

100. Young, A., "Models for Planning Recruitment and Promotion of Staff," *Brit. J. Ind. Rel.* **3**, Part 3: 301–310 (1965).

101. Young, A., and G. Almond, "Predicting Distribution of Staff," *Computer J.* **3**: 246–250 (1961).

I-5

AGGREGATE PRODUCTION PLANNING

Arnoldo C. Hax
Massachusetts Institute of Technology

1. INTRODUCTION

Production planning is concerned with the determination of production, inventory, and work force levels to meet fluctuating demand requirements. Normally, the physical resources of the firm are assumed to be fixed during the planning horizon of interest, and the planning effort is oriented toward the best utilization of those resources given the external demand requirements. A problem usually arises because the times and quantities imposed by the demand requirements seldomly coincide with the times and quantities which make for an efficient use of the firm's resources. Whenever the conditions affecting the production process are not stable in time (due to changes in demand, cost components, or capacity availability), production should be planned in an aggregate way to obtain effective resource utilization. The time horizon of this planning activity is dictated by the nature of the dynamic variations; for example, if demand seasonalities are present, a full seasonal cycle should be incorporated into the planning horizon. Commonly, the time horizon varies from six to eighteen months, twelve months being a suitable figure for most planning systems.

Usually, since it is impossible to consider every fine detail associated with the production process and still maintain such a long planning horizon, it is mandatory to aggregate the information being processed. This aggregation can take place by consolidating similar items into product families, different machines into machine centers, different labor skills into labor centers, and individual customers into market regions. The type of aggregation to be performed is suggested by the nature of the planning systems to be used, and the technical as well as managerial characteristics of the production activities. Aggregation forces the use of a consistent set of measurement units. It is common to express aggregate demand in production hours.

Once the aggregate plan is generated, constraints are imposed on the detailed production scheduling technique which decides the specific quantities to be produced of each individual item. These constraints normally specify production rates or total amounts to be produced per month for a given product family. In addition, crew sizes, levels of machine utilization and amount of overtimes to be used are determined.

When demand requirements do not change with time, and costs and prices are also stable, it may be feasible to bypass entirely the aggregate planning process, provided the resources of the firm are well balanced to absorb the constant requirements. However, when these conditions are not met, serious inefficiencies might result from attempting to plan production responding only to immediate requirements and ignoring the future consequences of present decisions. To illustrate this point, consider what happens when an order point-order quantity inventory control system,[1] that treats every item in isolation, is applied in the presence of strong demand seasonalities. Firstly, at the beginning of the peak season demand starts rapidly increasing and a large number of items simultaneously trigger the order point, demanding production runs of the amount specified by the order quantities. Being unable to satisfy all these orders and still maintain an adequate service level, management may react by reducing the production run lengths, thereby creating multiple changeovers of small quantities. This, in turn, reduces the overall productivity (because of the high percentage of idle machine time due to the large number of changeovers), increases costs, and deteriorates customer service levels. Secondly, items at the end of the season are produced in normal order quantities (typically large); thus, inventory is created that is inactive until the beginning of the next season or that must be liquidated at salvage values. An effective aggregate capacity planning system will prevent such inefficiencies.

---

[1] An order point-order quantity inventory control system releases a replenishment order for an item whenever the amount on hand, plus on order, minus backorders is equal to or less than a specified level, called the order point. The order point normally is calculated as the expected demand over the purchasing (or manufacturing) lead time plus a safety stock. The amount ordered is a fixed quantity (normally called the EOQ: economic order quantity) which minimizes the total cost involved, including inventory carrying cost and purchasing (or manufacturing) ordering costs. For details on the description of an order point-order quantity system see, for example, Buffa and Taubert [1972], or Magee and Boodman [1967].

1.1 Ways to Absorb Demand Fluctuations

There are several methods that managers can use to absorb changing demand patterns. These ways can be combined to create a large number of alternative production plans.

1. Management can change the size of the work force by hiring and laying off, which allows changes in the production rate to take place. Excessive use of these practices, however, can create severe labor problems.
2. While maintaining a uniform regular work force, management can vary the production rate by introducing overtime and/or idle time, or relying on outside subcontracting.
3. While maintaining a uniform production rate, management can anticipate future demand by accumulating seasonal inventories. The tradeoff between the cost incurred in changing production rates and holding seasonal inventories is the basic question to be resolved in most practical situations.
4. Management can also resort to planned backlogs whenever customers may accept delays in filling their orders.
5. An alternative which has to be resolved at a higher planning level is the development of complementary product lines with demand patterns which are counter seasonal to the existing products. This alternative is very effective in producing a more even utilization of the firm's resources, but it does not eliminate the need for aggregate planning.

1.2 Costs Relevant to Aggregate Production Planning

Relevant costs can be categorized as follows:

1. Basic production costs. These are the fixed and variable costs incurred in producing a given product type in a given time period. Included are direct and indirect labor costs, and regular as well as overtime compensations.
2. Costs associated with changes in the production rate. Typical costs in this category are those involved in hiring, training, and laying off personnel.
3. Inventory holding costs. A major component of the inventory holding cost is the cost of capital tied up in inventory. Other components are storing, insurance, taxes, spoilage, and obsolescence.
4. Backlogging costs. Usually these costs are very hard to measure and include costs of expediting, loss of customer good will, and loss of sales revenues resulting from backlogging.

McGarrah [1963] and Holt et al. [1960] provide a good discussion on the nature and structure of these cost elements.

1.3   The Role of Models in Aggregate Production Planning

Models have played an important role in supporting management decisions in aggregate production planning. Anshen et al. [1958] indicate that models are of great value in helping managers to:

1. Quantify and use the intangibles which are always present in the background of their thinking but which are incorporated only vaguely and sporadically in scheduling decisions.
2. Make routine the comprehensive consideration of all factors relevant to scheduling decisions, thereby inhibiting judgments based on incomplete, obvious, or easily handled criteria.
3. Fit each scheduling decision into its appropriate place in the historical series of decisions and, through the feedback mechanism incorporated in the decision rules, automatically correct for prior forecasting errors.
4. Free executives from routine decision making activities, thereby giving them greater freedom and opportunity for dealing with extraordinary situations.

In order to describe the different types of models that can be used in supporting aggregate planning decisions, it is useful to classify the models according to the assumptions they make about the structure of the cost components. In the following sections we will analyze first linear cost models, followed by quadratic cost models, fixed cost models, and then general nonlinear cost models.

2.   LINEAR COST MODELS

Some of the very first models proposed to guide aggregate planning decisions assume linearity in the cost behavior of the decision variables. These kinds of models are very popular even today because of the computational conveniences associated with LP. Moreover, these models are less restrictive then they first appear because nonlinear convex costs functions can be approximated to any degree of accuracy by piecewise linear segments. We now will see two important classes of linear models.

2.1   Fixed Work Force Model

First, let us consider the case where the work force is fixed. Hiring and firing to absorb demand fluctuations during the planning horizon are disallowed. Production rates can fluctuate only by using overtime from the regular work force.

The following notation is used to describe the model in mathematical terms. Parameters:

v_{it} = unit production cost for product i in period t

c_{it} = inventory carrying cost per unit of product i in period t
r_t = cost per manhour of regular labor in period t
o_t = cost per manhour of overtime labor in period t
d_{it} = demand for product i in period t
k_i = manhours required to produce one unit of product i
$(rm)_t$ = total manhours of regular labor available in period t
$(om)_t$ = total manhours of overtime labor available in period t
I_{io} = initial inventory level for product i
W_o = initial regular workforce level
T = time horizon, in periods
N = total number of products

Decision Variables:

X_{it} = units of product i to be produced in period t
I_{it} = units of product i to be left over as inventory at the end of period t
W_t = manhours of regular labor used during period t
O_t = manhours of overtime labor used during period t.

A simple version of the fixed work force-linear cost model is

$$\text{Min } z = \sum_{i=1}^{N} \sum_{t=1}^{T} (v_{it} X_{it} + c_{it} I_{it}) + \sum_{t=1}^{T} (r_t W_t + o_t O_t) \tag{1}$$

subject to:

$$X_{it} + I_{i,t-1} - I_{it} = d_{it}, \qquad t = 1, \ldots, T; \ i = 1, \ldots, N \tag{2}$$

$$\sum_{i=1}^{N} k_i X_{it} - W_t - O_t = 0, \qquad t = 1, \ldots, T \tag{3}$$

$$0 \le W_t \le (rm)_t, \qquad t = 1, \ldots, T \tag{4}$$

$$0 \le O_t \le (om)_t, \qquad t = 1, \ldots, T \tag{5}$$

$$X_{it}, I_{it} \ge 0, \qquad i = 1, \ldots, N; \ t = 1, \ldots, T. \tag{6}$$

The objective function (1) expresses the minimization of variable production, inventory, and regular and overtime labor costs. If the marginal production costs v_{it} are invariant over time, the terms $v_{it} X_{it}$ do not need to be included in the objective function (since total production is fixed). Similarly, if the payroll of regular work force W_t constitutes a fixed commitment, the terms $r_t W_t$ should be deleted from (1).

Constraints (2) represent the typical production-inventory balance equation. Notice that (2) and (6) imply that no backordering is allowed. The next model will show how backorders can be incorporated. Moreover, (2) assumes a deterministic demand, d_{it}, for every item in every time period. One way to allow for uncertainties in the demand forecast is to specify a lower bound for the ending inventory at each period; i.e., $I_{it} \geqslant ss_{it}$, where ss_{it} is the safety stock associated with item i in period t.[2]

Constraints (3) defines the total manpower to be used at every period. This model formulation assumes that manpower availability is the only constraining resource of the production process. It is a trivial matter to expand the number of resources being considered, provided that linearity assumptions are maintained.

Constraints (4) and (5) pose lower and upper bounds on the use of regular and overtime manhours in every time period.

We already have indicated how constraints (6) could be changed to incorporate safety stocks. One should bear in mind that if no terminal conditions are imposed to the inventories at the end of the planning horizon, the model will drive them to zero; i.e., it will make $I_{iT} = 0$ for all i. If total depletion of inventories is undesirable, a target inventory constraint should be added in the model. An additional constraint also should be attached if there are storage requirements that cannot be exceeded; for example, the constraint

$$\sum_{i=1}^{N} I_{it} \leq (sc)_t, \qquad t = 1, \ldots, T$$

implies that the total inventory at each period cannot be greater than the total storage capacity $(sc)_t$.

When it is necessary to assign products to different working centers with limited capacities, the decision variables are redefined to identify those decisions explicitly. For example, X_{ict} may denote the amount of product i produced at working center c during period t. It is straightforward to carry out the resulting transformations in the overall model.

Even the very simple model described by expressions (1) to (6) could present enormous computational difficulties if the individual items to be scheduled are not grouped in broad product categories. If we ignore constraints (4), (5), and (6), which merely represent upper and lower bounds for the decision variables, the model consists of $Tx(N + 1)$ effective constraints. When dealing with complex production situations, the total number of individual items, N, may be several thousands. For example, if the planning model has 12 time periods and 5,000 items, the model would have about 60,000 constraints, which exceeds the capabilities of a regular LP code.

---

[2]The magnitude of the safety stocks depends on the quality of the demand forecasts and the level of customer service to be provided. For a good discussion of how to compute safety stocks, see Brown [1967].

In most practical applications, however, it would not be functional to plan the allocations of the production resources at this level of detail. First, a detailed scheduling program should take into account a large number of technological and marketing considerations which cannot be included in the overall model, due to their highly qualitative nature. Second, as we have expressed before, many of the planning issues to be resolved with the model deal with broad allocations of resources, and excessively detailed information will obscure rather than enlighten these decisions. Third, aggregate forecasts are more accurate than detailed forecasts.

It is common practice, therefore, to aggregate items in family types. The criteria for aggregation are evident from the model structure: members of a single family type should share similar demand patterns (d_{it}), have similar cost characteristics $(v_{it}, c_{it}, r_t, o_t)$, and should require similar unit production time (k_i). Once the aggregate planning decisions are made, these decisions impose constraints that must be observed when performing detailed item scheduling.

Notice that this model, as well as any other planning model, requires the definition of a planning horizon T and the partitioning of this time horizon into multiple time periods. One may assume that this partitioning results in T equally spaced time periods; this need not be so. Many operational planning systems are better designed if this partitioning generates uneven time periods, so that the more recent time periods carry more detailed information. Due to the uncertain environment in which this planning effort is being conducted, only the first time period results usually are implemented. At the end of every time period new information becomes available which is used to update the model and recompute the next time period plans.

Broad technological, institutional, marketing, financial and organizational constraints also can be included in the model formulation. This flexibility, characteristic of the LP approach to problem solving, has made this type of model very useful and popular.

A simple version of the fixed work force LP model, having a transportation problem structure, was first proposed by Bowman [1956].

2.2 Variable Work Force Model

Whenever it is feasible to change the work force during the planning horizon as a way to counteract demand fluctuations, the composition of the work force becomes a decision variable whose values can change by hiring and firing personnel. Therefore, the corresponding hiring and firing costs should be part of the objective function. In addition, the model allows for shortages to be included; thus a backordering cost is part of the formulation. The model decision variables are

X_{it} = units of product i to be purchased at period t
W_t = manhours of regular work force at period t

O_t = manhours of overtime work force at period t
H_t = manhours of regular work force hired at period t
F_t = manhours of regular work force fired at period t
I_{it}^+ = units of ending inventory for product i at period t
I_{it}^- = units backordered for product i at the end of period t.

Using the above notation with that introduced in the previous model, the cost incurred during period t includes the following components:

Variable manufacturing cost	$v_{it} X_{it}$
Inventory holding cost	$c_{it} I_{it}^+$
Backorder cost	$b_{it} I_{it}^-$
Regular payroll cost	$r_t W_t$
Overtime payroll cost	$o_t O_t$
Hiring cost	$h_t H_t$
Firing cost	$f_t F_t$.

A simple version of the variable work force model can be formulated as:

$$\text{Min } z = \sum_{i=1}^{N} \sum_{t=1}^{T} (v_{it} X_{it} + c_{it} I_{it}^+ + b_{it} I_{it}^-) + \sum_{t=1}^{T} (r_t W_t + o_t O_t + h_t H_t + f_t F_t)$$

subject to:

$$X_{it} + I_{i,t-1}^+ - I_{i,t-1}^- - I_{it}^+ + I_{it}^- = d_{it}, \qquad i = 1, \ldots, N; \quad t = 1, \ldots, T \quad (7)$$

$$\sum_{i=1}^{N} k_i X_{it} - W_t - O_t \leqslant 0, \qquad t = 1, \ldots, T \quad\quad\quad\quad (8)$$

$$W_t - W_{t-1} - H_t + F_t = 0, \qquad t = 1, \ldots, T \quad\quad\quad\quad (9)$$

$$-pW_t + O_t \leqslant 0, \qquad t = 1, \ldots, T \quad\quad\quad\quad (10)$$

$$X_{it}, I_{it}^+, I_{it}^- \geqslant 0, \qquad i = 1, \ldots, N; \quad t = 1, \ldots, T$$

$$W_t, O_t, P_t, H_t, F_t \geqslant 0, \qquad t = 1, \ldots, T.$$

Constraints (7) represent the production-inventory balance equation. Notice that this is equivalent to the old balance equation

$$X_{it} + I_{i,t-1} - I_{it} = d_{it},$$

except that now

$$I_{i,t-1} = I_{i,t-1}^+ - I_{i,t-1}^-$$

and

$$I_{it} = I_{it}^+ - I_{it}^-.$$

In the present model the ending inventory, I_{it}, can be either positive ($I_{it}^+ > 0$ indicates that stock remains at the end of the period), or negative ($I_{it}^- > 0$ indicates an accumulation of backorders at the end of the period). Since there is a cost attached to both I_{it}^+ and I_{it}^-, those variables never will be positive simultaneously.

Constraints (8) limit production to available manpower.

Constraints (9) define the change in the work force size during period t; i.e., $W_t - W_{t-1} = H_t - F_t$. Labor has been added whenever $H_t > 0$, or has been subtracted whenever $F_t > 0$. Once again, since there is a cost attached to both hiring and firing, H_t and F_t will never simultaneously have positive values in a given time period.

Constraints (10) impose an upper bound on the total overtime available in period t as a function of the regular work force size; i.e., $O_t \leqslant pW_t$, where p is the percentage of overtime allowed to the regular work force.

Many of the comments we have made in the fixed work model regarding ways to expand or simplify the models and ways to aggregate items in item families are applicable here and are not repeated.

The first of this type of models was proposed by Hanssmann and Hess [1960]. Several alternative approaches have been suggested, particularly those by Von Lanzenaur [1970a], and O'Malley, Elmaghraby and Jeske [1966].

Lippman, et al. [1967a] have analyzed the form of the optimal policies for a single product problem assuming convex production costs, V-shaped manpower fluctuation costs, and increasing holding costs. In reference [1967b] the authors provide an efficient algorithm to solve the special case where all the cost functions are linear and demand requirements are either monotone decreasing or increasing. The algorithm is an iterative procedure that starts by guessing the value of W_T, the regular manpower at the end of the planning horizon. It provides, next, an optimum policy for this value of W_T, and checks this policy against an optimality test. If an improvement is possible the algorithm yields a better value of W_T and the process is repeated. Convergence is guaranteed in a finite number of iterations.

Whenever costs are linear and demand requirements are nondecreasing, there exists an optimum policy such that

$$W_{t+1} \geqq W_t, \qquad t = 1, \ldots, T - 1$$

$$O_{t+1} \geqq O_t, \qquad t = 1, \ldots, T - 1$$

$$\frac{O_{t+1}}{W_{t+1}} \geqq \frac{O_t}{W_t}, \qquad t = 1, \ldots, T - 1$$

$$(W_T - W_t)O_t = 0, \qquad t = 1, \ldots, T$$

This result is used throughout the computational process. Yuan [1967] extended this approach for a multiproduct problem.

In an early work, Hoffman and Jacobs [1954], and Antosiewicz and Hoffman [1954] considered a linear cost model for a single product, allowing for changes in the production rate to be represented in the objective function. They analyzed the qualitative properties of the optimum solution, and proposed simple procedures to compute that solution when demand requirements are monotone increasing. This work was extended by Johnson and Dantzig [1955].

Linear programming models can be expanded easily to cover production process with several stages. A comprehensive discussion of multistage LP models including multiple routings, multiple sources, product mix decisions, and multiple production and distribution decisions is given by Johnson and Montgomery [1974].

2.3   Advantages and Disadvantages of Linear Cost Models

The overwhelming advantage of linear cost models is that they generate LPs which can be solved by readily available and efficient computer codes. Linear programs permit models with a large number of decision variables and constraints to be solved expediently and cheaply. In addition, LP lends itself very well to the performance of parametric and sensitivity analyses; this feature can be helpful in making aggregate planning decisions. The shadow cost information can be of assistance in identifying opportunities for capacity expansions, marketing penetration strategies, new product introductions, etc.

As indicated before, the linearity assumptions which are implicit in these models are less restrictive than they appear. First, cost structures might behave linearly within the range of interest of the decision variables under consideration. Second, general convex separable functions can be treated with piecewise linear approximation. Moreover, with some ingenuity, certain functions which at first seem to present nonlinear characteristics can be linearized, as indicated in the cited references of Hanssmann and Hess [1960], and Von Lanzenaur [1970a].

The most serious disadvantage of LP models is their failure to deal with demand uncertainties in any explicit way. In some situations this could constitute a serious drawback. However, Dzielinski, Baker, and Manne [1963] have reported favorable experiences in using LP models under fairly uncertain and dynamic environments.

3.   QUADRATIC COST MODELS (LINEAR DECISION RULES)

Whenever quadratic cost models are used to solve the aggregate capacity planning problem, the decision rules that are generated possess a linear structure (because the differentiation of a quadratic function produces a linear function). Thus, these models are also known as *Linear Decision Rules*. The first model of this kind was developed by Holt, Modigliani, Muth, and Simon (HMMS) [1960] Subsequently, several extensions have been offered. We will now discuss the basic concepts underlying the HMMS model.

The HMMS model calls for a complete aggregation of all product types into a single category. This might require the use of appropriate compatible units that allow the transformation to be made. Thus, there are essentially two decision variables:

P_t = aggregate production rate for period t.
W_t = work force size at period t.

The remaining decision variable

I_t = ending inventory at period t

is specified automatically by the values of P_t and W_t, and the relationship that exists among the three variables. The optimum decision rules, therefore, require specification of the aggregate production and work force for each period that minimizes a quadratic cost function.

3.1 Cost Components

We now review in some detail the components of this quadratic cost function. The following cost categories are identified:

1. Regular Payroll Costs
    These costs are assumed to increase linearly with the workforce size, according to the following relationship:

    $$c_1 W_t + c_{13},$$

    where c_1 and c_{13} are cost coefficients to be determined externally to the model. Since c_{13} is a constant, it can be eliminated from further consideration.
2. Hiring and Firing Costs
    Both hiring and firing costs are assumed quadratic in the work force variation ($W_t - W_{t-1}$), thus allowing an increasing cost rate to be incorporated. The specific relationship is a U-shaped curve given by:

    $$c_2(W_t - W_{t-1} - c_{11})^2,$$

    where c_2 and c_{11} are constants to be evaluated. c_{11} is introduced to allow for asymmetry in the cost function.
3. Overtime and Idle Costs
    Given a work force size W_t there is a desirable production rate $c_4 W_t$. If the production rate exceeds that amount, there will be overtime cost; if it

is lower than that amount there will be a cost of idle time. The exact nature of these cost relationships is given by the expression

$$c_3(P_t - c_4 W_t)^2 + c_5 P_t - c_6 W_t + c_{12} P_t W_t,$$

where the three last terms are given to improve the accuracy of the cost relationships.

4. Inventory and Backorder Costs

The relationship which characterizes the inventory related costs is assumed to be of the following form:

$$c_7 [I_t - (c_8 + c_9 d_t)]^2,$$

where

$$d_t = \text{expected units of aggregate product demand at period } t.$$

The target inventory level is $c_8 + c_9 d_t$; when deviations from this target occur, either carrying or backorder costs are incurred which increase with the square of these deviations. In the original HMMS work, c_9 was set to zero.

The estimation of the cost coefficients is an expensive and time consuming activity requiring statistical analysis, accounting information, and managerial inputs. Extensive work has been done to improve the quality of these estimates (Van dePanne and Bosje [1962], Kriebel [1967]), and to develop aggregate cost functions which represent the cost characteristics of the individual items (Bergstrom and Smith [1970], Krajewski et al. [1973]).

3.2 Model Formulation

Given the cost structure discussed above, the aggregate capacity planning model can be formulated as:

$$\text{Min } z = \sum_{t=1}^{T} [(c_1 - c_6) W_t + c_2 (W_t - W_{t-1} - c_{11})^2 + c_3 (P_t - c_4 W_t)^2$$

$$+ c_5 P_t + c_{12} P_t W_t + c_7 (I_t - c_8 - c_9 d_t)^2] \tag{11}$$

subject to

$$P_t + I_{t-1} - I_t = d_t, \qquad t = 1, \ldots, T \tag{12}$$

$$P_t, W_t \geq 0, \qquad t = 1, \ldots, T. \tag{13}$$

The objective function (11) should be regarded as the minimization of expected costs. One of the interesting features of the model is that it does not assume the demand d_t to be deterministic. Simon [1956] proved that if the demand forecasts are unbiased and represent expected values, the linear decision rules resulting from the minimization of (11), subject to constraints (12) and (13) provide minimum expected costs.

3.3   The Linear Decision Rules

The above model will have a unique global minimum if the objective function is strictly convex. This condition usually is met by many cost functions encountered in practice, since the cost components often have increasing marginal costs.

Optimal solutions to the model are found by the use of Lagrangians. Several applications have been reported which illustrate the nature of the resulting rules (see Buffa and Taubert [1972]). In general, the form of the rules can be characterized by equations of the following type:

$$P_t = a_o d_t + a_1 d_{t+1} + \cdots + a_{T-t} d_T + b W_{t-1} + c - d I_{t-1} \tag{14}$$

$$W_t = e_o d_t + e_1 d_{t+1} + \cdots + e_{T-t} d_T + f W_{t-1} + g - h I_{t-1}. \tag{15}$$

Equation (14) describes the nature of the aggregate production rate which is dependent on future demand forecasts, previous work force size, and beginning inventory. The same comments apply to expression (15), which illustrates the form of the aggregate work force decision. The weights given to the demand forecasts (the a's and e's) decrease rapidly with time.

3.4   Extensions to the HMMS Model

Several extensions to the initial HMMS model have been reported in the literature. Bergstrom and Smith [1970] generalized the approach to a multiproduct formulation, and incorporated diminishing marginal revenues in the objective function. Their work was, in turn, further expanded by Hausman and McClain [1971] to allow for randomness in the items' demand. Chang and Jones [1970] also dealt with the multiproduct problem; they suggested procedures to solve situations when production cannot be started and completed in a given time period. Sypkens [1967] included plant capacities as an additional decision variable. Peterson [1971] proposed an extension to the HMMS model to allow the manufacturer, at a cost, to smooth distribution orders to achieve less pronounced fluctuations in work force, production, and inventory levels.

3.5   Advantages and Disadvantages of Quadratic Cost Models

The major advantages of quadratic cost models are that they allow for more realistic cost structure in the planning process, they provide linear decision rules which are easy to solve and implement, and they allow uncertainties to be handled directly, since the linear decision rules minimize the expected cost, provided that unbiased expected demand forecasts are given.

The more serious drawbacks are the strong need for aggregation, the elaborate estimation procedures that are required to assess the numerical values of the cost coefficients; and the numerical difficulties encountered when the number of decision variables and constraints increase, which limits the model dimensions to a small size.

Computational results (Van dePanne and Bosje [1962]) seem to indicate that decision rules are fairly insensitive to large errors in estimating cost parameters. This is a very attractive property due to the difficulty in providing accurate cost values.

In spite of the encouraging results reported on large savings that have been obtained by applying linear decision rules to actual managerial situations, these techniques have not been adopted by practicing managers. Probably the disadvantages listed outweigh the advantages that linear decision rules have, vis-a-vis LP models. Comparisons made by Kolenda [1970] between HMMS and Hannssmann-Hess type of models rank these two approaches very close in overall efficiency. Given the enormous computational capabilities of LP, this has to result in the more widespread use of linear cost models.

4. LOT SIZE MODELS (FIXED COST MODELS)

Whenever the manufacturing process is characterized by batch-type production operations (as opposed to continuous production), a cost is incurred when setting up the production facilities for a given run. Including the setup cost in the planning process creates many problems. First, every item that generates a setup (or a family of items sharing a common setup) has to be identified and treated independently. This expands the number of variables and constraints so that the dimensions of the model generate a large scale system which can be coped with only by using special computational techniques. Second, the inclusion of setup costs produces a problem of lot size indivisability, since a given batch has to be run incurring a single setup. This introduces integer variables in the model formulation. Finally, setup costs give rise to fixed cost components in the objective function. Moreover, the downtime which is characteristic of every setup operation introduces additional nonlinearities in the constraint set. The resulting large scale, integer, NLP model is hard to resolve computationally. We now review some of the most effective approaches that have been suggested to solve this problem.

4.1 The Uncapacitated Lot Size Model

The standard economic lot size formula, also known as the EOQ (economic order quantity) formula,[3] determines the production amount for an individual item when setup and inventory holding costs identify the cost tradeoffs. This formula does not account for any interaction that exists among the individual items to be scheduled for production. In particular, it ignores the capacity limitations which impose some of the more critical constraints for production planning.

Moreover, the EOQ formula assumes the demand to be constant and known over the planning horizon. When the demand is known but changing during the various time periods of the planning horizon, the EOQ lot size can provide very misleading recommendations. Wagner and Whitin [1958] suggested a DP model for a dynamic version of the economic lot size. We review their approach here because it plays an important role in the capacitated lot size models to be discussed later.

A simplified version of the uncapacitated lot size problem can be described as follows:

Minimize:

$$z = \sum_{t=1}^{T} [s_t \delta(X_t) + c_t I_t]$$

subject to

$$X_t + I_{t-1} - I_t = d_t, \qquad t = 1, \ldots, T$$
$$X_t \geq 0, \qquad t = 1, \ldots, T$$
$$I_t \geq 0, \qquad t = 1, \ldots, T$$

where

$$\delta(X_t) = \begin{cases} 0 & \text{if } X_t = 0 \\ 1 & \text{if } X_t > 0. \end{cases}$$

and as before:

X_t = amount to be produced in period t
I_t = ending inventory at period t
s_t = setup cost in period t
c_t = inventory holding cost in period t
d_t = demand during period t.

Notice that variable production costs are not included in the objective function since they are assumed to be constant throughout the planning horizon. Also, backorders are not allowed. A DP solution to this problem is straightforward. The functional equation that represents the minimum cost policy

[3]For a discussion on the various types of EOQ formulae that have been proposed in the literature, see, for example, Magee and Boodman [1967, Chapter 4].

(including only setup and inventory holding costs) for periods t through $T - 1$ is:

$$f_t(I_{t-1}) = \min_{\substack{X_t \geqslant 0 \\ X_t + I_{t-1} \geqq d_t}} [s_t \delta(X_t) + c_t(X_t + I_{t-1} - d_t) + f_{t+1}(X_t + I_{t-1} - d_t)]$$

In the last period T, the functional equation becomes:

$$f_T(I_{T-1}) = \min_{\substack{X_T \geqq 0 \\ X_T + I_{T-1} = d_T}} [s_T \delta(X_T)]$$

In this DP formulation we have assumed that no inventory is to be left over at the end of the planning horizon; i.e. $I_T = 0$. This assumption can be relaxed easily. A backward induction process can be applied to compute the optimum lot sizes during the planning horizon. However, this is not the most effective way to approach the problem.

In getting an efficient algorithm for this problem, Wagner and Whitin proved four important results about the structure of the optimal policy, assuming no initial inventory; i.e., $I_o = 0$.[4]

(1) There is always an optimal policy such that

$$I_{t-1} X_t = 0, \quad \text{for} \quad t = 1, \ldots, T.$$

This means that costs are never reduced by having incoming stock and producing in the same time.

(2) It is enough to consider optimal policies such that for all t

$$X_t = 0, \text{ or } X_t = \sum_{j=t}^{k} d_j \quad \text{for some } k, \quad t \leqq k \leqq T.$$

This implies that, at any given period, the production is either zero or the sum of consecutive demands for some number of periods into the future. When dealing with a time horizon of T time periods, the total number of production sequences to be considered is 2^{T-1}. These have been called the dominant production sequences. A DP approach requires the analysis of only $T(T + 1)/2$ of these

---

[4]If the initial inventory is not zero, subtract it from the demand requirements in the first period to obtain an adjusted requirement for that period. If the initial inventory exceeds the first period demand, continue with this adjustment process until all the inventory is used up. Then apply the proposed algorithm.

sequences.   This number can be reduced further by applying the following result:

(3) Whenever it is optimal to make $I_t = 0$ for any given period t, periods 1 through t, and $t + 1$ through T can be considered by themselves.

It is advantageous at this point to reformulate the DP approach as a forward process.

The functional equation that characterizes the forward induction procedure can be specified by letting $f(t)$ be the minimal cost program from period 1 to t, then

$$f(t) = \min \left\{ \min_{1 \leqslant j < t} \ [s_j + \sum_{h=j}^{t-1} \sum_{k=h+1}^{t} c_h d_k + f(j-1)] , s_t + f(t-1) \right\} \quad (16)$$

where $f(1) = s_1$, and $f(0) = 0$.

s_j represents the setup cost at period j, and $\displaystyle\sum_{h=j}^{t-1} \sum_{k=h+1}^{t} c_h d_k$ provides the inventory carrying cost from period $j + 1$ to t.   Numerical examples illustrating how to carry out the forward induction procedures are provided in the original reference of Wagner and Whitin [1958].

The last, and most important, result of Wagner and Whitin is the following:

(4) *Planning Horizon Theorem:* If at period t^* the minimum of (16) occurs for $j = t^{**} \leqq t^*$, then in periods $t > t^*$ it is sufficient to consider only $t^{**} \leqq j \leqq t$.   In particular, if $t^* = t^{**}$, then it is sufficient to consider programs such that $X_{t^*} > 0$.

If a forward DP is conducted, these results allow us to reduce the original problem into a succession of smaller problems by identifying periods in which the production orders are positive or, alternatively, in which the inventory levels are zero.

Wagner [1960] expanded this approach to include changing purchasing or manufacturing costs during the multiperiod planning horizon.   Eppen, Gould, and Pashigian [1969] and Zabel [1964] made significant extensions to the planning horizon theorem.   Zangwill [1969] showed how to treat backordering costs and provided a network representation of the problem.   Another approach for the inclusion of backorders was suggested by Elmaghraby and Bawle [1972], who analyzed the uncapacitated problem when ordering must be in batches greater than one, with and without setup costs.

The concept of dominant production sequences has been greatly exploited for computational purposes when dealing with capacitated lot size models.   This is shown in subsequent sections.

4.2 The Capacitated Lot Size Model

The capacitated lot size model deals with a multiitem production planning problem under changing demand requirements during the multiperiod planning horizon. The items are competing for limited capacity, and setup costs become an important element of the total cost to be minimized.

As before, we analyze first the fixed work force problem when only overtime can be added to expand the manpower availability; subsequently we examine the variable work force problem, when hiring and firing are permitted to change the total production rate.

Using the notation presented in the previous pages, a simple version of the fixed work force-capacitated fixed cost model can be expressed as follows:

$$\text{Min } z = \sum_{i=1}^{N} \sum_{t=1}^{T} [s_{it}\delta(X_{it}) + v_{it}X_{it} + c_{it}I_{it}] + \sum_{t=1}^{T} (r_t W_t + o_t O_t) \tag{17}$$

subject to:

$$X_{it} + I_{i,t-1} - I_{it} = d_{it}, \quad t = 1, \ldots, T, \quad i = 1, \ldots, N$$

$$\sum_{i=1}^{N} [a_i\delta(X_{it}) + k_i X_{it}] - W_t - O_t \leq 0, \quad t = 1, \ldots, T \tag{18}$$

$$0 \leq W_t \leq (rm)_t, \quad t = 1, \ldots, T$$

$$0 \leq O_t \leq (om)_t, \quad t = 1, \ldots, T$$

$$X_{it}, I_{it} \geq 0, \quad i = 1, \ldots, N, \quad t = 1, \ldots, T$$

where

$$\delta(X_{it}) = \begin{cases} 0 & \text{if } X_{it} = 0 \\ 1 & \text{if } X_{it} > 0. \end{cases}$$

Most of the comments we made when dealing with the fixed work force-linear cost model are also applicable now and will not be repeated. This model does not allow backorders, although it is easy to incorporate this added feature in the model formulation.

In expression (18) above, the term a_i represents the setup time consumed in preparing a production run for item i. The presence of $\delta(X_{it})$ both in the objective function (17) and in the constraints (18) completely breaks the linearity conditions of our previous models, and makes the computation of this model much more difficult. We now examine some of the methods that have been proposed to solve the model.

(A) Fixed Cost Model

Whenever the down time consumed by the setup operation is negligible, $a_i = 0$ in expression (18) and the lot size fixed work force model becomes a fixed cost LP model, also known as the fixed charge model. Since the objective function of the fixed charge model is concave and the constraint set is convex, the global minimum will occur at an extreme point. However, generally, many local minima also will exist at extreme points; a simplex type algorithm that terminates at a local minimum is not very effective to use.

Several approaches have been suggested to deal with this problem. Exact solution methods can be classified in two different categories: extreme point ranking procedures (Gray [1971], and Murty [1968]), and branch and bound solutions to MIP formulations of the problem (Jones and Soland [1962], and Steinberg [1970]). Exact methods are computationally limited to relatively small size problems and therefore have little practical value at the present. As a result of this limitation, several heuristic approaches have been proposed that generate near-optimal solutions. Generally, these heuristics start by producing a good extreme point solution, and by examining the adjacent extreme points a local minimum is determined. Then a move is made to an extreme point away from this local minimum, and the process is repeated until no further improvement is obtained or after completing a specified number of iterations. Effective heuristics have been provided by Balinski [1961], Cooper and Drebes [1967], Denzler [1969], Rousseau [1973], and Steinberg [1970].

(B) Linear Programming Approach

When the downtime, a_i, required to set up a production run for every item is not negligible, the resulting large scale nonlinear capacitated lot size model becomes extremely hard to solve in a direct way. In response to these computational difficulties, Manne [1958] suggested reformulation of the problem as an LP model. This approach subsequently was refined by Dzielinski, Baker, and Manne [1963], Dzielinski and Gomory [1965], and Lasdon and Terjung [1971].

The approach consists in incorporating setup costs by defining a set of possible production sequences. For a given item i, a production sequence over the planning horizon T is a set of T nonnegative integers; these identify the quantities of item i to be produced at each time period during the planning horizon so that the demand requirements for that item are met. As explained in the uncapacitated lot size model, it is enough to consider 2^{T-1} dominant sequences for each item.

Let us define

X_{ijt} = amount to be produced of item i by means of production sequence j in period t; $i = 1, \ldots, N$; $j = 1, \ldots, J$; $t = 1, \ldots, T$

and as usual, let d_{it} = demand for item i in period t.

To illustrate how these sequences are constructed, assume we have only three time periods. The number of dominant sequences for item i is $2^{3-1} = 4$; these four strategies for a given item i can be defined as follows:

Amounts to be produced at each sequence

Sequence No.	Time period		
	$t = 1$	$t = 2$	$t = 3$
$j = 1$	$X_{i11} = d_{i1} + d_{i2} + d_{i3}$	$X_{i12} = 0$	$X_{i13} = 0$
$j = 2$	$X_{i21} = d_{i1} + d_{i2}$	$X_{i22} = 0$	$X_{i23} = d_{i3}$
$j = 3$	$X_{i31} = d_{i1}$	$X_{i32} = d_{i2} + d_{i3}$	$X_{i33} = 0$
$j = 4$	$X_{i41} = d_{i1}$	$X_{i42} = d_{i2}$	$X_{i43} = d_{i3}$

It is easy to compute the total production, inventory holding and setup costs, t_{ij}, for each sequence. In the above example these costs are the following:

Setup and holding costs for each sequence (t_{ij})

Sequence	t_{ij}
$j = 1$	$t_{i1} = s_{i1} + v_{i1}(d_{i1} + d_{i2} + d_{i3}) + c_{i1}(d_{i2} + d_{i3}) + c_{i2}(d_{i3})$
$j = 2$	$t_{i2} = (s_{i1} + s_{i3}) + v_{i1}(d_{i1} + d_{i2}) + v_{i3}d_{i3} + c_{i1}d_{i2}$
$j = 3$	$t_{i3} = (s_{i1} + s_{i2}) + v_{i1}d_{i1} + v_{i2}(d_{i2} + d_{i3}) + c_{i2}d_{i3}$
$j = 4$	$t_{i4} = (s_{i1} + s_{i2} + s_{i3}) + v_{i1}d_{i1} + v_{i2}d_{i2} + v_{i3}d_{i3}$

In general

$$t_{ij} = \sum_{t=1}^{T} [s_{it}\,\delta(X_{ijt}) + v_{it}X_{ijt} + c_{it}I_{it}]$$

The total labor resources consumed by the production quantities X_{ijt} can be written as:

$$l_{ijt} = a_i\delta(X_{ijt}) + k_i X_{ijt}$$

If we assume, to simplify matters, that we have a prescribed work force at every time period, $(rm)_t$, that we cannot exceed, the fixed work force lot size model can be formulated as follows:

$$\text{Minimize } z = \sum_{i=1}^{N} \sum_{j=1}^{J} t_{ij} \theta_{ij} \qquad (19)$$

subject to

$$\sum_{i=1}^{N} \sum_{j=1}^{J} l_{ijt} \theta_{ij} \leqq (rm)_t, \qquad t = 1, \ldots, T \qquad (20)$$

$$\sum_{j=1}^{J} \theta_{ij} = 1, \qquad i = 1, \ldots, N$$

$$\theta_{ij} \geqq 0, \qquad i = 1, \ldots, N, \quad j = 1, \ldots, J \qquad (21)$$

where

   J = total number of dominant production sequences, and
   θ_{ij} = fraction of the jth production sequence used to produce item i.

Expression (19) states the objective of the model as the minimization of variable production, setup, and inventory holding costs. It is possible to expand the model to include regular and overtime labor costs, shortage costs, and hiring and firing costs. Constraints (20) force the total manpower consumed in the production schedules not to exceed the maximum labor availability at each time period. It also is simple to consider several types of production resources, and to include a variable work force as a decision variable with overtime capabilities (see Dzielinski, Baker and Manne [1963], Dzielinski and Gomory [1965], and Gorenstein [1970], for these model extensions).

Constraints (21) specify that for every item i, the total fractional production must add up to unity, plus the usual nonnegativity requirements on the decision variables. Since, by the very manner in which the various patterns of production in the above table were constructed, it is meaningless to have fractional θ's; the natural impulse is to insist on integer values of θ_{ij}, thus restricting them to 0 or 1. Unfortunately, these integrality constraints on the θ's renders a problem of any realistic size extremely difficult to compute. Worse still, it may result in a suboptimal solution since the optimal schedule may not be among the "pure strategies" represented by the given patterns of production. This is a subtle point which has escaped many researchers in this field. The possible deviation from these patterns is due to the presence of constraints on the available capacity for production.

Fortunately, solving the LP model of Eqs. (19)–(21) usually provides an excellent approximation of the "true" optimum. Since there are $T + N$ constraints in the model, there will be at most $T + N$ positive variables in the optimal LP solution; and at least one of these variables will be associated with each of the N constraints (21). Thus, there could be at most T instances for which more than one θ_{ij} is positive. Clearly, if only one θ_{ij} is positive for a given item i, that value of θ_{ij} should be 1, due to constraints (21). Consequently, whenever N is much larger than T, which is almost always the case in practical applications, the θ_{ij} fractional values are relatively only a few, and are rounded off in some arbitrary manner. The error thus introduced is usually insignificant.

As we have indicated before, it is possible to expand this model to include not only manpower availabilities but also any number, K, of limited resources. When this is the case, the split of production sequences is not significant whenever N (the number of items to be scheduled) is much greater than $K \times T$ (the number of resources times the number of time periods). This condition usually is satisfied in practice.

Regardless of the integrality problems posed by the variables θ_{ij}, the resulting LP is hard to solve by conventional methods. In some situations there might be several thousand items to schedule, and a model with that many rows can be impossible to compute with regular simplex procedures. In addition, each item generates 2^{T-1} dominant production sequences. If $T = 12$, there will be a $2^{12-1} = 2048$ variables for each item; and if there are one thousand items to schedule, the model will have more than two million θ_{ij} variables.

To bypass these difficulties, Dzielinski and Gomory [1965] suggested a Dantzig-Wolfe [1960] decomposition approach where the subproblem led to uncapacitated lot size models of the Wagner-Whitin type. These subproblems, which can be computed quite simply, are used to generate attractive entering production sequences so that there is no need to specify all the θ_{ij} variables from the very beginning.

The decomposition approach, however, has one severe limitation for this type of problem. As it is well known, the decomposition technique finds a near optimum solution relatively fast, but a large number of iterations might be spent in obtaining the optimum. In most applications, it is not very critical to get the final optimum. Lower bounds can be evaluated to determine how good an approximation to the optimum the current solution is, and stopping rules can be designed accordingly. In our problem, however, it is important to obtain the optimum since only then the integrality requirements for the production sequences are satisfied, and a feasible solution to the original problem is found.

To resolve this limitation, Lasdon and Terjung [1971] maintained the column generation procedure suggested by Dzielinski and Gomory (thus bypassing the computational problem introduced by the large number of columns); but instead of defining a decomposition master program, they solved the original LP formulation using generalized upper bounding techniques (Dantzig and Van Slyke [1967]), thereby taking advantage of the structure of the initial model.

We will now explain how the column generation procedure works. Let π_t, $t = 1, \ldots, T$, be the set of dual variables associated with constraints (20), and π_{T+i}, $i = 1, \ldots, N$, be the dual variables associated with the first set of constraints (21). The reduced costs corresponding to problem (19) to (21) are given by the expression

$$\overline{t_{ij}} = t_{ij} - \sum_{t=1}^{T} \pi_t l_{ijt} - \pi_{T+i}.$$

To choose the entering variable we want to find

$$\min_i \min_j \overline{t_{ij}}.$$

By introducing the values of t_{ij} and l_{ijt}, given by their respective expressions and rearranging the terms, the inner minimization becomes

$$\min_j \left[\sum_{t=1}^{T} \left\{ (s_{it} - \pi_t a_i) \delta(X_{ijt}) + (v_{ij} - \pi_t k_i) X_{ijt} + C_{it} I_{it} \right\} \right]. \quad (22)$$

Since $\pi_t \leqslant 0$, the above coefficients are all positive. The problem then involves a minimization of setup, variable manufacturing, and inventory carrying costs so that the production quantities X_{ijt} satisfy the demand requirements for item i over the multiperiod planning horizon. This is the uncapacitated lot size problem that can be resolved by the DP approach of Wagner and Whitin [1958], and Wagner [1960]. In practice, subindex j in expression (22) is somehow irrelevant, since its minimization does not require all the production sequences j to be enumerated. The application of the Wagner-Whitin approach will generate the optimum production schedule for item i at every time period t, which we called X_{ijt}.

To determine which column to enter in the basis, we subtract π_{T+i} from the optimum value of expression (22) corresponding to each item i. The minimum of these quantities identifies the entering column. The new LP problem thus generated is solved by the standard generalized upper bounded techniques.

Gorenstein [1970] used a similar model to support long range production decisions in a tire company. In addition, he linked the output of that model to a short range scheduling plan, and introduced precedence relationships in the production of finished and semifinished tires and their components. An alternative approach to the capacitated fixed cost problem was developed by Kortanek, Sodaro, and Soyster [1968].

Since the Lasdon and Terjung approach constitutes a continuous approximation to an IP problem, it is only applicable when the number of items, N, is much greater than the number of time periods, T. To eliminate this shortcoming, Newson [1971] suggested a heuristic procedure which is independent of column generation techniques and treats the lot size problem as a shortest route problem.

In this model, the work force size also becomes a decision variable. Using the notation defined previously, the model can be formulated as follows:

$$\text{Min } z = \sum_{i=1}^{N} \sum_{t=1}^{T} [s_{it} \, \delta(X_{it}) + v_{it} X_{it} + C_{it} I_{it}] + \sum_{t=1}^{T} (r_t W_t + o_t O_t + h_t H_t + f_t F_t)$$

subject to:

$$X_{it} + I_{i,t-1} - I_{it} = d_{it}, \quad i = 1, \ldots, N, \quad i = 1, \ldots, N; \quad t = 1, \ldots, T$$

$$\sum_{i=1}^{N} [a_i \, \delta(X_{it}) + k_i X_{it}] - W_t - O_t \leqq 0, \qquad t = 1, \ldots, T$$

$$W_t - W_{t-1} - H_t + F_t = 0, \qquad\qquad t = 1, \ldots, T$$

$$-pW_t + O_t \leqq 0, \qquad\qquad\qquad t = 1, \ldots, T$$

$$X_{it}, I_{it} \geqq 0, \quad i = 1, \ldots, N; \qquad t = 1, \ldots, T$$

$$W_t, O_t, H_t, F_t \geqq 0, \qquad\qquad t = 1, \ldots, T$$

where

$$\delta(X_{it}) = \begin{cases} 0 & \text{if } X_{it} > 0 \\ 1 & \text{if } X_{it} = 0. \end{cases}$$

The interpretation of the model should now be straightforward to the reader. One could easily add backorder costs following the procedure suggested in the linear cost-variable work force model.

The solution procedures used to deal with this model are identical to those employed with the lot size-fixed work force model; that is, a fixed cost model is generated whenever the downtime incurred in manufacturing setup (a_i) is negligible; otherwise the LP approximations suggested by Dzielinski and Gomory, or Lasdon and Terjung can be applied.

Newson [1971] proposed to attack the problem in two stages. The first stage deals with the detailed scheduling decision for each individual item over the multiperiod planning horizon, neglecting the manpower constraints. For a given product i, this stage can be formulated as follows:

$$\text{Min } z_i = \sum_{t=1}^{T} [s_{it} \, \delta(X_{it}) + v_{it} X_{it} + C_{it} I_{it}]$$

subject to

$$X_{it} + I_{i,t-1} - I_{it} = d_{it}, \quad t = 1, \ldots, T$$

$$X_{it}, I_{it} \geqq 0, \qquad\qquad t = 1, \ldots, T.$$

After this model is solved for each of the N items, the capacity required by the detailed schedule for each time period t is computed as:

$$\hat{P}_t = \sum_{i=1}^{N} [a_i \delta(X_{it}) + k_i X_{it}], \qquad t = 1, \ldots, T.$$

Then the second stage model dealing with the aggregate capacity decision is solved. The model is defined as follows:

$$\text{Min } z(\hat{P}) = \sum_{t=1}^{T} (r_t W_t + o_t O_t + h_t H_t + f_t F_t)$$

subject to

$$W_t + O_t - \hat{P}_t \geq 0, \qquad t = 1, \ldots, T$$

$$W_t - W_{t-1} - H_t + F_t = 0, \qquad t = 1, \ldots, T$$

$$-pW_t + O_t \leq 0, \qquad t = 1, \ldots, T$$

$$W_t, O_t, H_t, F_t \geq 0, \qquad t = 1, \ldots, T.$$

Newson suggested a heuristic iterative process that relates two models sequentially until a terminal criterion is met.

4.3 Advantages and Disadvantages of Lot Size Models

The primary advantage of these models is that they incorporate the scheduling issues associated with lot size indivisabilities into the capacity planning decisions. This, however, creates the need for a great deal of detailed information throughout the planning horizon, which is costly to gather and to process.

An alternative approach to coordinate the aggregate capacity planning and detailed scheduling decisions is represented by the construction of hierarchical planning systems (Hax and Meal [1975]).

5. GENERAL COST MODELS

The linear, quadratic, and lot size models we have analyzed, although appropriate for a great number of applications, impose several restrictions on the nature of the cost functions to be used. Some authors have argued that realistic industrial situations tend to exhibit cost functions which are nonlinear and discontinuous and, therefore, cannot be treated by any of the methods outlined previously. Buffa and Taubert [1972] report the following factors as mainly responsible for this cost behavior: supply and demand interactions, manufacturing or purchasing economies of scale, learning curve effects, quantum jumps in costs with addition of a new shift, technological and productivity changes, and labor slowdowns.

Several aggregate capacity planning methods have been suggested which attempt to be more responsive to the complexities introduced by the specific decision environment. Generally, these more realistic approaches do not guarantee that an optimum solution will be found. They can be classified roughly according to the following categories:

—Nonlinear analytical models, which provide a mathematical treatment of general nonlinear cost structures;
—Heuristic decision rules, which attempt to bring in the decision maker's intuition of the problem under consideration by incorporating "rules of thumb" that contribute to the solution of the problem;
—Search decision rules, which consist of the application of hill climbing techniques to the response surface defined by a nonlinear cost function and the problem constraints; and
—Simulation decision rules, which represent the problem under consideration by a set of programmed instructions. The decision maker is able to test various approaches in an iterative fashion, where the outcome of each run suggests what the subsequent run might be. Simulation is particularly suitable to treat the uncertainties that can be present in a decision.

We now review the major contributions that have been proposed in each of these catagories.

5.1 Nonlinear Analytical Models

During the last twenty years, a significant amount of work has been devoted to the analytical treatment of production planning models with general nonlinear cost functions. Much of this work has attempted to decompose the multiperiod planning problem by using DP principles. Due to the inherent complexities of the problem under consideration and the computational limitations of DP, these models seldomly can be implemented to support period-to-period planning decisions. However, they are effective in analyzing qualitative properties of the optimum solutions. Most of the models to be discussed in this section will be single product models.

Two types of single product models are covered in the literature. The first type does not penalyze changes in the production rate, and can be formulated as follows:

$$\text{Min } z = \sum_{t=1}^{T} [v_t(X_t) + c_t(I_t)] \tag{23}$$

subject to

$$X_t + I_{t-1} - I_t = d_t, \qquad t = 1, \ldots, T \tag{24}$$

$$\underline{I_t} \leq I_t \leq \overline{I_t}, \qquad t = 1, \ldots, T \tag{25}$$

$$\underline{X_t} \leq X_t \leq \overline{X_t}, \qquad t = 1, \ldots, T. \tag{26}$$

$v(X)$ and $c(I)$ are, respectively, the nonlinear production and inventory carrying cost functions. $\underline{I_t}$, $\overline{I_t}$, and $\underline{X_t}$, $\overline{X_t}$ are lower and upper bounds imposed on the total amount of inventory and production at every time period. By choosing $I_t = 0$ for all t, all backlogging is eliminated. Optimum solutions to this model can be obtained by using standard DP methods.

The second type of model introduces production change costs which depend both on the current as well as the past production levels. In this case, the objective function (23) is substituted by the following expression:

$$\text{Min } z = \sum_{t=1}^{T} \left[v_t(X_t) + c_t(I_t) + p_t(X_{t-1}, X_t) \right].$$

The production change cost function p is assumed to be zero whenever $X_{t-1} = X_t$, and nonnegative otherwise.

A number of different functional forms have been proposed to characterize the production change costs (Johnson and Montgomery [1974]):

$$p_t(X_{t-1}, X_t) = p_t |X_t - X_{t-1}| \tag{27}$$

$$p_t(X_{t-1}, X_t) = p_t(X_t - X_{t-1})^+ + p_t'(X_t - X_{t-1})^- \tag{28}$$

$$p_t(X_{t-1}, X_t) = p_t(X_t - X_{t-1})^2 \tag{29}$$

$$p_t(X_{t-1}, X_t) = \begin{cases} p_t, & \text{if } X_t > 0 \text{ and } X_{t-1} = 0 \\ 0, & \text{otherwise} \end{cases} \tag{30}$$

$$p_t(X_{t-1}, X_t) = \begin{cases} p_t, & \text{if } X_t > 0 \text{ and } X_{t-1} = 0 \\ p_t', & \text{if } X_t = 0 \text{ and } X_{t-1} > 0 \\ 0, & \text{otherwise.} \end{cases} \tag{31}$$

Functions (27) and (28) can be treated as linear functions (see, for example, Hanssmann and Hess [1960]). Expression (29) is a simple quadratic convex cost; (30) defines a start-up cost model; (31) includes start-up as well as shut-down costs (Sobel [1970b], and Zangwill [1966c]).

Models with production change costs do not lend themselves to be treated by standard DP techniques since they define two state variables: X_t and I_t. This creates serious computational difficulties.

It is important to recognize that constraints (24)-(26) can be represented by the following network formulation:

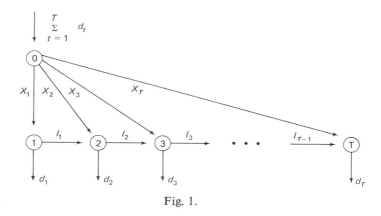

Fig. 1.

Nodes $1, 2, \ldots, T$ represent the various time periods in the planning horizon. Node 0 is an artificial source to provide a flow balance condition. Zangwill [1969] suggested this network representation and extended it to allow for backlogging. The network analogy has generated several important contributions to the production planning problem (Kalymon [1972], Veinott [1969], Zangwill [1968, 1969].

To facilitate an organized discussion of nonlinear analytical models we have classified them into three broad categories: convex cost models, concave cost models, and feedback and optimum control models.

Convex Cost Models. In practice, convex cost functions do not create problems. These cost functions can be approximated, to any desired degree of accuracy, by means of piecewise linear functions and the resulting production planning problem can be solved by LP procedures. Direct analytical treatment of convex cost models, however, provides important insights with regard to the nature of the optimum decision rules.

Veinot [1964] considered the problem of determining the optimum production quantities of a single product over a finite number of time periods so as to minimize convex production and inventory costs [expression (23)] subject to the constraints represented by expressions (24)-(26). When the total cost function is strictly convex, the optimum production quantities are unique. Veinott performed a parametric analysis to study the changes on the optimum production levels resulting from variations in demand requirements, and inventory and production bounds. His findings can be summarized as follows:

(1) The optimum production in a given period is a nondecreasing function of:
—the demand requirements in any given period $(d_1, d_2, \ldots, d_T)$
—the upper and lower production capacity bounds in the given period $(\overline{X_t}, \underline{X_t})$, and
—the upper and lower inventory bounds in the given period and all succeeding period $(\overline{I_k}, \underline{I_k},$ for $k = t, t+1, \ldots, T)$.
(2) the optimum production in a given period is a non-increasing function of:
—the upper and lower production capacity bounds in every other period $(\overline{X_k}, \underline{X_k},$ for $k = 1, 2, \ldots, t-1, t+1, \ldots, T)$, and
—the upper and lower inventory bounds in any preceeding period $(\overline{I_k}, \underline{I_k},$ for $k = 1, 2, \ldots, t-1)$.

Veinott exploited these results to develop simple and intuitive computational procedures for finding optimum production schedules for a range of parameter values. Karush [1958] suggested a DP approach to this problem.

Johnson [1957] studies a special case of this problem where no backlogging is allowed, no storage limits are permitted, and inventory carrying costs are linear. For this case, Johnson proved a very simple optimum rule: requirements should be satisfied in order of their due dates by the cheapest available means.

Modigliani and Hohn [1955] analyzed the problem for a convex and non-decreasing production cost function and linear inventory holding cost without production or storage limits. In addition, they assumed that production costs were unchanged for each period of the total time horizon. The problem then can be stated as follows:

$$\text{Min } z = \sum_{t=1}^{T} [v(X_t) + cI_t] \tag{32}$$

$$X_t + I_{t-1} - I_t = d_t, \qquad t = 1, \ldots, T \tag{33}$$

$$I_t \geqq 0, \quad X_t \geqq 0, \qquad t = 1, \ldots, T.$$

The derivative of $v(X_t)$, to be denoted $v'(X_t)$, is assumed to be nonnegative, monotone increasing, and continuous. In order to characterize the properties of the optimum solution to this problem, it is helpful to view the cumulative production schedules, $P_t = \sum_{k=1}^{t} X_k$ and the cumulative demand requirements, $D_t = \sum_{k=1}^{t} d_k$, as a piecewise linear functions of time formed by straight lines joining adjacent. points. Also, let K_t be the upper convex envelope of the cumulative demand requirements, D_t, and let $P_o = D_o = K_o = 0$.

If P_t^* denotes an optimum production plan, the following properties can be proved (Modigliani and Hohn [1955], Klein [1961]):

(1) $P_T^* = D_T$
(2) For any $t = 1, \ldots, T$, if $K_t = D_t$, then $P_t^* = D_t$. The periods in which this property holds are called *planning horizons*
(3) If D_t is concave, then $P_t^* = D_t$, $1 \leq t \leq T$.
(4) $D_t^* \leq K_t$, $t = 1, \ldots, T$.
(5) If D_t is convex, then P_t^* is convex.
(6) A *fundamental solution* to the problem is the set of production sequences X_t that minimizes the objective function (32), subject only to constraint (33). The fundamental solution satisfies the following condition on the marginal costs:

$$v'(X_{t+1}) = v'(X_1) + tc$$

Modigliani and Hohn proposed an algorithm based on fundamental solutions that can be implemented graphically. However, the qualitative properties associated with planning horizons are the most important results of Modigliani and Hohn's work. They proved that the total planning interval can be partitioned into subintervals, defined by planning horizons, within which the optimal plan is independent of requirements and costs during other periods. Furthermore, if inventory holding costs are negligible, a constant rate of production within each interval is optimum.

There are important practical implications that can be drawn. In production planning, when decisions are affected by strong seasonalities, the relevant horizon is unlikely to extend beyond the period of seasonally high sales of the current cycle, unless sales over the next seasonal cycle tend to be substantially higher than in the current one. Moreover, if the relevant horizon extends beyond the current cycle, this extension is likely to proceed by whole cycles.

Charnes, Cooper and Mellon [1955] extended the Modigliani-Hohn results for slightly more general production cost structures, and indicated that more than one product could be included in the model provided that suitable surrogates for total costs be utilized instead of output (for example, labor hours).

Klein [1961] combined the works of Modigliani and Hohn, and Hoffman and Jacobs [1954] to introduce piecewise linear costs associated with period-to-period fluctuations in the production rate. In an earlier work, Klein [1957] offered some insightful comments on the general shape of the optimum production schedules under a variety of costs and requirements conditions.

More recently, Lippman, et al. [1967a] have studied the form of optimum policies for a single product problem assuming convex production costs, V-shaped production smoothing costs, and increasing inventory costs. In a subsequent paper [1967b] the authors proposed a computational algorithm when the costs functions are linear and demand is either monotone increasing or decreasing. Yuan [1967] extended the algorithm when production costs are convex and demand requirements are arbitrary.

Concave Cost Models. Concave costs can result from setup charges, discounting, and efficiencies of scale in the production process. Since these situations occur frequently in practice, the study of production planning under concave cost functions has attracted significant attention in the past.

Let us concentrate first on the uncapacitated single product concave cost problem, ignoring production change costs. This problem can be formulated as

$$\text{Min } z = \sum_{t=1}^{T} [v_t(X_t) + c_t(I_t)]$$

subject to

$$X_t + I_{t-1} - I_t = d_t, \qquad t = 1, \ldots, T$$
$$X_t \geq 0, \qquad t = 1, \ldots, T$$

If backorders are not allowed, constraints

$$I_t \geq 0, \qquad t = 1, \ldots, T$$

should be added.

Zangwill [1966b] proved that it can be assumed without loss of generality that $I_o = I_T = 0$. Several algorithms proposed to solve the problem assume this condition.

The minimum of a concave function subject to linear constraints occurs at an extreme point of the convex set determined by the linear constraints. Concave cost functions could be minimized, therefore, by performing an exhaustive analysis of the extreme points of the constraint set. However, complete enumeration is seldom feasible for the general problem. Luckily, the optimum solution satisfies some important properties that can be exploited to develop effective DP approaches to this problem.

When no backorders are allowed the optimum solution is such that (Wagner and Whitin [1958]):

$$X_t I_{t-1} = 0, \qquad t = 1, \ldots, T.$$

This result was expanded for the backordering case (Zangwill [1969], Veinott [1969]) where the optimum solution satisfies the following conditions:

(1) $I_{t-1}^+ > 0$ implies $X_t = 0$,

(2) $X_t > 0$ implies $I_t^- = 0$, and

(3) $I_{t-1}^+ > 0$ implies $I_t^- = 0$.

These properties, together with the concepts of dominant schedules and planning horizons (see section 4.1), have played a fundamental role in the analysis of concave cost models.

A specially important class of concave cost production planning problems is represented by the lot size problem, where the objective function is characterized by setup costs and linear variable production and inventory costs. This problem has been discussed extensively in section 4 and it will not be treated here. In particular, section 4.1 considered the single product uncapacitated problem and described forward and backward DP algorithms to solve that problem. These dynamic approaches can be expanded easily to the general concave cost function (Johnson and Montgomery [1974], pages 212-224).

Zangwill [1966b] suggested a backward DP algorithm for a single product problem with or without backlogging. Backlogs are assumed to be filled at most α period after the scheduled delivery date. This condition can be expressed as follows:

$$I_t \geq - \sum_{k=t-\alpha+1}^{t} d_k,$$

where $d_k = 0$ for $k \leq 0$. If $\alpha = 0$, no backlogging is allowed. If $\alpha > T$, backlogging becomes unrestricted since the time horizon is limited to T time periods.

Zangwill considered concave production costs and piecewise concave inventory cost, allowing for a discontinuity in the origin so as to differentiate between backlogging and inventory carrying costs. These results were expanded by Zangwill [1966a] to include multiple facilities in parallel and in series. The lot size problem with multiple facilities was treated as a network problem by Zangwill [1969], and Kalymon [1972]. Kalymon analyzed the case of arborescence-structured production systems, in which each facility requires input from a unique immediate predecessor. A general discussion of the network approach for single product concave cost models is given by Zangwill [1968]. This approach can be extended to multiple product single source models.

Veinott [1969], using the characterization of extreme points of Leontief substitution systems, presented a unified theory to deal with single product concave cost problems, and extended Zangwill's results to an arborescence multiechelon structure.

Adding capacity constraints to the concave cost model

$$X_t \leq \overline{X_t}, \quad t = 1, \ldots, T$$

creates serious computational difficulties in the DP algorithms since these conditons break the structure of the optimum solution.

Florian and Klein [1971] studied the capacitated single product concave cost case under no backordering, and when backordering is limited to at most α periods. They analyzed the properties to develop a DP-shortest route algorithm for problems in which the production capacities are the same in every period. Florian and Robillard [1971] proposed a branch and bound procedure to solve the capacitated network problem with concave costs, which can be applied to this production planning problem.

Some work has been devoted to study the single commodity production planning problem, including concave production costs, concave inventory costs, and piecewise concave costs of changing the production level from period to period. Zangwill [1966c] analyzed the case of no backordering and nondecreasing demand requirements, i.e., $d_t \leqq d_{t+1}$, $t = 1, \ldots, T$. He studied the properties of the optimum solution under these conditions, and proposed algorithms for special cost structures. Sobel [1970b] made a similar analysis of the problem with smoothing start-up and shutdown costs.

Optimum Control and Feedback Models. Two important additional issues regarding production planning decisions have been studied by means of general cost analytical models. These are: extensions of production planning models to continuous time, and stability conditions of the suggested decision rules. The basic concepts that have been applied in dealing with these issues are the Pontryagin's optimum principle (Pontryagin, et al. [1962]) and feedback and servomechanism theory (Holt, et al. [1960, Chapter 19], Forrester [1961], and Simon [1952]). We will review now briefly the implications of this work.

Several approaches have been proposed in the literature to deal with aggregate production planning through continuous time. As with the previous analytical models we have examined, these approaches generally do not lead to practical computational procedures. They require a high level of aggregation (normally consisting of single product models), and their usefulness relies primarily on the characterization of the structure of optimal policies. Continuous time models are important in applications that involve high-speed control and where dynamic responses need to be examined.

One of the first studies dealing with a continuous time production model was proposed by Arrow, Karlin, and Scarf [1958, Chapter 7]. They suggested a continuous formulation to the problem of balancing inventory and production costs. If we denote by:

$I(t)$ = inventory level at time t
$X(t)$ = production rate at time t
$d(t)$ = demand requirements at time t
$v(X)$ = production cost associated with production rate X
$c(I)$ = inventory cost associated with inventory level I.

The problem can be formulated as follows:

$$\text{Min} \int_0^t \{v[X(t)] + c[I(t)]\} dt,$$

subject to

$$I(t) = I(O) + \int_0^t X(t) dt - \int_0^t d(t) dt.$$

An equivalent statement of this constraint is

$$\frac{dI(t)}{dt} = X(t) - d(t).$$

If no shortages are allowed, the following constraint should be added

$$I(t) \geq 0.$$

Arrow, Karlin, and Scarf studied this problem assuming linear inventory hold-ing costs, and production rate costs that are proportional to the rate of change for upward movements and zero for downward movements. They analyzed the properties of the optimum solution for various forms of the demand functions.

Hwang and Fan [1966], and Hwang, Fan and Erickson [1967] applied Pon-tryagin's optimum principle to the continuous production problem. In the production planning context, the optimum control actions correspond to the optimum level of the production quantities and the state variables correspond to the inventory levels. The problem can be stated as follows:

$$\text{Min} \int_0^t \{v[X(t) - X^*]^2 + c[I(t) - I^*]^2\} dt,$$

subject to

$$\frac{dI(t)}{dt} = X(t) - d(t).$$

In the objective function production and inventory costs have been approxi-mated by a quadratic expression. X^* and I^* are production and inventory targets assumed to be known and constant.

The application of Pontryagin's principle produces the following optimum solution to the problem:

$$I(t) = A_1 e^{\lambda t} + A_2 e^{-\lambda t} + [I(t)]_p$$

$$X(t) = A_1 \lambda e^{\lambda t} - A_2 e^{-\lambda t} + \frac{dI(t)_p}{dt} + d(t),$$

where $\lambda^2 = \dfrac{c}{v}$, A_1 and A_2 are to be determined by initial conditions, and $I(t)p$ is a particular solution to the equations to be decided by the forms and for the values of I^* and d (Hwang, Fan, and Erickson [1967]).

Nelson [1966] applied Pontryagin's principle to obtain necessary and sufficient conditions for a problem of manpower assignment in a labor and machine constrained production system.

Concepts such as feedback, lagged responses, types of control devices, and stability of the production system over time play a fundamental role in the design and operation of on-going production planning systems. Servomechanism theory provides the basis for a formal analysis of these concepts in the production environment. Holt and Simon [1954] and Hanssmann [1962, pp. 132–136] proved that the production rules derived by differentiating a quadratic cost expression can generate a very unstable system, creating unacceptable fluctuations in production and inventory levels unless demand forecasts during the planning horizon are perfect. Vassian [1955] proposed ways to construct stable feedback rules for this situation, and Holt and Simon [1954], and Simon [1952], indicated how the unstable rules can suggest the definition of stable classes of rules. However, as Hanssmann indicated, there appears to be no general theory available today to provide the practioner with a complete understanding of the stability of a proposed set of decision rules. This is particularly valid whenever external forecasts are introduced in the production planning model. At the present time, simulation seems to be the only way to explore exhaustively the degree of stability of the production planning decison rules.

For further discussion on this subject, the reader is referred to Holt, et al. [1960, Chapter 19].

5.2 Heuristic Decision Rules

Perhaps the most important attempt to incorporate management behavior in a systematic fashion to the aggregate capacity planning problem is Bowman's management coefficient approach [1963]. Bowman suggested that managers tend to determine production rates, inventory levels, and work force levels in a way which is responsive to the relevant costs that affect those decisions. However, they tend to overreact to the daily pressures of their work, occasionally creating expensive and erratic decisions which vary from their average pattern of past behavior. Moreover, since most cost functions exhibit a flat shape around the optimum, small deviations from the optimum are not going to generate heavy penalties.

From this, Bowman concluded that a decision rule with mean coefficients estimated from management's past performance should produce better results than those which actually occurred, and better results than those generated from analytical studies.

The actual structure of the decision rule to use can be suggested from analytical considerations like the linear decision rules obtained from quadratic cost functions; by intuitive reasoning; or by a combination of both. Bowman suggested the following example of a production scheduling rule:

$$P_t = \sum_{i=t}^{t+T-1} a_i S_i + x(P_{t-1} - S_t) + y(I_N - I_{t-1})$$

where

P_t = production scheduled in period t
S_t = sales forecast in period t
x, y = smoothing constants $(0 \leqq x \leqq 1), (0 \leqq y \leqq 1)$
I_N = "normal" inventory
I_{t-1} = ending inventory at period $t - 1$
a_i = weighting coefficient for sales forecast $S_i, a_t > a_{t+1} > \cdots > a_{t+T-1}$
T = planning horizon.

The numerical values of the coefficients a_i, x, and y are obtained not by analytical methods (as in the HMMS models) or by simulation techniques, but by performing regression analysis on past management behavior.

Bowman reported encouraging results by comparing the performance of his approach against linear decision rules and actual past costs in four industries.

5.3 Search Decision Rules

Jones [1967] combined a heuristic approach, defining the nature of the decision rules, and a search approach to compute the coefficients of the decision rules, and he developed a method for aggregate capacity planning that he called Parametric Production Planning. He started by postulating the existence of two linear decision rules to address work force level and production level decisions.

The work force decision rule takes the form of a smoothing expression:

$$W_t = W_{t-1} + A(W_D - W_{t-1})$$

where:

W_{t-1} = current work force level
W_t = planned work force level for the upcoming period
W_D = desired work force level to meet upcoming demand forecast
A = coefficient determining the fraction of the difference in the planned and current work force to be realized.

The desired work force W_D is expressed as a weighted sum of the work force required to meet future sales during the planning horizon, T.

$$W_D = \sum_{i=1}^{T} b_i K(S_{t+i-1}),$$

where

b_i = weighting coefficient for sales forecast S_{t+i-1}
$K(S_t)$ = number of workers required to produce S_t units at minimum cost.

After experimenting with several weighting functions, Jones suggested the following expression to determine values of the b_i coefficients:

$$b_i = \frac{B^i}{\sum_{i=1}^{T} B^i},$$

where

B = coefficient between 0 and 1 that determine the relative weight to be given to future forecasts.

Note that all the b_i coefficients, $i = 1, \ldots, T$, are expressed as a function of a single parameter B.

Moreover, Jones included a term to prevent inconsistencies in inventory depletion or buildup. Jones suggested the following corrective term to be added to the work force decision rule:

$$b_i K(I_t^* - I_{t-1}),$$

where

I_t^* = optimal inventory level at the end of the upcoming period (to be computed externally to the model).

The resulting work force decision rule becomes:

$$W_t = W_{t-1} + A\left[\sum_{i=1}^{T} b_i K(S_{t+i-1}) - W_{t-1} + b_1 K(I_t^* - I_{t-1})\right].$$

The production decision rule is similar to the work force rules, except that the production rates are expressed in production units rather than in number of workers:

$$P_t = K^{-1}(W_t) + C\left[\sum_{i=1}^{T} d_i S_{t+i-1} - K^{-1}(W_t) + d_1 (I_t^* - I_{t-1})\right],$$

where

$K^{-1}(W_t)$ = number of units that can be produced by W_t workers at minimum cost

C = coefficient between 0 and 1 indicating the fraction of the desired production increase or decrease to be achieved

d_i = weighting coefficient for sales forcast S_{t+i-1} .

The d_i coefficients are defined by an expression similar to the one used for the b_i coefficient; i.e.,

$$d_i = \frac{D^i}{\sum_{i=1}^{T} D^i} .$$

The numerical values of the four coefficients A, B, C, and D are obtained by applying search techniques over a five dimensional space determined by the firm's profitability and the four parameters. The profitability is determined by taking into consideration the general cost structure relevant to the production rate and work force decisions.

There are a large number of different search techniques available for optimization purposes. An extensive coverage of these techniques has been reported by Wilde [1964]. Among them the one that seems most promising is the Direct Search procedures developed by Hooke and Jeeves [1961]. Jones suggested that the response surface determined by the four coefficients and the associated profitability measure is unimodal, shallow, and smooth—highly desirable attributes for search techniques to be applied. Jones reported some encouraging results after testing the performance of his approach.

Another important application of search to aggregate capacity planning was developed by Taubert [1968]. There are some basic differences between Taubert and Jones' approaches. Taubert searches on the values of production rates, work force and inventory levels during each time period, while Jones searches only on the values of four coefficients (A, B, C, and D). The dimensionality of Taubert's search depends on the number of time periods contained in the planning horizon, which creates more computational difficulties.

Taubert suggests also the possibility of combining search with branch and bound procedures by partitioning the set of feasible solutions, using branch and bound methods, into simpler aggregate scheduling bounding problems that can be solved by applying search techniques. This approach, attractive in its potential, has not yet been tested. Another simple application of search to aggregate capacity planning was done by Goodman [1973].

5.4 Simulation Decision Rules

For a long time simulation has been recognized as an important modeling tool to deal with situations where analytical models either become computationally infeasible or provide a too simplified representation of a real world problem.[5] Vergin [1966] developed a general purpose simulator that is able to capture some of the special conditions that are present in practical scheduling problems that, by necessity, have been ignored in the analytical approaches to the capacity planning problem. The simulation can be adjusted to incorporate special conditions of a particular firm.

The simulation process starts with an initial schedule which is suggested by experience or represents the current conditions of the firm. An objective function, which has no restrictions in terms of its structure, is used to evaluate the performance of each schedule. A change is introduced in employment levels, overtime, inventories, subcontracting, etc., until a local minimum is achieved.

Vergin conducted a study on three manufacturing firms affected by strong seasonalities and reported a much better performance of simulation schedules against both operating schedules and linear decision rules schedules.

5.5 Advantages and Disadvantages of General Cost Models

One of the greatest advantages of the general cost models we have surveyed is the added realism they are capable of introducing to reflect more accurately the production planning environment, including uncertainties and special cost structure and constraints. In addition, they are more closely associated with the actual decision process, which makes them more acceptable by managers and easier to explain and justify.

However, these advantages have a price. Usually the models are expensive to develop and to run, and the computational procedures used to solve them seldom guarantee overall optimization. Some of the models require a high degree of aggregation; this creates problems of implementation when decisions need to be disaggregated at the lower levels. Moreover, general cost models do not lend themselves to handling a large number of interactive constraints, which easily can be managed by LP methods.

Analytical models are helpful in determining qualitative properties of the optimum solutions, but seldom generate practical algorithmic procedures.

Lee and Khumawala [1974] tested, in a practical environment, the performance of the Linear Decision Rule model against Bowman's Management

---

[5]For good references on simulation see Emshoff and Sisson [1970], and Naylor et al. [1966].

Coefficient Model, Jones' Parametric Production Planning Model, and Taubert's Search Decision Rule. They concluded that the Search Decision Rule clearly outperforms the other three models evaluated, and they provide a synthesis for implementing aggregate capacity planning models.

6. INTEGRATING THE PRODUCTION PROCESS

Economists define production as the process by which goods and services are created. In more specific terms, production can be defined as the process of converting raw materials into finished products. Of course, the terms "raw materials" and "finished products" are relative, since what constitutes a finished product for one industry, could be the raw material for another firm. An effective management of the production process should provide the finished products in appropriate quantities, at the desired times, of the required quality, and at reasonable costs.

6.1   A Framework for Production Decision Making

Production management encompasses a large number of decisions that affect several organizational echelons. To understand the role of OR in supporting those decisions it is helpful to classify them according to the taxanomy proposed by Anthony [1965] regarding strategic planning, tactical planning, and operations control (Hax [1976]):

Strategic Planning: Facilities Design. Strategic planning is mostly concerned with the establishment of managerial policies and with the development of the necessary resources the enterprise needs to satisfy its external requirements in a manner consistent with its specific goals. In the area of production management, the most important strategic decisions have to do with the design of the production facilities, involving major capital investments for the development of new capacity and the expansion of existing capacity. These decisions include the determination of location and size for new plants, the acquisition of new equipment, and the design of working centers within each plant. Other decisions, which require strong coordination with marketing, are the selection of new products, and the design of the logistics system (including warehouse location and capacity, transportation means, etc.)

These decisions are extremely important because, to a great extent, they are responsible for maintaining the competitive capabilities of the firm, determining its rate of growth, and, eventually, defining its success or failure. An essential characteristic of these strategic decisions is that they have long lasting effects, thus forcing long planning horizons in their analysis. This in turn, forces the recognition of the impact of uncertainties and risk attitudes in the decision making process. This imposes some problems for the proper use of mathematical programming models which, except for parametric analyses, do not allow for uncertainties to be properly handled.

Moreover, investments in new facilities and expansions of existing capacities are resolved at fairly high managerial levels, and are affected by information which is both external and internal to the firm. Thus, any form of rational analysis of these decisions has necessarily a very broad scope, requiring information to be processed in a very aggregated form to allow for all the dimensions of the problem to be included and to prevent top managers from being distracted by unnecessary operational details.

Tactical Planning: Aggregate Production Planning. Once the physical facilities have been decided upon, the basic problem to be resolved is the effective allocation of resources (e.g., production, storage and distribution capacities, work force availabilities, financial and managerial resources, etc.) to satisfy demand and technological requirements, taking into account the costs and revenues associated with the operation of the production and distribution process. When dealing with several plants, with many distribution centers, regional and local warehouses, with products requiring complex multistage fabrication and assembly processes, affected by strong randomness and seasonalities in their demand patterns, these decisions are far from simple. They usually involve the consideration of a medium range time horizon, divided into several periods, and the aggregation of the production items into product families. Typical decisions to be made within this context are utilization of regular and overtime work force, allocation of aggregated capacity resources to product families, accumulation of seasonal inventories, definition of distribution channels and selection of transportation and transshipment alternatives. This chapter dealt exclusively with model approaches to support aggregate production planning.

Operations Control: Detailed Production Scheduling. After making an aggregated allocation of capacity among product families, it is necessary to deal with the day-to-day operational and scheduling decisions which require the complete disaggregation of the information generated at higher levels into the details consistent with the managerial procedures followed in daily activities. Typical decisions at this level are the assignment of customer orders to individual machines, the sequencing of these orders in the work shop, inventory accounting and inventory control activities, dispatching, expediting and processing of orders, vehicular scheduling, etc.

6.2   The Need for a Hierarchical Decision Making System

To deal with these three distinct levels of decisions one has to recognize several complexities. First, the investment, location, allocation, and scheduling decisions cannot be made in isolation because they interact strongly among one another; therefore, an integrated approach is required if one wants to avoid the problems of suboptimization. Second, this approach, although essential, cannot be made without decomposing the elements of the problem in some way, within the content of a hierarchical system that links higher level decisions with lower level ones in an effective manner, and in which decisions that are made at higher levels provide constraints for lower level decision making. This hierarchical approach recognizes the distinct characteristics of the type of management participation, the scope of the decision, the level of aggregation of the required information, and the time framework in which the decision is to be made. In our opinion, it would be a serious mistake to attempt to deal with all these decisions at once, via a single mathematical model. Even if the computer and methodological capabilities could allow the solution of large detailed integrated production model, which is clearly not the case today, that approach is inappropriate because it is not responsive to the management needs at each level of the organization, and would prevent the interactions between models and managers at each organization echelon.

In designing a system to support the overall production management decisions it is imperative, therefore, to identify ways in which the decision process can be partitioned, to select adequate models to deal with the individual decisions at each hierarchical level, to design linking mechanisms for the transferring of the higher level results to the lower hierarchical levels which includes means to disaggregate information, and to provide quantitative measures to evaluate the resulting deviations from optimal performance at each level. Some suggestions on how to implement such an approach are provided in Hax [1974a].

Several hierarchical systems have been reported in the literature to deal with production decisions. Particularly, Hax [1973] describes an application for a continuous manufacturing process, Hax and Meal [1975] address the use of hierarchical systems in a batch processing environment, and Armstrong and Hax [1974], and Shwimer [1972] analyze an application for a job shop activity.

Some limited work has been conducted to integrate the production management process with the remaining managerial functional areas (e.g. marketing, finance, etc.). For examples of this type of work the reader is referred to Damon and Schram [1972], Starr [1972], and Thomas [1971].

Part of this work was supported by the Office of Naval Research under contract N00014-67-A-0204-0076.

REFERENCES

1. Anthony, R. N., *Planning and Control Systems: A Framework for Analysis*, Harvard University Graduate School of Business Administration, Boston (1965).

2. Antosiewicz, H., and A. J. Hoffman, "A Remark on the Smoothing Problem," *Management Sci.* **1**: 92–95 (1954).

3. Armstrong, R. J., and A. C. Hax, "A Hierarchical Approach for a Naval Tender Job Shop Design," Operations Res. Center, MIT (September 1974).

4. Arrow, K. J., T. H. Harris, and J. Marschak, "Optimal Inventory Policy," *Econometrica* **19**: 250–272 (1951).

5. ———, S. Karlin, and H. Scarf, *Studies in the Mathematical Theory of Inventory and Production*, Stanford University Press, (1958).

6. Balinski, M. L., "Fixed Cost Transportation Problem," *Nav. Res. Log. Quart.* **8**: 41–54 (1961).

7. Bergstrom, G. L., and B. E. Smith, "Multi-Item Production Planning - An Extension of the HMMS Rules," *Management Sci.* **16**: B614–B629 (1970).

8. Bowman, E. H., "Production Scheduling by the Transportation Method of Linear Programming," *Operations Res.* **4**: 100–103 (1956).

9. ———, "Consistency and Optimality in Managerial Decision Making," *Management Sci.* **9**: 310–321 (1963).

10. Brown, R. G., *Decision Rules for Inventory Management*, Holt, Rinehart and Winston, New York (1967).

11. Buffa, E. S., and W. H. Taubert, *Production-Inventory Systems: Planning and Control*, Richard D. Irwin, Inc. (1972).

12. Chang, R. H., and C. M. Jones, "Production and Workforce Scheduling Extensions," *AIIE Trans.* **2**: 326–333 (1970).

13. Charnes, A., W. W. Cooper, and B. Mellon, "A Model for Optimizing Production by Reference to Cost Surrogates," *Econometrica* **23**, 307–323 (1955).

14. Cooper, L. and C. Drebes, "An Approximate Solution Method for the Fixed Charge Problem," *Nav. Res. Log. Quart.* **14**: 101–113 (1967).

15. Damon, W. W. and R. Schramm, "A Simultaneous Decision Model for Production, Marketing and Finance," *Management Sci.* **19**: 161–172 (1972).

16. Dantzig, G. B., and R. M. Van Slyke, "Generalized Upper Bounding Techniques," *J. Computer and System Sci.* **1**: 213–226 (1967).

17. Dantzig, G. B., and P. Wolfe, "Decomposition Principle for Linear Programs," *Operations Res.* **8**: 101–111 (1960).

18. Denzler, D. R., "An Approximate Algorithm for the Fixed Charge Problem," *Nav. Res. Log. Quart.* **16**: 411–416 (1969).

19. Dzielinski, B. P., C. T. Baker, and A. S. Manne, "Simulation Tests of Lot Size Programming," *Management Sci.* **9**: 229–258 (1963).

20. ———, and R. E. Gomory, "Optimal Programming of Lot Sizes, Inventory and Labor Allocations," *Management Sci.* **11**: 874–890 (1965).

21. Elmaghraby, S. E., and V. Y. Bawle, "Optimization of Batch Ordering Under a Deterministic Variable Demand," *Management Sci.* **18**: 508–517 (1972).

22. Emshoff, J. R., and R. L. Sisson, *Computer Simulation Models*, Macmillan, New York (1970).

23. Eppen, G. D., and F. J. Gould, "A Lagrangean Application to Production Models," *Operations Res.* **16**: 819–829 (1968).

24. Eppen, G. D., F. J. Gould, and B. P. Pashigian, "Extensions of the Planning Horizon Theorem in the Dynamic Lot Size Model," *Management Sci.* **15**: 268–277 (1969).
25. Florian, M., and M. Klein, "Deterministic Production Planning with Concave Costs and Capacity Constraints," *Management Sci.* **18**: 12–20 (1971).
26. Florian, M. and P. Robillard, "An Implicit Enumeration Algorithm for the Concave Cost Network Flow Problem," *Management Sci.* **18**: 184–193 (1971).
27. Ford, L. R., and D. R. Fulkerson, *Flows in Networks*, Princeton University Press, Princeton, New Jersey (1962).
28. Forrester, J., *Industrial Dynamics*, M.I.T. Press (1961).
29. Goodman, D. A., "A New Approach to Scheduling Aggregate Production and Work Force," *AIIE Trans.* **5**: 135–141 (1973).
30. Gorenstein, S., "Planning Tire Production," *Management Sci.* **17**: B72–B81 (1970).
31. Gray, P., "Exact Solution of the Fixed-Charge Transportation Problem," *Operations Res.* **19**: 1529–1537 (1971).
32. Hanssmann, F., *Operations Research in Production and Inventory Control*, Wiley, New York (1962).
33. ——, and S. W. Hess, "A Linear Programming Approach to Production and Employment Scheduling," *Management Tech.* **1**: 46–51 (1960).
34. Hausman, W. H., and J. D. McClain, "A Note on the Bergstrom-Smith Multi-Item Production Planning Model," *Management Sci.* **17**: 783–785.
35. Hax, A. C., "Integration of Strategic and Tactical Planning in the Aluminum Industry," Operations Research Center, M.I.T., Technical Paper O.R. 026–73 (September 1973).
36. ——, "The Design of Large Scale Logistics Systems: A Survey and an Approach," Chapter 6 in *Modern Trends in Logistics Research*, W. H. Marlow, ed., M.I.T. Press, 1976.
37. ——, and H. C. Meal, "Hierarchical Integration of Production Planning and Scheduling," in TIMS Studies in Management Science, Vol. 1, Logistics, Murray Geisler, Ed.: 53–69 (January 1975).
38. Hoffman, A. J., and W. Jacobs, "Smooth Patterns of Production," *Management Sci.* **1**: 86–91 (1954).
39. Holt, C. C., F. Modigliani, J. F. Muth, and H. A. Simon, *Planning Production Inventories and Work Force*, Prentice-Hall, Inc., Englewood Cliffs, New Jersey (1960).
40. ——, and H. A. Simon, "Optimal Decision Rules for Production and Inventory Control," *Proc. Conf. on Operations Res. in Production and Inventory Control*, Case Institute of Technology (January 1954).
41. Hooke, R., and T. A. Jeeves, "Direct Search Solution of Numerical and Statistical Problems," *J. Assoc. Computing Machinery* **8**: 212–229 (1961).
42. Hwang, C. L., and L. T. Fan, "The Application of the Maximum Principle to Industrial and Management Systems," *J. Indus. Eng.* **17**: 589–593 (1966).
43. ——, ——, and L. E. Erickson, "Optimum Production Planning by the Maximum Principle," *Management Sci.* **13**: 751–755 (1967).
44. Johnson, L. A., and D. C. Montgomery, *Operations Research in Production Planning, Scheduling, and Inventory Control*, Wiley, New York (1974).
45. Johnson, S. M., "Sequential Production Planning Over Time at Minimum Cost," *Management Sci.* **3**: 435–437 (1957).
46. ——, and G. B. Dantzig, "A Production Smoothing Problem," *Proc. Second Symposium in Lin. Programming*, Washington, D.C. (January 1955).
47. Jones, C. H., "Parametric Production Planning," *Management Sci.* **13**: 843–866 (1967).
48. Kalymon, B. A., "A Decomposition Algorithm for Arborescence Inventory Systems," *Operations Res.* **20**: 860–874 (1972).
49. Karush, W., "On a Class of Minimum Cost Problems," *Management Sci.* **4**: 136–155 (1958).

50. Klein, M., "Some Production Planning Problems," *Nav. Res. Log. Quart.* **4**: 269–286 (1957).

51. ———, "On Production Smoothing," *Management Sci.* **7**: 286–293 (1961).

52. Kolenda, J. F., "A Comparison of Two Aggregate Planning Models," unpublished master's thesis, Wharton School of Finance and Commerce, The Univ. of Pennsylvania (1970).

53. Kortanek, K. O., D. Sodaro, and A. L. Soyster, "Multi-Product Production Scheduling via a Extreme Point Properties of Linear Programming," *Nav. Res. Log. Quart.* **15**: 287–300 (1968).

54. Krajewski, L. J., V. A. Mabert, and H. E. Thompson, "Quadratic Inventory Cost Approximations and the Aggregation of Individual Products," *Management Sci.* **19**: 1229–1240 (1973).

55. Kriebel, C. H., "Coefficient Estimation in Quadratic Programming Models," *Management Sci.* **13**: B473–B486 (1967).

56. Kuhn, H. W., and W. J. Baumol, "An Approximate Algorithm for the Fixed-Charge Transportation Problem," *Nav. Res. Log. Quart.* **9**: 1–16 (1962).

57. Lasdon, L. S., and R. C. Terjung, "An Efficient Algorithm for Multi-Item Scheduling," *Operations Res.* **19**: 946–969 (1971).

58. Lee, W. B., and B. M. Khumawala, "Simulation Testing of Aggregate Production Planning Models in Implementation Methodology," *Management Sci.* **20**: 903–911 (1974).

59. Lippman, S. A., A. J. Rolfe, H. M. Wagner, and J. S. C. Yuan, "Optimal Production Scheduling and Employment Smoothing with Deterministic Demands," *Management Sci.* **14**: 127–158 (1967a).

60. ———, ———, ———, "Algorithm for Optimal Production Scheduling and Employment Smoothing," *Operations Res.* **15**: 1011–1029 (1967b).

61. Magee, J. F., and D. M. Boodman, *Production Planning and Inventory Control*, McGraw-Hill, New York (1967).

62. Manne, A. S., "Programming of Economic Lot Sizes," *Management Sci.* **4**: 115–135 (1958).

63. McGarrah, R. E., *Production and Logistics Management*, Wiley, New York (1963).

64. Modigliani, F., and F. E. Hohn, "Production Planning over Time and the Nature of the Expectation and Planning Horizon," *Econometrica* **23**: 46–66 (1955).

65. Murty, K. G., "Solving the Fixed Charge Problem by Routing Extreme Points," *Operations Res.* **16**: 268–279 (1968).

66. Naylor, T., et al., *Computer Simulation Techniques*, Wiley, New York (1966).

67. Nelson, R. T., "Labor Assignment as a Dynamic Control Problem," *Operation Res.* **14**: 369–376 (1966).

68. Newson, E. F. P., "Lot Size Scheduling to Finite Capacity," unpublished doctoral thesis, Sloan School of Management, MIT (1971).

69. O'Malley, R. L., S. E. Elmaghraby, and J. W. Jeske, "An Operational System for Smoothing Batch-Type Production," *Management Sci.* **12**: B433–B449 (1966).

70. Peterson, R., "Optimal Smoothing of Shipments in Response to Orders," *Management Sci.* **17**: 597–607 (1971).

71. Pontryagin, L. S., V. G. Boltganskii, R. V. Gamkselidze, and E. F. Mishchenko, *The Mathematical Theory of Optimal Processes*, Wiley, New York (1962).

72. Rousseau, J. M., "A Cutting Plane Method for the Fixed Cost Problem," unpublished doctoral thesis, Sloan School of Management, MIT, (August 1973).

73. Shwimer, J., "Interaction Between Aggregate and Detailed Scheduling in a Job Shop," unpublished Ph.D. thesis, Sloan School of Management, MIT (1972).

74. Simon, H. A., "On The Application of Servomechanism Theory in the Study of Production Control," *Econometrica* **20**: 247–268 (1952).

75. ——, "Dynamic Programming under Uncertainty with a Quadratic Criterion Function," *Econometrica* 24: 74–81 (1956).
76. Sobel, M. J., "Smoothing Start-up and Shut-down Costs: Concave Case," *Management Sci.* 17: 78–91 (1970).
77. Starr, M. K., *Production Management-Systems and Procedures*, Prentice-Hall, Englewood Cliffs, New Jersey (1972).
78. Steinberg, D. I., "The Fixed Charge Problem," *Nav. Res. Log. Quart.* 17: 217–237 (1970).
79. Sypkens H. A., "Planning for Optimal Plant Capacity," unpublished master's thesis, Sloan School of Management, MIT (1967).
80. Taubert, W. H., "A Search Decision Rule for the Aggregate Scheduling Pattern," *Management Sci.* 14: B343–B359 (1968).
81. Thomas, J., "Linear Programming Models for Production-Advertising Decisions," *Management Sci.* 17: B474–B484 (1971).
82. Van dePanne, C., and P. Bosje, "Sensitivity Analysis of Lost Coefficient Estimates: The Case of Linear Decision Rules for Employment and Production," *Management Sci.* 9: 82–107 (1962).
83. Vassian, H. J., "Application of Discrete Variable Servo Theory to Inventory Control," *Operations Res.* 3: 272–282.
84. Veinott, A. F., "Production Planning With Convex Costs: A Parametric Study," *Management Sci.* 10: 441–460 (1964).
85. ——, "Minimum Concave-Cost Solution of Leontieff Substitution Models of Multi-Facility Inventory Systems," *Operations Res.* 17: 262–291 (1969).
86. Vergin, R. C., "Production Scheduling Under Seasonal Demand," *J. Indust. Eng.* 7: 260–266 (1966).
87. Von Lanzenaur, C. H., "Production and Employment and Scheduling in Multistage Production Systems," *Nav. Res. Log. Quart.* 17: 193–198 (1970).
88. ——, "A Production Scheduling Model by Bivalent Linear Programming," *Management Sci.* 17: 105–111 (1970b).
89. Wagner, H. M., "A Postscript to Dynamic Problems in the Theory of the Firm," *Nav. Res. Log. Quart.* 7: 7–12 (1960).
90. ——, and T. M. Whitin, "A Dynamic Version of the Economic Lot Size Model," *Management Sci.* 5: 89–96 (1958).
91. Wilde, D. J., *Optimum Seeking Methods*, Prentice-Hall, Englewood Cliffs, New Jersey 1964.
92. Yuan, S. C., "Algorithms and Multi-Product Model in Production Scheduling and Employment Smoothing," Technical Reprot No. 22, NSF GS-552, Stanford University, Stanford, California (August 1967).
93. Zabel, E., "Some Generalizations of an Inventory Planning Horizon Theorem," *Management Sci.* 10: 465–471 (1964).
94. Zangwill, W. I., "A Deterministic Multiproduct, Multifacility Production and Inventory Model," *Operations Res.* 14: 486–507 (1966a).
95. ——, "A Deterministic Multi-Period Production Scheduling Model with Backlogging," *Management Sci.* 13: 105–119 (1966b).
96. ——, "Production Smoothing of Economic Lot Sizes with Non-Decreasing Requirements," *Management Sci.* 13: 191–209 (1966c).
97. ——, "Minimum Concave Cost Flows in Certain Networks," *Management Sci.* 14: 429–450 (1968).
98. ——, "A Backlogging Model and Multi-Echelon Model of a Dynamic Economic Lot Size Production System - a Network Approach," *Management Sci.* 15: 506–527 (1969).

I-6

INVENTORY CONTROL*

Robert G. Brown
Consultant

1. INTRODUCTION

The theory of inventory management was one of the earliest fruitful areas of application for operations research (OR), since problems in the area are complex, the significant factors span at least three organizational divisions of the enterprise, and the solutions are highly profitable to manufacturing, processing, wholesaling, and retailing organizations. The first successful systems were implemented for spare parts inventories of large companies, where demand from a large population is based primarily on need (rather than promotion), there is no important substitutability of one item for another, and the costs and lead times are known with sufficient accuracy. Much of the early work was highly theoretical, but has been translated into successful practice with accurate rules of thumb that can be understood by the users.

Two independent streams of development have contributed to the state of the art. One was the abstract mathematical model of an inventory process (Dvoretsky [1952]; Arrow [1958]; Moran [1959]) looked at from purely an economic sense of minimizing costs within constraints on availability of stock to satisfy demand. The other was pragmatic (Magee [1958]), in which one had to show how to measure demand, for example, rather than merely stating—"assume the

---

*R. G. Brown's *Materials Management Systems* (Wiley-Interscience 1977) is an expanded version of the points covered in this chapter, with copious examples of implementation.

demand is described by $f(x)$." Whitin [1953] was one of the first significant attempts to bridge the gap between the two approaches.

1.1 Structure of the Inventory Problem

The total system for managing an inventory of any enterprise involved three different "levels" of systems:

(a) "First-level" systems applications are concerned with the processing of transactions, and the maintenance of files. The important inventory files show current stock on hand, stock due in from the sources on open orders, and stock due to customers when it becomes available. The record for any stocked item also includes various other data, such as cost, lead time, unit of measure, source, etc. There is only a finite number of different transactions (demand, issue, receipt from source, return, transfer, correction, etc.), but they occur in very large volumes. Data processing has made large contributions to the efficiency of processing and storing "first-level" information, especially since the rules for handling any transaction are logically unambiguous. The major systems-design problem is to assure the efficiency and reliability of the system.

(b) "Second-level" systems involve the decision rules for answering questions; especially WHEN to order to replenish stock, and HOW MUCH to order. The development of these decision rules has been of interest to OR since the middle 1950s, and the results are the principal concern of this chapter. Each decision rule is the optimal result for some particular problem. However, the user's real problems can have vastly different elements from one organization to another, so that it is necessary for the systems analyst to be familiar with the conditions under which one decision rule is preferable to another. Although the decisions are formally optimal, successful application requires a nice blending of the subjective judgement of middle managers with relevant experience—there is not necessarily one "right" answer to the exclusion of all others. The operating cycle of the second-level part of the system tends to be regular, but has monthly, as opposed to daily, processing of first-level transactions. Systems efficiency may be important, but relevance to the real operating environment is more important.

(c) "Third-level" systems provide management with simulations of alternative strategic choices among decision rules, and alternative tactical choices of policy in the rules chosen, to guide annual budgeting of the policy to be followed in the coming year. Monitors of actual performance against plan can help management decide whether and how to intervene, and when to manage the system rather than managing stocks of things. Financial monitors of performance against plan are often available through the accounting system. Still, it is also important to monitor some non-financial aspects of the operation, such as customer service. The design of appropriate simulations and monitors seems still to be highly personal to the manager involved.

1.2 Inventory Decision Rules

The second-level part of an inventory system for any enterprise must include some decision rule for both replenishment lot quantities and safety factors. Both require forecasts (see Chapter I-1) which measure the distribution of errors around the forecast. In each of the decision rules there is at least one *policy variable* for which management can choose values to affect the exchange of capital investment in stocks against some sort of operating expense. In the next two sections of this chapter, in which the decision rules are discussed, the third-level *exchange curves* will also be presented. They enable one to make a strategic choice among alternative rules, as well as the tactical choice of the value for the policy variable in the rule to be used.

In some systems there is also the need for a decision rule for allocating a finite resource (not necessarily scarce) among activities. These rules are discussed in section 4. The last section covers systems architecture—the alternative ways that these decision rules can be built into systems that make effective routine decisions about when to reorder, how much to order, and where to put it.

1.3 Stratification and Classification

The distribution across an inventory of items, of their sales rates in dollars per year, is universally representable by a lognormal distribution. The distribution can be plotted on lognormal graph paper (Figure 1), with one set of points representing the cumulative fraction of items, and another set representing the fraction of total revenue (or cost) from those items. Both are plotted against the annual sales rate. If the distribution is lognormal, the two lines will be parallel, and the common "slope" is called the *standard ratio*. For a normal distribution, about 16% exceeds the mean by more than one standard deviation, and about 84% exceeds a value one standard deviation below the mean. These percentages are marked with the heavy horizontal rulings in Figure 1. The parameter σ (which is not the standard deviation) of the lognormal distribution (i.e., the normal distribution of the natural logarithms of Sv) can be computed from the 16 and 50 percentiles by $\sigma = \ln 50 - \ln 5 = \ln 50/5 = \ln 10 = 2.3$ The ratio $50/5 = 10$ is referred to as the standard ratio. Let m denote the average sales per item per year and let $J = e^{1/2\sigma^2}$, then (Brown [1959]) the median item has sales of m/J, and half the sales are derived from items with sales exceeding mJ.

In many industries there is more than one inventory, in the sense of the market population it is intended to support, which will be indicated by evidence of two lognormal distributions with different means, but the same standard ratio. If there are two populations, the lines will not be straight, as indicated by the dashed lines in Figure 1. Observation of this phenomenon has led to the discovery that hotel suites are not merely more expensive hotel rooms, but have a different market; that there are two different physical processes in the formation

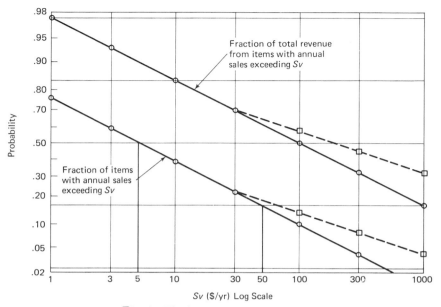

Fig. 1. The log normal distribution.

of drops in a spray-drying process; and that the characteristic market for industrial tools is quite different from the market for do-it-yourself, even though both sets of customers tend to buy quite similar tools. The marketing implications of recognizing these different populations can be quite as valuable as the improvement of inventory management. The detection of what discriminates among the various populations requires considerable imagination and investigative skill.

A more familiar representation is the Pareto curve that plots the percentage of revenue against the percentage of items, where items are ranked in descending sequence by annual dollar sales. If "20% of the items account for 80% of the sales" (they seldom do exactly), that is equivalent to a standard ratio of about 5, which would be characteristic of demand for consumer products at the retail level. The standard ratio for manufactured products is more often approximately 10, and for highly technological material such as aircraft or computer components, the standard ratio may be as high as 25.

A convenient way (Brown [1971a]) of plotting the distribution to find the standard ratio and to look for the possibility of nonhomogeneous populations is to plot the percentage of revenue against the percentage of items, with probability scales along both axes (Figure 2). If the distribution is lognormal, then the points fall along a straight line with a 45° slope. In Fig 2, 50% of the items contribute 99% of the revenue. It can be shown that 50% of the items contribute $F(\sigma)$ as a fraction of the total revenue, in this case 0.99. Since $F(.)$ is the cumulative normal distribution, from a table one can find the parameter $\sigma = 2.33$, so that the standard ratio is $\rho = e^{\sigma} = 10.15$, which agrees with the values computed above in conjunction with Figure 1.

In practice, the first few items on the list, which account for 50% of the revenue, are called Class A items, which deserve not only the best inventory management system, but also careful review by experienced managers who may improve on formal rules with extrinsic knowledge of special circumstances. There are few enough items to be watched, and the consequences of improving over formal rules can be large. The last half of the items are called Class C, and together represent only a small (1%) percentage of the total revenue. Very simple inventory systems may be justified for these items, since the loss caused by approximate controls may be very much smaller than the savings from using

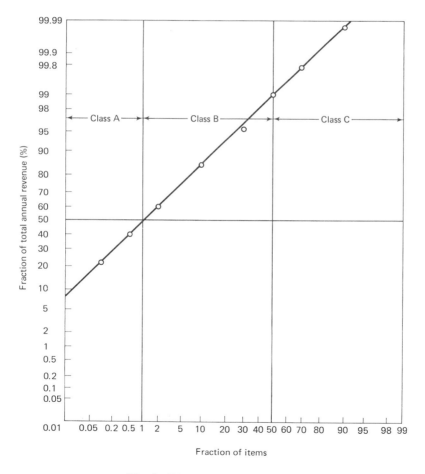

Fig. 2. Distribution by value.

simple procedures on so many items. The intermediate items, which account for nearly half the revenue and nearly half the items, merit sound systems but minimal intervention. They are called Class B.

For more refined control, items can be classified in several other ways: (a) raw materials vs. stocked components vs. finished goods at the plant, vs. finished products in the field distribution system, (b) items made within the plant vs. items supplied from independent vendors or other corporate divisions, and (c) items which customers can obtain from competition vs. items where this company is the sole source. Profit margins, time since introduction, and essentiality to the user are also the basis for classification in many corporations.

Throughout this chapter, an "inventory" is the group of stocked items with similar characteristics within this stratification. An enterprise might have from three to ten such inventories. Because of the difference in source and use of the items between one inventory and another, it is quite possible to make different strategic choices of decision rules for different inventories, and it is invariably true that management will want different tactical choices of the values of policy variables from one inventory to another.

1.4 What Items to Stock

There are two quite different motivations for carrying an inventory. One has the marketing connotations of service to the customer, to satisfy his needs quickly. The other has production connotations of service to the supplier, to buffer fluctuations in demand from the economics of smooth production. The decision whether to stock an item depends on the purpose of that inventory.

(a) In a customer-oriented inventory, the decision to add an item to the range in stock is usually based on the number of calls for that item. If there have been at least N calls in a period of time T, then the item is stocked. A decision table can be set up by marketing management giving the minimum values of (N, T) by inventory classification. There will, of course, be certain classes of items for which the item is stocked before the first call (essential repair parts for new machinery and pipeline stocks for a new product). It may take more evidence of demand to stock a noncurrent (spares only usage), nonfunctional part than to stock a current (also used in building products), essential part. Since the long-term marketing contribution of having an item in stock is only partially financial and always highly subjective, it is not likely to be productive to have very elaborate models of the costs of stocking an additional item. The manager making the decision should be aware of the cost consequences, but the model for making that prediction can be very simple, based on planning factors of inventory investment, space occupied, and the systems costs for first-level operations.

(b) In a producer-oriented inventory, there is a clearer economic basis for deciding whether to stock an item or to produce it (a generic term inferring either manufacture or purchase as appropriate) whenever there is demand. Suppose we sell N units a year, it costs A dollars to produce the item (a setup or ordering cost, not the invoice amount), the unit cost is v/piece, and management has set a carrying charge of r \$/\$/year on inventory investment. If the item is replenished p units at one time, the total annual cost is $NA/p + \frac{1}{2}rv$ (p-1). The costs of not stocking the item ($p = 1$) are less than the costs of making two when one is needed and carrying the other until it is used for $N \leqslant rv/A$. Hence, one would tend to make an expensive item, or one with very low setup costs, and to support from stock a high sales rate, cheap item or one that is expensive to setup.

(c) In a distribution network, with several warehouses, there have been many attempts to find an economical model for deciding which warehouses should carry a given item. A more practical approach is to consider each warehouse and decide what items should be stocked there. Rank all stockable items in descending sequence by number of calls (rather than the dollar value of annual demand). A relatively few items at the top of the list will account for 50% of all calls. These items should be stocked at all locations, to satisfy the largest number of requests with relatively small inventory costs because there are few items involved. The items in the middle of the list can be stocked regionally to reduce the number of inventory accounts to be managed, but still to gain the economy of transporting material in bulk into market areas, and to gain the marketing advantage of having products reasonably close to the customer for much of the remainder of the demand. The last half of the items on the list should be stocked in only one location to save the costs associated with multiple inventory accounts. The delays in supplying such material to the customer can't have serious marketing consequences since the demand rate is so low, and the transportation costs can't be large because there are so few demands.

Recently several corporations are beginning to explore the possibility of putting productive capacity "into stock" in the sense of having the ability to produce small amounts quickly rather than carrying the inventories of these low-demand items at all. A separate plant can "make one of anything over night, but two is a production run and we don't handle that," with numerical controlled machinery and special mechanics. Such a plant may be far less expensive than carrying physical stocks of finished products for which there is little demand, but what demand there is must be filled. It is important, however, that the process engineering for such a plant be wholly separate from traditional mass production.

In consumer goods especially there are often many similar products in stock, or potentially in stock, any one of which could satisfy the customer's needs. In this case most of the inventory theory (replenishment order quantities and safety stocks) applies to the aggregate group of substitutable merchandise as the planning unit. So long as the right total stock is available, the customer will make a choice and buy something from among what is in stock.

Some experimental work has been done which tends to show that there is a critical (broad) range of alternatives of the assortment. If there are too few items, the customer is less likely to buy any of them, even though they are the most popular in the whole line. If there are too many, the customer may become confused and unable to make a choice. Clearly, different companies create different images about the breadth of the assortment the customer is likely to find, and the size of the assortment seems to be relative to the customer's expectations for that store.

2. REPLENISHMENT LOT QUANTITY DECISION RULES

The first-level procedure for determining how much to produce (make or buy) when it is time to replenish stocks can in general either be to order a predetermined quantity (filed in the first-level system) or to order the difference between current *available stock* (on hand, plus on order, less commitments) and a maximum stocking objective (also in the first-level files). Sometimes the quantity ordered for each item is its fair share of space, weight or dollar constraints on the total order for a family of items. These procedures are discussed in Section 5 on systems architecture. Here we shall cover the second-level decision rules for the economical order quantities that can be used to establish the predetermined quantity or the maximum stocking objective for an item or for a family.

2.1 Assumptions about the Operating Environment

The various formulas for economical order quantities (Raymond [1931]) have to make one or another of the alternative assumptions under each of five basic headings. Under each heading the simplest assumption is given first. With each alternative there is a discussion of the circumstances under which the formulation using this alternative may be worth considering as a significant improvement over the first assumption. Since the assumptions under one heading are logically independent of the assumptions chosen under others, there are at least 120 possible combinations leading to different decision rules. Out of such a variety one should be reasonably close to the best obtainable, no matter what the environment, but the odds are high for choosing the wrong rule if one does not verify the real needs of the specific situation in which the rule is to be used.

1.(a) The entire quantity ordered is **delivered** as one lot. The model assumes that the stock on hand rises from the minimum to have the entire lot quantity on hand at the beginning of each cycle (Figure 3). (b) Material is delivered from the start of the production run over a period of time that is long enough for some part of the material to be consumed (issued, sold) before the entire

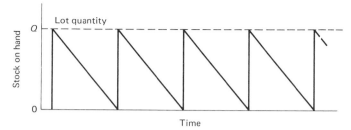

Fig. 3. Stock on hand with delivery of whole lot.

quantity has been delivered. In Figure 4, if material is delivered at the annualized rate P while being used at the annualized rate S, the maximum quantity on hand at the end of the production run is $Q(1 - S/P)$. Note that the total annual deliveries to stock will be of the order of S. P is the rate of delivery during the production run, so that the item is in production only a fraction S/P of the time. This alternative assumption is important if $P < 2S$, so that the fraction $(1 - S/P) > 0.5$. If $P < S$, this implies that there is more than one facility, each with a production rate P. Of these, $(n - 1)$ run continuously with no changeovers, and the last one runs intermittently to fill an effective annual demand of $S - (n - 1)P$ units per year.

2.(a) **Usage** will continue at a constant rate for an indefinite time, so that there will be more replenishments of the same quantity Q, and so that stock on hand will be diminished along a straight line as shown in Figures 3 and 4. "An indefinite time" turns out, in practice, to mean that there will be at least three more replenishment lots.

(b) Usage will continue at known or forecast rates which vary from period to period. This is the case that has received a great deal of attention in the OR literature in the past 15 years. The exact solution (Wagner, Whitin [1958]) requires dynamic programming. A number of plausible approximations have been proposed, but it has not always been recognized that they are approxima-

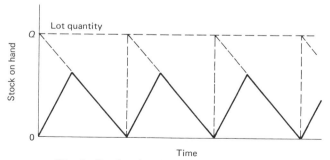

Fig. 4. Production into stock over time.

tions. If all the high demand is at one end of the planning horizon (e.g., a currently popular item that is dying rapidly, or a new product that is expected to have exponential growth) then none of the approximations work. If there are periods of high and low demand throughout the planning horizon, the distinction among alternative approximations is not significant and evaluations are usually predicated on the particular random samples chosen, rather than on basic inherent differences.

(c) If there is a significant random variation in demand, the minimum stock is not zero, as shown in Figures 3 and 4. However, there is safety stock. When lot quantities are increased over what they would be with the default assumption, there are fewer exposures to the risk of a shortage during a year; thus safety stock could be reduced for a given desired level of service. The total savings in jointly computing lot quantities and safety stocks is significant when the default lot quantity is smaller than the standard deviation of forecast errors over the replenishment lead time. For example, consider the case of a very expensive item with small setup costs, which might be made in a week's supply at a time, but where the usage is so erratic that one standard deviation is equivalent to a month's supply. The exact formulation requires iterative computations. A practical approximation is to increase the default lot quantity to be at least as large as the standard deviation. While this is not the lot quantity that results from the exact computations it is large enough that further refinement is not justified in terms of the cost of the computation.

(d) Usage will continue until there is an unexpected need to write off any stock that remains on hand (Brown [1971b]). Engineering changes that can be planned to take place far enough in the future to allow for balancing out present stocks can be taken into account by making the last lot sufficient to last only over the planned usage before that change. But when the Federal government decrees that a product is not safe and must be withdrawn immediately, then the carrying charge should be increased by the probability that such a change will arise within the next year.

(e) Finite remaining total demand. If usage will fall to zero some time within the planning horizon (end of contract, change in product model, discontinuance, etc.), then the last lot should be sufficient to cover the difference between current available stock and the total remaining demand. Dynamic programming is required to determine whether it is economical to produce the remaining demand in one, or in more than one lot, and if so, how large the first lot of the sequence should be. Closed forms have been developed for several possible models of the decline in demand. The difference between the first lot of an optimal sequence and the default lot quantity is important only when there are three or fewer remaining lots to be made.

3. **Setup cost.** These may include costs for setting up production, costs of administering the production schedule, and ordering and receiving costs that depend marginally on the number of orders processed during a year.

(a) Setup cost is incurred independently for each item ordered. (b) There is a major cost incurred for ordering a family of items with minor costs for including one more member of the family in the current order. Examples would include a list of merchandise bought from the same vendor, different products bottled in the same size bottles on a line, or parts stamped in progressive dies from the same gauge, width and material of coil stock. The joint order quantities are significant when the major setup cost is larger than the sum of the minor costs over all items in the family.

4. **Unit costs** are used in placing a capital value on the investment in stocks that result from making more at one time than is required immediately.

(a) Any reasonable quantity can be produced at any time for the same unit cost. (b) Anticipated price changes. If the cost on future orders is likely to be higher than present unit cost, the current replenishment order quantity should be larger than the default quantity to defer the expense at the higher rate. The extra time supply that it is economical to produce is proportional to the percentage price increase expected. The constant of proportionality is dominated by management's carrying charge or the rate used to discount future expenses to present value. The rate for this decision may be much higher than for the default case of repetitive replenishment orders under similar conditions.

(c) Quantity discounts. When the unit cost will be lower if a quantity larger than the default case is ordered each time stock is replenished, then the optimum lot quantity can be determined by comparing total costs for the default case with costs at each of the breakpoint quantities where the price changes. As a convenient rule of thumb, it is economical to order M months of supply over the default lot quantity only if the percentage reduction in unit cost is at least $2M\%$ (based on the typical case where management's carrying charge is in the range of 20–24% a year).

5. The **carrying charge** is an arbitrary policy variable which can be increased to reduce capital investment in stocks at the expense of processing a larger number of orders per year. The value of the carrying charge that would theoretically maximize return on investment is equal to the current corporate return on net assets employed—hence the popular values of 20–24% per annum. However, the carrying charge should be higher than that rate if management believes there is either more risk or less liquidity to an investment in inventories than in other capital investments of the firm. Thus, one major corporation sets lower carrying charges on raw materials than on finished goods, and a higher carrying charge on field stocks than on finished goods at the plant.

(a) The default case is a carrying charge on the financial investment in inventories. (b) Space occupied. If there are some relatively bulky items, and others that are relatively dense (in $/ft^3$), then management may set a second policy variable as a charge on space occupied which will reduce the lot quantities from the default case for bulky items. Note that in an inventory of glass bottles or building insulation, where all the items are bulky, it is not necessary to have a separate term in the model for space occupied—a higher charge on the financial investment will reduce the inventory to fit into the space available.

The carrying charge is, within limits, a management policy variable. If management chooses a value somewhat higher than corporate return on net assets, the lot quantities will be smaller with more frequent replenishment lots. A lower value of the carrying charge increases the capital investment but saves on the annual expense of processing replenishment orders.

There is a maximum practical limit on the value of the carrying charge for this purpose. When safety stocks are provided to protect customer service, the smaller and more frequent replenishment lots require additional safety stock to maintain the same level of service. Above some value of the carrying charge, the decrease in working stocks is offset by an increase in safety stock required, so that the only effect of increasing the carrying charge beyond that point is to increase the expense of ordering without a compensating reduction in total capital investment.

2.2   The Default Case

When usage is constant at the rate S units/year, the entire lot quantity Q is delivered to stock at one time, the setup cost A is incurred each time an item is ordered, the unit cost v $/piece applies for any reasonable quantity, and management policy is to charge r $/$/year for money invested in inventories. The economical quantity is $Q = \sqrt{2AS/rv}$. This standard economical order quantity (EOQ) formula was first published by Harris [1915], and is one of the first cost-optimization models to be developed by each new entrant into the OR profession.

The annual costs of processing replenishment orders $C_1 = AS/Q$, the costs of holding the resulting stocks $C_2 = \frac{1}{2}rvQ$, and the total costs $C(Q) = C_1 + C_2$ are plotted in Figure 5. Note that in the neighborhood of the EOQ the total cost curve is quite flat. If the quantity actually ordered is in the range from $Q/\sqrt{2}$ to $Q\sqrt{2}$, then the total annual cost will be less than 6% above the minimum. Hence, any error in estimating one of the factors in the formula that is in the range from double to half of the true value will not seriously impair the effectiveness of this rule in practice—unless, of course, one is so unlucky as to make errors on the high side for both factors in the numerator and on the low side in the denominator. Still, a factor of 2 is such a wide margin that most processes of estimation come well within that range.

2.3   The General Case

Most of the alternative assumptions can be accomodated in a more general formula. Cases of (a) known and random demand, (b) finite remaining de-

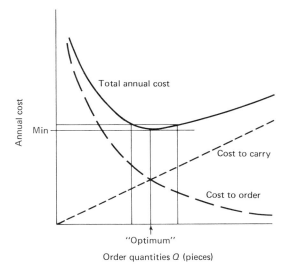

Fig. 5. Total annual inventory costs.

mand, and (c) changes in the price with quantity and time will be considered separately. Express the time that a lot will last as $T = Q/S = \sqrt{2A/rSv(1 - S/P)}$. Note that if P is large compared with S, the effect of the factor S/P becomes insignificant.

If there is a probability p that stock on hand will be written off unexpectedly within the next year, $T = \sqrt{2A/(r + p)Sv}$. If $p = 0$, this reduces to the default case.

Joint setups: Let A be the major setup cost incurred for ordering the family and a_j be the minor setup cost for including the j-th item of the family in the order. If a_j is dependent on the sequence of items, the travelling salesman problem can be formulated to find the optimum sequence of running individual members of the family and solved, for example, by branch and bound methods. In practice, the operating people know one of the nearly optimal sequences already, and will not contemplate any of the clearly uneconomical sequences. So it may not be worth the effort to find the optimum sequence: the improvement isn't worth the effort to find it. In any event, the a_j are the minor setup costs in the optimum (or nearly optimal) sequence.

If all items are produced on each cycle, the economical cycle will last

$$T = \sqrt{2\left(A + \sum a_j\right)/r \sum S_j v_j},$$

where the summations are taken over all items j in the family.

If slow-moving, cheap items are produced on every k-th cycle in a supply that will last k_jT years, the economical interval between lots becomes

$$T = \sqrt{2\left(A + \sum a_j / k_j\right) / r \sum k_j S_j v_j}.$$

There are two models for determining the economical frequency for including the slower-moving members of the family in the production order. One (Brown [1967]) is

$$k_j^2 = (a_j/S_j v_j) \left(\sum k_i S_i v_i \Big/ \left(A + \sum a_i / k_i\right)\right).$$

Start with all $k_j = 1$ on the right and solve for values on the left. Substitute them on the right and continue until the solution converges to the values assumed. The integral value of k_j can be obtained at each step by rounding the fractional part of the square root upward if the fractional part is larger than 0.4. A slightly different approach is given in Nocturne [1973].

All of these variations could be combined into one unwieldy formula. As each of the variables assumes its default value the formula simplifies.

2.4 Special Cases for Change in Cost

Figure 6 shows the cost curves for processing replenishment orders, holding inventory investment, and total costs in the case where the item's unit cost

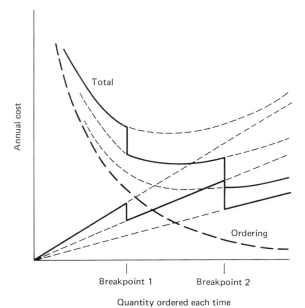

Fig. 6. Total inventory costs with quality discounts.

changes with the quantity ordered each time. There may be several solutions to the formula $Q = \sqrt{2AS/rv}$ for each of the unit costs v_i, but there is only one consistent solution where the quantity Q_i is in the range where the value v_i would apply. This quantity is the default case. The minimum total annual cost must occur either at this default quantity or at some larger quantity where the unit cost drops. The annual costs for a finite number of alternatives can be compared, to choose the value (Q^*, v^*) for which the costs would be the least.

If future unit costs are expected to be higher than now (as when a sale is over or when production is re-tooled to produce parts in spares quantities only after the end of an assembly model year) it is useful to formulate the present value $W(Q)$ of future expenses for alternative strategies about present and future lot quantities. $W(Q) = (A + Qv)/(1 - e^{-rQ/S})$. If all factors are at default conditions, formal differentiation of this expression gives the default EOQ as the least-cost strategy, in which the factor r is the rate at which management discounts future expenses to present value for comparison of alternatives.

When any quantity Q_1 can be produced at the current cost v_1, but future production will be at the higher cost v_2, then the optimum current quanity is

$$Q_1 = (S/r) \ln (r/Sv_1) (A_2 + Q_2v_2 + Sv_2/r),$$

in which Q_2 is the EOQ quantity after the price has increased to v_2. Under the usual case where the setup cost A is much smaller than the invoice amount Qv, this expression reduces approximately to

$$\frac{Q_1v_1 - Q_2v_2}{Sv_1} = (1/r) (v_2 - v_1)/v_1 + (2A_2S/rv_1 - Q_1^2)/2S^2.$$

If the second term on the right is approximately zero (the difference between squares of time supplies), the increase in quantity over the default quanity, expressed as a time supply, is proportional to the percentage price rise, and the constant of proportionality is the reciprocal of the carrying charge, or the discount rate.

2.5 Special Cases for Changes in Usage Pattern

If demand is known, planned, or forecast to vary significantly from a constant rate by period out to some future planning horizon, then the exact solution to the economical lot quantity problem can be solved by dynamic programming (Wagner and Whitin [1958]). The process can be visualized by plotting cumulative requirements as in Figure 7. Consider as one possibility making the total requirements in precisely three lots. The shaded area represents the total inventory carried for a particular choice of T_1 and T_2 as the times when the first two

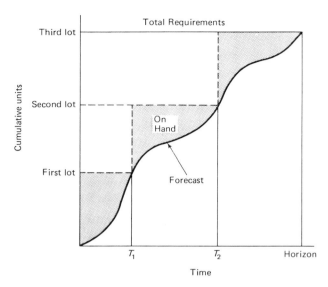

Fig. 7. Making total requirements in just 3 lots.

lots will be used up and the next lot due into stock. The third lot clearly is determined by the balance of the requirements out to the planning horizon.

There is a choice of (T_1, T_2) that minimizes the total inventory carried, and hence the cost of the strategy of providing the requirements in precisely three lots. Similar analyses can be made for $N = 1, 2, \ldots$ lots. When the reduction in cost of carrying the minimum inventory that results from going from N to $N + 1$ lots is less than the additional setup cost for one more lot, then we know the optimum number of lots, and hence the sequence of lot quantities under that optimum strategy.

Unless the cumulative plot of future requirements is very convex (upward or downward, indicating that all the high demand is at one end of the planning period) a satisfactory compromise is to use an artificial usage rate S as the average of planned requirements out to the horizon. Then compute the economical interval between lots by whichever of the cases discussed above is appropriate to that environment. The quantity actually planned for the first replenishment lot is the sum of the scheduled requirements during that economical interval.

Sometimes it is worth a slight improvement on this approximation. If the planned requirements during the last period (week, month, etc.) of the first interval are greater than the average S, then schedule a lot to cover one less period than the economical interval. In this case, the large planned withdrawal will be at the beginning of the second lot, rather than at the end of the first lot, reducing inventory investment.

There are two much publicized approximations: *least unit cost* and *part pe-*

riod balancing (deMatteis [1968]). These approximations are contrasted in Figure 8. The part period balancing quantity is chosen so that the triangular area, bounded by the quantity and the cumulative demand, is equal to A/rv. The least unit cost quantity is computed as a time supply such that the triangular area bounded below the cumulative demand is A/rv. If demand is at a constant annual rate S, the areas, and hence the quantities, are equal to the EOQ. When demand varies, the differences in results of the two algorithms is quite sensitive to the shape of the requirements curve at about the end of the period covered by the first lot.

Now consider the case where demand is declining exponentially: $S_t = S_o e^{-at}$. If it is now time for the last lot, the quantity should satisfy all remaining demand $Q = S_o/a$. If it were advisable to make the total demand in n more lots, there is a recursion relationship for the times T_j when the j-th lot will be exhausted and the next lot due into stock

$$a(T_j - T_{j-1}) = 1 - \exp -a(T_{j+1} - T_j).$$

Since T_n is infinite, $a(T_{n-1} - T_{n-2}) = 1$; and since the first lot must be made now, $T_0 = 0$ and $aT_1 = 1 - \exp -a(T_2 - T_1)$. The first lot that results from this sequence is materially different from the default EOQ only if $n \leqslant 3$.

2.6 Cycled Production

When a production facility is running at a rate that is sufficient to produce a year's supply of each of several items during a year, and each of the products is made in turn, the general rule is to continue making the item now in production

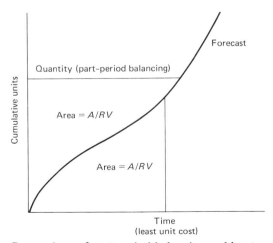

Fig. 8. Comparison of part-period balancing and least unit cost.

until either (a) stock of some other item is used up, or (b) too large a fraction of the stock is invested in the item now being produced, so that there is a danger of running out of two other products simultaneously.

From the model for the economical intervals between lots when there is a finite rate of delivery into stock, we can determine (Brown [1971a]) that the maximum inventory (twice the average) for any item is

$$I_j \Big/ \sum I_i = 2S_j\,(1 - S_j/P_j) \Big/ \sum S_i\,(1 - S_i/P_i).$$

If the stock of item j reaches this fraction of the total inventory, stop and shift to the item with the lowest time supply. That will allow making all products in reasonably economic lots, without running short of two of them simultaneously.

3. SAFETY FACTOR DECISION RULES

The first-level decision when to order a replenishment quantity is governed by comparing current available stock (on hand, plus already on order, less commitments to customers) with the maximum reasonable demand over the replenishment lead time, which is stored in the first-level files as an order point. The lead time starts when a demand transaction is posted that reduces the available balance below the order point quantity; it includes the internal time for processing the order, the vendor's lead time to fill the order, and any further internal time required to receive the materials and post it as available for use.

The maximum reasonable demand is the sum of the forecast over the lead time, plus a safety stock. The *safety stock* is the product $k\sigma$ of the *safety factor* and the standard deviation of errors in forecasting demand during the replenishment lead time.

In this section we shall assume that the forecasting system (Chapter I-1) provides an estimate of σ. If the lead times are known with reasonable accuracy in advance, the standard deviation can be estimated from the errors in forecasting demand. If lead times vary unpredictably, it is dangerous to use any model that alleges to convolve the distribution of lead times with the distribution of forecast errors. The variance of the resulting distribution is highly sensitive to assumptions about the statistical dependence (often assumed independent) between the two distributions. Scenarios can be constructed that show that the distributions are either negatively or positively correlated, and there is seldom enough evidence in practice to support the assumption of independence.

Lead times do, of course, vary. The first attack is to find the cause of the variation and eliminate it if possible. Many companies reach agreement with the source of supply for a specified delivery date, which makes the lead times known for purposes of computing the safety stock.

If it is impractical to control the lead times, measure demand-during-a-lead-time directly. When a replenishment order is triggered, that is by definition the beginning of a lead time. Record the demand year-to-date as part of the first-level file of open orders. Later, when the resulting material is received and posted to stock, that is by definition the end of the lead time. Subtract from today's year-to-date demand the value recorded when the order was triggered. The difference is demand-during-a-lead-time. This is the variable for which we require the standard deviation, with no assumptions made about dependence or independence between demand and lead time.

Examples will assume that the distribution of forecast errors is normal, with zero mean. A good forecast will produce zero mean forecast errors, and if the interval between successive revisions of the forecast is much shorter than about a third of the replenishment lead time, the relevant distribution is usually nearly normal. However, in cases where the lead times are short compared with the intervals between forecasts, and especially at stocking echelons close to the ultimate consumer, it pays to find out what form the distribution actually has, since it may be badly skewed. In any case, provided one uses the tables of the correct probability distribution, the results of the second-level decision rules in this section apply for all cases. For convenience, it is usually satisfactory to treat demand as a continuous variable rather than as a discrete random variable.

3.1 Measures of Service

The safety stock added to the forecast of lead-time requirements is expressed as $k\sigma$, where k is a safety factor usually limited to non-negative values as a matter of policy. Balancing out stocks at the end of a selling season might, however, require a negative value for the safety factor. The probability that demand during the next lead time will exceed the maximum reasonable demand is represented by $F(k)$ in standard units, $(x - \mu)/\sigma$. That is, if demand $(x = \mu + k\sigma)$ is equal to the order point quantity, then $(\mu + k\sigma - \mu)/\sigma = k$. The probability function is obtained by integrating the appropriate density function $p(k)$ from the right (the reverse of the usual statistical practice), which is the area under the upper tail of the probability function, from the maximum reasonable demand out to infinity. We shall also need the *partial expectation function*

$$E(k) = \int_{k}^{\infty} (t - k)p(t)\,dt.$$

Since the height of the probability curve is proportional to the chance that there will be a shortage, and $\sigma(t - k)$ is the corresponding number of units that will be short, $\sigma E(k)$ is the expected number of units short per replenishment cycle. Schlaiffer [1961] calls this function the "linear loss function" and IBM manuals call it the "service function." Its nomenclature has not yet been established in statistics. Tabulated values are given for the normal, exponential, uniform and lognormal distributions in (Brown [1959, 1963, 1967]).

There is no risk of any shortage just after a replenishment lot has been received; the risk occurs when stock is at the low point just prior to another receipt. Therefore, the expected number of shortage occurrences per year is $(S/Q)F(k)$, and the expected dollar value of demand that cannot be filled from stock per year is $(S/Q)\sigma v E(k)$. Both measures of service thus depend on the number of replenishment orders S/Q per year, and hence the safety factor k will depend on the replenishment frequency.

If demand that cannot be filled from stock is backordered and filled from the next lot received from the source, the average safety stock investment is $k\sigma v$. However, if demand that cannot be filled from stock is lost, nothing will be subtracted from the next receipt and the average investment will be higher at $v(k + E(k))\sigma$. The specific decision rules discussed in this section are based on the assumption that demand is backordered if it cannot be filled from stock. The derivations of the analogous cases where demand is lost are straightforward, using the above expression for average safety stock investment.

3.2 Exchange Curves

Each of the decision rules contains a *management policy variable* that can be used to control the exchange of capital invested in safety stocks [dimensions $] against some measure of service which includes [1/years] in the dimension. The measure may be shortages per year, dollar value of annual backordered demand, or the number of customer transactions per year that cannot be filled from stock. One choice of a value for the management policy variable results in high investment and good service—a different choice reduces the investment at the expense of service.

One of the important third-level simulations is the *exchange curve* which shows (graphically or in tabular form, depending on whether the reponsible manager is primarily a visual or an aural person) the consequences of alternative choices of the value for the policy variable. The ordinate of each point on the curve is $\sum k\sigma v$ over all items in that particular stratum of the corporate inventory (with the obvious addition if unfilled demand represents lost business) and the abscissa is $\sum (S/Q)v\sigma E(k)$ to represent annual backorders or $\sum (S/Q)F(k)$ to represent the number of shortage occurrences.

Figure 9 shows exchange curves developed for two alternative decision rules applied to the same inventory. The rules may be any of the ones discussed in sections 3.3 to 3.7; for generality we may call them "A" and "B". Clearly if backordered demand were the relevant measure of service, decision rule "A" is preferable to decision rule "B"; but if the number of shortage occurrences is more relevant, the order of preference is reversed.

Backorders (or lost business) are most often the primary measure of service in a "terminal" inventory from which demand from third-party customers is satis-

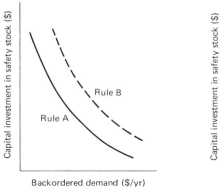
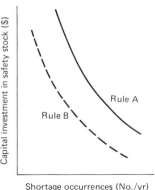

Fig. 9. Strategic comparison of two decision rules.

fied, and which is relatively isolated from the source of supply. The number of shortage occurrences may be of more concern in an inventory where it is possible to expedite a reasonable number of lots and get material in advance of the established lead time when demand is so much above forecast that the normal safety stock will be inadequate. The management of each enterprise must weigh the marketing and production reasons for having an inventory at all in order to decide which measure is more important in each instance.

Simpson [1958] has shown that to minimize the total inventory investment in a logistics system of several echelons, all of the risks of failure to meet demand should be taken at the final stage of inventory. At each earlier stage it is necessary to meet all the requirements. The base stock system (Magee [1958]) allows earlier stages to anticipate abnormal requirements and have material available on time, and effective expediting can often get material earlier than planned, even if intermediate stages do not carry safety stocks sufficient to meet all surges in demand.

Exchange curves are generated by assuming a range of alternative values for the management policy variable. Comparison with current safety stock investment and current actual service, as in Figure 10, aids the responsible manager to decide where on the curve he would like to operate for the coming year. Third-level exchange curves facilitate negotiation, in this case between the financial managers and marketing managers, by displaying the anatomy of alternative assumptions. The exchange of capital resources for marketing effectiveness is at the heart of entrepreneurial risk and is not an "ideal" value that can be measured objectively by an OR technician.

The next few sections describe in detail some of the common decision rules for determining a value of the safety factor k for all items in an inventory, with guidelines as to where each rule might be applicable.

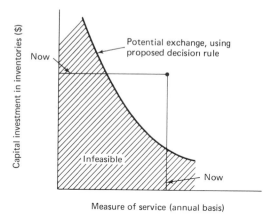

Fig. 10. Tactical choice of operating policy.

3.3 Weeks of Supply

Many existing inventory systems, otherwise quite sophisticated, include "3 weeks of supply" for safety stock where the value 3 is clearly the choice of a management policy variable. This rule fails utterly to take account of the fact that the coefficient of variation (ratio of the standard deviation to the mean forecast) varies by as much as a factor of 4 even among items with roughly the same forecast rate of sale. Hence, the effective safety factor for one item is quite low, resulting in poor service, and for another item quite high, resulting in an unnecessary inventory investment. This rule is quite a pet of the consultants in OR, if only because it is so easy to show a substantial gain in effectiveness with little effort.

3.4 Constant Safety Factor

In a system that needs a decision rule which is easy to develop, implement, document, maintain, and educate people in its use, a far preferable decision rule is to set safety stocks at "1.1σ" for all items in the inventory stratum. The value of the safety factor itself, here $k = 1.1$, is the policy variable. Because this rule takes explicit account of the standard deviation of forecast errors, it will have substantially less investment for any given level of service than the weeks-of-supply rule. The major complexity in this rule is to measure the standard deviation, which is properly part of the forecasting system, and required in any event if one is to obtain improvement in operating effectiveness.

This rule is often a useful transient stage in systems development that gets good results quickly and lets people in the organization become familiar with computing safety stocks from the standard deviation, rather than just the forecast itself, before going on to implement some more elegant rule.

3.5 Minimum Backorders

"Given a total capital budget for safety stocks, I_o, compute the safety factors for each item in the inventory stratum to minimize the value of annual backordered demand." This problem was formulated (Gerson [1970]) as a translation from the "managerese" of a very real objective of managers.

The expected dollar value of the backorders to be minimized is $\sum (S/Q)v\sigma E(k)$ per year, where each of the variables is subscripted for individual items in the inventory stratum. This minimization is subject to the constraint that the total safety stock $\sum k\sigma v = I_o$. Form the expression to be minimized, including an arbitrary multiple (Lagrange multiplier) λ times zero:

$$H(k_i, \lambda) = \sum (S_i/Q_i)v_i\sigma_i E(k_i) + \lambda\left(\sum k_i v_i \sigma_i - I_o\right) .$$

Set the partial derivative with respect to the safety factor for a particular item to zero, $\partial H/\partial k_j = 0$. Note that the terms for all other items in the summations are constants with respect to the differentiation, so that we are left with (S_j/Q_j) $v_j\sigma_j F(k_j) = \lambda v_j\sigma_j$, which results in the decision rule $F(k_j) = \lambda/(S_j/Q_j)$. The dimensions of the management policy variable λ are shortages per item per year. Note that the effect is to assure the same expected number of shortages per year for all items, taking account of the number of exposures based on the number of times the item is replenished. Values of the policy variable can be established by responsible management from a review of the exchange curve to satisfy either a capital budget constraint on investment (or space) or some marketing objective.

The effect of this rule is to compute larger safety factors for Class A items which are replenished frequently. For Class C items, which may be produced in a one- or two-year supply when needed, the formula may result in negative values for the safety factor, often arbitrarily limited to a minimum of zero. That is, for items replenished at long intervals, one obtains better service than the desired level with no safety stock at all. However, if additional money is available for investment, an increase in the safety stock for Class A items will reduce backorders more than the same investment added to the inventory for Class C items.

3.6 Minimum Number of Shortages

If the objective is to minimize the number of shortage occurrences for a given capital investment, the formulation of the problem is similar, replacing the expected number of shortages for the expected dollar value. The resulting decision rule is to find (if one exists) a safety factor k_j that satisfies $p(k_j) = \lambda v_j\sigma_j/$

(S_j/Q_j) where the management policy variable (Lagrange multiplier) λ has dimension $(1/\$)$ and can be interpreted as the marginal cost of a shortage that could be avoided by investing an incremental amount of capital in inventory. It is an imputed cost, not an accountable cost. The value to be implemented is a tactical choice to be reviewed annually by management with the aid of an exchange curve.

3.7   Other Decision Rules

Quite a wide variety of decision rules can be derived by changing the objective to be minimized within a budget constraint. For example, management may say that they want to minimize the number of customer calls (transactions) that can't be filled from stock. Brown [1972] shows that the solution to this problem has the extreme result of carrying stock for those items with low invoice values, and letting shortages occur for items with high invoice values Qv.

Another problem considers the administrative costs per customer transaction and the premium shipping charge per pound of material that has to be filled by referring an order to an alternative location when the point of demand entry is out of stock. The resulting decision rule is similar to section 3.5, and tends to reduce safety factors for light-weight material, or items where a single customer transaction is likely to be for a large quantity.

3.8   Interaction between Safety Stock and Replenishment Frequency

In the foregoing sections it was assumed that the frequency of exposure S/Q to shortages was already determined by the average order quantity Q and the annual sales rate S. The total annual cost of processing replenishment orders and of carrying the total investment in working stock $(\frac{1}{2}Q)$ and the safety stock is $C = \sum AS/Q + r \sum v(k\sigma + \frac{1}{2}Q)$, again with the obvious addition of $v\sigma E(k)$, if demand during a shortage is lost rather than backordered. To minimize this cost subject to a constraint B on the total dollar value of backorders, form

$$H(Q_j, k_j, \lambda) = C + \lambda\left(\sum(S_j/Q_j)\, v_j\sigma_j E(k_j) - B\right) \ ;$$

and turn the crank to get a pair of decision rules

$$F(k_j) = (r/\lambda)/(S_j/Q_j)$$
$$Q_j = \sqrt{2(A_j + \lambda v_j\sigma_j E(k_j))S_j/rv_j},$$

where it is clear that both the carrying charge r and the Lagrange multiplier λ are management policy variables. Figure 11 represents a three-dimensional exchange surface. The vertical axis represents total inventory investment $\sum v(k\sigma +$

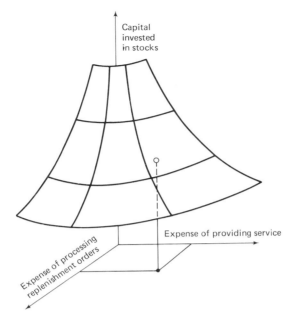

Capital
invested
in stocks

Expense of providing service

Expense of processing
replenishment orders

Fig. 11. A three-dimensional exchange surface.

$\frac{1}{2} Q$); the axis to the right represents service such as $\sum (S/Q)F(k)$; and the axis out of the plane of the page is the expense of processing replenishment orders $\sum AS/Q$. It is impractical to solve the two decision rules simultaneously for the safety factors k and the lot quantities Q, but they can be evaluated iteratively. First assume that the value for Q is some default lot quantity, and solve for k. Substitute that value in the second equation, solve for Q, and repeat. Usually, about three iterations gives a satisfactory convergence.

The results have been shown to be superior in total costs only when the default lot quantity would otherwise have been smaller than the standard deviation. Therefore, to save the expense of iterative computations, it is advisable to round the default lot quantity upward to at least the quantity of one standard deviation. This is not the quantity that would result from the decision rules above, but it is large enough to make it not worth while to compute the exact quantity.

Note that the expression $\lambda v \sigma E(k)$ could be considered as an additional expected expense of processing backordered demand that is incurred once each order cycle, just like the setup cost A. Thus the order quantity is larger than the simple default case, to reduce the frequency of exposure, which reduces the safety stock by more than enough to offset the increase in working stock. If any factor in this term is zero, the lot quantity is the default EOQ.

3.9 Stocks for Options in an Assembly

Consider now the case where the total number of trucks to be assembled in a given week has been fixed by the production schedule. Each truck has an optional feature which the customer may specify from a number of alternative choices. The particular mix of orders for the week in question is not known in advance. Therefore it is necessary to provide enough of each option to allow for building any reasonable order mix. Let us assume that the management objective is to minimize the number of shortage occurrences for any option, within a given constraint for the total investment in stocks for all alternatives for that option.

If the i-th option is ordered with probability p_i, then the distribution of the different order mixes is given by a multinomial distribution. The marginal distribution for the i-th option is a binominal distribution, which could be approximated for large assembly rates by the normal distribution. One degree of freedom is eliminated from the decision about how much to stock because the total number of orders to be filled must add to the total number of trucks to be assembled.

The decision rule is similar in form to section 3.6. The major difference being that we infer the relevant standard deviation from $\sigma = \sqrt{Npq}$, rather than from measuring forecast errors.

4. ALLOCATION

There are several ways in which a *finite resource* can be shared among *activities* in inventory systems. For example, a production batch of paint, or cereal, is to be filled into each of several different package sizes. The finished stock of a product is to be distributed through each of a number of field warehouses. The space in a rail car is to be shared by a number of products for the same destination. In each case there is a finite resource which is to be shared by several activities. These are all instances of a general allocation problem.

The decision rule for how much of the resource to devote to each activity usually works by computing the maximum objective for each that is consistent with the total resource available. Then enough of the resource is allocated to each, taking account of what is already available, to bring stock up to that objective.

Often one activity will already have more than its fair share of the total resource. In that case its resources and requirements are removed from consideration, and the allocation is computed with fewer activities. The result must converge in a finite number of iterations, with something to be allocated to at least one activity.

4.1 Criteria

There are several alternative criteria for determining the maximum stock objective for each activity. Perhaps the simplest to understand and to implement is to give each activity the same time supply. Let Q be the new amount to be shared among activities which have current usage rates S_i and current available stocks a_i. The total stock in the system will last $T = \left(Q + \sum a_i \right) / \sum S_i$. Therefore the amount to be sent to the i-th activity is $q_i = TS_i - a_i$, if the result is positive. Usually it is impractical to empty packages that are overstocked, and uneconomic to bring stock back from overstocked warehouses. If q_j is negative, remove S_j and a_j from the summations and recompute T', which will be smaller than before.

Meyer (see Brown [1967]) has worked out a rationale for allocation that minimizes the expected remnant stock. Suppose that a batch of product is filled into different size packages, and that a new production batch is required whenever the stock of any single package runs short. The stock at that time of the packages that haven't run short is called the *remnant stock*. Stock should be allocated among packages so that the probability that package j is the first one to run short is equal to the ratio $S_j / \sum S_i$. If demand is deterministic, there will be no remnant stock. It is difficult to work with the expression for the probability that package j will be the first to run short. Good results can be obtained by using T as the median time to run short for each product. Both the sales forecast $S_i(T)$ and the standard deviation $\sigma_i(T)$ depend on the length of time being covered. For each activity, compute a safety factor such that $F(k_j)$ is proportional to $\alpha S_j / \sum S_i$. The stocking objective is then $S_j(T) + k_j \sigma_j(T)$. The constant of proportionality $0.5 < \alpha < 0.693$, is a root of the polynomial $G(\alpha) = \prod_j$

$$\left(1 - \alpha S_j / \sum_i S_i \right) = 0.5.$$

Other criteria for allocation might be to minimize the expected total value of backorders or the number of shortages. Note that the safety stock decision rules in sections 3.5-9 were all derived by allocating a finite capital budget among items in the inventory stratum, in order to minimize some service criterion.

4.2 Evaluation

While each decision rule can be stipulated to achieve the objective set forth in stating the problem, the evaluation of alternatives should take note of side effects, such as the average stock in the system as a whole, the number of allocation decisions per year, and the expected number and size of shortages. It may be found that a simple rule, like equal time supplies, is quite robust and shows good performance on all measures, while a more elaborate rule might do well in one respect, but have unattractive side effects. A third-level simulation can often quickly discriminate among such alternatives, if the machinery is set up to measure several aspects of performance for any decision rule.

5. SYSTEMS ARCHITECTURE

From combinations of the building blocks described above, it is possible to construct a good many different inventory control systems. Some theoretical insight into replenishment decisions can be gained by exploring models with zero lead time or deterministic demand. Most practical systems for implementation have to deal with stochastic demand over a lead time. Most of the theory is developed on the assumption that the resulting decision rule will be applied repetitively but, in reality, lead times, costs, and the distribution of demand change appreciably over time. Thus, the replenishment decision taken now is merely the best decision in the light of the current outlook; the next time the decision has to be taken, the same rule may be applied, but result in vastly different numbers.

In this section we shall first consider several alternative ways of taking the first-level decision about when to reorder any particular stocked item, and how much to order. As special cases there are the "two-bin" system for Class C items and special techniques for dealing with "lumpy" demand. Later we shall consider joint orders for several related items, and finally we shall consider the physical distribution of products through several supply echelons.

5.1 Independent Orders

When it is possible to order any item in the inventory at any time without regard to the status of other items, there are basically three ways to answer the questions WHEN to order the item and HOW MUCH to order.

(a) *Order-point, order-quantity*. An order point, or reorder level, is computed for each item from the current forecast of requirements over the replenishment lead time, plus a safety stock. The safety stock is the product of the standard deviation of the distribution of forecast errors over the lead time, and a safety factor. The safety factor can be computed from any of the decision rules in section 3, or any applicable extension.

The first-level system keeps track of the available stock on hand, plus stock on order, less backorders or other commitments. When the available stock drops, because of a demand transaction, to or below the order point, then a replenishment order is triggered.

The quantity to order is computed from the applicable decision rule from section 2. The quantity may be rounded to convenient package quantities, time supplies, or handling units, without any significant loss in economic advantage.

The second-level decision rules are usually evaluated at regular intervals, such as once a month, and the results are stored in the first-level files.

This is the simplest procedure to comprehend and implement, and is frequently quite satisfactory. For example in the manufacture of paint and pharmaceuticals, tank sizes impose physical limits on the reorder quantities, so that it makes sense to reorder in pre-determined lot quantities.

(b) *Max/min* or (s, S). The minimum level s is computed the same way as the order point in the paragraph above entitled "Order-point, order-quantity." The maximum level S is the sum of this minimum and the order quantity suggested by the appropriate lot-size decision rule from section 2. These values are computed at regular intervals by the second-level system, and the results stored in the first-level files.

The first-level system continually keeps track of available stock. When it drops to the minimum, the quantity to order is the difference between the maximum objective and the available stock. If there is an opportunity to reorder after each unit of demand is posted (so that the available stock drops exactly to the minimum level), the system operates exactly like the order-point, order-quantity. However, if the records for the available stock are posted at long intervals, or if single demand transactions can be found for large quantities, there is a possibility that the available stock will be below the order point when the need to replenish is recognized, and the max/min system restores that deficit. This system has been studied extensively (Arrow [1958]), and is preferable to the order-point, order-quantity system when there may be significant deficits at the times when replenishment orders are triggered. Again, the suggested order quantity can be rounded to convenient packages, time supplies, and handling units.

(c) *Fixed interval.* If the source will not accept orders except at fixed intervals of time, there is no point in ordering between those times. For example, the manufacturing plant may process all orders on the 24th of the month when they prepare production schedules. Or a supply boat visiting ships of a fleet calls only once every 10 days. One might as well wait until the source is ready to accept orders to trigger new orders to replenish stocks.

In this case the reorder point, or minimum stock level, is based on a forecast of requirements during the replenishment lead time plus one additional interval between opportunities to order, plus a safety stock to cover errors in forecasting demand over that interval, as before. If the available stock at the time of review is below this reorder point, then a replenishment order is released either for the predetermined order quantity or for the difference between the available stock and the maximum level. Note that the minimum order quantity must always be sufficient to last at least the time between replenishment opportunities. This scheme is also used, in some instances, as an approximation to joint ordering (5.7) where several items should be coordinated.

In general, the values for the order point or minimum and the order quantity or maximum should be recomputed whenever the forecast is revised. In some systems, the order point is revised when there is a new forecast, but the order quantities or maximum values are computed only when an order is to be released.

5.2 Two-bin Control

The two-bin system is a special case of an order-point, order-quantity, system that requires a minimum of record keeping and is highly suitable for Class C materials. A quantity of stock equal to an order point is physically segregated into a reserve bin or sealed bag. The balance of the stock is in a working bin. Anyone is allowed to withdraw from the working bin as needed without records.

When the working bin is empty, the reserve bin is broken open. A travelling requisition is removed from the sealed bin to start the replenishment process. Good discipline is required to assure that this travelling requisition is retrieved and sent to the production control or purchasing department who can use it as the reorder document. The supplier can use it as a picking document and a shipping document, so that it comes back with the new material.

When the material is received, the reserve bin is refilled to the order-point quantity, the travelling requisition is placed inside, and the bin is sealed. The balance of the stock is put into the open working bin. The quantity ordered at one time should last much longer than the replenishment lead time so that there is never more than one order outstanding at any one time. This is true for Class C items in most inventories.

There may be some loss and unauthorized shrinkage of stock, but the elimination of all records except the travelling requisition may save far more in administrative costs than is lost by lax controls. Often, the system is not popular with accountants.

The usage rate can be inferred from the travelling requisition, which shows the quantity in the working bin and the date it was replenished. Since the reserve stock is also noted, the demand rate is the working stock quantity divided by the time elapsed since replenishment until the reserve stock is opened. The default EOQ, based on current purchase cost, is a good estimate of the replenishment order quantity. A one-time study to establish a variance-law relationship between average usage rate and the standard deviation of demand-during-a-lead-time can set up a table of 3σ safety stocks. The same table gives the order points, based on the current estimated usage rate.

5.3 Lumpy Demand

In most inventories, especially of repair parts for machinery, the demand is "lumpy"; that is, there are long random periods with no demand, periods with low demand, and occasional quite large peaks. If the large peaks can be anticipated, such as for special projects and contracts, it is wise to plan their procurement separately (5.4). When the demand is essentially unpredictable, classical methods of inventory control (especially forecasting) are in some difficulty.

The following system is now being used successfully by a number of corporations. Stock is replenished on a max/min (s, S) system. The order quantity used in computing the maximum should take account of the interaction between lot quantities and safety stocks (3.8), which can be approximated satisfactorily by assuring that the lot quantity is at least as large as σ.

The order point should be larger than the normal minimum by the amount of the *expected deficit*, or the average of the amounts by which the available stock is below the order point when a replenishment order is triggered. An estimate of this expected deficit is $\langle d^2 \rangle / 2 \langle d \rangle$, where the notation $\langle \cdot \rangle$ is for the expected value and d is the number of units on a single demand transaction, or a single posting to stock. Note that if all transactions were for the same quantity, the expected deficit reduces to half the expected demand quantity. For lumpy demand it is significantly larger.

Thus for normal items, the lumpy-demand control system reduces to a classical min/max system. "Lumpiness" is measured by the coefficient of variation (σ/μ) rather than the absolute level of demand. If the coefficient of variation (or any other convenient measure of relative variability) is larger than 1.0, the item can be considered to be lumpy. Items should not be reclassified more often than once a year, and there should be a "chatter" interval so that normal items become lumpy only if the coefficient of variation exceeds 1.2 and lumpy items become normal if it drops below 0.8. Marginal items, with ratios near 1, will be controlled much the same way in either case.

There is no information from current demand to warrant revising the max/min levels frequently. This is the significant difference from the second-level revisions of the max/min levels for the normal case. One can maintain statistics about the average demand quantity and the average square of demand quantities, revised after each demand posting by exponential smoothing. Lead-time demand can be posted at each receipt, to maintain statistics about the average and average of squared values. After at least 30 demand transactions, or a calendar year, whichever occurs first, use these statistics to recompute the max/min quantities.

5.4 Time-Phased Planning

The inventory control systems described above keep track only of the total balance of stock on order from all outstanding replenishment orders. The balance is credited with new replenishment orders and debited by receipts from the source (with suitable adjustments for orders that are closed short or long).

Future requirements are expressed as the total forecast over the lead time, plus a safety stock.

In some situations it is advisable to keep track of requirements and availability by time period, within the lead time, and far beyond. For example, if there are special large commitments for marketing programs, retrofit of customer equipment, lot-size withdrawals for assembly, or definite contracts, these requirements can be posted separately from the forecast of normal demand. In mail order of style merchandize and sales of air conditioners it is trade practice to accept return of goods sent out earlier, and it is necessary to keep track of a separate forecast of returns, by time period, as well as new material due from the source.

There are two reasons for keeping the more elaborate first-level records illustrated in Figure 12. (a) When dependent demand on lower levels of assembly is to be exploded from top-level production schedules, requirements must be projected quite some time ahead to allow for the offset times at each level of assembly. (b) When it is practical to expedite as an alternative to keeping safety stocks (3.6) the time-phased records give a more precise picture of which open order must be rescheduled, and what others can be moved back to provide capacity.

A typical record (Figure 12) has one column for each time period, and one row for each independently planned kind of requirement and for each source of material. Usually there is a *freeze period*, indicated by the heavy line between periods 8 and 9, during which orders on the source are considered firm and are not to be changed either in quantity or time due. Orders beyond this freeze period, which can be longer or shorter than the actual lead time, are *notional*. They are, for example, used as a basis for planning materials and labor, but are subject to change in time and quantity as requirements and current available stock change.

Notional orders are computed as follows. Set all notional orders to zero, beyond the freeze period. Compute the total planned requirements by time period as the algebraic sum of each kind of requirement record. The safety stock is the product of a suitable safety factor and the standard deviation σ, which is based on errors in forecasts of total requirements over the freeze period. In some cases safety stock also includes other reserve quantities.

The bottom row shows the *net stock* position by time period. In the first period the net stock is the excess of stock actually on hand over the planned safety stock, and it may be negative. Each period the net stock is computed from the net stock at the end of the previous period by adding firm orders and subtracting total planned requirements.

The first notional order is due in the time period (a) beyond the freeze and (b) where net stock falls to or below zero. (That is equivalent to saying that stock on hand is projected to fall to or below the planned reserve for safety

	1	2	3	4	5	6	7	8	9	10	11	12	13	14	15	16	17	18	19	20	21	22	23	…
Forecasts of normal demand	30	30	30	35	35	35	35	40	40	40	40	40	35	35	35	35	30	30	30	30	25	25	25	…
Dependent requirements, exploded from higher levels			600			100			300					500					700					
Special contracts and projects											1,000													
Forecasts of returned merchandise	0	0	0	0	0	0	0	0	0	0	5	5	5	5	10	10	10	10	15	15	15	15	15	…
Total planned requirements (Safety stock 200)	30	30	630	35	35	135	35	40	340	40	1,035	30	30	525	25	20	20	15	15	10	10	10		…
Firm orders		750				500																		
Net stock position (Stock on hand 250, Safety stock 50)	20	740	110	75	40	405	370	330	290	−50 / 1,075 / 1,035	0	555	525	0	40		20	0		25	0	·	·	…
Notional orders																65			40					

Fig. 12. Record format for time-phased planning period (e.g., weeks).

stock.) In the illustration, this occurs in period 9, which is beyond the freeze, where the projected net stock falls to −50 units. Thus a notional order is due in period 9.

The quantity for that notional order can be the sum of actual requirements over an economical number of planning periods (2.5) or for a fixed order quantity which may be dictated by quality control or manufacturing methods. In the case shown, the first notional order of 1125 covers the total planned requirements in the next three periods, plus the deficit of 50 units carried over from the freeze period. Then the net stock falls to zero in period 12 and another three-period supply is due in period 13.

The notional order now due in the first period beyond the freeze now becomes a firm order, not to be changed in subsequent periods when the planning process is repeated. Note that the firm order can be a zero quantity.

Chapters I-5 and I-9 go more deeply into the production processes which explode high-level requirements into requirements on parts and raw materials, and other matters of inventory planning in the manufacturing process.

5.5 Run-out Lists

Sometimes it is advisable to trigger orders in advance of need, to give production facilities enough work to use the planned capacity effectively. One method is to produce a list of notional orders for all products, sorted in sequence by due date, until a sufficient workload has been accumulated to assure that even with the most favorable conditions of productivity and yield there won't be a shortage of things to do.

5.6 Seasonal Stocking

In any industry where it is economically advisable to produce at a steady rate throughout the year, but demand is seasonal, it is necessary to plan the stocks of items to be built up during the slack season. First select only stockable items where it is prudent from marketing, shelf-life, and continued demand to carry a stock for a substantial portion of the year.

Now rank these items in sequence for the preference for seasonal stock, usually the ratio of man-hours (or machine hours) to the standard cost of materials. The aim is to stock those items with high labor (or machine) content at the minimum financial investment.

At the beginning of the slack season, when capacity is greater than required for current demand, select the first item on the preference list, and make enough of it to last through the next peak season. If there is additional capacity available, make the second item on the list.

Easy-to-make, expensive items are made to meet current demand throughout the year. The hard-to-make, cheap items are made in one lot, which stocks a great deal of productive capacity for relatively little financial investment.

5.7 Joint Orders

If there is a common cost incurred once for an order of a number of related items, then the whole family should be ordered at one time. For example, materials bought from the same vendor may have freight minimums or quantity discounts; various products can be bottled on one packaging line for one line setup; many different parts can be stamped from the same coil stock with a simple change of dies, etc.

One possibility is to trigger a replenishment order for the family at fixed intervals (5.1c). Another possibility is to trigger an order for the family whenever any item reaches its order point. However, that leads to substantial remnant stocks (4.1). A third possibility is to trigger a replenishment order when the aggregate projected shortage reaches some critical level. Estimate the probable stock level a lead time from now $I_i(L) = I_i(0) - L\mu_i$, where L is the common lead time for the family, and μ_i is the projected rate of usage for the i-th item. For some items $I_i(L)$ might be negative. The effective safety factor is $k_i = I_i(L)/\sigma_i$. The expected total shortage is then $\sum v_i\sigma_i E(k_i)$ for the family. If this expression is larger than $\lambda \sum \mu_i$, for some management policy λ, then it is time to order.

In the independent-item case it is not so usual to express the order point in terms of the expected shortage, but it holds there as well. This difference in point of view makes it practical to deal with joint orders.

All items are ordered on the basis of a common time supply T (2.3). For those items produced every cycle, order enough to bring supply up to $T\mu_i + k_i\sigma_i$. For items that are to be produced only on every n-th cycle, order enough to bring the supply up to $n_iT\mu_i + k_i\sigma_i$. However, if the available supply is now enough to last at least T, don't order that item at all.

If the order for a family is triggered when the available stock for any member reaches an order point, then coordinated orders for other items can be generated by comparing their available stocks with a "can-order" point, which is usually set as some fraction of the distance between the order point and a maximum stocking objective (Silver [1972]).

5.8 Multi-echelon Physical Distribution

There have been several scholarly papers on multi-echelon inventory management (Scarf [1963]). The "master/satellite" system has been implemented successfully in many government and industrial physical distribution networks, with considerable improvement in availability and reduction in inventory investment.

Each product that is stocked in more than one location (1.4) has one location designated as a *master warehouse*. The location of the master warehouse need not be the same for all products. In some industries it is the location nearest the plant or port of entry; in others it is in the center of the market concentration. The function of the master warehouse is to carry a *national safety stock* for redistribution to the satellites. Often the same physical location has a *satellite* function, to fill demand from customers in that market territory.

The *net available stock* in the system is the stock on hand, plus firm orders on the source, less any unfilled commitments to customers, less the sum of satellite order point quantities, and less any unredistributable excess. New orders on the source can be triggered by comparing this net available stock with a national order point, or by time-phased planning. In either case there is provision for a national safety stock based on the standard deviation of the error in forecasting aggregate demand, and a safety factor (3.6).

When material is received from the source, the national safety stock quantity is reserved at the master warehouse, and the balance of the stock is allocated among satellites (4.1).

Each satellite has an order point based on the forecast of demand in its territory during the redistribution lead time from the master warehouse, plus a safety stock based on the standard deviation of errors in those forecasts and a safety factor (3.5). The stock available to a satellite is the stock on hand, plus in transit, less unfilled commitments to local customers. When the available stock reaches the order point a *redistribution* is triggered. The national safety stock is now considered available (not reserved as in the initial distribution of a receipt) and the total system stock is allocated among all locations. Only the fair share due to the location needing more material is actually shipped. The balance is held at the master warehouse until some other location trips its reallocation order point.

If during the allocation computation some satellite has more than its fair share already, that excess is the *unredistributable excess*, which is subtracted from total system net available stock in deciding whether to order more material from the source. If the excess is large, some enterprises temporarily designate that location as a master warehouse, to distribute the material to other locations as needed, in which case the excess is clearly not unredistributable.

There are many variations on this theme. In some cases the initial distribution is computed before shipment so that the source can ship directly to each location. The total country considered as one system may be only the warehouses west of the Rockies for commodities such as paint and bricks that aren't shipped long distances. There may be some commodities where it is impractical to redistribute stock, so that orders on one warehouse are transferred to another when the normal stocking location runs short (3.7). There may be good marketing reasons for biasing the allocations to assure that one territory is kept in good supply even when the total system is short of stock, as for certain medicines used by a few large medical centers (1.3).

When production lead times are measured in months and quarters but redistribution lead times are measured in days and weeks, the long lead time is buffered by only one safety stock, the national safety stock. It is not usually true that forecast errors for local sales territories are statistically independent, but it has been common to find that the standard deviation of errors in forecasting total demand is appreciably less than the sum of the standard deviations of errors, territory by territory. The redistribution allows one national safety stock effectively to protect the whole country.

Class A items tend to have most of their safety stock at the satellites, and Class C items tend to have most of their safety stock at the master warehouse, because of the recommended decision rules for computing the two kinds of safety factors. See Magee [1968] for further details and elaboration of planning for the transport and storage of materials in such a system.

6. IMPLEMENTATION

Modern theories of inventory management have gained wide acceptance in the United States and by progressive managers of corporations elsewhere in the world. Yet many of the attempts to implement well-designed systems have failed. A common source of failure is to "use the computer to solve our inventory problems" rather than to solve the problems, using the computer when advisable. Another common source of failure is to design a total system to be implemented all at once. It takes appreciable time for people, from clerks to vice presidents, to absorb the real implications of a radically new system. When a large system is well planned, but implemented in a series of small steps: (a) people can keep up with the change; (b) the track record of successful changes makes further changes easier; (c) preliminary tangible results are available early as proof of the validity of the theory, and as a real, if small, advantage to the organization; (d) options are left open about how to deal with some aspects of the system until there is ample operating evidence to aid in the decision among alternatives.

6.1 Time for an Inventory to React

The third-level simulations that produce exchange curves indicate the service, number of replenishment orders, and inventory investment in the steady state. Often there is a long transition period before the predicted results will be seen on the third-level operating monitor reports.

As a part of the implementation of each part of a new system, there should also be a simulation to project the inventory and service, month by month, starting from current stock status until the new conditions are reached. There is a characteristic time constant for an inventory, which includes the lead time from a reorder decision until stock is on hand, and the distribution of times until present stock status reaches the new order point. Brown [1967] has worked out expressions involving the parameters of the order-quantity decisions and the lognormal distribution of usage rates for the expected fraction of the ultimate effect, as a function of the elapsed time after a change is introduced. In practice it is usually simpler to use a brute-force simulation.

In conglomerate enterprises, managers who have become subjectively aware of the time constant in one segment of the business may be alarmed at the vast difference in another kind of industry. An appropriate third-level simulation can help them condition their expectations so that there will be no surprises.

6.2 Excess Stocks

Inevitably, some of the current stock is excessive—if not under present rules, then under the proposed change in decision rules and values for policy variables. It is important to identify these excesses, and to take action to get rid of the most serious ones.

The maximum reasonable stock on hand could be as much as a full replenishment lot quantity, plus twice the safety stock (on the grounds that the minimum reasonable stock is zero, and the average on hand before a receipt is the safety stock). Any actual stock on hand above this amount is excess.

The total available stock (on hand plus on order) could be as large as the maximum stock objective, or the order point plus the order quantity. If available stock is above this level, the difference is excess.

To screen out the trivial excesses, one usually ignores excess stock that will be worked off in a short span of time at the forecast rate of usage, say three or four months, or excess amounts that are small in value, say less than $1000.

The excesses which represent more than three months of supply and more than $1000 can be listed in descending sequence by the dollar value of the excess, so that if there isn't time to deal with them all, at least the most important will receive attention first. If the excess is caused by an open order, cancel the order, defer delivery, or cut the quantity. Even a cancellation penalty can be small compared with the cost of writing off excess material later. If the excess stock is already on hand, then more careful consideration is required to find the best way to salvage it.

Often the accountants will have a view as to the best time to take a tax write-off on the excess. Marketing may have views on the danger of letting material get into disposal channels that would compete with the profitable products, or they may have ingenious suggestions for special marketing campaigns to sell off the excess.

An economic model of the cost of retention versus salvage of material, when the demand forecast is rising or will continue long enough to use up the material, indicates that it is better to retain the excess than to write it down. However, if the stock on hand is more than the forecast of total requirements for the remainder of the life of the product, then any excess over an all-time supply should be written off, at any loss.

For spare parts for automobiles and other machinery there is good evidence (Brown [1963]) that the population declines exponentially, and that "an all-time supply is a five-year supply"—meaning that the total remaining usage for a part, once it is in the declining phase, is about five times the actual usage in the most recent year, at any time.

REFERENCES

Arrow, K. J., S. Karlin, *Studies in the Mathematical Theory of Inventory and Production* Stanford University Press, Stanford, California (1958).

Brown, R. G., *Statistical Forecasting for Inventory Control*, McGraw-Hill, New York (1959).

——, *Smoothing, Forecasting and Prediction*, Prentice-Hall, Englewood Cliffs, New Jersey (1963).

——, *Decision Rules for Inventory Management* Holt, Rinehart and Winston, New York (1967).

——, *Management Decisions for Production Operations*, Dryden (1971 a).

——, "Economic order quantities for materials subject to engineering changes" *Production and Inventory Management* 12 No. 2: 89–91 (1971 b)

——, "Improved customer service at the HAL division" *Proc. Am. Production and Inventory Control Conf.*, Toronto, 152–177 (October 1972)

deMatteis, J. J., A. G. Mendoza, "Part-period algorithm" *IBM Syst. J.* 7 No. 1: 30–46 (1968).

Dvoretsky, A., J. Kiefer, J. Wolfowitz, "The inventory problem," *Econometrica* XX: 187–222 and 450–466 (1952).

Gerson, G., and R. G. Brown, "Decision rules for equal shortage policies," *Nav. Res. Log. Quart.* 17 No. 3: 351–358 (September 1970).

Harris, F. W., *Operations and cost*, A. W. Shaw, Chicago (1915).

Magee, J. F., *Production Planning and Inventory Control*, McGraw-Hill, New York (1958).

——, *Industrial Logistics*, McGraw-Hill, New York (1968).

Mennell, R. F., "Early history of the economic lot size," *Am. Production and Inventory Control Soc. Quart. Bull.* 2 No. 2: 19–22 (April 1961).

Moran, P. A. P., *The Theory of Storage*, Methuen, London (1959).

Nocturne, D. H., "Economic ordering frequency for several items jointly replenished," *Management Sci.* 19, No. 9: 1093–1096 (May 1973).

Raymond, F. E., *Quantity and Economy in Manufacturing*, McGraw-Hill, New York (1931).

Scarf, H. E., D. M. Guilford, M. W. Shelly (eds.), *Multi-Stage Inventory Models and Techniques*, Stanford University Press, Stanford, California (1963).

Schlaiffer, R. *Introduction to Statistics for Business Decisions*, McGraw-Hill, New York (1961).

Silver, E. A., J. P. Schaack, "A procedure, involving simulation, for selecting the control variables in an :S,c,s) joint ordering strategy," *INFOR J.* **10** No. 2 (May 1972).

Simpson, K. F., "In-process inventories," *Operations Res.*, **6** No. 6: 863–873 (September 1958).

Wagner, H., T. M., Whitin, "Dynamic version of the economic lot size model," *Management Sci*, **5**: 89–96 (1958).

Whitin, T. M., *The Theory of Inventory Management*, Princeton University Press, Princeton, New Jersey (1953).

I-7

COMPUTER AND INFORMATION SYSTEMS

Alan G. Merten
University of Michigan

1. INTRODUCTION

Since its introduction in the early 1940's, the digital computer has had a significant effect on the operations of business, scientific, and educational organizations throughout the world. Computer hardware, computer software, and the people assigned to the design and maintenance of computer systems represent a sizeable resource of an operating organization. Because of this, operating organizations and researchers have been intrigued with the vast number of allocation of resource problems associated with computer systems. Computer systems have been modeled and analyzed by various techniques of OR (Hanssman [1971]). In this chapter the various classifications of computer and information systems will be defined, the activities of designing, operating, evaluating, and managing computer systems will be specified, and various ramifications of applying OR techniques to specific problems will be presented.

Operations research techniques have been used to analyze various components and levels of digital computers. In order to delineate the various applications we will define various system classifications of computers. The *hardware system* represents the lowest level; it usually includes the central processing unit, primary memory, secondary memory, peripherals, and control functions. There are only a few published reports of the use of OR to aid in the design of these hardware devices.

Most often we refer to a *computer system* as the combination of hardware and software provided by the vendors, such as the operating system and the language processors (compilers, assemblies, etc.). The operating system is a collection of computer programs used to control and direct the wide range of user programs run on the computer system and to allocate resources to these programs. Operating systems also perform other functions such as resource charging and accounting. Most of the applications of OR techniques to computer and information science have been directed toward design of the components of an operating system and the interface of operating systems to the various hardware components.

Most organizations, both business and scientific, make little or no change to the hardware and software provided by the computer vendor. They use these resources to write application programs and design file systems to meet their specific information processing requirements. The collection of application software and computer system hardware and software is often referred to as a *computer-based*, *information processing system*. Until recently, there have been few applications of OR techniques to determine efficient ways to develop application programs using the facilities of the computing system. Most of the applications have been in the area of the design of user files.

A computer is a device for storing, maintaining, and processing data for use by people. In many organizations a computer-based, information processing system is an integral part of the organizational *information system*. However, the information system also contains many noncomputerized and manual functions. Included in these are those activities associated with preparing input for computer systems and for the use of computer output by various technical and managerial personnel. Operations research techniques have been used to design and evaluate information systems and have been used to determine the effective use of computers within the information systems.

In order to classify the use of OR techniques in the area of computer and information science we also distinguish the point in time in which these techniques are applied to the particular system. The techniques may be used in design, operation, management, and evaluation of any of the system classifications listed in this section.

The life cycle of development of any of the four system types can be viewed as being divided into the following stages:

1. Perception of Need
2. Logical System Design
3. Physical Systems Design
4. Construction
5. Testing
6. Operation and Evaluation
7. Maintenance and Modification

During the perception of need there is a recognition of the desire to produce a system. During the logical system design phase, the system is specified in terms of requirements. During physical systems design there is a detailed specification of the procedures necessary to construct the system. During construction, the system is built using the available components. During testing, the system is tested under various conditions both idealistic and operational. The system is then operated over time, evaluated, and, possibly, maintained and modified. During the maintenance and modification, a number of the other steps of the life cycle may be repeated.

In general, OR techniques have been used during the physical systems design phase of the four levels of system classification. In some cases, OR techniques have been used to evaluate and compare various alternatives. Also, OR techniques have been used to decide how to monitor the operation of computer systems and, based on this monitoring, make appropriate modifications.

Various OR techniques have been used to study the different system levels during the various phases of the life cycle specified above. The difficulty in comparing the techniques lies in the fact that there is often a fine line between the use of mathematical notations in the analysis of a computer system, the use of simple quantitative analysis, or the use of OR techniques to study the system. The three most widely used classes of OR techniques are queuing theory, optimization theory, and computer simulation. Queuing theory models of various components of computer operating systems constitute a large class of the applications of OR. These applications have, for the most part, looked at a computing system as one or more resources requested by users of one or more types. These analyses have been done both at the secondary memory device level and the operating systems component level.

Mathematical programming techniques have been applied to computer systems design by various authors during the past ten years. In most cases the authors have formulated optimization problems involving time-shared or spaceshared resources of a computer system in an attempt to solve these problems through the use of mathematical programming techniques such as IP. Some of these applications are in the areas of scheduling in a multiprogramming environment, organization of primary and secondary memory, and design of file organizations to support an information processing system (McWhorter [1971]).

Computer simulation models have been designed to aid in the development of various systems. Besides the simulation models designed by the computer vendors, there have also been computer simulation models designed to assist users in the selection of a computer system based on a set of predetermined requirements. Simulation models have also been designed to study various components of hardware and operating systems.

In the remaining sections of this chapter, specific examples of the use of OR techniques in the area of computer and information systems will be described.

The examples will be classified according to the system type to which the model and technique were applied. The technique used will be explicit, but the time within the life cycle should be self-evident.

2. COMPUTER SYSTEMS

The designer of computer systems software (operating systems, compilers, data management systems, etc.) is constrained by the resources provided in the hardware system, and wants to produce the most cost-effective software for the programmers and file designers that will use his software (*computer system*).

The application of OR techniques to the design of a computer system are usually concerned with the allocation of memory and the distribution of processor time to a set of programs. The published results can be classified into the following three categories:

1. design of scheduling and allocation schemes for a particular memory device
2. assignment of user files to memory when there is more than one class of memory
3. design of scheduling schemes to be used in a multiprogramming or time-sharing environment

Frank [1969] developed models of movable head secondary storage devices. Expected seek time and expected rotational delay were used as measures of performance of the disk. The following aspects of disk file behavior were considered: the speed characteristics of the mechanism and its effect on seek time; effects of the probability distribution of requests for information stored on tracks; track overflow of records; dynamic queuing strategies; reduction of rotation time by buffered read techniques; and strategies for using multiple-armed devices. He developed analytic stochastic models of the transfer characteristics of this class of storage devices.

Based on these models, Frank was able to state a number of conclusions. If very active records are stored in the central portion of the disk, the average seek time can be reduced. A significant reduction in seek time can be made by utilizing the properties of the queue of service requests rather than using a FCFS policy. If records are large relative to track capacity, buffers can be effectively used to reduce rotational delay. Additional results were stated concerning the use of multiple independent disk heads.

Seaman, et al. [1966] developed a queuing model for analyzing alternative ways of storing direct access files on secondary storage systems. They derived formulas for system response time and for utilization factors of the file modules and channels. They also discussed modifications to the basic model necessary for estimating performance obtained in using indexes in large sequential files.

Abate, Dubner, and Weinberg [1968] used queuing theory to analyze the performance of a mass storage device in a real-time environment. A trade-off analysis was performed between the throughput of a stochastic service device and the response time for each service request. The analysis was applied to the IBM 2314 disk storage facility. The results were presented in a series of graphs showing the file system response time versus the throughput for several distributions of record length and user requests, as represented by disk arm movement. The authors claim that any disk whose seek time characteristic can be approximated by a piecewise linear continuous function can be analyzed by the methods presented.

Lauer [1967] developed an analytic model to aid in the comparison of a IBM 360-67, using a drum as a paging memory, and an IBM 360/67 using bulk core for a paging memory. Models of the drum and bulk core systems were constructed and used to determine that the drum could not support the paging rate except under conditions which impose high system costs.

Denning [1967] analyzed the effect of various queue disciplines on the performance of disks and drums. He compared the performance of three scheduling methods for movable head devices. The basic scheduling method was one in which requests are processed on a FCFS basis. In an effort to reduce the head movement and the expected seek time of the FCFS, scheduling procedures in which all waiting requests are considered as candidates for the next request to be serviced were also examined. In one of these scheduling schemes, the next request processed was the one that could be satisfied in moving the head the shortest distance (shortest-seek-time-first (SSTF)). The other scheduling scheme was a modification of SSTF. Denning showed that SSTF methods reduce the expected seek time and consequently the expected service and completion time, but that the variance of completion time is often very large because of long delays encountered in servicing requests for information in the inner and outer regions of the storage device. In this model, Denning approximated the movement of the head with continuous random variables and computed the expected value of this random variable as a measure of performance to be used in comparison of the alternative schemes. Merten [1970] and Teorey and Pinkerton [1972] extended and modified Denning's results. Analytic and simulation models are presented which are used to compare various disk scheduling policies with respect to the mean and variance of different performance variables.

Coffman [1969] developed mathematical models of drum scheduling disciplines in which requests arrived singly and at random. The models were analyzed and the following results were presented: a measure of drum utilization, a generating function for the queue length probabilities at equilibrium, and a procedure for computing the mean queue length and the mean waiting time.

Various authors have applied quantitative techniques to the allocation of primary memory to computer jobs. Kelley [1961] developed a model to assign subroutines to available primary memory. Kelley defined three allocation problems using space requirements, processing time, and the functional capabilities of various routines as parameters. In one model, memory space was minimized, subject to processing time constraints. In the other, processing time was minimized, subject to memory space constraints. The models developed were IP and DP models. Although the author indicates that the variables in the models must take on the values of either 0 or 1, he does not explicitly state that these are discrete optimization problems and generally cannot be solved using classical LP techniques.

Knuth [1968] reports the results of simulations on various primary memory replacement algorithms. A commonly accepted scheme used to satisfy requests for memory was shown to be inferior to another scheme which is easier to implement. Additional simulation results relate the total size of the memory resource to the amount of memory needed to satisfy an individual request.

Pinkerton [1968] developed stochastic models to study the problem of increasing productivity of a computing system by improving primary memory allocation.

The models described in this section have considered the allocation of memory resources at a particular memory level. In third-generation computing systems, various levels of memory are available to the designer of a computer system. Some research has been reported on the use of OR techniques to allocate and manage programs and files in computer systems with multiple memory types.

Ramamoorthy and Chandy [1970] developed a model for the selection of types and sizes of memory devices to minimize the average access time to an information block subject to cost constraints. A program was partitioned into equal size blocks and each block was assigned a relative frequency of usage. Analytic and mathematical programming models were developed for assigning program and data (information blocks) to a particular component of the memory hierarchy. They also considered the case in which memories are constructed out of indivisible modules. Considering these indivisible modules, an IP formulation of the memory hierarchy problem was provided. They proposed a branch and bound algorithm for the solution of the formulated programming problem.

Hellerman and Smith [1970] presented an analytic model of a computing system in order to compute the performance of various channel and memory configurations. The object of the paper was to gain insight into the bounds on system throughput performance and to give equations useful for checking computer simulations. The model assumed that the resources of the computing system were a single central processing unit, main storage, auxiliary storage consisting of one or more devices, and channels for controlling transmission between main and auxiliary storage.

Anacker and Wang [1967] studied the memory hierarchy problem by analyzing data flow between different levels of memory. A method to determine data processing rates and the relative utilization of memories for various system configurations under a variety of program loads was presented. The statistics of data flow in the memory hierarchy were obtained by analyzing a number of recorded address traces of executed programs. A combination of queuing theory and simulation models for the analyses of processor and memory operations were presented. These models were used to analyze two computer programs: a FORTRAN compiler computing a source program and a FORTRAN object program.

Gecsei, et al. [1970] presented quantitative techniques that eliminate much of the effort required in the use of simulation to evaluate storage hierarchies. Procedures were presented to determine the exact frequency of access to each level of a memory hierarchy. These procedures were applied to a large class of memory replacement algorithms used to determine which program or data file should be moved to a slower, cheaper memory device to make room for another file.

Various third-generation operating systems are based on the concept of virtual memory. A programmer can write a computer program as if he has an unlimited amount of memory available. In other words, while the actual memory available is limited, the "virtual memory" available to the programmer is unlimited. The operating system manages the movement of portions of the user program to main memory and maps the virtual memory to the actual memory assigned to the program.

Denning [1970] presented an overview and introduction to virtual memory computer systems. He studied the allocation problems associated with the use of virtual memory and showed how various analytic and simulation techniques had been used to contrast different memory allocation schemes. He presented a set of analytic equations for selecting the size of pages, for selecting the proper replacement policy, and for moving information between primary and secondary memory. The paper described the mechanisms for effecting virtual memory and the policies for using the mechanisms. The principal mechanisms were segmentation under which the address space was organized into variable size segments of contiguous addresses and paging under which the address space is organized into fixed size pages of contiguous addresses. The paper reviewed and presented analytic models to compare and contrast the policies and the implementation mechanisms.

Aho, et al. [1971] addressed the problem of optimal page replacement in computer systems that use virtual memory. The objective in this paper was to determine a paging policy which minimizes the aggregate page wait time accumulated while executing. The problem was expressed as a DP problem.

McKinney [1969] reviewed previous papers which described queuing models of time-sharing systems. The paper also delineated the parameters which distinguished the different analytic models. The techniques used in analyzing various classical scheduling algorithms, such as round-robin models, and multiple-level queue models with and without priorities were emphasized. An excellent annotated bibliography was included.

Moore [1971] and Buzen [1973] applied network queuing models to the analysis of multi-programming and time-sharing systems. Moore represented a time-sharing system as a set of independent resources. Based on this independence assumption, independently operating queues were represented as a time-continuous Markov process. The model was validated on a time-sharing operating system, and was used to compare the two memory allocation schemes used in virtual memory systems (paging and segmentation).

Buzen [1973] used the network queuing models to design operating systems. The models were used to determine the optimal buffer size for sequential devices. Next, certain models were used for the optimal allocation of processing requests among a set of functionally equivalent peripheral processors. In addition, the models were used to select the optimal degree of multi-programming in paging systems.

3. COMPUTER-BASED INFORMATION PROCESSING SYSTEMS

Industrial, commercial, and government organizations, whose activity is not the development of computer systems, employ programmers and system analysts to build computer-based *information processing systems* (user programs and files), which use the computer system provided by the hardware manufacturers and/or software vendor. Examples of such information processing systems are payroll programs and files, inventory programs and files, and student registration programs and files.

Operations research techniques have been applied to the design of user programs and files, given the resources of the hardware and operating system. Most of the work has been in the area of the analysis and design of data files. Simulation techniques have also been applied to the design of programs.

Simulation techniques have been applied to the analysis of an information processing system (Ihrer [1967] and Sutherland [1971]). These computer system simulations are sets of special purpose programs which simulate a defined workload (programs and files) on a specified computing system (hardware, operating system, and, possibly, file management system). The proposed workload is defined on a set of pre-defined forms or in a specification language. Characteristics of files include such information as blocking factor, number of records, record length, and packing density. Each individual program in the workload, whether batch or real-time, is described in a machine independent form. The description of a program includes the processing required and the generated file activity. The technical characteristics of the hardware and software of a set of machine configurations are maintained in a library to be accessed in a particular simulation. The hardware characteristics used by the simulator include descriptions of the central processor, peripheral devices, and communication equipment. Similarly, software characteristics include descriptions of operating systems, problem-oriented language processors, sort packages, and report generators. The computer system simulator accepts these inputs, simulates the proposed workload and configuration, and then prints various reports. Outputs include a summary of file activity, device utilization, and response times.

Thiess [1965], Day [1965], Chu [1968] presented mathematical programming formualtions of file organizations and file allocation. Day used IP to determine which file should be searched in order to satisfy a group of requests. The objective was to minimize total tape search time subject to the constraint that each request must be satisfied. He assumed that only one file could be searched at once, and that the entire file must be searched even though the request might be satisfied after only one part of the file has been searched. He also presented a modification of the above model to allow for the simultaneous interrogation of two data files.

Chu [1968] developed a mathematical model to allocate sets of files that are required in common by several computers in a computer network. The model considers storage cost, transmission cost, file sizes, usage rates of the various files, the maximum allowable access time to various files at each computer, and the storage capacity of each computer. The criterion of optimal allocation is minimal overall operating costs (storage and transmission). The model was formulated into a zero-one IP problem with nonlinear constraints that can be reduced to linear constraints.

Thiess [1965] addressed the problem of optimally blocking records in a number of files so that input/output time is minimized over a series of computer runs. He assumed that the files were on magnetic tape and that processing was done without buffering of input/output operations. He also assumed that the number of data records in each of a number of input and output files in a series of computer runs was given, as was the amount of computer storage available for internally storing input and output data. An additional constraint specifies that the number of characters per data record could not be altered, and no data record could split. He formulated this problem as a NLP problem with linear constraints and a nonlinear objective function. He relaxed the assumptions of the basic model to permit buffering, satellite computers, different types of tape units, etc. General NLP algorithms are used to solve the integer problem. The noninteger solutions are truncated to arrive at integer blocking factors. He treated the problem of assigning files to various available types of tape units so as to minimize the read-write time of each run. After the blocking factors have been determined, a model was proposed to select the tape unit assignment which will move the files the fastest. The result was a transportation problem.

A file simulation model FOREM written in FORTRAN was introduced by Senko, et al. [1968]. Tables describing logical files, records, fields, device parameters, and search strategies were used as input. Queries were generated from query specifications, and the size of the response set depended on the descriptions in the tables. Simulation modules describing specific designs was embedded into the model and were driven with simulated query transactions. Processing time was evaluated by equations in the modules. Extensive simulation results for the Indexed Sequential Access Method were reported by Lum, et al. [1970]. The use of GPSS in simulating file access methods was discussed by Martin [1967].

Nyssen [1971] and Behymer, et al. [1974] evaluated the relative merits of an indexed sequential file organization and a direct file organization, in both transaction-oriented and batch-oriented modes. The papers also evaluated a technique for efficiently updating a direct file in a batch processing mode. Behymer, et al. developed a simulation model to generate tables which could be used to select among the various file organizations and processing modes, based on a specification of user requirements and file specifications.

A data base simulation model was introduced by Cardenas [1973]. File structure modules were embedded in the system, and the system estimated total storage costs and average access time, given a specific data collection, query characterization, and device related specifications. Without considering update activity, the simulations of different file organizations were performed on several data collections.

The need for using generalized file models in the evaluation and selection of file organization was recognized by Severance [1972]. Models were constructed to represent file structures and search mechanisms, and each was characterized by a small set of parameters. For a given design problem, a model was used to generate a spectrum of alternative file organizations by varying the parameters of the generalized model. The model developed by Severance did not simulate the transactions that query or modify the data maintained by a file organization. Instead, he developed a model and computer program to "simulate" what a file designer does in the selection of a good file organization. Using a model of a generalized file organization, the computer program implicitly evaluated a large set of file organizations with respect to a set of user file requirements that were input to the computer program. Based on a user supplied objective function which specified the relative importance of primary and secondary memory space and processing time, the program evaluated those file organizations which might be of interest to the file designer. Certain file organizations could be ignored due to specific dominance characteristics. The program then displayed the selected set of file organizations.

In order to model and study file organizations, most authors developed explicit models of the data to be stored, the user activities on the data, and the hardware devices and software system used to store and maintain the data. In order to demonstrate the components of most of these models, the model proposed by Severance and Merten [1972] will be discussed in more detail.

The model includes explicit specification of data, user activity, and storage parameters. The set of data is described by the number of records, the fields within each record, and the specification of the field which can be used to uniquely identify a record. For example, the set of data contains 1000 logical records, each consisting of 10 attribute-value pairs which constitute the description of one employee entity. Each logical record has a unique employee pass number.

The user activity is described in terms of record deletions, additions, and modifications, and in terms of user requested extracts from the data set. An example of a modification would be that approximately five telephone number changes are processed each month. User specified extracts are stated in terms of an extract key, a projection schema, an ordering criteria, and a frequency of occurrence. For example, each month the system must retrieve the name and pass number of all employees in division A sequenced in numerically ascending order by pass number.

The storage facility is also described with respect to a set of predetermined parameters which specified the characteristics of the hardware (e.g. rotation speed of a disk) and the system software (e.g. procedures used to logically connect two elements of stored data). The file organizations were evaluated with respect to linear combinations of the following cost components:

1) the space required by the file organization,
2) the time required to retrieve an extract from the file organization,
3) the time spent on the maintenance of the file organization.

Kennedy [1973] presented a model for constructing file structures with doubly-chained trees, by the use of access frequencies of data. The basic problem is minimization of the weighted path length of a tree. For the equally weighted case, an approximated solution was given by Sussenguth [1963], and an exact solution was given by Stanfel [1970] as an IP problem. The problem was shown to correspond to binary tree minimization and a type of machine scheduling problem. A branch and bound algorithm was introduced to obtain a solution.

Ramamoorthy and Blevins [1971] developed a heuristic procedure to study the arrangement of frequency dependent data on sequential memory. The heuristic is applicable to a general class of objective functions corresponding to seek time functions constrained to be a monotonically increasing, piecewise linear. Results include development of bounds for achieving a locally optimum arrangement, proofs for finiteness and feasibility, comparison of the procedure with a modified version, and simulation experiences. The techniques employ a directed graph formulation.

Yao [1974] developed a file design system to select good file organizations from a large number of alternatives. The design system took its design requirement parameters from the data collection, user activities, and machine characteristics. The output of the design system is a suggested file structure, and the details of the actual file structure can be determined by simulation or other techniques.

The model is based on the fact that all access mechanisms are gradually-refining processes, and that they hierarchically decompose the search space. Within a data base, the access paths of most file structures were modeled by an access tree. The access tree was represented by two sets of variables. One set of variables characterized the configuration of the tree, and the other set of variables determines the implementation of the branches of the tree.

The access tree model provided a mapping from the space of file structures to an n-dimensional variable space. Design requirements were incorporated into a cost function defined over this variable space. A NLP algorithm was used to locate a set of minimal cost values for the variables which, in turn, determined a minimal cost file design.

4. INFORMATION SYSTEMS

Organizations use information in conjunction with its various functional activities. For example, sales reports and the marketing models are used to adjust salesman routes and commissions. Computer programs and files can store and process data in support of these functional activities of the organization. However, the flow and control of information to support this activity requires manual procedures and other noncomputerized activities; for example, the conversion of source documents into machine readable form, and the delivery of the computer output to the responsible manager.

Nunamaker [1971] and Teichroew and Sayani [1971] developed procedures to use OR techniques to assist in the automation of the design of computer-based information systems. The fundamental concept of the research is that a complete information system can be generated by the computer from a precise statement of the processing requirements of the system. The design methodology consists of a set of submodels which are solved using mathematical programming, graph theory, and heuristic procedures. The algorithm used is a multi-level decision model where the decision variables of one level became the constraints at the next level.

A formal language was proposed for stating the requirements of the information system independent of processing procedures. The algorithm selected a set of hardware, and generated the specifications for the set of programs and files that satisfied timing requirements, core memory, and secondary storage constraints, such that the cost of hardware system was minimized. The algorithm was limited to the design of uni-programmed batch systems, sequential auxiliary storage organization, linear data structures, and the selection of a single, central processing unit. Mathematical programming models were used to optimize the blocking factors for all files, specify the number and type of auxiliary memory devices, assign files to memory devices, and generate an operating schedule for running program modules.

Teichroew *et al* [1974] and Merten and Teichroew [1972] extended the concept of using the computer itself as an aid to designing computer based information systems. The fundamental concept is that the description of user requirements should be recorded in machine readable form as early as possible in the process.

The description of the requirements of an information processing system requires identification and naming of a number of types of objects and of the relationships among them. First, the objects which are involved in producing, storing, or using information from the system must be identified. The physical units by which data is transported or stored must be identified. Next, the units of data and the process which operate on the data must be specified. The dynamic behavior is described by stating the conditions or situations which trigger events over time, and the actions which follow events. Finally, the size of the proposed system must be described by identifying the parameters which determine size.

Based on the formal description of user requirements, algorithms are being developed to assist the analyst in the design of computer programs, files, and data bases. In particular, algorithms are being devised to group and present user requirements in a form that corresponds with the input specifications of the file design models discussed in the previous section.

5. CONCLUSION AND SUMMARY

This chapter has classified and reviewed the application of OR techniques to computer and information science. The major contributions appear to have been in the application of these techniques to the scheduling of operations on a large auxiliary memory. Recent published work has presented some successes in the application of OR techniques to the problems directly related to a user, that is, the design of an information processing system and/or an information system.

Various factors have limited the achievements in this area of application. First, most designers and evaluators of computer and information systems are unable to specify the objective and/or constraints of their problem. In other cases, there exists more than one objective to be optimized.

Second, many of the problems associated with computer and information systems are either scheduling, ordering, or allocation problems. In most cases, these problems lead to discrete optimization problems. The lack of efficient computational tools in this area has been a drawback. Finally, it is very often difficult to combine design algorithm, developed for different allocation problems, into a model which can be used at a higher level of design. This is often a problem, but appears more severe in this application area. A major contribution to this problem is in the wide range of time units for the activities of the design. For example, in a time sharing system, while the effectiveness of the system is a function of both the user at a terminal and a particular arithmetic processor, the time variables associated with the user are often measured in minutes or seconds, while those of the processor are measured in microseconds and nanoseconds.

Future applications of OR techniques to computer and information sciences will have to address these basic problems. Similarly, more research will be directed to the design problems of the eventual user of a computer. The optimal design of information processing systems and information systems remains the research challenge.

REFERENCES

Abate, J., H. Dubner, and S. Weinberg, "Queuing Analysis of the IBM 2314 Storage Facility," *J. ACM* **15**, No. 4: 577–589 (October 1968).

Aho, A. V., P. J. Denning, and J. D. Ullman, "Principles of Optimal Page Replacement," *J. ACM* **18**, No. 1: 80–93 (January 1971).

Anacher, W. and C. P. Wang, "Performance Evaluation of Computing Systems with Memory Hierarchies," *IEEE Trans. Electronic Comput.* **EC-16**, No. 6: 764–772 (December 1967).

Behymer, J., A. Merten, and R. Ogilvie, "Analysis of Indexed Sequential and Direct Access File Organizations," *ACM-SIGFIDFT Workshop on Data Description, Access and Control* (May 1–3, 1974).

Buzen, J. P., "Computational Algorithm for Closed Queuing Networks with Exponential Servers," *Communications ACM* **16**, No. 9: 527–531 (September 1973).

Cardenas, A. F., "Evaluation and Selection of File Organization—A Model and System," *Communications ACM* **16**, No. 9: 540–548 (September 1973).

Chu, W. W., "Optimal File Allocation in a Multicomputer Information System," *Proc. IFIP Conf.*, North-Holland, Amsterdam, F80–F85 (1968).

Coffman, E., "Analysis of a Drum Input/Output Queue Under Scheduled Operation in a Paged Computer System," *J. ACM* **16**, No. 1: 73–90 (January 1969).

Day, R. H., "On Optimal Extracting from a Multiple File Data Storage System: An Application of Integer Programming," *Operations Res.* **13**, No. 3: 482–492 (1965).

Denning, P. J., "Effects of Scheduling on File Memory Operations," *Spring Joint Comput. Conf.* 9–21 (1967).

———, "Virtual Memory," *Computing Surveys* **2**, No. 3: 152–189 (September 1970).

Frank, H., "Analysis and Optimization of Disc Storage Devices for Time-Sharing Systems," *J. ACM* **16**, No. 4: 602–620 (October 1969).

Gecsei, J., D. R. Slutz, I. L. Traiger, and R. L. Mattson, "Evaluation Techniques for Storage Hierarchies," *IBM Syst. J.* **9**, No. 2: 78–117 (1970).

Hanssmann, F., Editor, *Operational Research in the Design of Electronic Data Processing Systems, Proceedings of a NATO Conference*, Munich, West Germany, The English Universities Press, Ltd, London, Crane, Russak & Co., Inc., New York (1971).

Hellerman, H. and H. J. Smith, "Throughput Analysis of Some Idealized Input, Output, and Complete Overlap Configurations," *Computing Surveys* 2, No. 2: 111-118 (June 1970).

Ihrer, F. C., "Computer Performance Projected Through Simulation," *Comput. and Autom.* 17: 22-27 (April 1967).

Kelley, J. E., Jr., "Techniques for Storage Allocation Algorithms," *Communications ACM* 4, No. 10: 449-454 (October 1961).

Kennedy, S. R., *The Use of Access Frequencies in Data Base Organization*, Ph.D. Dissertation, Cornell University (1973).

Knuth, D., *The Art of Computer Programming*, Vol. 1, Addison-Wesley, Reading, Massachusetts (1968) pp. 435-455.

Lauer, H. C., "Bulk Core in an IBM 360/67 Time Sharing System," *Fall Joint Computer Conference* (1967) pp. 601-609.

Lum, V. Y., H. Ling, and M. E. Senko, "Analysis of a Complex Data Management Access Method by Simulation Modeling," *Proc. Fall Joint Computer Conference*, 211-222 (1970).

Martin, J., *Design of Real-Time Computer System*, Prentice-Hall, Englewood Cliffs, New Jersey, (1967).

McKinney, J. M., "A Survey of Analytical Time Sharing Models," *Computing Surveys* 1, No. 2: 105-116 (June 1969).

McWhorter, A., Jr., "A Survey of the Application of Mathematical Programming to the Optimization of Information Processing Systems," unpublished paper (1971).

Merten, A. G., *Some Quantitative Techniques for File Organization*, Ph.D. Thesis, Technical Report No. 15, University of Wisconsin Computing Center (1970).

Merten, A. and Teichroew, D., "Impact of Problem Statement Languages in Software Evaluation," *Fall Joint Computer Conference*, 849-857 (1972).

Moore, Charles G., III, "Network Models for Large-Scale Time Sharing Systems," Technical Report #71-1, ISDOS Research Project (April 1971).

Nyssen, G. M., "Indexed Sequential versus Random," *IAG J.* 4, No. 1: 29-37 (March 1971).

Nunamaker, J., "A Methodology for the Design and Optimization of Information Processing Systems," *Spring Joint Computer Conference*, AFIPS Press, Montvak, New Jersey, 283-294 (1971).

Pinkerton, T., *Program Behavior and Control in Virtual Storage Computer Systems*, Ph.D. Thesis, The University of Michigan (1968).

Ramamoorthy, C. V. and P. R. Blevins, "Arranging Frequency Dependent Data on Sequential Memories," *Spring Joint Computer Conference*, 545-556 (1971).

———, and K. M. Chandy, "Optimization of Memory Hierarchies in Multiprogrammed Systems," *J. ACM*, 17, No. 3: 426-445 (July 1970).

Seaman, P., R. Lind, and T. Wilson, "An Analysis of Auxiliary Storage Activity," *IBM Syst. J.* 5, No. 3: 158-170 (1966).

Senko, M. E., V. Lum, and P. Owens, "A File Organization Evaluation Model (FOREM)," *Proc. Intl. Federation of Info. Processing Congress* 68 (1968): 514-519.

Severance, D. and Merten, A., "Performance Evaluation of File Organizations through Modeling," *Proc. ACM* (1972) pp. 1061-1072.

Severance, D. G., *Some Generalized Modeling Structures for Use in Design of File Organizations*, Ph.D. Dissertation, The University of Michigan (1972).

Stanfel, L. E., "Tree Structures for Optimal Searching," *J. of ACM* 17, No. 3: 508-517 (July 1970).

Sussenguth, E. H., "Use of Tree Structures for Processing Files," *CACM* 6 5: 272-279 (May 1963).

Sutherland, J. W., "Tackle System Selection Systematically," *Comput. Decisions* **3**, No. 4: 14–19 (April (1971).

Teichroew, D., Hershey, E. A., and Bastarache, M., "An Introduction to PSL/PSA," ISDOS Working Paper #86, University of Michigan (1974).

———, and H. Sayani, "Automation of System Building," *Datamation*: 25–30 (August 15, 1971).

Teorey, T. and T. Pinkerton, "A Comparative Analysis of Disk Scheduling Policies," *Communications ACM* **15**, No. 3: 177–184 (March 1972).

Thiess, H. E., "Mathematical Programming Techniques for Optimal Computer Use," *Proc. ACM*: 501–512 (1965).

Yao, B., *Evaluation and Optimization of File Organizations Through Analytic Models*, Ph.D. Thesis, The University of Michigan (1974).

I-8

FACILITIES LOCATION AND LAYOUT[1]

Richard L. Francis
University of Florida

John A. White
Georgia Institute of Technology

I. INTRODUCTION

In this chapter the application of operations research (OR) methodology to the study of facilities location and layout problems is presented. Even though facility location problems have been the subject of mathematical analysis since at least the seventeenth century, it was not until the emergence of OR that the subject received renewed attention from a number of academic disciplines. Today, there exists a strong interdisciplinary interest in facilities location and layout. As examples, architects, economists, engineers, geographers, logisticians, management scientists, operations researchers, systems analysts, and urban planners are among those who have discovered a commonality of interest in their concern for the location and layout of facilities.

The term "facility" can be defined very broadly. As examples, a facility can be a manned space vehicle, a school, a student to be bused to a school, a machine tool, a hospital, a remote computer terminal, a fire station, an ambulance, a sewage treatment plant, a book in a library, an airport, a police cruiser, a radar station, a computer program to be stored on magnetic tape, a warehouse, a console display, or an office within an office building. Due to the very general interpretation which can be given to the term facility, it is not

[1] Much of the material presented in this chapter is from Francis and White [1974]. Materials reprinted are by permission of Prentice-Hall, Inc., Englewood Cliffs, New Jersey.

229

surprising to find that facilities location and layout research papers are published in a large number of seemingly unrelated professional journals.

Since 1960, over 500 papers have been written on the subject of facilities location and layout. Based on the variety of problems considered thus far, it is possible to establish a taxonomy of facilities location and layout problems. Specifically, six major elements may be considered in formulating a given facilities location and layout problem: new facility characteristics, existing facility locations, new and existing facility interactions, solution-space, distance measure, and criterion. These elements are depicted in Figure 1.

One aspect to be treated in formulating facilities location and layout problems involves the number of new facilities involved. Furthermore, the new facilities can be considered to occupy either point locations or area locations. In those cases where area locations are involved and the configuration of the areas for the new facilities are decision variables, the problem is often called a facilities layout problem. Thus, facilities layout problems can be considered as area location problems. In some facilities location problems the number of new facilities is a decision variable, rather than a parameter of the problem. Finally, the location of a new facility can be either dependent on or independent of the location of the remaining new facilities.

The location of the existing facilities is the second category to be considered in formulating a facilities location problem. Depending on the size of an existing facility, it can be considered to have a point location or an area location. Additionally, the location of an existing facility can be treated as either static or dynamic, as well as either deterministic or probabilistic. When the location of

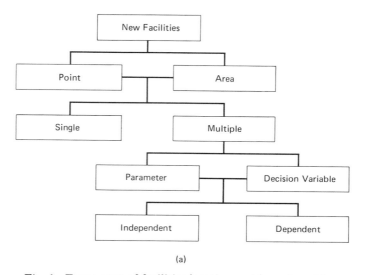

(a)

Fig. 1. Taxonomy of facilities location and layout problems.

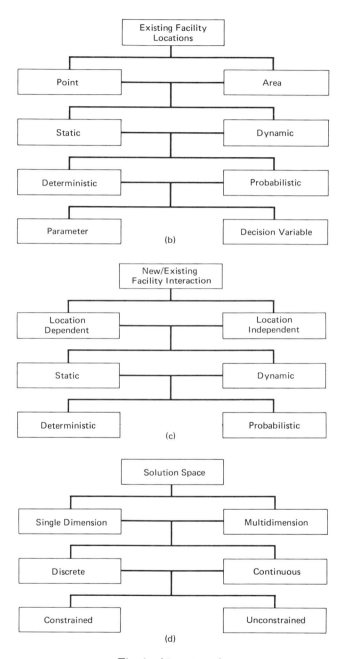

Fig. 1. (*Continued*)

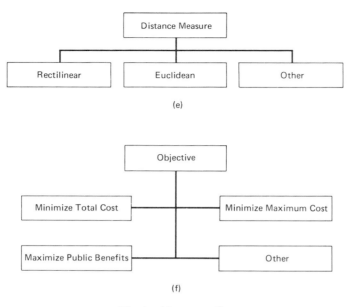

Fig. 1. (*Continued*)

an existing facility is a decision variable, a relocation problem exists; if the location and configuration of the area for an existing facility is a decision variable, a re-layout problem occurs.

The interaction of the new and existing facilities is another aspect to be treated in formulating the problem. In some cases, the level of the interaction is dependent upon the location of the new facilities. Furthermore, the magnitude of the interaction can be either static or dynamic, either deterministic or probabilistic, and either a parameter or a decision variable.

The fourth category considered in formulating a facility location problem concerns the solution space involved. In some cases the solution space is one dimensional; however, more commonly a two- or three-dimensional solution space exists. Additionally, the solution space can be either discrete or continuous. In the case of a discrete space, a finite number of sites are available for locating the new facilities; whereas, an infinite number of feasible sites exist when a continuous space is assumed.

The distance measures involved in a facility location problem provide another aspect to consider in formulating location problems. In some cases, rectilinear or Euclidean distances are computed as needed to approximate the actual distances involved; otherwise, actual distances must be measured and kept for subsequent computations.

The final category in formulating location problems is the criterion employed in solving the problem. A number of different criteria can be employed; however, the criteria encountered most frequently in the literature treating private sector location problems are the minimization of a total cost function and the minimization of the maximum cost involving pairs of facilities. Alternatively, in the public sector a criterion of maximizing public benefits may be employed.

In addition to its use in formulating location problems, the structure provided in Figure 1 can be used to classify the growing body of research literature on location problems. We make use of the structure in organizing the subsequent discussion. Specifically, point location problems having a continuous solution space are treated in Sections 2 and 3. In Section 2 the number of new facilities is a parameter; whereas, in Section 3 the number of new facilities is a decision variable. A related area location (layout) problem having a continuous solution space is presented in Section 4. In Section 5, the layout problem presented in Section 4 is solved for the case of a discrete solution space. In Sections 6 and 7, discrete solution spaces are assumed for the location problems treated in Sections 2 and 3, respectively. Additionally, in Section 7 are presented a number of constrained, discrete location problems which occur commonly in the public sector.

Due to the large number of variations of facilities location and layout problems which have been studied, it is not possible to provide an exhaustive discussion of the subject in this chapter. As an illustration, the subjects of computerized plant layout programs, network location problems, and minimax location problems have not been addressed.

A large number of computerized plant layout programs have been developed in recent years. Among these are ALDEP (Seehof and Evans [1967]), CORELAP (Lee and Moore [1967]), Interactive CORELAP (Moore [1971]), CRAFT (Armour and Buffa [1963]), and PLANET (Apple and Deisenroth [1972]). For a discussion of a number of these programs, see Francis and White [1974].

The problem of locating facilities on a network has received considerable attention since Hakimi's [1964] early work. Among the contributors to the study of locating facilities on networks are Christofides and Viola [1971], Donath [1968], Frank [1966], Gilbert and Pollack [1968], Goldman [1969, 1971, 1972a], Goldman and Witzgall [1970], Hakimi [1964, 1965, 1972], Hakimi and Maheshwari [1972], Levy [1967], Minieka [1970], and Wendell and Hurter [1972].

With the exception of the discussion on covering problems in Section 6, the previous treatment of facility location and layout problems employs the objective of minimizing the weighted sum of distances between facilities. An alternate objective, which has a number of applications, is a minimax objective in which new facilities are located, such that the maximum weighted distance is minimized. Minimax facility location and layout problems have been studied by

Dearing and Francis [1972], Elzinga and Hearn [1972a, 1972b, 1973], Francis [1967c, 1973], Goldman [1972b], Nair and Chandrasekaran [1971], and Wesolowsky [1972b].

2. CONTINUOUS FACILITIES LOCATION PROBLEMS

The facility location problem treated in this section is a generalization of a location problem variously referred to as Fermat's Problem, Steiner's Problem, the Weber Problem, and the Steiner-Weber Problem. Mathematically, the problem can be stated as follows. Let m existing facilities be located at known distinct points $P_1, \ldots, P_m$, and let n new facilities be located at points $X_1, \ldots, X_n$ in the plane. Let $d(X_j, P_i)$ represent the distance between the locations of new facility j and existing facility i, and $d(X_j, X_k)$ be the distance between the locations of new facilities j and k. Let the annual cost per unit distance between new facility j and existing facility i be denoted w_{ji}, with v_{jk} being the corresponding value for new facilities j and k. The total annual transportation cost associated with new facilities located at $X_1, \ldots, X_n$ is given by

$$f(X_1, \ldots, X_n) = \sum_{1 \leqslant j < k \leqslant n} v_{jk} d(X_j, X_k) + \sum_{j=1}^{n} \sum_{i=1}^{m} w_{ji} d(X_j, P_i). \qquad (1)$$

Properly defining v_{jk} as the annual cost per unit distance due to item movement *between* new facilities j and k, it is only necessary to sum over those values of j which are less than k, and over those values of k from 2 to n. The multifacility location problem can be stated as the selection of locations $X_1^*, \ldots, X_n^*$ of the new facilities such that total annual cost is minimized.

2.1   Rectilinear Distance Problems

For the case when distances are rectilinear, when $X_j = (x_j, y_j)$ and $P_i = (a_i, b_i)$,

$$d(X_j, X_k) = |x_j - x_k| + |y_j - y_k| \qquad (2)$$

and

$$d(X_j, P_i) = |x_j - a_i| + |y_j - b_i|. \qquad (3)$$

On substituting (2) and (3) into (1) and rearranging terms, the following expression is obtained:

$$f(X_1, \ldots, X_n) = f_1(x_1, \ldots, x_n) + f_2(y_1, \ldots, y_n), \qquad (4)$$

where

$$f_1(x_1, \ldots, x_n) = \sum_{1 \leqslant j < k \leqslant n} v_{jk} |x_j - x_k| + \sum_{j=1}^{n} \sum_{i=1}^{m} w_{ji} |x_j - a_i| \qquad (5)$$

and

$$f_2(y_1, \ldots, y_n) = \sum_{1 \leqslant j < k \leqslant n} v_{jk} \, |y_j - y_k| + \sum_{j=1}^{n} \sum_{i=1}^{m} w_{ji} \, |y_j - b_i|. \qquad (6)$$

Subsequent reference to the total cost expressions f_1 and f_2 will be to the expressions defined by (5) and (6) respectively unless otherwise indicated. The expressions f_1 and f_2 give the total cost incurred due to "travel" in the x and y directions, respectively.

From (4), it follows that

$$\min f(X_1, \ldots, X_n) = \min f_1(x_1, \ldots, x_n) + \min f_2(y_1, \ldots, y_n).$$

Thus, optimum x coordinates of the new facilities can be found independently of optimum y coordinates. Further, it is the case that f_1 and f_2 have the same form, so any procedure developed for minimizing f_1 will also apply to f_2 on replacing x_j by y_j and a_i by b_i.

The procedure used to minimize f_1 or f_2 depends on the idea of transforming it to an equivalent linear programming (LP) problem; any optimum solution to the LP problem will provide optimum x coordinates of the new facilities.

The determination of an equivalent LP problem will now be considered. The following fact is needed: given numbers $a, b, p,$ and q, if $a - b - p + q = 0, p \geqslant 0,$ $q \geqslant 0$, and $pq = 0$, then $|a - b| = p + q$. Thus, minimizing f_1 is equivalent to the following problem:

$$\text{Minimize} \quad \sum_{1 \leqslant j < k \leqslant n} v_{jk}(p_{jk} + q_{jk}) + \sum_{j=1}^{n} \sum_{i=1}^{m} w_{ji}(r_{ji} + s_{ji})$$

Subject to

$$x_j - x_k - p_{jk} + q_{jk} \qquad\qquad = 0, \quad 1 \leqslant j < k \leqslant n$$

$$x_j \qquad\qquad\qquad - r_{ji} + s_{ji} = a_i, \quad i = 1, \ldots, m \ \text{ and } \ j = 1, \ldots, n$$

$$p_{jk}, q_{jk} \qquad\qquad\qquad\qquad \geqslant 0, \quad 1 \leqslant j < k \leqslant n$$

$$r_{ji}, s_{ji} \ \geqslant 0, \quad i = 1, \ldots, m \ \text{ and } \ j = 1, \ldots, n$$

$$x_j \text{ unrestricted} \qquad\qquad , \quad j = 1, \ldots, n$$

$$p_{jk} \times q_{jk} \qquad\qquad\qquad = 0, \quad 1 \leqslant j < k \leqslant n$$

$$r_{ji} \times s_{ji} = 0, \quad i = 1, \ldots, m \ \text{ and } \ j = 1, \ldots, n.$$

Notice that, with the exception of the last two sets of multiplicative constraints, the above problem is a LP problem (call the above problem P0, and call P1 the LP problem obtained by deleting the multiplicative constraints from P0). Since P1 is a less constrained problem than P0, the minimum value of its objective function will be at least as small as the minimum value of the objective function of P0. If a minimum feasible solution to P1 satisfies *all* the constraints of P0 (i.e., the multiplicative constraints as well as the others), it is therefore a minimum feasible solution to P0.

In solving P1, the theory of LP guarantees that some basic feasible solution will be a minimum feasible solution. For any basic feasible solution, if p_{jk} is in the basic feasible solution, q_{jk} will not be, and vice versa; likewise, if r_{ji} is in the basic feasible solution, s_{ji} will not be, and vice versa. Since variables not in the basic feasible solution are zero, the multiplicative constraints will therefore be satisfied for every basic feasible solution. Thus, P0 and P1 are equivalent optimization problems, and we can employ LP to solve the rectilinear location problem.

A straightforward LP solution of P1 can be time consuming when a large number of new and existing facilities are involved. Specifically, from P0 we observe there can be as many as $n^2 + 2mn$ variables and $n(n-1)/2 + mn$ constraints involved in determining the x coordinates for the new facilities. Of course, depending on the values of v_{jk} and w_{ji}, the actual number of variables and constraints can be considerably less than the maximum number given above. However, it is apparent that, for large sized problems, more efficient solution procedures are desired. Cabot, et al. [1970] formulate the dual of P1, and convert the dual problem to a network flow problem to obtain an efficient solution to P1.

For the case of a single new facility, a simple procedure can be used to solve the rectilinear location problem. Specifically, by letting the w_i value be referred to as the "weight" between the new facility and existing facility i, it can be shown that an optimum x coordinate (y coordinate) location for the new facility is a *median location*. A median location is defined to be a location such that no more than one-half of the cumulative weight is to the left of (below) the new facility location and no more than one-half of the cumulative weight is to the right of (above) the new facility location.

In addition to the single facility location problem being easily solved, one can also construct contour lines of the total cost function. Contour lines (lines of constant total cost) provide considerable insight into the shape of the surface of the total cost function, as well as providing a useful means of evaluating alternative locations for the new facility. A procedure for constructing contour lines for the rectilinear distance problem is given below. The procedure will be employed subsequently, in Section 4, to obtain warehouse layout designs.

1. Plot the points $(a_1, b_1), \ldots, (a_m, b_m)$, and draw perpendicular lines (parallel to the x and y axes) through each point. (See Figure 2).
2. Consider the vertical lines to be numbered $1, 2, \ldots, p$ from left to right, and the horizontal lines to be numbered $1, 2, \ldots, q$ from bottom to top.
3. Call the x intercept of the j-th vertical line c_j; the y intercept of the i-th horizontal line d_i. Denote the region delimited by vertical lines j and $j+1$

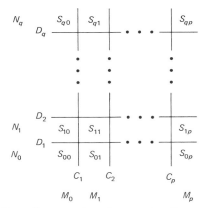

Fig. 2. Illustration of a procedure for constructing contour lines.

and horizontal lines i and $i + 1$ by $[i, j]$. (In order that all regions are numbered, *imagine* there is a vertical line numbered 0 to the left of vertical line 1, a vertical line numbered $p + 1$ to the right of vertical line p, a horizontal line numbered 0 below horizontal line 1, and a horizontal line $q + 1$ above horizontal line q).

4. Let C_j and D_i be the sums of the weights associated with vertical line j and horizontal line i, respectively. (For example, if the points $(5, 3)$ and $(5, 10)$ have the associated weights of 6 and 8 respectively, and the second vertical line has an x intercept of 5, then $C_2 = 14$). It is convenient to place the numbers C_j at the bottom of the corresponding vertical lines, and the numbers D_i at the left of the corresponding horizontal lines.

5. Compute the numbers

$$M_0 = -\sum_{j=1}^{p} C_j = -\sum_{i=1}^{m} w_i \qquad N_0 = -\sum_{i=1}^{q} D_i = -\sum_{i=1}^{m} w_i$$

$$M_1 = M_0 + 2C_1 \qquad\qquad N_1 = N_0 + 2D_1$$

$$M_2 = M_1 + 2C_2 \qquad\qquad N_2 = N_1 + 2D_2$$

$$\vdots \qquad\qquad\qquad\qquad \vdots$$

$$M_p = M_{p-1} + 2C_p = \sum_{i=1}^{m} w_i \qquad N_q = N_{q-1} + 2D_q = \sum_{i=1}^{m} w_i$$

and place them as indicated in Figure 2.

6. The slope, S_{ij}, of any contour line passing through region $[i, j]$ is computed as follows:

$$S_{ij} = -M_j / N_i.$$

When N_i is zero, the contour line is vertical in region $[i, j]$.

7. To find a point (x^*, y^*) which minimizes the total cost expression, there are four cases to consider:

   i) $M_{t-1} < 0, M_t > 0, N_{s-1} < 0, N_s > 0$; take $x^* = c_t, y^* = d_s$.

   ii) $M_{t-1} < 0, M_t = 0, N_{s-1} < 0, N_s > 0$; take x^* to be any point between c_t and $c_{t+1}, y^* = d_s$.

   iii) $M_{t-1} < 0, M_t > 0, N_{s-1} < 0, N_s = 0$; take $x^* = c_t$, take y^* to be any point between d_s and d_{s+1}.

   iv) $M_{t-1} < 0, M_t = 0, N_{s-1} < 0, N_s = 0$; take x^* to be any point between c_t and c_{t+1}, and y^* to be any point between d_s and d_{s+1}.

8. Given the above information, a contour line can be constructed, beginning at any point except a minimum point. As a check, the line should always "end" at the same point where it "begins."

2.2   Euclidean Distance Problems

For the case when distances are Euclidean, when $X_j = (x_j, y_j)$ and $P_i = (a_i, b_i)$, then in (2.1)

$$d(X_j, X_k) = [(x_j - x_k)^2 + (y_j - y_k)^2]^{1/2} \tag{7}$$

and

$$d(X_j, P_i) = [(x_j - a_i)^2 + (y_j - b_i)^2]^{1/2}. \tag{8}$$

On substituting (7) and (8) into (1), the multifacility Euclidean problem is formulated as follows:

$$\text{Minimize } f(X_1, \ldots, X_n) = \sum_{1 \leqslant j < k \leqslant n} v_{jk} [(x_j - x_k)^2 + (y_j - y_k)^2]^{1/2}$$

$$+ \sum_{j=1}^{n} \sum_{i=1}^{m} w_{ji} [(x_j - a_i)^2 + (y_j - b_i)^2]^{1/2} \tag{9}$$

The notation employed is the same as introduced for the multifacility, rectilinear distance problem. The necessary conditions for optimal locations of new facilities are that the partial derivatives of $f(X_1, \ldots, X_n)$ with respect to $X_1, \ldots, X_n$ be zero (or change sign) at the optimum locations.

Taking the partial derivatives of $f(X_1, \ldots, X_n)$ with respect to x_j and y_j, respectively, gives

$$\frac{\partial f}{\partial x_j} = \sum_{\substack{k=1 \\ k \neq j}}^{n} v_{jk}(x_j - x_k)/D_{jk} + \sum_{i=1}^{m} w_{ji}(x_j - a_i)/E_{ji}, \quad j = 1, \ldots, n \tag{10}$$

and

$$\frac{\partial f}{\partial y_j} = \sum_{\substack{k=1 \\ k \neq j}}^{n} v_{jk}(y_j - y_k)/D_{jk} + \sum_{i=1}^{m} w_{ji}(y_j - b_i)/E_{ji}, \quad j = 1, \ldots, n, \quad (11)$$

where

$$D_{jk} = [(x_j - x_k)^2 + (y_j - y_k)^2]^{1/2}$$

and

$$E_{ji} = [(x_j - a_i)^2 + (y_j - b_i)^2]^{1/2}.$$

Notice that, if new facilities j and k have the same location ($D_{jk} = 0$), and new facility j and existing facility i have the same location ($E_{ji} = 0$), then both $\partial f/\partial x_j$ and $\partial f/\partial y_j$ are undefined.

Geometrically, each cost term included in (9) represents the equation of a right circular cone. Consequently, (9) represents the sum of cones. The sharp points of the cones involved in the summation result in the undefined derivatives, and produce the *knife-edged surface* referred to by Vergin and Rogers [1967]. Since a cone is a limiting form of a hyperboloid, if the cones are replaced by hyperboloids, a smooth approximating function, $\hat{f}$, is obtained. Furthermore, since hyperboloids are strictly convex functions and $\hat{f}$ is the sum of hyperboloids, $\hat{f}$ is a strictly convex function, assuming at least one $w_{ji} > 0$ for each j.

The equation for a hyperboloid centered on the point (a_i, b_i) in the x–y plane can be expressed as

$$\hat{f}_{ji} = w_{ji}[(x_j - a_i)^2 + (y_j - b_i)^2 + \epsilon]^{1/2}.$$

The addition of the constant, ϵ, essentially results in the replacement of the point of a cone by a smooth hyperbolic surface. Consequently, by introducing ϵ, the partial derivatives exist everywhere. Furthermore, the smaller the value of ϵ, the closer the hyperboloid approximates the cone.

Letting

$$\hat{D}_{jk} = [(x_j - x_k)^2 + (y_j - y_k)^2 + \epsilon]^{1/2}$$

and

$$\hat{E}_{ji} = [(x_j - a_i)^2 + (y_j - b_i)^2 + \epsilon]^{1/2},$$

the new optimization problem can be given as

$$\text{Minimize } \hat{f}(X_1, \ldots, X_n) = \sum_{1 \leqslant j < k \leqslant n} v_{jk}\hat{D}_{jk} + \sum_{j=1}^{n}\sum_{i=1}^{m} w_{ji}\hat{E}_{ji}, \quad (12)$$

where

$$\lim_{\epsilon \to 0} \hat{f}(X_1, \ldots, X_n) = f(X_1, \ldots, X_n).$$

Therefore, solving (12) using a very small value of ϵ yields a solution which is approximately the same as that obtained by solving (9).

Taking the partial derivatives of $\hat{f}$ with respect to x_j and y_j, setting the partials equal to zero and solving for x_j and y_j gives the following iterative expressions,

$$x_j^{(h+1)} = \frac{\sum_{\substack{k=1 \\ k \neq j}}^{n} v_{jk} x_k^{(h)}/\hat{D}_{jk}^{(h)} + \sum_{i=1}^{m} w_{ji} a_i/\hat{E}_{ji}^{(h)}}{\sum_{\substack{k=1 \\ k \neq j}}^{n} v_{jk}/\hat{D}_{jk}^{(h)} + \sum_{i=1}^{m} w_{ji}/\hat{E}_{ji}^{(h)}} \tag{13}$$

$$y_j^{(h+1)} = \frac{\sum_{\substack{k=1 \\ k \neq j}}^{n} v_{jk} y_k^{(h)}/\hat{D}_{jk}^{(h)} + \sum_{i=1}^{m} w_{ji} b_i/\hat{E}_{ji}^{(h)}}{\sum_{\substack{k=1 \\ k \neq j}}^{n} v_{jk}/\hat{D}_{jk}^{(h)} + \sum_{i=1}^{m} w_{ji}/\hat{E}_{ji}^{(h)}}, \tag{14}$$

where the superscripts denote the iteration number.

The iterative expressions (13) and (14) are subsequently referred to as the hyperboloid approximation procedure or HAP (Eyster, et al. [1973]). It is known that if a convergent solution is obtained, it will be an optimum solution. Although it has not been shown that (13) and (14) will always yield a convergent solution, considerable computational experience with HAP has not produced a case in which the procedure has failed to converge. It has been shown that (13) and (14) reduce to the iterative expressions used in gradient search procedures; however, the size of the gradient step used in HAP is not "optimum." For further discussion of HAP, see Eyster, et al. [1973].

For the case of a single new facility and ϵ set equal to zero, (13) and (14) reduce to

$$x^{(h+1)} = \frac{\sum_{i=1}^{m} w_i a_i/E_i^{(h)}}{\sum_{i=1}^{m} w_i/E_i^{(h)}} \tag{15}$$

and

$$y^{(h+1)} = \frac{\sum\limits_{i=1}^{m} w_i b_i / E_i^{(h)}}{\sum\limits_{i=1}^{m} w_i / E_i^{(h)}} \tag{16}$$

respectively, where

$$E_i^{(h)} = [(x^{(h)} - a_i)^2 + (y^{(h)} - b_i)^2]^{1/2}.$$

The convergence of (15) and (16) to the optimum location has been studied recently by Kuhn [1973], among others. Cooper [1963, 1964, 1967], Kuhn and Kuenne [1962], and Miehle [1958] are among those who have employed (15) and (16) in solving the single facility, Euclidean distance, location problem.

3. CONTINUOUS LOCATION-ALLOCATION PROBLEMS

The multifacility location problems treated previously considered the situation in which the values of the weights v_{jk} and w_{ji} were not dependent on the locations of the new facilities. We will treat briefly a class of location problems, called location-allocation problems, in which all v_{jk} values are zero, and the w_{ji} values are decision variables, as are the locations for the new facilities. Our treatment of the location-allocation problem in this section will concentrate on the continuous solution space problems examined by Cooper [1963, 1964, 1967], and in Section 7 we examine discrete solution space formulations.

A very general statement of the location-allocation problem would involve a determination of the number of new facilities, as well as their locations, and the allocation of item movement between the new and existing facilities. A common example involves the location of distribution centers which will receive products from production facilities and distribute products to retail or wholesale outlets; another example arises when a number of branch banks are to be located in a metropolitan area. Instead of branch banks or warehouses, the new facilities could easily be, say, hospitals or grocery stores. In the case of branch banks, hospitals, and grocery stores, the existing facilities would include the residences of the consumers.

A mathematical formulation of the location-allocation problem can be given as follows:

$$\text{Minimize } \Psi = \sum_{j=1}^{n} \sum_{i=1}^{m} z_{ji} w_{ji} d(X_j, P_i) + g(n) \tag{17}$$

subject to

$$\sum_{j=1}^{n} z_{ji} = 1, \quad i = 1, \ldots, m, \quad n = 1, 2, \ldots, m,$$

where w_{ji} is the cost per unit time per unit distance if new facility j interacts with existing facility i; z_{ji} equals 1, if new facility j interacts with existing facility i, and equals 0, otherwise; $X_j = (x_j, y_j)$ is the coordinate location of a new facility j; $P_i = (a_i, b_i)$ is the coordinate location of existing facility i; $g(n)$ represents the cost per unit time of providing n new facilities; and Ψ is the total cost per unit time.

The decision variables in (17) are n, z_{ji}, x_j, and y_j. Each constraint insures that each existing facility interacts with only one new facility. Since no capacity constraints are given, it is assumed that a new facility is capable of handling all interchanges with existing facilities. Additionally, it is normally assumed that $w_{1i} = w_{2i} = \ldots = w_{ni}$, since identical new facilities are to be located. Unfortunately, an optimum solution to (17) is not easily obtained. The difficulty is presented by the decision variables n and z_{ji}. One approach which has been used to solve the problem is to fix the value of n and consider all possible combinations of z_{ji}. For each combination of z_{ji}, an "optimum" solution is obtained by solving the associated single facility location problems. Next, the minimum cost combination of z_{ji} is determined for the particular value of n. Finally, an optimum solution is obtained by performing a search over n.

The above procedure is not feasible for moderate to large sized problems since the number of combinations of z_{ji}, which must be considered for each value of n, is given by the Stirling number of the second kind,

$$S(n, m) = \sum_{k=0}^{n} \frac{(-1)^k (n-k)^m}{k! \, (n-k)!}$$

Recall, the computation of the number of combinations is based on the assumption that the new facilities are identical; otherwise, even more combinations would have to be considered.

Since considerable computational effort can be required to solve the location-allocation problem exactly, a number of heuristic methods have been employed to obtain "good" solutions to the problem; for example, see Cooper [1964, 1967]. Kuenne and Soland [1971] present a branch and bound algorithm and Sherali and Shetty [1977] present a bilinear programming algorithm for determining the optimum allocations and locations of n new facilities.

4. CONTINUOUS FACILITY LAYOUT PROBLEMS

In the previous section, we formulated a number of facility location problems in which both the new and existing facilities were idealized as points and a continuous solution space was assumed. In this section, we treat the new facilities as areas, rather than points. Due to the physical context in which such a formulation arises, we refer to the location problems as facility layout problems. In the subsequent discussion we will find it convenient to develop the discussion in a warehouse design context, where the items to be stored in the warehouse are the new facilities, and the shipping and receiving docks are the existing facilities. It is assumed that no interaction exists between the new facilities.

To facilitate the discussion, some additional notation must be established. In particular, suppose the warehouse is to include m items; the set of points in the plane which item i takes up will be represented by S_i, and it will be assumed that S_i has a known area, represented by A_i. It will further be assumed that for any two items i and j, the sets S_i and S_j do not overlap. Since the sets $S_1, \ldots, S_m$ specify the locations of all m items, it will be convenient to speak of the collection $\{S_1, \ldots, S_m\}$ as being a layout. It will be assumed for any layout that each set S_i is contained in a known region L, which might represent, for example, the plot of ground on which the warehouse is to be placed. The collection of all layouts will be denoted by $H_m(L:A)$. It will be assumed that the warehouse will have n docks, at known locations $P_1, \ldots, P_n$. Given any layout $\{S_1, \ldots, S_m\}$, under an equal likelihood assumption, and letting $|X - P_j|$ represent the distance between X and P_j, the average distance that item i travels to or from dock j may be represented by:

$$\int_{S_i} (1/A_i) |X - P_j| \, dX.$$

The cost of the travel of item i, to and from dock j, for a given time period, will be assumed to be directly proportional to the average distance, with w_{ij} being the nonnegative constant of proportionality, so that the total cost of movement of item i to and from dock j for a given time period is given by:

$$w_{ij} \int_{S_i} (1/A_i) |X - P_j| \, dX.$$

The total cost of movement of all items is then given by:

$$F(S_1, \ldots, S_m) = \sum_{i=1}^{m} \sum_{j=1}^{n} w_{ij} \int_{S_i} (1/A_i) |X - P_j| \, dX. \tag{18}$$

It will be assumed that the matrix $W = (w_{ij})$ factors; the assumption is equivalent to the assumption that $w_{ij} = c_i w_j$, where $c_i = \sum_{j=1}^{n} w_{ij}$ for $i = 1, \ldots, m$ and

$$w_j = \sum_{i=1}^{m} w_{ij} \Big/ \sum_{i=1}^{m} \sum_{j=1}^{n} w_{ij}.$$

The factoring assumption is satisfied whenever the total number of pallets of item i travelling in and out of storage from dock j per time period (w_{ij}), can be obtained by multiplying the total number of pallets of item i travelling in and out of storage per time period (c_i), by the fraction of all pallets travelling in and out of storage from dock $j(w_j)$.

Given the factoring assumption, (18) may be rewritten, on interchanging the order of summation and integration, as follows:

$$F(S_1, \ldots, S_m) = \sum_{i=1}^{m} (c_i/A_i) \int_{S_i} f(X) \, dX, \tag{19}$$

where

$$f(X) = \sum_{j=1}^{n} w_j \, |X - P_j|. \tag{20}$$

In order to develop the conditions for an optimum layout, it is useful first to establish some notation. Given any layout $\{S_1, \ldots, S_m\}$, the union of S_1, $\ldots, S_q$, denoted by $\bigcup_{i=1}^{q} S_i$ for $q = 1, 2, \ldots, m$, is defined to be the collection of all points in at least one of the sets $S_1, \ldots, S_q$. In a warehousing context, $\bigcup_{i=1}^{q} S_i$ simply specifies the location of all the items 1 through q, and will have an area of B_q, where B_q is defined by $B_q = A_1 + \cdots + A_q$, for $q = 1, \ldots, m$. Figure 3 illustrates a layout $\{S_1^*, S_2^*\}$, as well as the resultant design $\bigcup_{i=1}^{2} S_i^*$.

The following property states a sufficient condition for a least cost layout design.

Property 1: Let $\{S_1^*, \ldots, S_m^*\}$ be a layout in $H_m(L:A)$. Given that

$$c_1/A_1 \geqslant \cdots \geqslant c_m/A_m > 0,$$

then

$$F(S_1^*, \ldots, S_m^*) \leqslant F(S_1, \ldots, S_m),$$

where $\{S_1, \ldots, S_m\}$ is any other layout in $H_m(L:A)$, if $\{S_1^*, \ldots, S_m^*\}$ has the following property: there exist numbers $k_1 \leqslant \cdots \leqslant k_m$ such that, for $q = 1, \ldots, m$,

$$f(X) \leqslant k_q \quad \text{for every point} \quad X \text{ in} \bigcup_{i=1}^{q} S_i^*, \text{and}$$

$$f(X) \geqslant k_q \quad \text{for every point} \quad X \quad \text{not in} \quad \bigcup_{i=1}^{q} S_i^*.$$

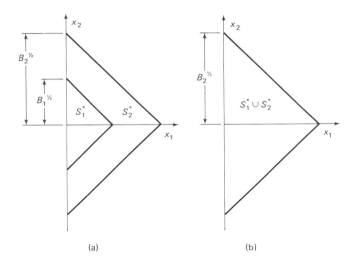

Fig. 3. Multi-item, single dock (a) storage area layout and (b) warehouse design.

Based on Property 1, a warehouse design is obtained by plotting contour lines of the total cost function (19). From the discussion of Section 2.2, the docks are treated as existing facilities, and w_j denotes the "weight" between the items to be stored in the warehouse and existing facility j. The contour line corresponding to a cost of k_1, and enclosing a region of $B_1 = A_1$, provides the storage area used for the storage of item 1; the contour line corresponding to a cost of k_2, and enclosing a region of area $B_2 = A_1 + A_2$, provides the storage area used for the storage of items 1 and 2, etc. The items to be stored are numbered according to the ratio c/A, with the "fast moving" items tending to be located nearer the docks. Thus, when rectilinear item movement is used, contour lines are plotted using the procedure outlined in Section 2.1.

If the total cost of the optimum warehouse design is desired, it is useful to develop a single integral expression for least cost layouts. To facilitate the development define the function $q(k)$ to be the area of the set $\{X \in L: f(X) \le k\}$; under a weak assumption, $q(k)$ is strictly increasing and has an inverse function, say $r(t)$, such that $q(r(B_i)) = B_i$ and $r(q(k_i)) = k_i$. Finally, both the terms $r(B_0)$ and k_0 will represent the minimum value of the function $f(X)$.

Property 2: Suppose there exist numbers $k_0 < k_1 < \cdots < k_m$ such that $\{S_1^*, \ldots, S_m^*\}$ is a layout in $H_m(L:A)$, where

$$S_i^* = \{X \in L: k_{i-1} \le f(X) \le k_i\}, \quad i = 1, \ldots, m.$$

Then, for $i = 1, \ldots, m$, $k_i = r(B_i)$, and

$$\int_{S_i^*} (1/A_i) f(X) \, dX = (1/A_i) \int_{r(B_{i-1})}^{r(B_i)} q'(z)z \, dz. \tag{21}$$

where $q'(z)$ is the first derivative of $q(z)$ with respect to z.

Property 2 provides a convenient means of computing the expected distance traveled per unit time for item i. Thus, the expected total cost of movement of all items can be given by

$$F(S_1^*, \ldots, S_m^*) = \sum_{i=1}^{m} (c_i/A_i) \int_{r(B_{i-1})}^{r(B_i)} q'(z)z \, dz. \tag{22}$$

As an illustration of the use of Properties 1 and 2, consider the warehouse designs for a single item in Fig. 4. Layout designs (a) and (b) suggest that the single dock should be located in the middle of the warehouse in order to minimize expected distance traveled per unit time. If travel is rectilinear, the diamond shaped layout is obtained; if travel is Euclidean a circular design is obtained. If the dock must be located along the periphery of the warehouse, designs (c) and (d) are obtained for the cases of rectilinear and Euclidean travel, respectively. If two docks are located as shown, travel is rectilinear, and $w_1 = w_2 = \frac{1}{2}$, the layout design obtained is given by design (e). Also shown in Figure 4 is the resulting expected total cost, $F(S^*)$, for each design.

This discussion of warehouse designs has, of necessity, been brief; for additional discussion, including proofs of the properties presented in this section and a treatment of rectangular warehouse designs, see Francis [1967a, 1967b].

The continuous formulation of facility layout and location problems introduced in this section can also be extended to include location problems in which the new facilities are idealized as points and the existing facilities are either points or areas (Wesolowsky and Love [1971b]).

In a sense, the continuous warehouse design and layout problem treated in this section can be considered to be a special case of the more general problem of regional design. The regional design problem can be defined as the determination of optimal regions in the plane following some appropriate criteria. Thus, the regional design problem involves a partitioning of a given region into subregions. Examples of regional design problems include the partitioning of a state into congressional districts, the partitioning of a county into school districts, the division of a given region into districts of telephone subscribers, the design of a source region for a business with several branch offices, the design of a parking lot based on the destinations of the people who park in the lot, and the design of a warehouse based on dock locations. For a discussion of regional design as it relates to facility layout and location, see Corley and Roberts [1972].

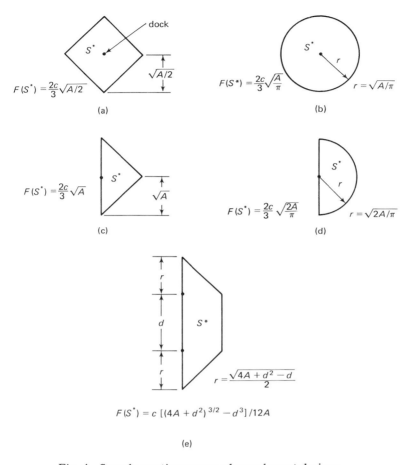

Fig. 4. Sample continuous warehouse layout designs.

5. DISCRETE FACILITY LAYOUT PROBLEMS

Our previous discussion of a warehouse layout problem was based on a continuous solution space. In this section we formulate the layout problem in a discrete solution space, and continue to assume that no interchange occurs between new facilities.

To facilitate the discussion of the discrete facility layout problem, we again consider a warehouse layout problem. In particular, suppose that a region L, which might be that part of the floor of a warehouse where items can be stored, is subdivided into n grid squares of equal size, numbered in any convenient manner from 1 to n. Suppose that m items are to be stored in the warehouse, and let the total number of grid squares which item i will take up be denoted by A_i; for example, if item 3 takes up 4 grid squares, then $A_3 = 4$. Let the warehouse have p docks, the locations of which are known, and denote by d_{kj} an appropriately determined distance between dock k and the center of grid square j. Denote by S_i the collection of the numbers of grid squares which are taken up by item i; for example, if item i takes up 4 grid squares, which have the numbers 12, 13, 29, and 30, then $S_i = \{12, 13, 29, 30\}$. Given the assumption, for a given storage region for an item, that an item is equally likely to travel between dock k and any grid square taken up by item i, the average distance item i travels between dock k and its storage region is given by

$$\sum_{j \in S_i} (1/A_i) \, d_{kj};$$

that is, the average distance is the sum of the distances between dock k and all the grid squares taken up by item i divided by A_i. Finally, let w_{ik} represent a known total cost per unit of average distance incurred in transporting item i between dock k and its storage region, for a given time period. Typically, if items are stored on pallets, for example, w_{ik} would be directly proportional to the number of pallet loads of item i moving between dock k and the storage region of item i, for some given time period. Thus,

$$w_{ik} \sum_{j \in S_i} (1/A_i) \, d_{kj} \tag{23}$$

is the total average cost of transporting item i between dock k and the storage region for item i. The total average cost per time period due to transporting items to and from storage is given by

$$F(S_1, \ldots, S_m) = \sum_{i=1}^{m} \sum_{k=1}^{p} w_{ik} \left[\sum_{j \in S_i} (1/A_i) \, d_{kj} \right]. \tag{24}$$

The warehouse layout problem consists of finding storage regions for each item (given that no more than one item can take up any grid square) which will minimize the total cost expression (24).

In order to convert the layout problem into a generalized assignment problem, define the decision variable x_{ij}, as one if item $i = 1, \ldots, m$ takes up grid square $j = 1, \ldots, n$, and equals zero, otherwise. It will be assumed, for the time being, that the total number of grid squares to be taken up by items is the same as the total number of grid squares, that is, $\sum_{i=1}^{m} A_i = n$. Since item i takes up a total of A_i grid squares, it follows that

$$\sum_{j=1}^{n} x_{ij} = A_i \quad \text{for} \quad i = 1, \ldots, m.$$

Since each grid square is also taken up by one item, it also follows that

$$\sum_{i=1}^{n} x_{ij} = 1 \quad \text{for} \quad j = 1, \dots, n.$$

Given the definition of the variables x_{ij}, S_i is the collection of all grid squares j for which $x_{ij} = 1$, that is, $S_i = \{j : x_{ij} = 1\}$, so the expression (23) is equivalent to the expression

$$w_{ik} \sum_{j=1}^{n} (1/A_i) d_{kj} x_{ij},$$

and the total cost expression (24) is equivalent to the expression

$$\sum_{i=1}^{m} \sum_{k=1}^{p} w_{ik} \left[\sum_{j=1}^{n} (1/A_i) d_{kj} x_{ij} \right]. \tag{25}$$

If the term c_{ij} is defined by

$$c_{ij} = (1/A_i) \sum_{k=1}^{p} w_{ik} d_{kj}, \quad \text{for} \quad i = 1, \dots, m \quad \text{and} \quad j = 1, \dots, n,$$

then the total cost expression (25) may be rewritten, on rearranging the order of summation, as

$$\sum_{i=1}^{m} \sum_{j=1}^{n} c_{ij} x_{ij}.$$

The generalized assignment problem version of the layout problem may now be stated:

$$\text{Minimize} \sum_{i=1}^{m} \sum_{j=1}^{n} c_{ij} x_{ij}$$

subject to

$$\sum_{j=1}^{n} x_{ij} = A_i, \, i = 1, \dots, m$$

$$\sum_{i=1}^{m} x_{ij} = 1, j = 1, \dots, n$$

$$x_{ij} \in \{0, 1\}, \quad i = 1, \dots, m$$

$$j = 1, \dots, n.$$

In some cases, the number of items and number of grid squares will yield a generalized assignment problem too large to solve efficiently, using existing computer codes. Fortunately, an assumption, which is realistic in many cases, can be made which permits a least cost layout to be found by a procedure simpler than the generalized assignment approach. Specifically, as in Section 4, it is assumed that w_{ik} can be factored such that $w_{ik} = c_i w_k$ for $i = 1, \ldots, m$ and $k = 1, \ldots, p$.

Given the factoring assumption, $F(S_1, \ldots, S_m)$ can be rewritten, on rearranging the order of summation, as follows:

$$F(S_1, \ldots, S_m) = \sum_{i=1}^{m} (c_i/A_i) \sum_{j \in S_i} f_j,$$

where

$$f_j = \sum_{k=1}^{p} w_k d_{kj} \quad \text{for} \quad j = 1, \ldots, n.$$

Letting the items be numbered such that

$$c_1/A_1 \geqslant c_2/A_2 \geqslant \cdots \geqslant c_m/A_m,$$

the problem of interest is to find a layout $\{S_1^*, \ldots, S_m^*\}$, such that $F(S_1^*, \ldots, S_m^*) \leqslant F(S_1, \ldots, S_m)$, where $\{S_1, \ldots, S_m\}$ is any other layout.

The procedure for finding a least cost layout may now be stated. For $j = 1, \ldots, n$, compute

$$f_j = \sum_{k=1}^{p} w_k d_{kj},$$

and let $j_1, j_2, \ldots, j_n$ be a permutation of $1, 2, \ldots, n$, such that $f_{j1} \leqslant f_{j2} \leqslant \cdots \leqslant f_{jn}$. A least cost layout $\{S_1^*, \ldots, S_m^*\}$ in $H_m(L:A)$ is then given, on defining $B_i = \sum_{h=1}^{i} A_h$, for $i = 1, \ldots, m$, by

$$S_1^* = \{j_1, \ldots, j_{B_1}\}$$
$$S_2^* = \{j_{B_1+1}, \ldots, j_{B_2}\}$$
$$\cdot$$
$$\cdot$$
$$\cdot$$
$$S_m^* = \{j_{B_{m-1}+1}, \ldots, j_{B_m}\}.$$

A justification of the solution procedure is given by Francis and White [1974].

6. DISCRETE FACILITIES LOCATION PROBLEMS

In Section 2, facilities location problems were treated as continuous space problems. Discrete counterparts of those problems are considered in this section. Since interchanges are allowed between pairs of facilities, the resulting discrete location problem is commonly referred to as a quadratic assignment location problem, due to the fact that it can be formulated (although we shall not do so) as an assignment problem with a quadratic objective function.

We find it instructive to let $a(j)$ denote the number of the site to which facility j is assigned, and let $\mathbf{a}$ be the assignment vector

$$\mathbf{a} = (a(1), a(2), \ldots, a(n)),$$

where there are n new facilities to be located and n sites. (If the number of sites exceeds the number of new facilities, then an appropriate number of "dummy" facilities are defined). As an illustration, the assignment vector, $\mathbf{a} = (4, 1, 2, 3)$, indicates facility 1 is assigned to site 4, facility 2 is assigned to site 1, facility 3 is assigned to site 2, and facility 4 is assigned to site 3.

Given an assignment of facilities to sites, the next step is to compute a total cost for the assignment. For all integer values of g and h between 1 and n, let $d(g, h)$ denote an appropriately determined distance between sites g and h. As a subsequent notational convenience, it will be useful to assume that $d(g, h) = d(h, g)$ for all g and h. Suppose, finally, that v_{jk} is a constant of proportionality converting the distance between new facilities j and k, for all $j < k$, into a cost, so that if facility j is at site $a(j)$ and facility k is at site $a(k)$ the total cost for new facilities j and k is $v_{jk} d(a(j), a(k))$. Let the distance between existing facility i and site h be given by $c(i, h)$, with w_{ji} the constant of proportionality converting into a cost the distance between existing facility i and new facility j, so that if new facility j is located at site $a(j)$, the total cost for facilities i and j is $w_{ji} c(a(j), i)$. The total cost for an assignment of facilities to sites is then as follows:

$$TC(\mathbf{a}) = \sum_{1 \leqslant j < k \leqslant n} v_{jk} d(a(j), a(k)) + \sum_{j=1}^{n} \sum_{i=1}^{m} w_{ji} c(a(j), i) \qquad (26)$$

Thus, the quadratic assignment location problem involves the determination of an assignment vector, $\mathbf{a}$, such that (26) is minimized.

If there exist costs which are not proportional to distance, they can be added to (26) to obtain

$$TC(\mathbf{a}) = \sum_{1 \leqslant j < k \leqslant n} [v_{jk} d(a(j), a(k)) + p(a(j), a(k))]$$

$$+ \sum_{j=1}^{n} \sum_{i=1}^{m} w_{ji} c(a(j), i) + \sum_{j=1}^{n} q(a(j)), \qquad (27)$$

where $p(a(j), a(k))$ is the non-distance related cost of locating new facilities j and k at sites $a(j)$ and $a(k)$, respectively, and $q(a(j))$ is the non-distance related cost of assigning new facility j to site $a(j)$. To simplify the subsequent discussion, our concern will be with (26), rather than (27). However, the presentation can be extended to (27).

Procedures which have been developed to attempt to find least cost solutions to (26) are of two types: exact and heuristic. Exact procedures do in fact find least total cost assignments. With the exception of total enumeration, all of the exact procedures of interest developed thus far are branch and bound, or implicit enumeration, procedures. Branch and bound procedures, to date, have not proved to be generally computationally satisfactory; it has been estimated that they are unable to solve problems when n is greater than fifteen. One exact solution procedure, total enumeration, may be ruled out immediately, since it requires the explicit consideration of all $n!$ assignments. For these reasons, heuristic solution procedures have received considerable attention. For the problem being considered, a heuristic procedure may be characterized as one which has intuitive appeal and seems reasonable; such a procedure might be called a "common sense" procedure. A number of heuristic procedures have been developed for solving the problem being considered, and several will be discussed in the sequel.

One of the most successful heuristic procedures developed to obtain solutions to the quadratic assignment problem may be considered to be a steepest decent, pairwise interchange procedure (Armour and Buffa [1963]). This procedure, referred to more commonly as the CRAFT (Computerized Relative Allocation of Facilities Technique) procedure, begins with an initial assignment vector, $\mathbf{a}$, and considers the change in cost produced by interchanging pairs of facility locations. From among all pairs of interchanges the one which produces the greatest cost reduction is chosen and the associated interchange is made, yielding a new assignment vector, $\mathbf{a}'$. Given a new assignment vector, the procedure is repeated to obtain a second improved assignment, $\mathbf{a}''$, where

$$TC(\mathbf{a}) > TC(\mathbf{a}') > TC(\mathbf{a}''). \qquad (28)$$

The process continues until no pairwise interchange will yield a cost reduction. The final assignment generated by the procedure is specified as the solution to the quadratic assignment problem.

A number of other heuristic procedures have been developed to solve the quadratic assignment problem. For a comparison of several of the available heuristic procedures, see Hillier and Conners [1966], Hanan and Kurtzberg [1972], and Nugent et al. [1968].

The heuristic procedures we have considered are *improvement* procedures since an initial assignment is required and subsequent iterations yield improved solutions. An alternate approach which has been used is to develop a *construc-*

tion procedure in which a final solution is obtained by constructing a complete assignment. Construction procedures begin with a null vector and assign one of the facilities to one of the location sites. Next, another facility is chosen and it is assigned to one of the remaining sites. The process continues until all facilities have been assigned to sites. For a discussion of construction procedures, see Hanan and Kurtzberg [1972].

A number of branch and bound approaches have been developed to obtain exact solutions to the quadratic assignment problem. Among these are the procedures due to Gavett and Plyter [1966], Gilmore [1962], and Lawler [1963]. A discussion of a branch and bound procedure based on the works of Gilmore and Lawler is presented by Francis and White [1974]. For extensive reviews of solution procedures for quadratic assignment problems, see Hanan and Kurtzberg [1972] and Pierce and Crowston [1971].

7. DISCRETE LOCATION-ALLOCATION PROBLEMS

In Section 3 a continuous space formulation of the location-allocation problem was considered. In this section, a discrete space formulation is presented for the location-allocation problem. The discrete space problem is more commonly referred to as the plant location problem and the warehouse location problem, due to the context within which the problem occurs.

7.1 Plant Location Problems[2]

The plant location problem typically involves a determination of the number, location, and sizes of plants (warehouses) required to supply products to customers. The locations of a finite number of potential plant sites and customers are assumed to be known.

Balinski [1964] was among the first to formulate the discrete plant location problem as a mixed integer programming (MIP) problem. To facilitate the presentation of the MIP formulation, let m be the number of customers; n be the number of possible plant sites; y_{ij} represent the fraction or portion of the demand of customer i which is satisfied by a plant located at site j; $i = 1, \ldots, m$; $j = 1, \ldots, n$; c_{ij} denote the cost of supplying the entire demand of customer i from a plant located at site j; and f_j be the fixed cost resulting from locating a plant at site j. The decision variable, x_j, equals one if a plant is located at site j, and equals zero, otherwise.

Based on the above notation, the following discrete plant location problem, called the *simple plant location* problem, is formulated:

$$\text{P0.} \quad \text{Minimize} \quad z = \sum_{i=1}^{m} \sum_{j=1}^{n} c_{ij} y_{ij} + \sum_{j=1}^{n} f_j x_j \tag{29}$$

[2] The authors wish to acknowledge the contributions of Leon F. McGinnis to this section. For a review of plant location research results, see McGinnis [1977].

$$\text{subject to } \sum_{i=1}^{m} y_{ij} \leqslant mx_j, \quad j = 1, \dots, n \tag{30}$$

$$\sum_{j=1}^{n} y_{ij} = 1, \quad i = 1, \dots, m \tag{31}$$

$$y_{ij} \geqslant 0 \quad \text{for all} \quad i, j$$

$$x_j = (0, 1) \quad \text{for all } j.$$

The objective function (29) gives the cost when $\sum_{j=1}^{n} x_j$ plants are to be located at those sites corresponding to positive valued x_j. Constraints (30) indicate the total fraction of customer demand supplied by a plant at site j either equals zero when x_j equals zero, or cannot exceed the number of customers when x_j equals one. By (31) all demands for customer i must be met by some combination of plants. Typically, the c_{ij} are transportation costs. If there were no fixed costs, the optimum solution to the problem would be to build a plant at every site. On the other hand, if there were no transportation costs, the optimum solution to the problem would be to build one plant at the site with the smallest fixed cost. Thus, we see that in the general problem a balance must be achieved between transportation costs and fixed costs.

More generally, models of the plant location problem define y_{ij} as the *amount* of the demand of customer i which is satisfied by a plant located at site j. Additionally, constraints are often placed on the capacity of a plant at site j. Incorporating these features in P0 gives the *capacitated plant location problem*, P1.

$$\text{P1. Minimize} \quad z = \sum_{i=1}^{m} \sum_{j=1}^{n} c_{ij} y_{ij} + \sum_{j=1}^{n} g_i \left(\sum_{i=1}^{m} y_{ij} \right)$$

$$\text{subject to} \quad \sum_{i=1}^{m} y_{ij} - Q_j x_j \leqslant 0$$

$$\sum_{j=1}^{n} y_{ij} = d_i$$

$$y_{ij} \geqslant 0, \quad x_j = (0, 1),$$

where

Q_j = capacity of a facility at site j;
c_{ij} = cost of transporting a demanded unit from j to i
$g_i(\ )$ = cost function for the proposed facility at site j, which may include a fixed cost

y_{ij} = amount supplied to customer i from site j

d_i = amount to be supplied to customer i

Variations of P1 include the consideration of nonlinear forms of $g_j(\ )$, as well as nonlinear distribution costs. Also, additional constraints may be added to P1 to restrict the configuration of plants. Configuration constraints, for example, might be included to prevent the location of a plant at site j if a plant is located at, say, site k. For a consideration of a number of these variations, see Ellwein and Gray [1971], Sá [1969], Spielberg [1969a, 1969b], Soland [1971], and Elshafei [1974a, 1974b], among others.

P1 can be expressed in matrix notation as follows:

$$P2. \quad \text{Minimize} \quad \mathbf{fx + CY}$$

$$\text{subject to} \quad \mathbf{A_1 x + A_2 Y = b}$$

$$\mathbf{Y} \geqslant 0$$

$$\mathbf{x} \in \mathbf{X}$$

$$x_j = (0, 1),$$

where $\mathbf{X}$ is the set of feasible combinations of plant sites defined by any configuration constraints, $\mathbf{A_1}$ and $\mathbf{A_2}$ are appropriately defined matrices and $\mathbf{b}$ is a column vector.

P2 is a mixed integer linear programming problem (MILP) whose integer variables are restricted to the values 0 and 1. Procedures proposed for solving P2 can be classified as "enumeration methods" to include "relaxation algorithms" and "partitioning algorithms." Both algorithmic approaches are characterized by a tree diagram representing a systematic search for the optimal binary variables, x_j.

For P2 each node of the search tree corresponds uniquely to a partition of the indices of the binary variables:

  (i) $K_0 = \{j: x_j$ is set equal to $0\}$
  (ii) $K_1 = \{j: x_j$ is set equal to $1\}$
  (iii) $K_2 = \{j: x_j$ is not assigned a value$\}$.

Any x_k for $k \in K_2$ is called a *free variable*. There are, at most, two branches emanating from any node, ν, in the tree. The two *successor nodes* correspond to choosing a free variable, x_k, at ν, and forming two new partitions by alternately requiring that $k \in K_0$ and $k \in K_1$, and is referred to as *branching* on x_k.

It will be convenient to let RP denote P2 with the integer restrictions relaxed. Thus, RP is the LP problem formed by removing the binary restriction on x_j in P2. If all the free variables in the LP optimal solution are integer, then a feasible solution has been obtained to P2; otherwise, some noninteger x_k is chosen for branching.

Likewise, it will be convenient to let SP denote a subproblem of P2 when values have been assigned to $x \in X$. In particular, for a specified $x \in X$, there is a corresponding optimal Y, denoted by Y_x, given by the *subproblem*

$$\text{SP} \quad \text{Minimize} \quad \mathbf{CY}$$

$$\text{subject to} \quad \mathbf{A_2 Y = b - A_1 x}$$

$$\mathbf{Y \geqslant 0}$$

Partitioning algorithms involve a search over X. The x are evaluated by solving SP, and are referred to as *designs*. The value of a design, x, is $Z(x) = \mathbf{fx} + \mathbf{CY_x}$.

The distinction between relaxation algorithms and partitioning algorithms centers on the nature of RP and SP. In RP, there are some as yet unspecified binary variables, but they are treated as continuous variables. In SP, however, all the binary variables have been specified, so that the only variables to be determined are the continuous variables, y_{ij}. In terms of the enumeration tree, RP can be solved at any node, while SP is solved only at "terminal nodes;" i.e., those nodes for which K is empty. In the sequel, the term "branch and bound" is associated with procedures employing RP, and the term "implicit enumeration" is associated with those procedures involving SP.

Before considering procedures for solving RP and SP, it is worthwhile to consider a third procedure for solving P2 due to Benders [1962]. Although not computationally attractive, Bender's partitioning algorithm leads to improvements in the enumeration methods. Bender's algorithm requires that P2 be partitioned as:

$$\text{BP.} \quad \text{Min} \quad \left\{ \begin{array}{l} \mathbf{fx} + \min \mathbf{CY} \\ \\ \mathbf{A_2 Y = b - A_1 x} \\ \mathbf{Y \geqslant 0} \end{array} \right.$$

$$\text{subject to}$$
$$x \in X$$
$$x_j = 0, 1$$

As can be seen, the portion of BP contained in braces is the formulation SP. The dual of SP is:

$$\text{DSP.} \quad \text{Max} \quad \mathbf{u}(\mathbf{b} - A_1 \mathbf{x})$$

$$\text{subject to} \quad \mathbf{uA_2 \leqslant C}$$

$$\mathbf{u \geqslant 0},$$

where $\mathbf{u}$ is the vector of dual variables. If BP is feasible and unbounded, SP can be replaced by DSP in BP to obtain

BP1. Min $\quad$ $\left\{\begin{array}{l} \mathbf{fx} + \max \mathbf{u}(\mathbf{b} - A_1\mathbf{x}) \\[1em] \end{array}\right.$

$\quad$ subject to

$\quad \mathbf{x} \in X$ $\qquad \mathbf{u}A_2 \leqslant C$

$\quad x_j = 0, 1$ $\qquad \mathbf{u} \geqslant 0$ $\qquad \left.\begin{array}{c}\\\\\\\end{array}\right\}$

To motivate the procedure to be used in solving P2, suppose, for a given value of $\mathbf{x}$, that DSP is unbounded. Consequently, there exists a dual extreme point, $\mathbf{u}^t$, and a dual direction vector $\mathbf{u}^r$, such that

$$(\mathbf{u}^t + \theta\mathbf{u}^r)A_2 \leqslant C \quad \text{and} \quad (\mathbf{u}^t + \theta\mathbf{u}^r)(\mathbf{b} - A_1\mathbf{x}) \to \infty \qquad \text{as} \quad \theta \to \infty.$$

This implies that

$$\mathbf{u}^r(\mathbf{b} - A_1\mathbf{x}) > 0.$$

If DSP is unbounded for some $\mathbf{x}$, then SP is infeasible. Consequently, $\mathbf{x}$ must satisfy

$$\mathbf{u}^r(\mathbf{b} - A_1\mathbf{x}) \leqslant 0 \qquad \forall r \in R,$$

where R is the index set of directions of extreme rays of $\mathbf{u}A_2 \leqslant C$.

Let T be the index set of all extreme points of $\mathbf{u}A_2 \leqslant C$. Then we can rewrite BP1 as

$\quad$ BIP $\quad$ Minimize $\quad x_0$

$\qquad$ subject to $\quad x_0 \geqslant \mathbf{fx} + \mathbf{u}^t(\mathbf{b} - A_1\mathbf{x}) \qquad t \in T \qquad$ (32)

$\qquad\qquad\qquad 0 \geqslant \qquad \mathbf{u}^r(\mathbf{b} - A_1\mathbf{x}) \qquad r \in R \qquad$ (33)

$\qquad\qquad \mathbf{x} \in X$

$\qquad\qquad x_j = 0, 1 \qquad \forall j.$

BIP is a MILP with one continuous variable, x_0. In solving BIP, the sets T and R are initially empty; i.e., the extreme rays and extreme points of DSP have not yet been identified. Some $\mathbf{x}$ is chosen and DSP is solved, generating either an extreme point or an extreme ray. The corresponding constraint, either (32) or (33), is appended to BIP and the problem is resolved, using any MILP technique, to obtain a new $\mathbf{x}$.

The solution procedure iterates between BIP and DSP until some $\mathbf{x}$ is obtained which satisfies

$$x_0 - \mathbf{fx} = \max \mathbf{u}(\mathbf{b} - A_1\mathbf{x})$$

$$\text{subject to} \quad \mathbf{u}A_2 \leqslant C$$

$$\mathbf{u} \geqslant 0.$$

Finiteness of the procedure is assured since there are only a finite number of extreme points and extreme rays. For additional discussion of the iterative solution technique, see Garfinkel and Nemhauser [1972].

Returning to a consideration of relaxation algorithms, recall from P1 and P2 at node ν in the search tree, RP can be written as

$$\text{RP}^\nu \quad \min \sum_{j \in K_1 \cup K_2} \sum_i c_{ij} y_{ij} + \sum_{j \in K_1} f_j + \sum_{j \in K_2} f_j x_j$$

$$\text{subject to} \quad \sum_{j \in K_1 \cup K_2} y_{ij} = d_i$$

$$\sum_i y_{ij} - Q_j x_j \leqslant 0, \qquad j \in K_2$$

$$\sum_i y_{ij} \leqslant Q_j, \qquad j \in K_1$$

$$y_{ij} \geqslant 0$$

$$0 \leqslant x_j \leqslant 1, \qquad j \in K_2$$

$$x \in X.$$

If there are configuration constraints (side conditions), then RP^ν must be solved directly as an LP problem. However, if there are no side conditions the optimal solution will have

$$\sum_i y_{ij} - Q_j x_j = 0, \qquad j \in K_2.$$

Thus, on solving for x_j in terms of y_{ij}, we obtain

$$x_j = \frac{1}{Q_j} \sum_i y_{ij},$$

such that $0 \leqslant x_j \leqslant 1$. Substituting for x_j in RP^ν yields a formulation involving y_{ij} alone;

$$\text{RP1}^\nu \quad \min \sum_{j \in K_1} \sum_i c_{ij} y_{ij} + \sum_{j \in K_2} \sum_i \left(c_{ij} + \frac{f_j}{Q_j} \right) y_{ij} + \sum_{j \in K_1} f_j$$

$$\text{subject to} \quad \sum_{j \in K_1 \cup K_2} y_{ij} = d_i, \qquad i = 1, \ldots, m$$

$$\sum_i y_{ij} \leqslant Q_j, \qquad j \in K_1 \cup K_2$$

$$y_{ij} \geqslant 0, \qquad j \in K_1 \cup K_2, \quad i = 1, \ldots, m.$$

Sá [1969] and Davis and Ray [1969] solved RP1^ν as a transportation problem. If the plant location problem has no side conditions, and is uncapacitated such that P2 reduces to P0, it is convenient to redefine y_{ij} and c_{ij} by letting y'_{ij} represent the fraction of the demand for customer i, satisfied by a plant at site j, and letting c'_{ij} become the cost of supplying the entire demand of customer i from a plant located at site j. Thus, if $y'_{ij} = y_{ij}/d_i$, $c'_{ij} = c_{ij} d_i$, and $Q_j = \sum_{i=1}^{m} d_i$, then RP1$^\nu$ reduces to

$$\text{RP2}^\nu \quad \min \sum_{j \in K_1} \sum_{i=1}^{m} c'_{ij} y'_{ij} + \sum_{j \in K_2} \sum_{i=1}^{m} \left(c'_{ij} + \frac{f_j}{m} \right) y'_{ij}$$

$$\text{subject to} \quad \sum_{j \in K_1 \cup K_2} y'_{ij} = 1, \quad \forall i$$

$$y'_{ij} \geq 0, \quad \forall i, \ j \in K_1 \cup K_2.$$

Defining a new term g_j such that

$$g_j = \begin{cases} 0, & \text{if } j \in K_1 \\ f_j, & \text{if } j \in K_2, \end{cases}$$

then an optimum solution to RP2$^\nu$ is obtained by inspection. For each i, choose j^* such that

$$mc'_{ij^*} + g_{j^*} = \min (mc'_{ij} + g_j),$$

and let

$$y'_{ij} = \begin{cases} 1, & \text{if } j = j^* \\ 0, & \text{otherwise.} \end{cases}$$

Optimum values of x_j are obtained from the relation

$$x_j = \frac{1}{m} \sum_{i=1}^{m} y'_{ij}.$$

Efroymson and Ray [1966] first employed the above procedure in a branch and bound algorithm to solve P0. Khumawala [1972, 1973] subsequently developed a variety of node selection rules and branching rules which produced computational efficiencies in solving P0.

In using partitioning algorithms to solve P2, notice that the specification of a complete design, say $\mathbf{x}^{(k)}$, such that K_2, the set of free binary variables, is empty, reduces SP to

$$\text{SP}(k) \quad \min \sum_{j \in K_1} \sum_{i=1}^{m} c_{ij} y_{ij}$$

$$\text{subject to} \quad \sum_{j \in K_1} y_{ij} = d_i, \quad i = 1, \ldots, m$$

$$\sum_{i=1}^{m} y_{ij} \leqslant Q_j, \qquad j \in K_1$$

$$y_{ij} \geqslant 0, \qquad j \in K_1, \quad i = 1, \ldots, m.$$

Notice that the constraints of SP (k) are the same as those for RP1$^{\nu}$ when K_2 is empty, and that there are no side conditions. Thus, the comments relating to RPI$^{\nu}$ and its descendants apply as well to SP (k).

Spielberg [1969a, 1969b] presents an implicit enumeration algorithm for the uncapacitated problem with side conditions, which he indicates can accommodate the capacitated problem. Ellwein and Gray [1971] and Elshafei [1973] present algorithms for the uncapacitated problem with configuration constraints, and Bulfin and Unger [1973] provide an algorithm for the capacitated problem without configuration constraints.

7.2 Set of Covering Location Problems

A location problem which is related to the plant location problem is the set covering location problem. In a facility location context, the problem of determining the number and location of, say, warehouses such that a warehouse is within 100 miles of each customer, can be formulated as a set covering problem. In addition to the location of plants and warehouses, a number of other facility location problems can be formulated as covering problems. As an illustration, one can formulate as a covering problem the problem of determining the number and location of community colleges within a state, such that a student will be within a one hour drive of a college. Additionally, the problem of locating fire stations within, say, five minutes driving time from all points in a city can be formulated as a covering problem.

The set covering problem can be formulated as follows:

P3. Minimize $z = \sum_{j=1}^{n} c_j x_j$

subject to $\sum_{j=1}^{n} a_{ij} x_j \geqslant 1, i = 1, \cdots, m$

$$x_j = (0, 1), j = 1, \cdots, n.$$

The a_{ij} values in P3 are referred to as covering coefficients, and take on the value of one if customer i is *covered* by site j; otherwise, a_{ij} equals zero. Likewise, x_j is set equal to one if a facility is assigned to site j and to zero, otherwise. By the constraint in P3 it is required that each of the m customers be *covered* by at least one of the n facilities. The objective, then, is to cover the customers at minimum cost, where c_j is the cost of assigning a facility to site j.

As an illustration of the meaning of the term "cover," consider the customers to be residences in a community, the facilities to be fire stations, and let residence i be covered if there is a fire station located within a five minute drive of the residence. As another example, let the facilities be plants, and let customer i be covered or served by a plant if it is assigned to either sites 1, 2, or 3. Thus, $a_{i1} = a_{i2} = a_{i3} = 1$ and all other a_{ik} are zero for $k \neq 1, 2, 3$.

Since P3 is also an integer LP problem, any appropriate integer programming solution procedure can be used to solve P3. However, due to the special structure of P3, a number of algorithms have been developed especially for covering problems. Generally speaking, there are four broad approaches reported in the literature for solving covering problems: implicit enumeration procedures, cutting plane methods, reduction techniques, and heuristic methods. For a general review of the covering problem and its applications, see Garfinkel and Nemhauser [1972].

A common facilities location application of a set covering problem involves the determination of the minimum number of facilities required to cover a set of customers. In such a situation, P3 reduces to what is called the total cover problem, P4, by letting all c_j equal one in P3. Toregas, et al. [1971] demonstrates that a number of emergency service facility location problems can be formulated as total cover problems.

A zero-one programming problem, which is related to the *total cover problem*, is the *partial cover problem*. The total cover problem involves a determination of the minimum number and locations of facilities such that *all* customers are covered; the partial cover problem involves the determination of the location of a given number of facilities such that the maximum number of customers is covered. In a number of practical situations, it is not possible to provide the number of facilities required to *totally* cover all customers, rather, the number of facilities available for location is only sufficient to *partially* cover the set of customers. For such situations, a partial cover formulation is appropriate.

Mathematically, the partial cover problem can be formulated, as follows:

$$\text{P5. Maximize } \tilde{Z} = \sum_{i=1}^{m} \max_{1 \leqslant j \leqslant n} a_{ij} x_j$$

$$\text{subject to } \sum_{j=1}^{n} x_j \leqslant K$$

$$x_j = (0, 1), \quad j = 1, \cdots, n,$$

where K is the maximum number of facilities available for assignment to sites; a_{ij} and x_j are as defined for P3.

As indicated by the term $\max_j a_{ij} x_j$, in the objective function of P5, if a particular customer is covered by more than one of the facilities which have been assigned to sites, only the maximum a_{ij} value is included in the computation of $\tilde{Z}$. The constraint in P5 indicates that, at most, K facilities are to be assigned to sites. Notice: if $\tilde{Z}$ equals m, the number of customers, then K is sufficiently large to totally cover the set of customers. Thus, the total cover problem (P4) can be solved by solving the partial cover problem (P5) for various values of K; the solution to P5 (involving the smallest value of K), which results in $\tilde{Z}$ equaling m, will be an optimum solution to P4. However, one would not normally solve P4 in this way, since more direct (and efficient) solution procedures are available.

P5 has received very little attention in the location literature. However, a more general formulation of a minimization version of P5 has been studied extensively. Thus, P5 can be solved by using procedures appropriate for the more general formulation. By generalizing the definition of a_{ij}, the following formulation, defined as the *generalized partial cover* problem, is obtained:

$$
\text{P6.} \quad \text{Minimize } \tilde{Z} = \sum_{i=1}^{m} \min_{j \in \theta(x)} a_{ij}
$$

$$
\text{subject to } \sum_{j=1}^{n} x_j \leqslant K
$$

$$
x_j = (0, 1), \quad j = 1, \cdots, n,
$$

where $\theta(x)$ is the set of indices of sites which are assigned facilities; thus, $\theta(x) = \{j: x_j = 1\}$. Letting a_i be the customer population at community i, and d_{ij} be the distance between community i and site j, then in P6 a_{ij} equals $a_i d_{ij}$. Thus, the objective is to locate at most K facilities, such that the total distance traveled between communities and facilities is minimized. The term, $\min_{j \in \theta(x)} a_{ij}$, indicates that if a community can be served by more than one assigned facility, the community will be served by the closest facility. (Note: $\theta(x)$ must be non-empty.)

Due to the physical contexts in which P6 has been applied, it is referred to in the literature as the central facilities location problem (Revelle and Swain [1970]), the p-median problem (Hakimi [1965]), and a warehouse location problem (Shannon and Ignizio [1970]). To complete the correspondence between P6 and the central facilities location problem, in P6 each community is designated as a potential site for a facility; thus, n is set equal to m.

Exact solutions to P6 have been obtained using dynamic programming, branch and bound, and a dual procedure. However, the exact procedures are not felt to be computationally feasible for $n \geqslant 20$ and $K \geqslant 10$. Consequently, a number of heuristic procedures have been developed to solve P6 (Khumawala, [1974], Maranzana [1964], Shannon and Ignizio [1970], Teitz and Bart [1968]).

8. SUMMARY

Due to the large body of research and applications literature dealing with the location and layout of facilities, it is not possible to provide an exhaustive treatise on the subject in a single chapter. Consequently, we have endeavored to provide a taxonomy of the subject, as well as formulations of a variety of facilities location and layout problems, in order to illustrate not only the wide variety of applications which are possible, but also the role that OR has played in the study of the subject.

To date, the literature has emphasized the development of either new formulations of facilities location and layout problems, or new solution techniques for old formulations. Relatively little has been published on the application of the formulations to real world problems. Yet, a number of successful applications have been made. As appears to be the case with a number of the subject areas treated in other chapters of the handbook, many of those involved in solving real world facilities location and layout problems have not published accounts of their work.

Many of the quantitative techniques presented in this chapter have been applied in the location and/or layout of plants, warehouses, fire stations, hospitals, branch banks, post offices, production machines, and storerooms—to mention but a few. For a more detailed treatment of the subject, as well as the presentation of a number of example problems illustrating the variety of applications, see Francis and White [1974].

In summary, significant progress has occurred in the past decade in the formulation of analytical models of facilities location and layout problems, as well as in the development of efficient solution procedures for many of these models. In the future, it is anticipated that the current widespread, interdisciplinary interest in the subject will manifest itself in the application of the models to a greater number and variety of real world problems.

REFERENCES

Apple, J. M., and Deisenroth, M. P., "A Computerized Plant Layout Analysis and Evaluation Technique (PLANET)," *Proceedings*, American Institute of Industrial Engineers, 23rd Annual Conference and Convention, Anaheim, California (1972).

Armour, G. C. and Buffa, E. S., "A Heuristic Algorithm and Simulation Approach to the Relative Location of Facilities," *Management Sci.* 9, No. 2: 294-309 (1963).

Balinski, M. L., "On Finding Integer Solutions to Linear Programs," Mathematica, Princeton, New Jersey (May 1964).

Benders, J. F., "Partitioning Procedures for Solving Mixed-Variables Programming Problems," *Numerishe Mathematik* 4: 238-252 (1962).

Bindschedler, A. E., and Moore, J. M., "Optimal Location of New Machines in Existing Plant Layouts," *J. Ind. Eng.* 12, No. 1: 41-48 (1961).

Bulfin, R. L. and Unger, V. E., "Investigation of Surrogate Constraints in a Plant Location Algorithm," Georgia Institute of Technology, Atlanta, Georgia (1973).

Cabot, A. V., Francis, R. L., and Stary, M. A., "A Network Flow Solution to a Rectilinear Distance Facility Location Problem," *AIIE Trans.* **2**, No. 2: 132–141 (1970).

Christofides, N., and Viola, P., "The Optimum Location of Multi-Centres on a Graph," *Operational Res. Quart.* **22**, No. 2: 145–154 (1971).

Cooper, L., "Location-Allocation Problems," *Operations Res.* **11**, No. 3: 331–334 (1963).

——, "Heuristic Methods for Location-Allocation Problems," *SIAM Rev.* **6**, No. 1: 37–52 (1964).

——, "Solution of Generalized Locational Equilibrium Models," *J. Regional Sci.* **7**, No. 1: 1–18 (1967).

——, "The Transportation-Location Problem," *Operations Res.* **20**, No. 1: 94–108 (1972).

Corley, H. W., Jr., and Roberts, S. D., "A Partitioning Problem with Applications in Regional Design," *Operations Res.* **2**, No. 5: 1010–1019 (1972).

Curry, G. L. and Skeith, R. W., "A Dynamic Programming Algorithm for Facility Location and Allocation," *AIIE Trans.* **1**, No. 2: 133–138 (1969).

Davis, P. S. and Ray, T. L., "A Branch-Bound Algorithm for the Capacitated Facilities Location Problem," *Nav. Res. Log. Quart.* **16**, No. 3: 331 (1969).

Dearing, P. M., and R. L. Francis, "A Network Flow Solution to a Multi–Facility Minimax Location Problem Involving Rectilinear Distances," *Transport. Sci.* **8**, No. 2: 126–141 (1974).

Donath, W. E., "Statistical Properties of the Placement of a Graph," *SIAM J. Appl. Math.* **16**, No. 2: 439–457 (1968).

Efroymson, M. A. and Ray, T. L., "A Branch-Bound Algorithm for Plant Location," *Operations Res.* **14**, No. 3: 361–368 (1966).

Eilon, S., Watson-Gandy, C. D. T., and Christofides, N., *Distribution Management: Mathematical Modelling and Practical Analysis*, Hafner Publishing Company, New York (1971).

Ellwein, L. B. and Gray, P., "Solving Fixed Charge Allocation Problems with Capacity and Configuration Constraints," *AIIE Trans.* **3**, No. 4: 290–298 (1971).

Elshafei, A. N., "Optimal Location of Facilities," Ph.D. Thesis, University of Birmingham, England (May 1973).

——, "On Solving the Capacitated Facilities Location Problem with Concave Cost Functions– Part I: Features of a Search Procedure," OR Report No. 92, North Carolina State University at Raleigh, Raleigh, North Carolina (1974).

——, "On Solving the Capacitated Facilities Location Problem with Concave Cost Functions –Part II: Algorithmic Aspects and Computational Experience," OR Report No. 93, North Carolina State University at Raleigh, Raleigh, North Carolina (1974).

Elzinga, J. and Hearn, D., "Geometrical Solutions For Some Minimax Location Problems," *Transport. Sci.* **6**, No. 4: 379–394 (1972).

——, "The Minimum Covering Sphere Problem," *Management Sci.* **19**, No. 1: 96–104 (1972).

——, "A Note on a Minimax Location Problem," *Transport. Sci.* **7**, No. 1 (1973).

Eyster, J. W., White, J. A., and Wierwille, W. W., "On Solving Multifacility Location Problems Using a Hyperboloid Approximation Procedure," *AIIE Trans.* **5**, No. 1: 1–6 (1973).

Francis, R. L., "A Note on the Optimum Location of New Machines in Existing Plant Layouts," *J. Ind. Eng.* **14**, No. 1: 57–59 (1963).

——, "Sufficient Conditions for Some Optimum-Property Facility Designs," *Operations Res.* **15**, No. 3: 448–466 (1967).

——, "On Some Problems of Rectangular Warehouse Design and Layout," *J. Ind. Eng.* **18**, No. 10: 595-604 (1967).

——, "Some Aspects of a Minimax Location Problem," *Operations Res.* **15**, No. 6: 1163-1168 (1967).

——, "A Minimax Facility Configuration Problem Involving Lattice Points," *Operations Res.* **21**, No. 2: 101-111 (1973).

—— and Cabot, A. V., "Properties of a Multifacility Location Problem Involving Euclidean Distances," *Nav. Res. Log. Quart.* **19**, No. 2: 335-353 (1972).

—— and Goldstein, J. M., "Location Theory: A Selective Bibliography," *Operations Res.* **22** (1974).

—— and White, J. A., *Facilities Layout and Location: An Analytical Approach*, Prentice-Hall, Inc., Englewood Cliffs, New Jersey (1974).

Frank, H., "Optimum Location on a Graph with Probabilistic Demand," *Operations Res.* **14**, No. 3: 409-421 (1966).

Gavett, J. W. and Plyter, N. V., "The Optimal Assignment of Facilities to Locations by Branch and Bound," *Operations Res.* **14**, No. 2: 210-232 (1966).

Garfinkel, R. S. and Nemhauser, G. L., *Integer Programming*, John Wiley and Sons, New York (1972).

Gilbert, E. N. and Pollack, H. O., "Steiner Minimal Trees," *J. Soc. Ind. and Appl. Math.* **16**, No. 1: 1-29 (1968).

Gilmore, P. C., "Optimal and Suboptimal Algorithms for the Quadratic Assignment Problem," *SIAM Journal*, **10**, No. 2: 305-313 (1962).

Goldman, A. J., "Optimal Locations for Centers in a Network," *Transport. Sci.* **3**, No. 4: 352-360 (1969).

——, "Optimal Center Location in Simple Networks," *Transport. Sci.* **5**, No. 2: 212-221 (1971).

——, "Approximation Localization Theorems for Optimal Facility Placement," *Transport. Sci.* **6**, No. 2: 195-201 (1972).

——, "Minimax Location of a Facility on a Network," *Transport. Sci.* **6**, No. 4: 407-418 (1972).

—— and Witzgall, C. J., "A Localization Theorem for Optimal Facility Placement," *Transport. Sci.* **4**, No: 406-408 (1970).

Hakimi, S. L., "Optimum Locations of Switching Centers and the Absolute Centers and Medians of a Graph," *Operations Res.* **12**, No. 3: 450-459 (1964).

——, "Optimum Distribution of Switching Centers in a Communication Network and Some Related Graph Theoretic Problems," *Operations Res.* **13**, No. 3: 462-475 (1965).

——, "Steiner's Problem in Graphs and Its Implications," *Networks* **1**, No. 2: 113-134 (1972).

—— and Maheshwari, S. N., "Optimum Locations of Centers in Networks," *Operations Res.* **20**, No. 5: 967-973 (1972).

Hanan, M., and Kurtzberg, J., "A Review of the Placement and Quadratic Assignment Problems," *SIAM Rev.* **14**, No. 2: 324-342 (1972).

Hillier, F. S., and Connors, M. M., "Quadratic Assignment Problem Algorithms and the Location of Indivisible Facilities," *Management Sci.* **13**, No. 1: 43-57 (1966).

Järvinen, P., Rajala, J., and Sinerro, J., "A Branch-and Bound Algorithm for Seeking the p-median," *Operations Res.* **20**, No. 1: 173-178 (1972).

Katz, Norman, "On the Convergence of a Numercial Scheme For Solving Some Locational Equilibrium Problems," *SIAM J. Appl. Math.* **17**, No. 6: 1224-1231 (1969).

Khumawala, B. M., and Whybark, D. C., "A Comparison of Some Recent Warehouse Location Techniques," *Log. Rev.* **7**, 3-19 (Spring 1971).

——, "An Efficient Branch and Bound Algorithm for the Warehouse Location Problem," *Management Sci.* **18**, No. 12: 718-731 (1972).

——, "An Efficient Heuristic Procedure for the Uncapacitated Warehouse Location Problem," *Nav. Res. Log. Quart.* **20**, No. 1: 109-122 (1973).

——, "An Efficient Algorithm for the p-median Problem with Maximum Distance Constraints," *Geograph. Anal.* **5**, No. 4: 309-321 (1974).

Koopmans, J. C., and Beckman, M., "Assignment Problems and the Location of Economic Activities," *Econometrica* **25**, No. 1: 53-76 (1957).

Kuenne, R. E., and Soland, R. M., *The Multisource Weber Problem: Exact Solutions by Branch and Bound*, IDA Economic Papers, H. Williams (ed.), Program Analysis Division, 400 Army-Navy Drive, Arlington, Virginia (1971).

Kuhn, Harold, W. and Kuenne, Robert E., "An Efficient Algorithm for the Numercial Solution of the Generalized Weber Problem in Spatial Economics," *J. Regional Sci.* **4**, No. 2: 21-33 (1962).

——, "A Note on Fermat's Problem," *Math. Prog.* **4**, No. 1: 98-107 (1973).

Lawler, E. L., "The Quadratic Assignment Problem," *Management Sci.* **9**, No. 4: 586-599 (1963).

Lee, R. C., and Moore, J. M., "CORELAP—Computerized Relationship Layout Planning," *J. Ind. Eng.* **18**, No. 3: 195-200 (1967).

Levy, J., "An Extended Theorem for Location on a Network," *Operational Res. Quart.* **18**, No. 4: 433-442 (1967).

Love, Robert F., "Locating Facilities in Three-Dimensional Space by Convex Programming," *Nav. Res. Log. Quart.* **16**, No. 4: 503-516 (1969).

——, "A Computational Procedure for Optimally Locating a Facility With Respect to Several Rectangular Regions," *J. Regional Sci.* **12**, No. 2: 233-242 (1972).

Mallette, A. J. and Francis, R. L., "A Generalized Assignment Approach to Optimal Facility Layout," *AIIE Trans.* **4**, No. 2: 144-147 (1972).

Maranzana, F. E., "On the Location of Supply Points to Minimize Transport Costs," *Operations Res. Quart.* **15**, No. 3: 261-270 (1964).

Marsten, R. E., "An Algorithm for Estimating the Medians of a Weighted Graph Subject to Side Constraints and An Application to Rural Hospitals in British Columbia," Unpublished Ph.D. Thesis, University of British Columbia, Vancouver (1971).

McGinnis, L. F., "A Survey of Recent Results for a Class of Facilities Location Problems," *AIIE Trans.* **9**, No. 1: 11-18, (1977).

Miehle, William, "Link-Length Minimization in Networks," *J. Operations Res.* **6**, No. 2: 232-243 (1958).

Minieka, Edward, "The m-Center Problem," *SIAM Rev.* **12**, No. 1: 138-139 (1970).

Moore, J. M., "Optimal Locations For Multiple Machines," *J. Ind. Eng.* **12**, No. 5: 34-38 (1961).

——, "Computer Program Evaluates Plant Layout Alternatives," *Ind. Eng.* **3**, No. 8: 19-25 (1971).

Nair, K. P. K. and R. Chandrasakaran, "Optimal Location of a Single Service Center of Certain Types," *Nav. Res. Log. Quart.* **18**, 503-510 (1971).

Nugent, C. E., Vollmann, T. E., and Ruml, J., "An Experimental Comparison of Techniques for the Assignment of Facilities to Locations," *Operations Res.* **16**, No. 1: 150-173 (1968).

Pierce, J. F. and Crowston, W. B., "Tree-Search Algorithms for Quadratic Assignment Problems," *Nav. Res. Log. Quart.* **18**, No. 1: 1-36 (1971).

Revelle, C., Marks, D., and Liebman, J. C., "An Analysis of Private and Public Sector Location Models," *Management Sci.* **16**, No. 11: 692-707 (1970).

—— and Swain, R., "Central Facilities Location," *Geographical Analysis*, **2**, No. 1: 30–42 (1970).

Rojeski, P. and Revelle, C., "Central Facilities Location Under an Investment Constraint," *Geograph. Anal.* **2**, No. 3: 343–350 (1970).

Roth, R., "Computer Solutions to Minimum-Cover Problems," *Operations Res.* **17**, No. 3: 455–465 (1969).

Sa, G., "Branch-and Bound and Approximate Solutions to the Capacitated Plant Location Problem," *Operations Res.* **17**, No. 6: 1005 (1969).

Scott, A. J., "Location-Allocation Systems: A Review," *Geograph. Anal.* **2**, No. 2: 95–119 (1970).

Seehof, J. M. and Evans, W. O., "Automated Layout Design Program," *J. Ind. Eng.* **18**, No. 12: 690–695 (1967).

Shannon, R. E. and Ignizio, J. P., "A Heuristic Programming Algorithm for Warehouse Location," *AIIE Trans.* **2**, No. 4: 334–339 (1970).

Sherali, A. D. and Shetty, C. M., "The Rectilinear Distance Location-Allocation Problem," *AIIE Trans.* **9**, No. 2: 136–143 (1977).

Soland, R. M., "Optimal Plant Location with Concave Costs," presented to the 39th National Meeting of the Operations Research Society of America, Dallas, Texas (May 1971).

Spielberg, K., "Algorithms for the Simple Plant-Location with Some Side Conditions," *Operations Res.* **17**, No. 1: 85–111 (1969).

——, "Plant Location with Generalized Search Origin," *Management Sci.* **16**, No. 3: 165–178 (1969).

Teitz, Michael B., and Bart, P., "Heuristic Methods for Estimating the Generalized Vertex Median of a Weighted Graph," *Operations Res.* **16**, No. 5: 901–1092 (1968).

Toregas, C., Swain, R., Revelle, C., and Bergman, L., "The Location of Emergency Service Facilities," *Operations Res.* **19**, No. 6: 1363–1373 (1971).

Vergin, R. C. and Rogers, J. D., "An Algorithm and Computational Procedure for Locating Economic Facilities," *Management Sci.* **13**, No. 6: 3240–3254 (1967).

Vollman, T. E., Nugent, C. E., and Zartler, R. L., "A Computerized Model for Office Layout," *J. Ind. Eng.* **19**, No. 7: 321–327 (1968).

Wendell, R. E. and Hurter, A. P., Jr., "Optimal Locations on a Network," *Transport. Sci.* **6**, 18–33 (1972).

——, "Location Theory, Dominance, and Convexity," *Operations Res.* **21**, No. 1: 314–320 (1973).

Wesolowsky, G. O., "Location in Continuous Space," *Geograph. Anal.* **5**, No. 2: 95–112 (1972).

——, "Rectangular Distance Location Under the Minimax Optimality Criterion," *Transport. Sci.*, **9**, No. 2: 103–113 (1972).

—— and Love, R. F., "The Optimal Location of New Facilities Using Rectangular Distances," *Operations Res.* **19**, No. 1: 124–130 (1971).

——, "Location of Facilities with Rectangular Distances Among Point and Area Destinations," *Nav Res. Log. Quart.* **18**, No. 1: 83–90 (1971).

——, "A Nonlinear Approximation Method for Solving a Generalized Rectangular Distance Weber Problem," *Management Sci.* **18**, No. 11: 656–663 (1972).

White, J. A. and Case, K. E., "On Covering Problems and the Central Facilities Location Problem," *Geograph. Anal.* **6**, No. 3: 281–293 (1974).

I-9

SCHEDULING AND SEQUENCING

Michael S. Salvador
Ernst and Ernst

1. INTRODUCTION

The words "scheduling" and "sequencing," in the context of OR applications, have come to be associated with a wide range of quantitative problems. Generically speaking, sequencing refers to the mere ordering of a collection of jobs or. tasks to be performed, whereas scheduling is concerned with the assignment of points or times for each job or task that stipulate when it is to be performed.

In a totally deterministic environment, scheduling and sequencing are often referred to interchangeably, simply because when all the problem characteristics are known *a priori*, and jobs are started as soon as possible, a sequence determines a schedule and vice versa. In cases where uncertainty exists with respect to problem characteristics (e.g., the time required to complete a job), a scheduling methodology necessarily implies only a means for sequencing or ranking jobs, inasmuch as a "schedule" cannot be ascertained.

Despite the distinction just drawn, it is common in actual applications of the subject matter of this chapter to make reference to a "scheduling" problem that is rightfully a "sequencing" problem only. Likewise, there is a tendency to identify some of the more generalized methodology in this area as "scheduling" theory when it properly contains "sequencing" theory. Accordingly, the literature (including this chapter) will often be characterized by this inconsistency of terminology. Nevertheless, an understanding of the simple, yet fundamental, differences between scheduling and sequencing, as noted above, is sufficient to compensate for this fact.

In the next section, a taxonomy of the scheduling problems addressed in this chapter is developed. Clearly, it has not been possible to include all scheduling-related problems in such a scheme. In fact, some specialized application areas, such as project scheduling, have been treated separately in another chapter of this Handbook, because of the extensive work that has been done in these areas. The material in this chapter does, however, represent the bulk of what is generally referred to as scheduling (and sequencing) theory, and it provides the foundation on which to proceed with an organized presentation of the vast research that has been done in this area.

The remainder of the chapter will consist of a discussion of the scheduling and sequencing models that have been developed thus far within the framework of the taxonomy. Generalized methodologies, which, it is hoped, will provide some guidance to the practitioner in treating any specialized scheduling problems, are also presented.

2. A CLASSIFICATION OF SCHEDULING PROBLEMS

It has been difficult to develop a standard classification scheme or taxonomy of scheduling problems, mostly because of the diversity of scheduling applications. What is needed is not only a logical framework in which to categorize the bulk of applications, but also a vocabulary that can somehow be used to describe the basic characteristics of each application.

2.1   The Job-Shop Process

A major contribution to the classification of scheduling problems is the concept of the job-shop, the setting for much of the research expended thus far in the area of scheduling theory. In fact, many of the scheduling problems for which solution techniques have been developed are special cases of the ubiquitous *job-shop scheduling problem*. The basis for the commonality of these scheduling problems is the *job-shop process*, a concept that embodies the elementary (and often idealistic) assumptions usually associated with applied scheduling problems, and that is a good foundation upon which a classification scheme or taxonomy of scheduling problems can be devised.

One of the more thorough efforts to isolate the concept of the job-shop process appears in the pioneering textbook *Theory of Scheduling* by Conway *et al.* [1967]. The material to be subsequently introduced is adopted from this work.

The basic unit of the job-shop process is the *operation*. In fact, a job is considered to be some finite collection of operations. Each operation associated with a job must be "processed" on a specific *machine* for a specific duration of time (the processing time) unique to the job and machine.

A *job-shop* is the set of all machines that are identified with a given set of jobs or, equivalently, a set of operations. A *job-shop process* is the machine, jobs, operations, and a statement of the disciplines or physical constraints that restrict the manner in which an operation can be assigned to the corresponding machine.

The generalized *job-shop scheduling problem* consists of finding an ordering of the operations to be performed on each machine in a job-shop subject to the job-shop process specifications (as well as any other constraints), and such that some measurable function of that ordering is optimized (viz., minimized or maximized). Typically, these constraining specifications include the following at a minimum:

(1) Each machine is continuously available; i.e., there is no inherent provision for shutdown or breakdown time.
(2) Operation sequences are strictly ordered; i.e., for a given operation and job, there is at most one other operation that immediately precedes it, and at most one operation that immediately succeeds it.
(3) Each operation can be performed by only one type of machine in the job-shop.
(4) There is only one of each type of machine in the job-shop.
(5) Operation preemption is not allowed; i.e., once an operation is started on a machine, it must be completed before a different operation can begin on that machine.
(6) A job can be in process on at most one machine at any given time.
(7) A machine can be processing at most one operation at any given time.

Each of the above assumptions is often violated in practice; consequently, much of the analytical results in scheduling theory reflect idealized situations.

In addition to the above, the specification of the job-shop process includes:

● Any additional job/operation characteristics (e.g., how many jobs, how the jobs arrive to be processed).
● Any additional machine characteristics (e.g., how many machines).
● Any additional restrictions on the ordering of operations on machines.
● The criterion by which the resulting schedule will be evaluated.

In the next section, the scheduling problems and their solution techniques to be presented in this chapter will be classified according to these four specification areas. In addition, it will be convenient to assume that the seven specific process constraints (sometimes said to describe the "simple" job-shop process) delineated above are binding in all cases unless stated otherwise.

One final comment on the generality of the job-shop process itself is warranted. Because of the nomenclature used (viz., "job," "machine," etc.), it is natural for one to associate the problem with activities such as production orders in a manufacturing facility or repair orders in a servicing center. Clearly, however, the problem description does not necessarily restrict itself to such environments. For example, without loss of continuity, the task of scheduling in a criminal justice system could be a form of the general job-shop scheduling problem. In this case, the jobs could be criminal suspects; the operations could be incarceration, trial, bonding, probation, etc.; and the machines could be jails or prisons, courts or judges, bondsmen, probation boards, etc.

2.2   A Classification Scheme

Given the simple job-shop process, the first major distinction that can be drawn between different scheduling problems is the fundamental concept of deterministic versus probabilistic shop characteristics. A *deterministic scheduling problem* will be one in which all job characteristics (number of jobs, their availability times, their processing times on machines, routings, etc.) and all shop characteristics (number of machines, their availability, etc.) are fixed and known in advance. A *probabilistic scheduling problem* will be one in which any of those characteristics vary stochastically.

Within the deterministic and probabilistic problem groupings, the *single machine* case will be treated separately. Subsequently, the *multiple-machine* case will be further divided into three categories:

(1) The cases in which all jobs require only one operation, which can be performed by any machine in the shop (essentially the *single-stage parallel machine* cases).

(2) The cases in which all jobs involve the same operations, and the sequence of the operations is fixed for all jobs (commonly referred to as the *multistage flow-shop*).

(3) All other cases (these will be referred to as *hybrid job-shops*).

The final subdivision of scheduling problems is, of course, by the schedule evaluation criterion used. Some of the more common criteria are discussed in the next section. Others will be either self-explanatory or described as they are introduced.

In subsequent sections of the chapter, this entire classification scheme will serve as a framework for presenting the various techniques available for solving common scheduling and sequencing problems. A diagram of this scheme (including some sub-classifications) is given in Figure 1.

3. COMMON SCHEDULE EVALUATION CRITERIA

The most critical factor in any scheduling problem—even more critical than the process constraints—is the schedule evaluation criterion. In almost any scheduling environment, it is more likely that schedules are feasible with respect to process constraints than that they are efficient with respect to stated schedule criteria. Furthermore, the feasibility of a schedule is generally more explicit than its efficiency.

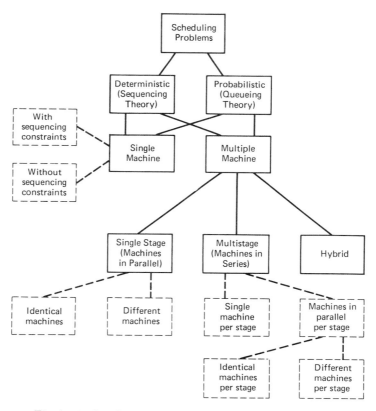

Fig. 1.   A classification scheme for scheduling problems.

Schedule criteria are normally expressed in terms of job-related or shop-related variables whose values are determined by a particular schedule or scheduling discipline. The job-related variables include:

- *Completion-time*—the time at which processing of the last operation of the job is completed.
- *Flow-time*—the total time that the job spends in the shop.
- *Waiting-time*—that portion of the flow-time that the job spends waiting for operations to be performed.
- *Lateness*—the difference between the completion-time of a job and some pre-specified *due date* associated with that job.
- *Tardiness*—equivalent to lateness when lateness is positive, otherwise equal to zero.

Typically, shop-related variables that affect schedule evaluation are restricted to:

- *Utilization*—the ratio of time spent by a machine processing a job to the total time available (the latter is usually equated to maximum job flow-time).
- *Work-in-process*—generally, the amount of "work" that has not yet completed processing; could be measured a variety of ways, including the number of jobs in the shop and the total processing time represented by the jobs in the shop.

Schedule evaluation criteria invariably involve one or more of the above variables, the specific objective being to minimize or maximize the mean, total, maximum, or minimum value achieved by the schedule. The most common criterion is minimization of the maximum flow-time, which is sometimes termed minimization of "makespan." Another popular criterion is minimization of total tardiness, since most real-world scheduling problems involve jobs that are characterized by due dates and tardiness penalties.

In some cases, the overriding consideration is cost; i.e., the objective is to minimize some cost incurred by the schedule. Often these criteria are merely extrapolated from the variables already mentioned, by assigning some fixed unit cost to the value of the variable; in other situations, the relationship may not be linear but still a function of one or more of these variables. In any event, rarely is a cost minimization criterion effectively different from a minimization or maximization of some function of said variables. Common examples of this are minimization of work-in-process, maximization of utilization, and minimization of total tardiness criteria, all of which have direct proportional costs readily associated with them.

One final point about schedule evaluation concerns equivalences of criteria.

It is easy to show that:

- The mean flow-time is directly proportional to the mean work-in-process inventory (as measured by the number of jobs).
- The mean flow-time differs from the mean lateness and the mean waiting-time by a constant.
- A scheduling procedure that is relatively good with respect to either the mean total processing time per job, mean availability time (due date less arrival date, the latter being zero in the static case), the number of machines in the shop, or the mean utilization of the machines in the shop is comparably good with respect to each of the others.
- A scheduling procedure that minimizes mean flow-time also minimizes mean lateness, mean waiting-time, and the mean work-in-process inventory (as measured by the number of jobs).

Along these lines, Elmaghraby [1968] has well demonstrated the relationships between some common inventory considerations and other schedule criteria.

Despite these results and others, such conclusions are not always immediately obvious. For example, a schedule that minimizes mean flow-time also minimizes mean lateness, but one that minimizes maximum flow-time does not necessarily minimize maximum lateness. One is cautioned to investigate potential criteria equivalences carefully.

4. DETERMINISTIC SCHEDULING MODELS

The key feature of deterministic scheduling problems that uniquely sets them apart from probabilistic scheduling problems is the fixed nature of the problem characteristics. This fact alone renders most deterministic scheduling problems as pure sequencing problems. In other words, under the conditions of the deterministic problem, it is sufficient to know only the starting time of the first operation of the first job and the sequence in which operations are performed on each machine. If one assumes that each operation is started as soon as possible, a schedule can be determined. For this reason, deterministic scheduling problems are almost exclusively referred to in the literature as deterministic sequencing problems.

In the sections that follow, an attempt is made to document some of the more significant results of the research performed in the area of deterministic scheduling. In most cases, it is not practical to reproduce any formal results; hence, only appropriate references will be cited.

The presentation will be made in terms of the classification scheme presented earlier. All the restrictions of the simple job-shop process are assumed to hold unless explicitly stated otherwise.

4.1 The Single Machine Case

The single-machine sequencing problem seems, on the surface, to be too elementary for any worthwhile analysis. Yet, its study is meaningful from at least two points of view. First, there exist several operational systems that can be modeled as a single-machine system. These include, for example, certain segments of the process industries, paint manufacturing, and data processing. Second, there is always the possibility of and, indeed, precedent for the fact that a study of the simplest case may lead to solutions of more general, complex scheduling problems.

One of the more prevalent assumptions found in sequencing research in general is the immediate availability of all the jobs to be scheduled. In fact, it is rare not to find this constraint expressly stated along with some of the fundamental job-shop process constraints listed earlier. One reason for this situation is the relationship the constraint has to the even more common preemption constraint of the simple job-shop processes. Along these lines, Conway *et al.* [1967] point out that, in the single-machine case, different job-availability times require consideration of preemption or inserted idleness. They conclude that no interesting results have been found for this situation with the exception that, if jobs that are preempted can be started from the point of interruption, the problem is essentially the same as one with simultaneous arrivals. For these reasons, it will be assumed that all jobs are simultaneously available unless stated otherwise.

As one may expect, the solutions to some single-machine deterministic sequencing problems are relatively straightforward. In fact, in these cases, an optimal sequence of jobs is found by simply ordering the jobs according to some set of values of a job-related variable. Three of the more fundamental results in this category are:

- If the jobs are sequenced according to their respective processing times arranged in non-decreasing order, the following measures are minimized:
  1) Mean job flow-time;
  2) Mean job completion-time;
  3) Mean job waiting-time;
  4) Mean job lateness;
  5) Minimum job flow-time;
  6) Minimum job completion-time;
  7) Minimum job waiting-time;
  8) Mean work-in-process.

  This discipline of sequencing is usually called the "shortest processing time" rule, abbreviated SPT.
- If the jobs are sequenced according to their respective due dates arranged in non-decreasing order, the following measures are minimized:
  1) Maximum job lateness;
  2) Maximum job tardiness.

- If one assigns a "weight" to the measure attributed to each job, and then sequences the job according to a non-decreasing sequence of ratios of their respective processing times to their respective weights, the following measures are minimized:
  1) Mean weighted flow-time;
  2) Mean weighted lateness;
  3) Mean weighted waiting-time.

There are, of course, many other single-machine problems that are much less straightforward. A notable example is the case in which sequence-dependent "setup" times exist between contiguous jobs. In this situation, there is assumed to be a unique, positive amount of machine idle-time that must elapse between the processing of any ordered pair of distinct jobs. Thus, the setup time required prior to processing a job is not solely a function of the job itself, but also its position in the job schedule sequence.

Most efforts to solve the single-machine sequencing problem with sequence-dependent setup times have addressed a criterion of minimization of maximum flow-time, which is equivalent to minimization of total setup-time for this problem. (Investigations of other criteria, such as minimization of mean flow-time, have been sparse.) This criterion reduces the problem to the famous "Traveling Salesman Problem"; i.e., finding the sequence in which a salesman should visit each of n cities and return to his origin, so that some total function of the traverse between each pair of cities in the sequence (usually, simply the distance between them) is minimized. A variety of solution techniques for this problem have been developed, including the well-known "branch-and-bound" algorithm devised by Little *et al.* [1963], and the dynamic programming techniques offered by Bellman [1962] and Held and Karp [1962]. More recently, Held and Karp [1970, 1971] have developed an efficient implicit enumeration algorithm for solving a special version of the problem, based upon its relationship to the minimum spanning tree problem of network theory.

In general, the variety of deterministic single-machine scheduling problems that have been solved is extensive, well beyond the common schedule evaluation criteria delineated thus far. Some of the more interesting work (along with an appropriate reference) are itemized below in terms of the schedule measure minimized and any extraneous constraints imposed on the problem:

(1) Mean flow-time when certain disjointed, fixed subsequences of jobs (called "strings") are pre-specified; Smith [1956].

(2) Mean flow-time with consideration of job precedence constraints; Conway *et al.* [1967].

(3) Total penalty when jobs are "related" to each other; Elmaghraby [1968].

(4) Total cost of processing when the machine is characterized by a single-state variable; Gilmore and Gomory [1964].

(5) Total cost of tardiness, where the cost of tardiness for a job is any non-decreasing linear function of the tardiness of the job; McNaughton [1959], Schild and Fredman [1961], Elmaghraby [1968].

(6) Number of "changeovers," where jobs are production lots whose sizes are determined by a demand schedule and where a changeover is incurred when a new lot is initiated; Glassey [1968].

(7) Total job deferral cost, where the deferral cost is any continuous, bounded, monotone non-decreasing function of the job completion-time; Lawler [1964].

(8) Maximum job deferral cost, as defined in (7); Moore [1968].

(9) Total cost of production and inventory, where jobs are production lots whose sizes are determined by a demand schedule; Magee [1958], Rogers [1958], Eilon [1962], Bomberger [1966], Brown [1967], Madigan [1968], Dooley and Bernholtz [1969], Baker [1970], Elmaghraby and Mallik [1973], and Doll and Whybark [1973].

(10) Number of late jobs; Moore [1968].

(11) Total tardiness; Emmons [1970], Shwimer [1972].

(12) Total weighted tardiness and total weighted flow time; Gelders and Kleindorfer [1974].

One final point should be noted. Many of the single-machine sequencing problems that have been discussed in this section explicitly represent research into the single-machine sequencing problem *only*. In addition to this class of problems, however, there are also the single-machine (degenerate) versions of both the single-stage parallel machine case and the multi-stage flow-shop. Hence, any additional solution techniques introduced in subsequent sections for these other classes of scheduling problems should be considered a supplement to the findings presented above for the single-machine problem.

4.2   The Single-Stage Parallel Machine Case

The generalization of the single-machine case that will first be considered is the case in which there is still only one operation per job, but there are multiple machines on which each of the jobs can be processed. This obviously represents the elimination of constraint (4) in the list of constraints presented earlier to define the simple job-shop process, although all other constraints and assumptions hold. As with the single-machine case results, it is assumed that all jobs are immediately available.

One of the more elementary results in this class of sequencing problems is provided by McNaughton [1959], for the case in which the parallel machines are identical. It involves a version of the simplistic SPT discipline presented earlier for the single-machine case. If the number of machines, say m, is greater than the number of jobs, say n, assign the n jobs to any n machines. Otherwise, first sequence the jobs in order of non-decreasing processing times. Next, assign the first m jobs in the sequence to the first m machines (assume the machines are arbitrarily numbered). Successive jobs in the sequence are assigned to the first available machine. This rule will minimize:

(1) Mean flow-time;
(2) Mean waiting-time;
(3) Mean lateness;
(4) Mean completion-time.

It is interesting to note that the rule does not necessarily minimize either the maximum flow-time or the mean work-in-process, as does SPT in the single-machine case.

A major catalyst in the sophistication of parallel machine scheduling was the paper by McNaughton referenced above. He first considered the situation in which jobs could be "split" on any of m identical processors (the opposite of constraint (6) of the simple job-shop process), and provided guidelines for scheduling to minimize the maximum flow-time. Returning to the problem of minimization of the total cost of tardiness, he showed that optimal solutions may involve splitting, but that, when all due dates are zero, no splitting is required for optimality. Of course, with all due dates equal to zero, tardiness is equivalent to completion-time. Accordingly, the objective translates into minimizing the total of linear costs of job completion-time. Note that these were referred to as "deferral" costs in some of the single-machine results.

Pursuant to the work of McNaughton, several complex algorithms have been developed for parallel machine scheduling problems. However, the criterion addressed by each has been consistently unchanged. Although some contributors have included additional considerations such as setup time/cost (*not* sequence-dependent), the algorithms usually address minimization of some total job-related "loss function," e.g., deferral costs, that are functions of either tardiness or completion-times.

Eastman *et al.* [1964] investigated lower bounds on the minimum total deferral costs of parallel machine scheduling problems and produced the following useful corollary to their findings: Given $m > 1$ identical processors, the minimum total deferral cost of a schedule of n jobs is lower on a single-machine operating at m times the speed of any one of the original processors than on the m original processors. Because of the definition of deferral costs, this conclusion also holds for total or mean completion-time, flow-time, and waiting-time (assuming immediate availability of all jobs). This result possibly offers some insight into the emphasis that has been placed on minimization of total deferral costs in parallel machine problems.

Other research into this class of scheduling problems that has resulted in solution algorithms, is summarized below according to the measure minimized, as in the previous section:

(1) Total of deferral costs (not necessarily linear) where processing times are equal; Lawler [1964].

(2) Total tardiness when all due dates are equal; Root [1965].

(3) Total of deferral costs (not necessarily linear), setup costs, and machine operating costs, when machines are not necessarily identical with respect to job processing-time; Rothkopf [1966].

(4) Total of deferral costs, setup costs, and machine operating costs; Arthanari and Ramamurthy [1970].

(5) Total weighted flow time; Baker and Merten [1973].

(6) Total of tardiness penalty costs; Elmaghraby [1969].

(7) Total of tardiness penalty costs when all jobs are immediately available, due dates are equal to processing times, and tardiness penalty costs are linear; Elmaghraby and Park [1974].

(8) Total of (linear) processing and waiting costs; Gupta and Walvakar [1970].

(9) Makespan when processing times are equal, Hu [1961].

(10) Makespan when processing times are equal and there are precedence relationships between jobs; Coffman and Graham [1972], Fujii, Kasami, and Ninomiya [1969], and Graham [1969, 1972].

In addition to the above, Schrage [1970] and Garey and Johnson [1974] have researched the problem of finding *feasible* schedules for the assignment of m jobs to n identical processors, when the jobs are characterized by precedence constraints and resource requirements and the resources available are limited. Bounds related to the minimum makespan schedule for this problem have also been developed by Graham [1966, 1969] and Garey and Graham [1974].

An excellent survey of 30 papers related to the problem of scheduling jobs on parallel processors has been prepared by Elmaghraby and Elshafei [1975]. The survey contains useful summaries of the findings and/or algorithmic procedures developed in each paper.

4.3 The Multi-Stage Flow-Shop

The multi-stage flow-shop describes a situation in which processing a job involves more than one operation but is restricted to a fixed number and sequence of operations for each job to be processed. The research into this class of scheduling problems has been extensive, although many of the solution techniques are heuristic and do not guarantee optimal solutions within reasonable limits of computational feasibility.

As with the previous cases, most of the research into the deterministic sequencing of the multi-stage flow-shop assumes that all jobs are immediately available. Another characteristic of this research is the preponderance of a minimization of maximum flow-time (or "makespan") criterion. This is in sharp contrast to the parallel machine cases discussed previously.

One of the more intriguing properties of multi-stage flow-shops that have set the stage for most of the research efforts is the following: When one is scheduling an m-stage flow-shop with a criterion of minimization of maximum flow-time, and all jobs are immediately available, one need only consider schedules in which the same job order is prescribed on machines 1 and 2, and the same job order is prescribed on machines $m - 1$ and m. (Machine numbers correspond to the fixed sequence of operations associated with each job.)

What this result reveals is that, for flow-shops with up to three stages, the optimal sequence of jobs is necessarily the same on all machines. Hence, it is sufficient to investigate a set of job permutation sequences without concern for the optimal sequence being possibly different on each machine. When there are more than three stages, the number of potentially optimal schedules is formidable, since one must consider individual machine sequences. For example, a 5-machine, 10-job problem involves $(10!)^3$, or 4.78×10^{19} possible job sequences. Consequently, the solution to such m-stage problems with $m \geq 4$ is necessarily relegated to heuristic, restricted enumeration, or similar techniques for approximate solutions.

As a result of this finding, there is a natural dichotomy present in multi-stage static sequencing. On the one hand, relatively few and simple techniques that provide exact solutions exist for the two- and three-stage problems. On the other hand, the techniques that apply to the m-stage ($m \geq 4$) generally inject special assumptions, are computationally infeasible, or provide only approximate solutions. Of course, many of the m-stage techniques can be applied to the two- and three-stage cases, although they have been developed primarily for the larger flow-shops.

Just as McNaughton paved the way for research into the single-stage parallel machine scheduling problem, Johnson [1954] instigated a similar movement in flow-shop scheduling. His solution to the two-machine flow-shop problem was the prelude to extensive research into this class of scheduling problems. To summarize his elegant, albeit simple result, let

A_i = the processing-time (including setup, if any) of the first operation of the ith job, and

B_i = the processing-time (including setup, if any) of the second operation of the ith job.

With all jobs simultaneously available, and an objective of minimization of makespan, an optimal sequence (recall that it should be identical on each machine) is one where

$$\min (A_j, B_{j+1}) < \min (A_{j+1}, B_j),$$

for any contiguous pair of jobs, j and $j + 1$, in the sequence.

The next logical step was, of course, to address the three-machine problem, which was appealing since it was known that the optimal sequence specified identical sequences on each machine. Surprisingly, however, the results of the two-machine case could not be easily extended to the three-machine case. In fact, in his paper, Johnson showed that job j precedes job $j + 1$ in an optimal sequence for the three-machine flow-shop if

$$\min (A_j + B_j, C_{j+1} + B_{j+1}) < \min (A_{j+1} + B_{j+1}, C_j + B_j),$$

and if $\min A_i \geqslant \max B_j$ or $\min C_i \geqslant \max B_j$. ($C_j$ is the processing time of job j on the third machine.) The latter constraint is by no means trivial, and the result prompted others to search for an alternative solution to the problem. The more prominent results in this regard include the IP model of Giglio and Wagner [1964] and the B&B methods of Ignall and Schrage [1965], Lomnicki [1965], and McMahon and Burton [1967]. Progressing to four or more machines, the flow-shop scheduling problem becomes, as stated earlier, particularly less susceptible to an exact algorithmic solution. Three basic approaches have appeared in the literature: (1) combinatorial analyses, (2) mathematical programming, and (3) B&B controlled enumeration. Virtually all developments treat the minimization of makespan criterion. Furthermore, with the exception of some of the mathematical programming methods, all assume that the job sequence on each machine is identical (sometimes called a "no passing" constraint). Clearly, this eliminates assurance of optimality since it only applies to optimal solutions of flow-shops with less than four machines.

Dudek and Teuton [1964] were among the first to offer a combinatorial solution to the problem. Aside from its explicit complexity, Karush [1965] found a counterexample to the optimality of the algorithm, which was later modified accordingly by Smith and Dudek [1967]. The new algorithm manifested considerably improved efficiency, but unfortunately no relief in complexity.

The key ILP formulation appeared in an early paper by Wagner [1959]. As demonstrated by the results of a subsequent application of this formulation to the three-machine problem (as few as five jobs was sometimes a formidable problem), the approach offered no hope for computational feasibility in large flow-shops.

The B&B solutions to the multi-stage flow-shop with no passing are unquestionably the most diverse. There have been no less than six different B&B solution techniques offered, notably by Ignall and Schrage [1965], Brown and Lomnicki [1966], McMahon and Burton [1967], Nabeshima [1967], Ashour [1970], and Gupta [1970]. Five of these methods were extensively compared by Ashour and Quraishi [1969] by applying them to various flow-shop structures; the algorithms were executed on an IBM 360/50 computer. Their findings were that the "composite-based" bounding technique of McMahon and Burton consistently required fewer iterations than the others, but required more computer time to compute the bounds. On the other hand, the technique of Brown and Lomnicki consistently required less computer time than any of the others; thus, it was the recommended choice.

There have been, of course, several variations of the three approaches discussed above. Wismer [1972] and Salvador [1973] have shown that, when no intermediate queues of jobs are allowed between contiguous stages, the problem can be modeled as a Traveling Salesman Problem. Campbell *et al.* [1970] offered a solution that segments the problem into $p(p \leqslant m - 1$, where m is the number of stages) auxiliary n-job, 2-machine sub-problems to which Johnson's algorithm can be applied. Gupta [1969] has developed a solution method that uses the special technique called "lexicographic search." In all these methods, however, the assumption of preservation of job sequence on machines is retained, and the schedule criterion is still minimization of makespan.

A final comment on multi-stage flow-shop scheduling concerns the tacit assumption of common job sequencing in a shop of more than three machines. On the surface, it appears that the assumption is made for convenience; e.g., to reduce the number of feasible schedules from $(n!)^m$ to $n!$ (where n is the number of jobs and m the number of machines), to elicit the use of combinatorial and straightforward enumeration schemes, or to make schedules easier to implement, all at the expense of optimality. Such motivations are not altogether unjustified, since relaxing the assumption literally renders the problem unsolvable for any practical purposes. A study by Heller [1960], however, has revealed evidence that the assumption may not only be convenient, but also may often produce near optimal solutions.

What Heller did was randomly generate a set of 100 jobs with integer processing times uniformly distributed between zero and nine units of time on each machine in a ten-machine flow-shop. Then, using only the first 20 of the set of 100 jobs, he generated 9,037 schedules with an independent permutation of the integers 1 through 20 for the ordering on each machine, and plotted the makespan achieved by each schedule. Next, he generated 12,000 more schedules for the same 20 jobs, with the order of the jobs arbitrarily fixed on each machine, and also plotted the results. His findings are presented in Figure 2. Not only did the fixed job sequence schedules effect smaller makespans than the random sequence schedules, but the difference between the maximum makespan of the former and the minimum makespan of the latter was more than 400 time units!

This experiment clearly gives strong support to the credibility of the assumption of preservation of job sequences on machines in a multi-stage flow-shop. Most important, however, it assures the practitioner that the numerous techniques of flow-shop scheduling that rely on the assumption are more than just theoretical exercises. When used judiciously, they are powerful tools for solving real-world problems.

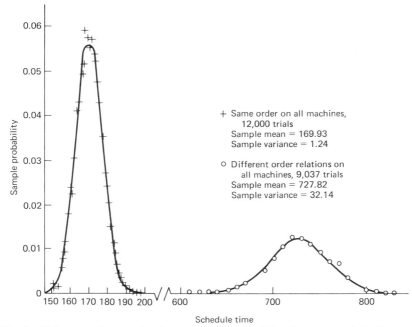

Fig. 2. Makespan for randomly generated schedules for twenty jobs in a 10-machine flow-shop (Heller, 1970).

4.4. Hybrid Job-Shops

Beyond the single-machine, parallel-machine, and flow-shops, results of deterministic scheduling research for the remaining class of hybrid shops are diverse and of dubious computational value with respect to deriving optimal solutions. Although algorithms have been formulated to model even the most general deterministic job-shop scheduling problems, many are not unlike some of the attempts at solving large flow-shop problems in that they are not even amenable to the computational potential of computers. Nevertheless, these solution attempts are certainly not entirely futile; not only do they possess some utility for small-scale hybrid problems, but also give some foundation as well as direction for future research efforts.

One of the more interesting hybrid shops to consider is the straightforward generalization of the previous two cases; viz., a multi-stage flow shop with parallel machines at each stage. All jobs have the same number and sequence of operations, each of which can be performed on one of several machines (not necessarily the same number for each operation). A solution has been offered by Salvador [1973] for a modified version of this problem. When all jobs are immediately available, no jobs are allowed to wait between stages, and the sequence of jobs leaving a stage is the same for each stage, an optimal solution can be found. The technique involves an algorithm that combines a DP model with a B&B scheme. Although computational experience is not promising for large shops, the technique has been successfully applied in the process and chemical industries.

The more intriguing problem is, of course, the general job-shop scheduling problem described earlier in Section 2.1. Each job has a unique set of operations to be performed, and there is only one machine capable of performing each different operation.

A solution to the two-machine job-shop problem, where no job has more than two operations, has been given by Jackson [1956]. There is also a graphical procedure for solution to a two-job, m-machine job-shop problem, first suggested by Akers and Friedman [1955]. More effective solutions were subsequently proposed by Swarc [1960] and Hardgrove and Nemhauser [1963].

Algorithms for solution to the unrestricted, general job-shop problem have been formulated as IP models by Bowman [1959], Wagner [1959], and Manne [1960]; a B&B technique has been given by Brooks and White [1965]. Unfortunately, for problems of reasonable size, none of these particular formulations is very useful. For example, a problem with 4 machines and 10 jobs translates to 220 variables and 390 constraints in the integer program of Manne. Furthermore, Brooks and White concede that their technique is computationally prohibitive for problems of practical dimensions.

About the only techniques for generalized deterministic job-shop scheduling that hold any promise for obtaining practical (but not necessarily optimal) solutions are those of the family of heuristic schedule generation procedures. One of the oldest and most popular of these is the well-known Gantt chart, which allows one to generate feasible schedules by arranging variable length blocks (operations) on a two-dimensional graph. Other such techniques incorporate the popular concept of a dispatching rule, which is basically some rationale for scheduling local activities; e.g., the operations to be performed on a single machine or simply the operations of a single job, so as to optimize some local schedule measure. More sophisticated procedures involve adjustment of local schedules interactively as they are generated.

Extensive simulation experiments have been made, using various schedule generation procedures to verify any potential they may have for even approximating optimality. The results are encouraging but too voluminous to report with any reasonable comprehensiveness. For a thorough treatment of the availability and utility of heuristic solutions to the general job-shop scheduling problem, one is referred to Conway et al. [1967].

4.5   General Methods of Deterministic Scheduling

In this section, the general methodology for solving deterministic scheduling problems is discussed, and some guidelines for solving those problems for which no efficient solution is readily available are presented.

As demonstrated in most of the research documented thus far, deterministic scheduling is a sequencing problem. Simply stated, schedules for deterministic problems are given by job sequence. Furthermore, since deterministic scheduling involves job and machine characteristics that are known *a priori*, the set of sequences from which a schedule is to be chosen is similarly known and fixed.

Elmaghraby [1968] has pointed out that the methodology for selecting optimal or "near" optimal sequences has thus far involved four basic approaches: (1) combinatorial, (2) general mathematical programming, (3) reliable heuristics, and (4) Monte Carlo sampling.

Combinatorial approaches in this context refer to techinques that involve "switching" pairs of jobs of a given sequence in a controlled fashion until the resulting sequence is optimal. The foundation of this approach was generalized in a theorem by Smith [1956], and appears in the sequencing research of Johnson [1954, 1959], Jackson [1956], McNaughton [1959], Mitten [1959], Gilmore and Gomory [1964], Gapp, *et al.* [1965], and Root [1965].

Mathematical programming solutions include linear, dynamic, quadratic, convex, and integer programming, as well as some applications of network theory and Lagrangian methods. Many of these formulations are cumbersome, in that they do not lead to exact results without inordinate computational problems. Their usefulness, however, lies in the mere existence of such mathematical models of sequencing problems and the incentive they provide for finding computationally feasible methods of solution for these formulations. Examples of uses of these techniques are seemingly endless. Those already mentioned in previous sections are representative.

One of the more potentially useful tools for large-scale problems is the family of heuristic methods, particularly the controlled enumeration techniques such as B&B. Such methods are usually just one step removed from the complete enumeration of all possible sequences, the latter being clearly the least efficient method for finding an optimal sequence. What renders them both sophisticated and significantly efficient in many cases, however, is a unique feature that allows for the elimination of certain sequences on the basis of bounding, feasibility, or dominance, before those sequences are ever evaluated in terms of the schedule criterion. Several examples of this approach have already been mentioned, particularly in the discussion of the multi-stage flow-shop.

A final alternative that has been seriously explored is the random search for potentially optimal sequences via Monte Carlo sampling. In a paper already cited, Heller [1960] spawned the technique by generating 3,000 random sequences for a flow-shop of 10 machines. When processing times on each machine were assigned by sampling a uniform distribution between zero and nine units, the result was that makespan was normally distributed. Although random processing times are in the realm of probabilistic scheduling, Elmaghraby [1968] shows how a similar methodology can be useful in general deterministic scheduling problems by using statistical properties of sequences, e.g., distribution of makespan, to control an iterative selection technique. The sampling could be bounded by a predetermined sample size that would allow a statistically significant inference to be made about the makespan of the "best" sequence selected, or it could be performed according to some exogenous factor such as the cost of sampling. When the marginal cost of sampling exceeds the marginal benefit of schedule improvement, the sequence selected thus far with the lowest makespan is implemented. Other "stopping" rules could be developed according to the characteristics of the particular scheduling problem being addressed.

The four categories above encompass the findings of a vast amount of research. Despite the fact that scheduling is one of the most common application areas of OR, a relatively small amount of that research has actually been applied. The principal reason for this, of course, has already been stated: Many of the solution methods are grossly impractical for use in large-scale problems.

For the practitioner, there will seemingly always be a need for solution methods that provide "good" schedules in a relatively efficient manner, regardless of the scope of the problem. Of the four categories above, only the last two offer any promise in this regard. The basic tenets of these two approaches suggest the following guidelines in addressing deterministic scheduling problems for which exact solutions are neither readily available nor otherwise feasible to generate:

(1) Examine the set of all possible sequences to see if it can be significantly reduced by eliminating obviously infeasible members. Many applied problems involve environments in which technological constraints automatically exclude certain sequences. Some are trivial (e.g., a hole cannot be tapped before it is drilled), and others are not so trivial (e.g., the chemical constraints of a dyeing process). Alternatively, it is sometimes not difficult to generate the set of feasible sequences (instead of the infeasible ones) if the constraints are rigid. If the resulting feasible sequences are reasonably few in number, explicit enumeration may be meaningful.

(2) If available, examine the set of feasible sequences to see if some of the sequences can be further eliminated because of the schedule criterion. This is often possible by determining a lower bound on the optimal schedule measure, such as with the results of Eastman *et al.* [1964] for the parallel machine case. Again, the alternative, generation of potentially optimal sequences, is also desirable but rarely possible. Johnson [1954]

did devise such a procedure for the two- and three-machine flow-shop problems.

(3) When neither of the above tends to warrant complete enumeration—the number of feasible sequences is still excessive—it may be possible to emulate the exercise in a controlled enumeration scheme such as the B&B technique or the general technique developed by Giffler and Thompson [1960]. Sequences can be systematically evaluated so that several are implicitly eliminated by the investigation of others. Such schemes are sometimes readily available because of peculiarities of the scheduling problem at hand.

(4) When none of the above prove fruitful, another potentially useful approach is to investigate relaxation of some problem constraints which would elicit use of an acceptable solution technique to solve a modified problem. The most striking example of this approach is found in multi-stage flow-shops with four or more machines. Although the optimal solution need not dictate identical job sequences on each machine, researchers such as Ignall and Schrage [1965], Lomnicki [1965], Smith and Dudek [1967] and McMahon [1967] assumed this to be the case so as to make the problem more palpable.

In another example it was shown in an actual scheduling application by Salvador [1973] that imposing the constraint of no inter-stage inventory in a flow-shop not only rendered the problem solvable and resulted in improved schedules, but also reduced a large capital investment by eliminating the need for inter-stage storage.

In general, the best way to uncover such benefits is to first identify which existing constraints need relaxation or which new constraints need imposition in order to make a problem more manageable. Next, identify the conditions (e.g., processing time inequalities) necessary to satisfy (or violate) the relaxation or imposition. Sometimes, those conditions are sufficiently common (or rare) in an actual setting to warrant the change in the problem description.

(5) If the problem is still unmanageable, another useful technique for finding near optimal schedules in an efficient way is problem segmentation. For example, one can consider finding optimal schedules for each machine individually or possibly for some sub-group of machines.

(6) When no systematic enumeration or approximation technique is appropriate, always consider random schedule generation, i.e., random sampling of the set of all possible sequences, or preferably only the set of feasible sequences if it is discernible. With the use of a computer, thousands of schedules may be easily evaluated and statistics of schedule measures may be compiled. Reasonable schedules can then be generated by using Monte Carlo sampling, as discussed earlier.

5. PROBABILISTIC SCHEDULING MODELS

Unlike deterministic problems, where all the parameters specifications are known *a priori*, probabilistic scheduling problems include those whose parameters vary stochastically; i.e., according to some probability distribution function. The analysis of such problems has not been restrictive, although the thrust has been toward those with random job availability (or arrival characteristics) and random job (operation) processing times. Other considerations have included random shop size (machine availability), job routings, and job due dates.

The crucial difference between deterministic and probabilistic scheduling problems lies in the concept of optimization of schedule evaluation measures. In the deterministic problem, since key job- and shop-related variables can be measured exactly, scheduling disciplines can be (theoretically) uncovered that unequivocally optimize some aggregate measure. In the probabilistic problem, however, the effect of scheduling disciplines on aggregate measures of job- and shop-related variables is necessarily expressed in probabilistic terms, and the optimization exercise is of a different nature. The parallel methodology in probabilistic scheduling problems is to derive the probability distribution of the aggregate measure of interest, e.g., flow-time, and then evaluate the resulting characteristics of that distribution, e.g., mean flow-time. Another way of drawing this distinction is to realize that probabilistic scheduling models are necessarily only *descriptive* whereas, with deterministic scheduling, it is both possible and desirable to construct *prescriptive* models. Note, however, that some recent advances in the application of optimization theory to queueing problems have led to prescriptive probabilistic models as well.

The concept of a scheduling discipline likewise differs for deterministic and probabilistic scheduling problems. In deterministic problems, a sequence (of a known set of jobs) to be processed by a machine is determined. In the probabilistic case in which jobs arrive in a random pattern, one is normally dealing with continuous queues of jobs waiting to be processed by each machine; the sequence in which those jobs are to be processed by a machine can only be determined by some *selection discipline* (often used interchangeably with *priority rule* or *dispatching rule*) that specifies which one of the jobs waiting in a queue of any composition is to be processed as soon as the machine is available for processing.

It should be kept in mind that probabilistic scheduling problems are by definition in the realm of the theory of queues. The vast body of literature on this subject is accordingly relevant to our discussion here. Subsequent material reflects scheduling research only and does not necessarily exhaust the applied queueing theory results that may also be useful in this context. (See Chapter III-2 of the first volume for a more thorough discussion of queues.)

As with the treatment of deterministic scheduling, a summary of the research on probabilistic scheduling will be given below in terms of the classification scheme presented earlier.

The following notation will be used throughout to represent random variables:

P = job processing-time;
W = job waiting-time;
F = job flow-time;
N = the number of jobs in the system under steady-state conditions.

In addition, all results to be presented are based on the following universal assumptions about the random behavior of job arrivals and processing times:

(1) The job arrival process is described by a Poisson distribution with parameter λ; i.e., during an arbitrary time interval of length t, the probability that the number of jobs arriving, denoted by A, is equal to n is given by

$$P\{A = n\} = e^{-\lambda t} \frac{(\lambda t)^n}{n!}, \qquad n = 0, 1, \cdots$$

(Other arrival distributions have been studied by researchers. Nevertheless, the Poissonian assumption above dominates the literature.)
(2) The mean processing *rate*, $1/\&(P)$, where P is the random variable describing the processing time of a job, is always greater than the mean arrival rate, λ. In other words, it is always assumed that $\lambda \&(P) < 1$; otherwise, the queue size would grow monotonically and be unbounded, regardless of the selection discipline. The quantity $\lambda \&(P)$ will be denoted ρ.

5.1   The Single-Machine Case

Investigations of the single-machine probabilistic scheduling problem, or, to use queueing theory nomenclature, the single-channel queueing problem, has been quite extensive. Comprehensive treatments of the problem from both the scheduling and queueing points of view can be found in Conway *et al.* [1967] and Saaty [1961], respectively.

The bulk of the scheduling research usually retains the simple job-shop process constraints mentioned earlier, with the single exception that allowance for various types of job preemption appears in numerous models.

Below is an itemization of the more prominent selection disciplines for single-machine probabilistic scheduling, along with any appropriate references. In some cases, the moments of the distributions of waiting-time, flow-time, and the number of jobs in the system resulting from each are given.

(1) FCFS—The job which has waited the longest is the next to be processed. Under this discipline

$$\&(W) = \frac{\lambda \&(P^2)}{2(1 - \rho)},$$

$$\mathcal{E}(W^2) = \frac{\lambda\mathcal{E}(P^3)}{3(1-\rho)} + \frac{(\lambda\mathcal{E}(P^2))^2}{2(1-\rho)^2},$$

$$\mathcal{E}(F) = \mathcal{E}(P) + \frac{\lambda\mathcal{E}(P^2)}{2(1-\rho)},$$

$$\mathcal{E}(F^2) = \mathcal{E}(P^2) + \frac{\rho\mathcal{E}(P^2)}{1-\rho} + \frac{\lambda\mathcal{E}(P^3)}{3(1-\rho)} + \frac{(\lambda\mathcal{E}(P^2))^2}{2(1-\rho)^2},$$

and

$$\mathcal{E}(N) = \rho + \frac{\lambda^2\mathcal{E}(P^2)}{2(1-\rho)}.$$

Contributors of these results are numerous; see Avi-Itzhak *et al.* [1965].

(2) LCFS—The job which has waited the least is the next to be processed. Under this discipline, the mean waiting-time and flow-times are identical to those resulting from the FCFS discipline. However,

$$\mathcal{E}(W^2) = \frac{\lambda\mathcal{E}(P^3)}{3(1-\rho)^2} + \frac{(\lambda\mathcal{E}(P^2))^2}{2(1-\rho)^3},$$

and

$$\mathcal{E}(F^2) = \mathcal{E}(P^2) + \frac{\rho\mathcal{E}(P^2)}{1-\rho} + \frac{\lambda\mathcal{E}(P^3)}{3(1-\rho)^2} + \frac{(\lambda\mathcal{E}(P^2))^2}{2(1-\rho)^3}.$$

(3) Non-preemptive priority (NP)—When jobs arrive, they are assigned to one of a finite number of priority classes; the job which has waited the longest within the highest priority class is the next to be processed; Cobham [1954].

(4) SPT—When jobs arrive, they are assigned to priority classes that are constructed according to the job processing-time distribution; the job with the highest priority (least expected processing time) is the next to be processed; Phipps [1956].

(5) Preemptive repeat priority (PRP)—Same as NP, except that when jobs with higher priority than the one being processed arrive, the one being processed is preempted and returned to the head of the queue of its class; there are several researchers, notably White and Christie [1958], Heathcote [1960], Gaver [1963], and Avi-Itzhak [1963].

(6) Preemptive resume priority (PRS)—Same as PRP, except that when a preempted job is restarted, it commences from the point of preemption rather than from the start of processing; White and Christie [1958], Heathcote [1960], and Miller [1960].

(7) Shortest remaining processing-time (SRPT)—Similar to the SPT discipline

for the non-preemptive cases, except that preemption is allowed and pro-cessing-time for preempted jobs is only the processing time needed to complete the job; Schrage [1965], and Miller and Schrage [1965].

In a study by Conway *et al.* [1967], most of the above were compared, via simulation, with respect to their effect on mean flow-time. The experiments were conducted assuming varying arrival rates and both exponential and uniform distributions of processing-time. The more salient observations are paraphrased below:

- Compared with the SRPT discipline, which in all cases produced minimum mean flow-time, the other processing-time dependent rules seem to perform quite well in reducing mean flow-time below the value achieved by the FCFS discipline.
- There is no major advantage to preemptive rules which, incidentally, are generally difficult to implement in a real-world setting.
- In at least a two-class priority discipline, it is possible and likely for the case of exponential processing-times for a non-preemptive discipline to perform better than a preemptive-resume discipline. The situation reverses as the number of classes increases.
- Mean flow-time is always greater under FCFS when processing-times are ex-potentially distributed, and always less under FCFS when they are uni-formly distributed; the reverse is true for SRPT. Results are mixed (depend-ing on the arrival rate) for the other disciplines.

Single-machine probabilistic scheduling research has not avoided the issues of setup-time or due dates, although the findings in either case are relatively limited.

The principal contributor to the study of the cases involving setup-time has been Gaver [1963]. One aspect of his work with the FCFS discipline under con-ditions of random setup-time has led to the following result.

Assume that there are r classes of setup, such that setup-time (a random vari-able S) is incurred only when a job immediately succeeds a job from a different class. Assume also that the rate of arrival of jobs of class r is equal to λ/r for all classes. Then, the time required to process a job is P with probability $1/r$ and $P + S$ with probability $(r - 1)/r$. When jobs are processed according to an FCFS discipline, without regard for classes, the mean waiting- and flow-times are

$$\mathcal{E}(W) = \frac{\lambda}{2(1 - U)} \left[\mathcal{E}(P^2) + \left[\frac{r - 1}{r} \right] \ [(2\mathcal{E}(P)\mathcal{E}(S) + \mathcal{E}(S^2)] \right]$$

and

$$\mathcal{E}(F) = \mathcal{E}(W) + U/\lambda,$$

where

$$U = \rho + \left[\frac{r-1}{r}\right] \lambda \, \&(S).$$

Due date analysis, which leads to consideration of lateness and tardiness measures, is considerably less straightforward than any of the results presented thus far. What little is known (and mostly conjectured) about this class of problems is mostly due to Jackson [1960, 1961, 1962].

5.2 The Single-Stage Parallel Machine Case

The parallel machine probabilistic scheduling problem has invoked neither extensive nor varied research. The same is generally true of the queueing theory equivalent, the multiple-channel single-stage queueing problem. Of the results that are available, most consider only a single common queue from which the next job is chosen to be processed on the next available machine. The more interesting cases of assigning jobs to one of several machine queues upon arrival, and allowing the job to change queues before it is processed, have not been generalized.

The most frequently cited result for this type of problem assumes a common queue, FCFS selection discipline, identical machines, and processing-times on any single machine characterized by a negative exponential distribution with parameter μ. Let m represent the number of parallel machines, and for notational convenience, let $r = \lambda/\mu$ (note that $\rho = \lambda/m\mu$ in this case). Then,

$$\&(W) = \frac{P_o r^{m+1}}{\lambda(m-1)! \, (m-r)^2},$$

$$\&(F) = \&(W) + (1/\mu),$$

$$\&(N) = \lambda \&(W) + r,$$

where

$$P_o = \left\{ \left[\sum_{n=0}^{m-1} \frac{r^n}{n!} \right] + \left[\frac{r^m}{m! \left(1 - \frac{r}{m}\right)} \right] \right\}^{-1}.$$

5.3 The Multi-Stage Flow-Shop

The probabilistic multi-stage flow-shop has received very little attention in the literature. Nevertheless, this situation does not necessarily constitute any significant imbalance because of an important result involving the decomposition of the problem as stated.

The result, presented by Reich[1957], considers the following assumptions:

- Jobs arrive at machines from either an external source (according to a Poission process) or a machine performing a previous operation.
- Jobs may exit the shop from any machine with a given probability.
- Processing-times are distributed according to a negative exponential distribution.
- The selection discipline for any machine in the shop is independent of processing-time.

When these general conditions are met, it is sufficient to analyze each machine in the shop as if it were independent. The Poisson arrival rate for each machine can be determined as a composite of the exogenous arrival rates and exit probabilities. (Incidentally, a similar result was developed for the general job-shop by Jackson [1963], as will be discussed in the next section.)

Since the conditions above are not uncommon in probabilistic flow-shops, the decomposition result makes much of the research on the single-machine case available for analysis of the multi-stage flow-shop. Nevertheless, variations of the problem, such as those that limit queue sizes between stages or those that require each job to be processed on each machine, have been independently studied. See Elmaghraby and Ginsberg [1964], Avi-Itzhak [1965], and Friedman [1965] for examples of such research.

5.4 Hybrid Job-Shops

The same general comments about the status of research in the area of probabilistic flow-shop scheduling can be made about generalized probabilistic job-shop scheduling. The situation is due to the famous Jackson Decomposition Principle developed by Jackson [1963]. The result applies to "queueing networks," or hybrid probabilistic job-shops, which satisfy the following assumptions.

- Jobs arrive from outside the shop according to a Poisson distribution.
- The processing times at each machine are distributed according to a negative exponential distribution.
- The jobs are routed to machines or out of the shop according to a given set of probabilities.
- The selection discipline for any machine in the shop is independent of processing-time.

Under these conditions, each machine in the shop can be considered to consitute an independent single-machine scheduling (queueing) problem. Accordingly, analysis of hybrid shops satisfying these conditions can fully utilize the results of the abundant single-machine models. As with the probabilistic flow-shops, this decomposition result has rendered the analysis of composite hybrid job-shops not only scarce, but also of dubious practical value.

5.5   General Methods for Analysis of Probabilistic Job-Shops

Becuase of the nature of probabilistic job-shops, the effects of various selection disciplines on certain schedule evaluation criteria are virtually impossible to ascertain analytically beyond the single machine case. The only alternative is direct measurement, a highly costly and impractical task in an actual setting, but one that has been made relatively efficient by the advent of the digital computer.

The singly most powerful and effective methodology for studying probabilistic job-shops is the application of the family of simulation techniques, particularly Monte Carlo simulation, to the data storage, processing, and retrieval potential of the computer. The underlying procedure is relatively simple:

- All system status is maintained by the computer. This includes, for example, where each job is located, the number of jobs in a machine queue and their identifying characteristics, the time when each machine has been idle, and the total time spent waiting by each job.
- The occurrence of random events such as job arrivals, the completion of processing a job, and the routing of a job to the next machine is simulated by the random sampling of a probability distribution function that describes the actual occurrence of these events.
- The occurrence of deterministic events, such as the selecting of a job from a machine queue when the machine becomes available, is controlled by maintenance of a chronological list of those events. The list is continually updated by the occurrence of sampled random events and the system status data. The events are implemented by merely updating the system status according to the effect the event has on the system. For example, when a machine becomes available, a certain job is removed from the queue according to the selection discipline. Then, the waiting-time of the job is updated, the time when the machine will be next available is updated, etc.

When such a process is terminated, the system status, depending on the extent to which it has been maintained, will contain the information of interest; e.g., the mean job flow-time, the mean number of jobs waiting, the mean lateness of jobs with due dates, etc.

The simulation of job-shops has attracted many researchers. The problem assumptions generally concur with those of the simple job-shop process as well as the two common probabilistic job-shop assumptions; viz., Poisson arrivals and probability $p < 1$ for the selection of each machine in the shop as the "next" job processor. Because of the generality of the approach, however, there has been no limit to either the job or shop characteristics that have been allowed to vary stochastically, the selection disciplines simulated, or the schedule evaluation measure monitored. Accordingly, it would be neither possible nor desirable to summarize here the variety of simulation analyses that have been undertaken. An adequate treatment would require an inordinate expansion of the chapter contents, including almost twice as many bibliographical references as included thus far.   For an exceptionally good, comprehensive synopsis of this area of research, refer to the survey of Day and Hottenstein [1970].

6. THE FUTURE OF APPLIED SCHEDULING AND SEQUENCING THEORY: A POSTSCRIPT

Scheduling and sequencing research has resulted in models, algorithms, procedures, etc., ranging from the manual Gantt chart to the most sophisticated of optimization models.   Clearly, the range of theoretical problems which have prompted that research has been equally diversified.   Unfortunately, however, a large number of these scheduling and sequencing problems are combinational in nature, and their respective solution methodologies, when applied in a real-world environment, are naturally cumbersome, usually iterative, and almost always costly and time-consuming computational procedures.   Some of these "solutions" may literally never be useful in a practical setting.

Some very recent work in "complexity theory" (see Cook [1971], Karp [1972], and Ullman [1973]), helps put this problem into perspective.   According to this theory, specific combinational problems are classified as "P-time" or "NP-time" problems, indicating that their solution "time" is either bound by a polynomial function or it is not.   Applying the theory to scheduling and sequencing problems (Brucker et al. [1975]), some problems have been *proven* to be of the NP-variety (also called NP-complete problems); this suggests that only enumerative solutions, such as the generalized B&B technique, are justified in these cases.

It is hoped that such results will direct the future of scheduling and sequencing theory research toward finding more efficient methods of determining "good schedules," rather than more possibly inefficient ones that promise optimal schedules.   Responding to this tradeoff will mean both a challenge to the researcher and hope for the practitioner.

REFERENCES

Akers, S. B., Jr., and J. Friedman, "A Non-Numerical Approach to Production Scheduling Problems," *Operations Res.* 3, No.: 429-442 (November 1955).

Arthanari, T. S. and K. G. Ramamurthy, "A Branch and Bound Algorithm for Sequencing n Jobs on m Parallel Processors," *Opsearch* 7, No. 3: 147-156 (September 1970).

Ashour, Said and M. N. Quraishi, "Investigation of Various Procedures for Production Scheduling Problems," *Int. J. Prod. Res.* 7, No. 13: 249-252 (1969).

——, "A Branch and Bound Algorithm for Flow Shop Scheduling Problems," *AIIE Trans.* 2, No. 2: 172-176 (June 1970).

Avi-Itzhak, B., "Preemptive Repeat Priority Queues as a Special Case of the Multi-Purpose Server Problem—I and II," *Operations Res.* 11, No. 4: 597-617 (July 1963).

——, "A Sequence of Service Stations with Arbitrary Input and Regular Service Times," *Management Sci.* 11, No. 5: 553–564 (March 1965).

——, W. L. Maxwell, and L. W. Miller, "Queuing with Alternating Priorities," *Operations Res.* 13, No. 2: 306–318 (January-February 1965).

Baker, K. R., "On Madigan's Approach to the Deterministic Multi-Production and Inventory Problem," *Management Sci.* 12, No. 9: 636–638 (May 1970).

—— and A. G. Merten, "Scheduling with Parallel Processors and Linear Delay Costs," *Nav. Res. Log. Quart.* 20, No. 4: 193–804 (1973).

Bellman, R., "Dynamic Programming Treatment of the Travelling Salesman Problem," *J. Assoc. Comp. Mach.* 9, No. 1: 61–63 (January 1962).

Bomberger, Earl, "A Dynamic Programming Approach to a Lot Size Scheduling Problem," *Management Sci.* 12, No. 11: 778–784 (July 1966).

Bowman, E. H., "The Schedule-Sequencing Problem," *Operations Res.* 7, No. 1: 621–624 (September 1959).

Brooks, G. H. and C. R. White, "An Algorithm for Finding Optimal or Near-Optimal Solutions to the Production Scheduling Problem," *J. Ind. Eng.* 16, No. 1: 34–40 (January 1965).

Brown, A. P. G. and Z. A. Lomnicki, "Some Application of the 'Branch-and-Bound' Algorithm to the Machine Scheduling Problem," *Operational Res. Quart.* 17, No. 2: 173–186 (June 1966).

Brown, R. G., *Decision Rules for Inventory Management*, Holt, Rinehart, and Winston, New York 46–55 (1967).

Brucker, P., J. K. Lenstra, and A. H. G. Rinnooy Kan, "Complexity of Machine Scheduling Problems," Dept. of Math. Dec. Sc., BW 43/75, Mathematish Centrum, Amsterdam (April 1975).

Campbell, Herbert G., Richard A. Dudek, and Milton L. Smith, "A Heuristic Algorithm for the n Job, m Machine Sequencing Problem," *Management Sci.* 16, No. 10: B630–B637 (June 1970).

Cobham, A., "Priority Assignment in Waiting Line Problems," *Operations Res.* 2, No. 1 (February 1954).

Coffman, E. G., Jr. and R. L. Graham, "Optimal Scheduling for Two-Processor Systems," *Acta Informatica*, 1: 299–213 (1972).

Conway, Richard W., William L. Maxwell, and Louis W. Miller, *Theory of Scheduling*, Addison Wesley Publishing Company, Reading, Massachusetts (1967).

Cook, S. A., "The Complexity of Theorem-Proving Procedures," in *Proc. 3rd Annual ACM Symp. on Computing*, 151–158 (May 1971).

Day, J. E. and M. P. Hottenstein, "Review of Sequencing Research," *Nav. Res. Log. Quart.* 17, No. 1: 11–40 (1970).

Doll, C. L. and D. C. Whybark, "An Iterative Procedure for the Single-Machine Multi-Product Lot Scheduling Problem," *Management Sci.* 20, No. 1: 50–55 (1973).

Dooley, J. E. and Ben Bernholtz, "A Many-Product Single-Machine Recursive Scheduling Procedure," *CORS J.* 7, No. 3: 165–176 (November 1969).

Dudek, Richard A. and Ottis Foy Teuton, Jr., "Development of M-Stage Decision Rule for Scheduling n Jobs Through m Machines," *Operations Res.* 12, No. 3: 471–497 (May-June 1964).

Eastman, W. L., S. Even, and I. M. Isaacs, "Bounds for the Optimal Scheduling of n Jobs on m Processors," *Management Sci.* 11, No. 2: 268–279 (1964).

Eilon, Samuel, *Elements of Production Planning and Control*, Macmillan, New York, Chapter 14 (1962).

Elmaghraby, S. E., "On the Sequencing of n Jobs on One Machine to Minimize the Number of Jobs," *Management Sci.* **18,** No. 7: 389 (March 1972).

——, "The One Machine Sequencing Problem with Delay Costs," *J. Ind. Eng.* **19,** No. 2: 105-108 (February 1968).

——, "The Sequencing of n Jobs on m Parallel Processors with Extensions to the Scarce Resources Problem of Activity Networks," presented at the Inaugural Conference, The Scientific Computation Center, Cairo, Egypt (December 17-20, 1969).

——, "The Machine Sequencing Problem-Review and Extensions," *Nav. Res. Log. Quart.* **15,** 2, 205-232 (June 1968).

——, "The Sequencing of n Jobs on m Parallel Processors," Research Memorandum (January 1968), North Carolina State University at Raleigh, N.C.

——, "The Sequencing of 'Related' Jobs," *Nav. Res. Log. Quart.* **15,** No. 1: 23-32 (March 1968).

—— and A. N. Elshafei, "The Scheduling of Jobs on Parallel Processors: A Survey and Annotated Bibliography," presented at the Logististics Research Conference, George Washington University, Washington, D.C. (May 8-10, 1975).

—— and A. S. Ginsberg, "A Dynamic Model for the Optimal Loading of Linear Multi-Operation Shops," *Management Tech.* **4,** No. 1: 47-58 (June 1964).

—— and A. Mallik, "The Scheduling of a Multi-Product Facility," *Proceedings of the Symposium on the Theory of Scheduling and Its Application*, Springer-Verlag, Berlin (1973) pp. 244-277.

—— and S. Park, "On the Scheduling of Jobs on a Number of Identical Machines," *IE Trans.* **6,** No. 1: 1-13 (1974).

Friedman, H. D., "Reduction Methods for Tandem Queueing Systems," *Operations Res.* **13,** No. 1: 121-131 (January-February 1965).

Fujii, M., T. Kasami, and K. Ninomiya, "Optimal Sequence of Two Equivalent Processors," *SIAM J. Appl. Math.* **17,** No. 4: 784-789 (1969).

Gapp, W., P. S. Mannkekar, and L. G. Mitten, "Sequencing Operations to Minimize In-Process Inventory Costs," *Management Sci.* **11,** No. 3: 476-484 (January 1965).

Garey, M. R. and R. L. Graham, "Bounds for Multiprocessor Scheduling with Resource Constraints," Bell Telephone Labs., Murray Hill, New Jersey (1974).

—— and D. S. Johnson, "Complexity Results for Multiprocessor Scheduling Under Resource Constraints," Bell Telephone Labs., Murray Hill, New Jersey (1974).

——, "Scheduling Tasks with Nonuniform Deadlines on Two Processors," Bell Telephone Labs., Murray Hill, New Jersey (1975).

Gaver, D. P., Jr., "A Comparison of Queue Disciplines when Service Orientation Times Occur," *Nav. Res. Log. Quart.* **10,** No. 3: 219-235 (September 1963).

Gelders, L. and P. R. Kleindorfer, "Coordinating Aggregate and Detailed Scheduling Decisions in the One-Machine Job Shop: Part I, Theory," *Operations Res.* **22,** No. 1: 46-60 (January-February 1974).

Giffler, B. and G. L. Thompson, "Algorithm for Solving Production-Scheduling Problems," *Operations Res.* **8,** No. 4: 487-513 (July-August 1960).

Giglio, R. J. and H. M. Wagner, "Approximate Solutions to the Three-Machine Scheduling Problems," *Operations Res.* **12,** No. 2: 305-324 (March 1964).

Gilmore, P. and R. E. Gomory, "Sequencing of One State-Variable Machine," *Operations Res.* **12,** No. 5: 655-679 (September-October 1964).

Glassey, C. R., "Scheduling Several Products on One Machine to Minimize Changeovers," *Operations Res.* **16,** No. 2: 342-352 (March-April 1968).

Graham, R. L., "Bounds on Multiprocessing Timing Anomalies," *SIAM J. Appl. Math.* **17:** 416-429 (1969).

——, "Bounds on Multiprocessing Timing Anomalies," *Bell Syst. Tech. J.* **45**: 1563–1581 (November 1966).

——, "Bounds on Multiprocessing Anomalies and Related Packing Algorithms," *AFIPS Conf. Proc.* 205–217 (1972).

Gupta, J. N. D., "A Functional Heuristic Algorithm for the Flow Shop Scheduling Problem," *Operations Res. Quart.* **22**, No. 1: 39–47 (March 1971).

——, "A General Algorithm for the nxm Flow Shop Scheduling Problem," *Int. J. Prod. Res.* 7, No. 3: 241–247 (1969).

——, "M-Stage Flow Shop Scheduling by Branch and Bound," *Opsearch* **7**, No. 1: 37–43 (March 1970).

—— and A. Walvakar, "Sequencing n-Jobs on m-Parallel Processors," *Opsearch* **6**, No. 3: 295–298 (1970).

Hardgrave, William W. and George L. Nemhauser, "A Geometric Model and A Graphical Algorithm for a Sequencing Problem," *Operations Res.* **11**, No. 6: 889–900 (November–December 1963).

Heathcote, C. R., "A Single Queue with Several Preemptive Priority Classes," *Operations Res.* **8**, No. 5: 630–638 (September 1960).

Held, M. and R. M. Karp, "A Dynamic Programming Approach to Sequencing Problems," *SIAM J. of Appl. Math.* **10**, No. 2: 196–210 (March 1962).

Heller, J., "Some Numerical Experiments for an M × J Flow Shop and Its Decision-Theoretical Aspects," *Operations Res.* **8**, No. 2: 178–184 (March-April 1960).

Hu, T. C., "Parallel Sequencing and Assembly Line Problems," *Operations Res.* **9**, No. 6: 841–848 (November-December 1961).

Ignall, Edward and Linus Schrage, "Application of the Branch and Bound Technique to Some Flow Shop Scheduling Problems," *Operations Res.* **13**, No. 4: 400–412 (May-June 1965).

Jackson, J. R., "An Extension of Johnson's Results on Job-Lot Scheduling," *Nav. Res. Log. Quart.* **3**, No. 3: 201–204 (September 1956).

——, "Jobshop-Like Queueing Systems," Research Report 81, Management Sciences Research Project, UCLA (January 1963).

——, "Queues with Dynamic Priority Discipline," *Management Sci.* **8**, No. 1: 18–34 (October 1961).

——, "Scheduling a Production Line to Minimize Maximum Tardiness," Research Report 43, Management Sciences Research Project, UCLA (January 1955).

——, "Some Problems in Queueing with Dynamic Properties," *Nav. Res. Log. Quart.* **7**, No. 3: 235–249 (September 1960).

——, "Waiting-Time Distribution for Queues with Dynamic Priorities," *Nav. Res. Log. Quart.* **9**, No. 1: 31–36 (March 1962).

Johnson, S. M., "Optimal Two- and Three-Stage Production Schedules with Setup Times Included," *Nav. Res. Log. Quart.* **1**: 61–68 (1954).

——, "Discussion: Sequencing n Jobs on 2 Machines with Arbitrary Time Lags," *Management Sci.* **5**, No. 3: 299–303 (April 1959).

Karp, R. M., "Reducibility Among Combinatorial Problems," in *Complexity of Computer Computations*, Miller and Thatcher, Eds., Plenum Press, pp. 85–103, New York (1972).

Karush, William, "A Counterexample to a Proposed Algorithm for Optimal Sequencing of Jobs," *Operations Res.* **13**, No. 2: 323–325 (March 1965).

Lawler, Eugene L., "On Scheduling Problems with Deferral Costs," *Management Sci.* **11**, No. 2: 280–288 (November 1964).

Held, M. and R. M. Karp, "The Traveling Salesman Problem and Minimum Spanning Trees," *Operations Res.* **18**, No. 6: 1138–1162 (November-December 1970).

——, "The Traveling Salesman Problem and Minimum Spanning Trees," *Math. Prog.* **1**, No. 1: 6–25 (October 1971).

Little, J. D. C., K. G. Murty, D. W. Sweeny, and C. Karel, "An Algorithm for the Traveling Salesman Problem," *Operations Res.* **11**, No. 6: 972–989 (November 1963).

Lomnicki, Z. A., "A 'Branch-Bound' Algorithm for the Exact Solution of the Three-Machine Scheduling Problem," *Operational Res. Quart.* **16**, No. 1: 89–100 (March 1965).

Madigan, J. G., "Scheduling a Multi-Product Single Machine System for an Infinite Planning Period," *Management Sci.* **14**, No. 11: 713–719 (July 1968).

Magee, J. F., *Production Planning and Inventory Control*, McGraw Hill, New York, pp. 44–66 (1958).

Manne, A. S., "On the Job-Shop Scheduling Problem," *Operations Res.* **8**, No. 2: 219–223 (March 1960).

McMahon, G. B. and P. G. Burton, "Flow-Shop Scheduling with the Branch-and-Bound Method," *Operations Res.* **15**, No. 3: 473–481 (May-June 1967).

McNaughton, Robert, "Scheduling with Deadlines and Loss Functions," *Management Sci.* **6**, No. 1: 1–12 (October 1959).

Miller, L. W. and L. Schrage, "The Queue M/G/1 with the Shortest Remaining Processing Time Discipline," RAND Paper P-3263 (November 1965).

Miller, R. G., Jr., "Priority Queues," *Ann. Math. Stat.* **31**, No. 1: 86–103 (1960).

Mitten, L. G., "A Scheduling Problem," *J. AIIE* **10**, No. 2: 131–135 (March-April 1959).

Moore, J. Michael, "An N Job One Machine Sequencing Algorithm for Minimizing the Number of Late Jobs," *Management Sci.* **15**, No. 1: 102–109 (September 1968).

Nabeshima, Ichiro, "One the Bound of Makespans and Its Application in M Machine Scheduling Problem," *J. Operations Res. Soc. Japan* **9**, Nos. 3 & 4: 6–44 (July 1967).

Palmer, D. S., "Sequencing Jobs Through a Multi-Stage Process in the Minimum Total Times," *Operational Res. Quart.* **16**, No. 1: 101–108 (March 1965).

Phipps, T. E., Jr., "Machine Repair as a Priority Waiting-Line Problem," *Operations Res.* **4**, No. 1: 76–86 (February 1956).

Reich, E., "Waiting Times When Queues are in Tandem," *Ann Math. Stat* **28**, No. 3: 768–772 (1957).

Rogers, Jack, "A Computational Approach to the Economic–Lot Scheduling Problem," *Management Sci.* **4**, No. 3: 264–291 (April 1958).

Root, James G., "Scheduling with Deadlines and Loss Functions in k Parallel Machines," *Management Sci.* **11**, No. 3: 460–475 (1965).

Rothkopf, Michael, "Scheduling Independent Tasks on Parallel Processors," *Management Sci.* **12**, No. 5: 437–477 (January 1966).

Saaty, Thomas L., *Elements of Queueing Theory*, McGraw-Hill Book Company, Inc., New York (1961).

Salvador, Michael S., "A Solution to a Special Class of Flow-Shop Scheduling Problems," *Proceedings of the Symposium on the Theory of Scheduling and Its Applications*, Springer-Verlag, Berlin (1973) pp. 83–91.

Schild, A., and I. J. Fredman, "Scheduling Tasks with Linear Loss Functions," *Management Sci.* **7**, No. 3: 280–285 (April 1961).

Schild, A. and I. J. Fredman, "Scheduling Tasks with Deadlines and Nonlinear Loss Functions," *Management Sci.* **9**, No. 1: 73–81 (October 1962).

Schrage, L. E., "A Survey of Priority Queueing," Master's Thesis, Cornell University (February 1965).

——, "Solving Resource-Constrained Network Problems by Implicit Enumeration–Nonpreemptive Case," *Operations Res.* **18**, No. 2: 263–278 (1970).

Shwimmer, J., "On the N-Job, One-Machine, Sequence-Dependent Problem with Tardiness

Penalties: A Branch-and-Bound Approach," *Management Sci.* 18, No. 6: B301-313 (February 1972).

Smith, Richard D. and Richard A. Dudek, "A General Algorithm for Solution of the n-Job m-Machine Sequencing Problem of the Flow Shop," *Operations Res.* 15, No. 1: 71-82 (January 1967).

Smith, W. E., "Various Optimizers for Single-State Production," *Nav. Res. Log. Quart.* 3, No. 1: 59-66 (March 1956).

Stankard, M. F. and S. K. Gupta, "A Note on Bomberger's Approach to Lot Size Scheduling: Heuristic Proposed." *Management Sci.* 15, No. 7: 449-452 (March 1969).

Swarc, Wlodzimierz, "Solution of the Akers-Friedman Scheduling Problem," *Operations Res.* 8, No. 6: 782-788 (November-December 1960).

Ullman, J. D., "Polynomial Complete Scheduling Problems," *Operating Systems Review* 7, No. 4: 96-101 (1973).

Wagner, H. M., "An Integer Linear-Programming Model for Machine Scheduling," *Nav. Res. Log. Quart.* 6, No. 2: 131-140 (June 1959).

White, H. and L. S. Christie, "Queueing with Preemptive Priorities or Breakdown," *Operations Res.* 6, No. 1: 79-95 (January 1958).

Wishart, D. M. G., "Queueing Systems in Which the Discipline is Last-Come, First-Served," *Operations Res.* 8, No. 5: 591-599 (September 1960).

Wismer, D. A., "Solutions of the Flowshop-Scheduling Problem with No Intermediate Queues," *Operations Res.* 20, No. 3: 689-697 (May-June 1972).

I-10

PROJECT SELECTION, PLANNING AND CONTROL

William E. Souder
University of Pittsburgh

1. INTRODUCTION

A project is a series of interrelated jobs which must be completed within a given time frame and with a given set of resources. The effective management of projects has become of particular concern in R&D (research and development), where nearly all modern efforts are organized around the project entity. The stereotyped lone scientist in a laboratory has been replaced by interdisciplinary teams of engineers and scientists whose work must be coordinated with other teams, outside contractors, etc.

In its broadest sense, a "project" often begins its life cycle with a nebulous idea for a product, design, etc., and ends with a transfer of developed technology to another party, such as marketing, the customer, etc. This project life cycle concept is depicted in a general way in Figure 1.

The effective administration of a total project effort and its environment requires attention to many behavioral, economic, financial, organizational, and systems optimization aspects. Some of these aspects are within the domain of OR while others are not. For example, idea generation and the stimulation of potential project ideas (Figure 1) has been extensively studied, for example, by Rubenstein [1963, 1970]. The findings indicate that the organizational rewards system and the degree to which organizational goals and constraints are clearly delineated will have a major impact on the quality of the ideas generated.

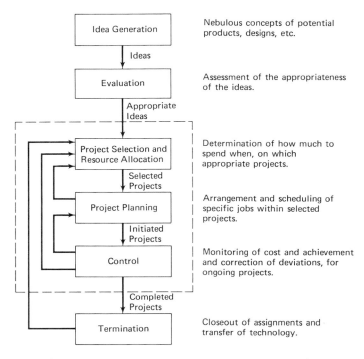

Fig. 1. Project life cycle concept with areas of operations research concentration inside the dashed line.

"Optimum" conditions are not apparent however, and, at the time this is being written, there is no substantive OR literature on this aspect.

Those aspects of the life cycle dealing with the evaluation of generated ideas (Figure 1) usually involve a rational assessment of ideas against delineated organizational goals. A variety of relevant analysis models have been developed to assist managers in this aspect, such as that by Cetron [1967]. However, since the evaluation of generated ideas is usually highly heuristic and qualitative in nature, the determination of a classical OR optimum is usually impossible.

Project selection and resource allocation (Figure 1) involve a determination of which of the appropriate ideas to initiate as project efforts. The selection process is normally closely related to project planning, which involves scheduling the jobs and tasks to be carried out. As discussed later in this chapter, there are substantial OR contributions in these areas. Project planning also involves the specification of systems organizational relationships (e.g., Cleland and King [1970]).

Control of ongoing efforts (Figure 1) consists of assessing the cost and achievement status of the project relative to planned costs and achievements, and correcting for significant variances (e.g., replanning or reselecting). Control is closely interrelated within planning, which provides the cost and achievement standards, and selection-allocation, which reallocates funds among projects in accordance with their relative achievement/cost status over time. OR methods can be of value in dealing with control problems, as noted later in this chapter.

Termination of completed projects (Figure 1) is also closely related to the project selection process, since termination renders previously committed resources available for reallocation. However, technology transfer (the transfer of the project outputs to the marketing department, the customer, etc.) is largely organizational in nature and not readily amenable to rigorous OR analysis (e.g., Douds [1971]).

To date, the OR contributions to project administration are primarily in the areas of (1) project selection, (2) project planning, and (3) control. The purpose of this chapter is to survey these contributions.

2. PROJECT SELECTION PROBLEMS

Prior to World War II, many industrial firms did not view project selection as a particularly important function. The need for firms to systematically plan risky investments such as R&D, large-scale engineering design (e.g., commercial aircraft), and discovery efforts (e.g., oil drilling) did not become significant until the 1950's, when many of the post-war markets matured. About 1955, systematic planning techniques began to be developed for determining which R&D projects to work on and how much to spend on them.

Since then, the term "project selection" has come to have many different connotations. In its narrowest sense, "project selection" means determining which of several alternative projects, tasks, jobs, programs, etc. to initiate now, start work on next, etc., given that more projects exist than can be initiated and concurrently pursued with the available resources. In its broadest sense, "project selection" means more than simply *selecting* the next project to be initiated or prioritizing a given set of available alternatives. The project selection process may also include the determination of the "optimum" (in some sense) allocation of limited resources among the available projects. Thus, prioritizing projects may be looked upon as a zero-one subproblem (select or not select) of the overall resource allocation problem, which is to determine how much to spend on which projects.

The overall selection-allocation process may be viewed as a sequential portfolio determination process: the decision maker wishes to know how much to spend on which of several alternative projects over several time periods. Portfolios are redetermined at the end of each time period, with a consideration of the projects available at that time. The set of available projects includes both those that are currently ongoing and those in the backlog awaiting initiation.

The determination of such optimum portfolios is highly important to the organization, since portfolio decisions entail large organizational commitments that can have significant opportunity costs. Thus, it is important to know that only the "best" projects have been selected and funded in the "best" overall fashion. However, the optimization of project selection decisions in real situations is extremely difficult, because they are often characterized by splintered selection and allocation responsibilities and by a diffuseness of organizational responsibility for the selection of projects.

In splintered responsibilities, the projects are selected and prioritized at one level of the organization, while the resources are assigned to them at a different level of the organization. Since the two organizational levels may have different viewpoints of the prevailing objectives and constraints sets, this confounds the possibilities for achieving an overall optimum. For example, it is not uncommon for the long range planning function of an organization to establish the acceptable programs, from which the operating departments may select particular projects. However, a hierarchy of budgets comes into play in determining the fundings for these projects. Divisions have total budgets. Departments within these divisions have budgets. Projects within divisions also have budgets. The structure is

$$D^- \leqslant \sum_{j \in D} x_j \leqslant D^+$$

$$d^- \leqslant \sum_{j \in d} x_j \leqslant d^+$$

$$p_j^- \leqslant x_j \leqslant p_j^+,$$

where D^+ and D^- are upper and lower division budgets, d^+ and d^- are upper and lower department budgets, p_j^+ and p_j^- are upper and lower project budgets, and x_j is the amount spent on project j. Thus, the amount of funds allocated to a project is heavily influenced by higher level budgetary constraints. Furthermore, divisional and departmental level budgets are often set largely on headcount or other bases for annual periods of time, without regard to new projects which may be selected during that year.

Diffuseness refers to the fact that project selection decisions may naturally occur at many different points in an organization. The decisions can be highly uncoordinated with each other. At the policy level; e.g., the corporate planning level, there may be a selection among alternative disciplines, technologies, or product areas (Souder [1971]). At the operational level; e.g., the departmental level, a similar selection process may go on with respect to alternative methodologies for carrying out the project (Souder [1970]). At both levels, it is likely that many different persons will be involved in the project selection decision making. Some of these persons will supply information to the process; e.g., the marketing department may supply information about the potential market returns from the project. Other persons will supply constraint-type information.

In an extensive study of project selection and budget procedures in a large organization, Shumway, et al. [1975] and Baker, et al. [1976] provide an interesting illustration of both splinteredness and diffuseness. The budgetary process within this organization, as diagramed in Figure 2, is sequential in nature. Budget guidance is issued from each superordinate level to its immediate subordinate levels, based, in turn, on the guidance it has received and on its decision as to how the budget should be further apportioned. Budget guidance is also issued according to technical areas. For example, a laboratory will receive guidance regarding its total budget, programs, and activities. The laboratory will issue guidance for its subordinate organizations and for its project subentities. Once these guidances reach the lowest organizational level, the information flow is reversed: each subordinate proposes to its superordinate how it

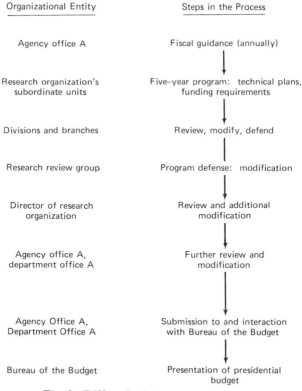

Fig. 2. Diffuse budgetary process.

would allocate the guidance budgets if they were, in fact, to be authorized. These proposed allocations are integrated at each level and are then communicated to the next level. This upward-downward cycling may recur many times until the highest organizational level receives a proposed budget allocation either consistent with the figures it originally issued as guidance or otherwise acceptable to it. The final acceptable budget is then issued as a set of guidelines, in a fashion that is analogous to the original issuance of guidance figures. Frequently, these final budgets must be revised during the year to take into account new influences that have developed since the budget was specified. Accordingly, several times during the year each organizational level is faced with a resource allocation decision which is characterized by a large number of budgetary constraints, defined both by organizational entity and activity type (Shumway, et al. [1975] p. 10). An empirical examination of the process for one budgetary cycle indicated that many, many small changes in the allocations were made by numerous persons throughout the organization. This resulted in a final budget which was not representative of the objectives of any one of the involved entities (divisions, branches, agencies, etc.)!

3. PROJECT SELECTION MODELS

The purpose of a project selection model is to assist the administrator in prioritizing and funding the available projects. Three general categories of "models" have been developed: (1) checklists, (2) economic indexes, and (3) portfolio models. Checklists and economic indexes have been developed and used largely by practicing managers and their staffs. Portfolio models have largely been developed by academicians and OR specialists. Checklists and indexes deal with the problem of prioritizing projects; portfolio models deal with the problem of determining optimum funding allocations.

3.1 Checklists

Where the projects are highly exploratory, such as a basic R&D project, only qualitative information may exist and the decision variables may be highly uncertain. In this case, proposed projects are often selected or rejected on the basis of the viewpoints of a few scientists or others closely connected with the technologies involved (Gee [1971]). A checklist of criteria or performance requirements which acceptable projects must meet is often a helpful aid to judgment. A list of some often-used criteria is shown in Figure 3, along with an example of an evaluation for a hypothetical project. Such evaluations provide systematic summaries, and are primarily of value at the "evaluation" stage of Figure 1.

Criteria	High	Medium	Low
Patentability	X		
Market potential			X
Probability of success		X	
Cost to produce	X		
R & D costs		X	

Evaluation

Fig. 3. Proposed checklist for a hypothetical project.

Where more information is available with respect to the relative importance of the criteria and where the projects may be measured along a scale of at least ordinal level, it is a short step to go from checklists to scoring models. In a scoring model, each of $j = 1, \ldots, n$ candidate projects are scored along a scale for each of $i = 1, \ldots, m$ criteria. These criterion scores for each project are then combined with their respective criterion importance weights, W_i, to achieve a total score, T_j, for each project. Projects may then be ranked according to their T_j values. For example, a simple additive scoring model would be

$$T_j = \sum_i s_{ij} W_i,$$

where s_{ij} is the score on the ith criterion for project j. An example is shown in Figure 4. Examples of varieties of scoring model-checklists are given by Sullivan [1961], Harris [1961] and Moore [1968].

Baker and Moore [1969] have rather extensively investigated the procedures

Factor	Weight	X	Score* for Project A	=	Criterion Score
Probability of success	3		5		15
Profit	2		10		20
Cost	1		3		3

*Scoring scale: excellent = 10
poor = 1

$T = 38$

$\% T = 38/[(3 \times 10) + (2 \times 10) + (1 \times 10)]$
$= 38/60 = 63.3\%$

Fig. 4. Example of a scoring model.

for using the scoring model form. The starting point is the determination of a time-table and representative set of criteria or factors for judging project proposals. A Delphi-like method for collecting such a list has been developed and successfully used by Souder [1973b]. The second step is the development of a performance measurement scale for rating candidate projects. For quantitative criteria, such as cost, profit, etc., one may construct a performance scale based on either historical data or expected future performances. As an example consider the criterion *project cost* (see Baker [1970]). Suppose the range of project costs experienced over the past two years is $500,000 to $1,500,000, and for 21 actual projects, assume we would find the distribution shown in Figure 5. Further, assume it is decided that this distribution is appropriate for judging the projects currently under consideration. Then, the next step is to divide the distribution into a number of categories from which a scale can be constructed. For purposes of illustration, assume that 3 such categories are specified. Relative to the project cost example, the categories might be (as illustrated by broken horizontal lines) 10 or less, between 10.5 and 13.5, and greater than 13.5. A new project which is being evaluated might be scored 3, 2, or 1, according to its estimated cost. Here, the basis for assigning categories is simply statistical: the middle two-thirds of the data (score of 2) are taken to be "typical." The choice of a basis for assigning categories, as well as the number of categories, is determined largely by the user and his needs (see Moore [1968]). For qualitative criteria; e.g., probability of success, one begins with scale descriptors such as "low," "medium," etc., and converts these to scale values such as 1, 2, etc. Thus, scoring models permit the combining of qualitative and quantitative assessments.

3.2 Economic Indexes

A variety of economic indexes have been developed for use in prioritizing candidate projects at the "evaluation" and at the "project selection and resource

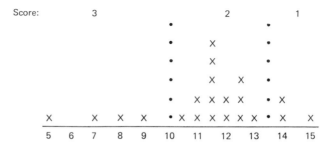

Fig. 5. Project cost in $100,000.

allocation" stages of Figure 1. Many such models exist in the literature (e.g., Kiefer [1964]). Some examples of economic index models are given below.
  Ansoff's [1962] index is:

$$\text{Figure of Merit} = \frac{rdp\,(T+B)\,E^*}{\text{total investment}},$$

where r = the probability of research success, d = the probability of development success, p = the probability of market success, T and B are indexes of technical and business merit, and E^* is the present value of earnings from the project. Olsen's (see Kiefer [1964]) index is:

$$\text{Value} = \frac{rdpSPn}{\text{project cost}},$$

where S = annual sales volume in units, P = unit profit, n = number of years of product life, and the other variables are the same as in Ansoff's index. Hart's [1965] index is:

$$\text{Capital Return} = pG^*/[(R^*) + (D^*) + (F^*) + W],$$

where G^* = present value gross profits, R^* = discounted direct cost of the research, D^* = discounted direct cost of the development, F^* = discounted direct cost of fixed capital, W = the working capital, and p is defined above. Viller's [1964] index is:

$$\text{Project index} = rdp\,\frac{E^* - R^*}{\text{cost}},$$

where the above notations are used. Disman's [1962] index is:

$$\text{Maximum expenditure justified} = rp\,(v^* - X^*),$$

where v^* = the present value dollar return from the project, X^* = the present value dollar cost of production, marketing and engineering services, and r and p are as defined above. Dean and Sengupta's [1960] index is:

$$V = \sum_{i}^{n} [c_i(1+r)^{-i}],$$

where V = present value of the research opportunity, c_i = net cash flow in the ith year, r = expected annual rate of return, i = time index by year, and n = total number of years that the income is expected. The values of c_i and r are subjectively estimated, and are based on past experience and future expectations of the company. This method can be extended to consider a variable rate of return, r_i.

Due to their simplicity of use and ease of understanding, indexes of this nature have been used by many administrators. Although such indexes permit the user to evaluate candidate projects at more than one funding level, the hand evaluation of several projects at several alternative funding levels becomes exhausting. Thus, economic index models have been used only as a rapid way to prioritize candidate projects at a single funding level, thereby gaining only limited insight into the "best" priority of projects. Unless the user recognizes that the resulting priorities are relevant to only one of many possible funding levels, there is danger of accepting the priorities as representative of all project funding levels.

3.3 Portfolio Models

In a portfolio model, candidate projects are implicitly prioritized by the amount of funds allocated to them. The general format of all such models is

$$\max \sum_j v_j(x_j) \tag{1}$$

$$\text{subject to} \quad \sum_j x_j \leqslant B, \tag{2}$$

where x_j is a project expenditure, B is the total budget for $j = 1, \ldots, n$ candidates (projects) for funding, and the value function, $v_j(x_j)$, can be nonlinear, linear, or single-valued. In the single-valued case (one value of v_j and one cost x_j for each jth project), the portfolio model is an index model with v_j as the prioritizing index.

A variety of "values" may be used in equation (1) above. Many portfolio models use expected values, so that equation (1) becomes

$$\max \sum_j v_j p_j(x_j),$$

where $p_j(x_j)$ is the probability of achieving v_j. Other portfolio models use a total score; e.g., a T_j "value" from a scoring model. In addition to equation (2), a typical constraint is

$$b_j^- \leqslant x_j \leqslant b_j^+,$$

where b_j^- and b_j^+ are lower and upper project expenditure bounds. Also, portfolio models have been developed for multiple time periods; e.g.,

$$\max \sum_{ij} v_{ij}(x_{ij})$$

$$\text{subject of} \quad \sum_{ij} x_{ij} \leqslant B,$$

where $i = 1, \ldots, m$ time periods.   Some examples of portfolio models are presented below.

Dean and Nishry's method [1965] is a mathematical programming approach using a scoring model framework.   Their model finds that set of $x_j = 0$ or 1 for each of the n projects which

$$\text{maximizes} \quad \sum_j x_j T_j,$$

$$\text{subject to} \quad \sum_j x_j R_j \leqslant R,$$

where R_j is the amount of the total resources allocated to the jth project, R is the total resource budget, and the value of x_j (the selection variable) depends on whether project j is not selected ($x_j = 0$) or is selected ($x_j = 1$).   Integer programming methods are used to solve the problem.

Bell, et al. [1967] have developed a LP model in which each project is allowed several project versions that correspond to different rates (e.g., fast, medium, slow) of carrying out the project.   The ith version of the jth project is defined by the zero-one variable x_{ij}.   To ensure that each project appears no more than one time, the inequalities

$$\sum_{i=1}^{m_j} x_{ij} \leqslant 1$$

are included for $j = 1, \ldots, n$ candidate projects available for selection and funding in the portfolio, where m_j is the number of versions of project j.   The model maximizes

$$\sum_{j=1}^{n} \sum_{i=1}^{m_j} b_{ij} x_{ij},$$

where b_{ij} is the expected benefit from each project version.

Watters [1967] uses a zero-one integer programming approach to maximize the total expected portfolio utility u where

$$E(u) = \sum_j (\mu_j - K\sigma_j^2) x_j, \quad j = 1, \ldots, n \text{ projects}, \quad x_j = 0, 1.$$

Here, μ_j and σ_j^2 are the mean and variance of net returns from the jth project, and K is the coefficient of risk aversion.   The maximization is subject to a budgetary constraint in each period, expressed as the probability of exceeding a limit B_q which is less than or equal to a stipulated amount β_q.   To wit:

$$Pr\{t_q > B_q\} \leqslant \beta_q, \quad q = 1, 2, \ldots, Q \text{ planning periods},$$

where t_q is a variable representing the total cost of all projects undertaken in period q.

The Rosen-Souder model [1965] uses a dynamic programming format to maximize the "netback" to R&D, where

$$\text{Maximum Netback} = \max_{\{x\}} \sum_j [G_j P_j(x_j) - x_j],$$

$$\text{subject to } \sum_j x_j \leq B, \quad j = 1, 2, \ldots, n \text{ projects.}$$

Here, G_j is the present value gross profit if the project succeeds, $P_j(x_j)$ is the probability of success function, B is the total budget, and x_j is the allocation to project j. Additional constraints, $S^j_{max.}$ = maximum total project expenditure, $S^j_{min.}$ = minimum total project expenditure, and x_j = project expenditure in any time period, are incorporated into the dynamic programming algorithm. The recurrence relation is

$$f_2^j(y) = \max_{x_j \geq 0} [G_j P_j(x_j) - x_j + \rho(1 - P_j(x_j) f_1^j(x_j + y))],$$

where $f_2^j(y)$ is the maximum expected profit from project j with two time periods to go, and ρ is a discount factor. Hess [1962] has a dynamic programming model which is similar and antecedent to the Rosen-Souder model. Hess considers a complex probability function form, $P_n(x_n, y_n)$ where x_n is the project budget in the nth period, and y_n is a weighted sum of research and development expenditure on the project in periods prior to the nth.

A large number of portfolio models have been proposed in the literature. In 1964, Baker and Pound published their survey of the literature and reported an analysis of ten portfolio model types. In 1967, Cetron, et al. reported their study of thirty such models cited in the literature. In 1970, Souder [1970b] reported an analysis of forty-one such models in the open literature. These models differ from each other with respect to the variables which are maximized and the nature of the parameters and the mathematics which are used to represent the real world system. The models were classified into the following six categories: linear, nonlinear, zero-one, scoring, profitability index, and utility types. Linear and nonlinear models have linear and nonlinear objective functions, respectively. Zero-one models use integer variables and integer mathematics, scoring models use interval scores in place of the financial variables used in the other models, while profitability index models maximize a single point index of return. The utility models maximize the subjective utility of the dollars invested. The literature sources for the models are cited, by model type, in Table 1.

TABLE 1. PORTFOLIO MODELS

Linear models

D. T. Asher, "A Linear Programming Model For the Allocation of R&D Efforts," *IRE Transactions on Engineering Management*, EM-3, (December 1962), 154–157.

F. T. Hanssmann, *Operations Research Techniques for Capital Investment*, New York: John Wiley (1968), 94–104.

A. B. Nutt, "An Approach to Research and Development Effectiveness," *IEEE Transactions on Engineering Management*, EM-10 (September 1965), 103–112.

W. H. Pound, "Research Project Selection: Testing A Model In the Field," *IEEE Transactions on Engineering Management*, EM-9 (March 1964), 16–22.

D. Sobin, *Proposal Generation and Evaluation Methods in Research and Exploratory Development*. Research Analysis Corporation Report RAC-R-11, Roanoke, Virginia (1965).

W. E. Souder, *Operations Research in R&D*. The Monsanto Company, St. Louis, Missouri, (March 1966).

Nonlinear models

Richard Burton, *A Model For Project Selection in Developing Countries*, The Boeing Company, Renton, Washington (1969).

A. H. Bobis, et al., "A Funds Allocation Method to Improve the Odds of Research Success," *Research Management* (March 1971), 34–49.

Leon Cooper, *A Method for Selecting R&D Projects*, The Monsanto Company (February 1970).

S. C. Daubin, "The Allocation of Development Funds," *Naval Research Logistics Quarterly*, 3 (September 1958), 263–276.

S. W. Hess, "A Dynamic Programming Approach to R&D Budgeting and Project Selection," *IRE Transactions on Engineering Management*, EM-9 (December 1962), 170–179.

Charles Matheny, *A Budget Model for Procurement of Army Equipment*. Technical Report Processing Center Report ARO-13-D493-A, Radford, Virginia (1964).

F. M. Scherer, "Research and Development Resource Allocation Under Rivalry," *The Quarterly Journal of Economics*, 81 (August 1967), 359–394.

W. E. Souder and E. M. Rosen, "A Method For Allocating R&D Expenditures," *IEEE Transactions on Engineering Management*, EM-11 (September 1965), 87–93.

A. R. Washburn, *A Mathematical Approach to Program Planning*, The Boeing Company, Renton, Washington (1969).

Zero-one models

A. G. Beged-Dov, "Optimal Assignment of R&D Projects in A Large Company Using An Integer Programming Model," *IEEE Transactions on Engineering Management*, EM-12 (December 1965), 138–142.

R. J. Freeman, "A Stochastic Model for Determining the Size and Allocation of the Research Budget," *IRE Transactions on Engineering Management*, EM-7 (March 1960), 2–7.

F. T. Hanssmann, *Operations Research Techniques for Capital Investment*, New York: John Wiley (1968), 104–134.

A. L. Minkes and J. M. Samuels, "Allocation of Research and Development Expenditures in the Firm," *Journal of Management Studies*, 3 (February 1966), 62–72.

S. S. Sengupta and B. V. Dean, "On a Method for Determining Corporate Research and Development Budgets," *Management Science Models and Techniques*, ed. C. W. Churchman and M. Verhulst, New York: Pergamon Press (1960), 210–225.

M. Soewarso, "Long Range Planning in a National Telephone System," Ph.D. Dissertation, Munich Technical University, Munich, Germany (1967).

TABLE 1. (*Continued*)

Scoring models

V. Bakanas, *An Analytical Method to Aid in The Choice of Long Range Study Tasks*, Ithaca, New York: Cornell Aeronautic Laboratory (May 1964).

B. V. Dean, *Project Evaluation: Methods and Procedures*, American Management Association Report No. 39, New York (1970).

G. R. Gargiulo, J. Hannoch, D. B. Hertz, and J. Zang, "Developing Systematic Procedures for Directing Research Programs," *IRE Transactions on Engineering Management*, EM-8 (March 1961), 24–29.

D. B. Hertz, "Selection, Evaluation and Control of R&D Projects," *Operations Research in Research and Development*, ed. B. V. Dean, New York: John Wiley (1963), 170–188.

J. S. Harris, "Evaluating New Project Proposals," *Chemical and Engineering News*, 15 (April 17, 1961), 14–18.

C. M. Mottley and R. D. Newton, "The Selection of Projects for Industrial Research," *Operations Research* (November–December 1959), 740–751.

M. J. Nishry, "Evaluation, Selection and Assignment of Industrial Research Projects," The Boeing Company, Renton, Washington (1964).

Profitability index models

H. I. Ansoff, "Evaluation of Applied R&D in A Firm," *Technological Planning on the Corporate Level*, J. R. Bright, ed. Cambridge: Harvard University Press (1964), 12–19.

Saul Disman, "Selecting R&D Projects for Profit," *Chemical Engineering*, 11 (December 1962), 87–90.

Carl Gloskey, "Research on A Research Department: An Analysis of Economic Decisions on Projects," *IRE Transactions on Engineering Management*, 11 (December 1960), 166–172.

J. H. Hirsch and E. K. Fisher, "The Alternative Service Concept In R&D Evaluation," *Gulf Research and Development Company*, Pittsburgh, Pennsylvania (1962).

H. V. Nyland and G. R. Towle, "How We Evaluate Return From Research: Experience of An Oil Company," *National Association of Cost Accounts Bulletin*, 37 (May 1956), 1092–1099.

J. J. Olsen, "Winds of Change in Industrial Chemical Research," *Chemical and Engineering News*, 12 (March 23, 1964), 95–96.

G. Pappas and D. McLaren, "An Approach to Research Planning," *Chemical Engineering Progress*, 57 (May 1961), 65–69.

D. Sobelman, "A Model For R&D," *Naval Research Quarterly*, 6 (September 1966), 19–24.

Utility models

R. Cramer and B. Smith, "Decision Models For the Selection of Research Projects," *The Engineering Economist*, 9 (January–February 1964), 1–20.

P. E. Green, "Risk Attitudes and Chemical Investment Decisions," *Chemical Engineering Progress*, 59 (January 1963), 35–40.

Harry Markowitz, *Portfolio Selection*, New York: John Wiley, 1960.

W. F. Sharpe, "A Simplified Model For Portfolio Analysis," *Management Science* (January 1963), 277–293.

3.4 Evaluation of Models

In recent papers (Souder [1972a, 1972b]), these models were evaluated for their suitability, using a scoring model methodology. In this methodology, c_{ij} denotes the ith characteristic within the jth criterion, as listed in Table 2. Also, w_{ij} is

TABLE 2. THE CRITERIA AND THEIR CHARACTERISTICS

Realism Criterion	*Capability Criterion*
Multiple objectives	Future times analyses
Multiple constraints	Optimization analyses
Orthogonal variables	Simulation analyses
Market risk variable	Selection analyses
Technical risk variable	Allocation analyses
Manpower limits parameter	Scheduling analyses
Facility limits parameter	
Data uncertainty variable	*Ease of Use Criterion*
Premises uncertainty variable	Low sensitivity
	Familiar variables
Flexibility Criterion	Discrete variables
Applied projects	Computer not needed
Basic projects	Special persons not needed
Priority decisions	Special interpretation not needed
Initiation decisions	Low amount of data
Budget allocation applications	Easily obtainable data
Project funding applications	Easy to estimate parameters
	Cost Criterion
	Low set-up costs
	Low use costs
	Low personnel costs
	Low computer time
	Low data costs

the relative importance factor weighting of c_{ij}, where $w_{ij} = 1, 2, \ldots, \lambda$, and x_{ij} is a designation variable, which assumes a value of one where the model fulfills the ith characteristic within the jth criterion, and a value of zero otherwise, in accordance with established definitions (see Souder [1972a]). Then,

$$\sum_i w_{ij} x_{ij} = S_{1j},$$

where S_{1j} is the raw score for a model relative to the jth criterion. Then,

$$S_{1j} / \sum_i w_{ij} = S_{2j},$$

where S_{2j} is the relative score for a model relative to the jth criterion. Letting r_j denote the relative value of the jth performance criterion, then

$$r_j S_{2j} = S_j,$$

where S_j is the suitability score for a model relative to criterion j. Thus, the total suitability, T, of a model is given by:

$$T = \sum_j \left[\left(\sum_i w_{ij} x_{ij} \middle/ \sum_i w_{ij} \right) r_j \right].$$

The criteria and characteristics are shown in Table 2. The values assigned to the r_j's were: realism = 4, flexibility = 3, capability = ease of use = 2, cost = 1. Criterion, characteristics, and r_j values were empirically determined.

Tables 3 and 4 show the results for one class of models. Total suitability, T, scores were determined for each of the forty-one models, and for each class of models. In general, the linear, nonlinear, and zero-one model types were found to have the highest realism, flexibility, and capability, while scoring and profitability index types had the best use and cost performance scores. Aside from the utility models, nonlinear types had the lowest usability and worst cost performance.

3.5 Applications of Portfolio Models

Portfolio models appear to be appropriate tools for a portfolio administrator who must decide how to allocate the scarce resources at his disposal among the many different available projects, so as to maximize the effectiveness of the total resources used. His portfolio decision will normally result in some projects which are not funded and which are therefore added to the backlog list of projects available for possible funding in some future time period. As time passes, he may wish to reallocate resources among the available projects (both ongoing and backlog) many times in order to take changing conditions and new information into account. Portfolio models can be used to prescribe portfolios in response to the questions: "Of those projects available, how much of the total annual budget *should* be programmed for which project, with respect to the subsequent annual budgetary horizon?," and "Now that *new* information is available, how *should* the resources be *reallocated* among all the available projects with respect to the subsequent annual budgetary horizon?" (Souder [1973a]).

In a field study, Souder [1973a] examined the analytical effectiveness of four generic types of project selection models. Analytical effectiveness refers to the ability of a model to select higher valued portfolios than a manager actually selects. In the study, it was shown that the choice of an analytically effective, project selection model type depended upon (1) the manager's objectives and (2) the life cycle stage of the set of available projects. Where the objective was the maximization of expected gross profits, either nonlinear or linear types of models were effective. Where the objective was the maximization of expected gross profit tempered by a desire to control the expenditures on ultimate failure projects, the results indicated that either zero-one or profitability index type models may be effective aids. Where the objective was the maximization of expected gross profit tempered by the maintenance of an ex-post optimal portfolio, e.g., shift funds out of potential failure projects and into potential success projects as they are identified, the results indicated that either the linear,

TABLE 3. CHARACTERISTICS AND SCORES FOR THE REALISM CRITERION, FOR SIX LINEAR MODELS

	Characteristics and x_{ij} values											
Model Name	Multiple Objectives	Multiple Constraints	Orthogonality	Market Risk	Technical Risk	Manpower Limits	Facility Limits	Budget Limits	Data Uncertainty	Premise Uncertainty	S_{1j}	S_{2j}
Asher	0	1	1	0	1	1	0	0	0	0	28	0.51
Hanssmann	0	1	1	0	1	0	1	0	0	0	27	0.49
Nutt	0	1	0	0	1	1	1	1	0	0	27	0.49
Pound	0	0	1	0	1	0	0	1	1	0	17	0.31
Sobin	0	0	1	1	1	1	1	1	1	0	28	0.51
Souder	0	0	0	1	1	0	1	0	0	0	17	0.31
$w_{ij} =$	10	9	8	7	6	5	4	3	2	1	$\sum_i w_{ij} = 55$	

TABLE 4. SUITABILITY SCORES FOR THE LINEAR MODELS

Model Name	Realism	Flexibility	Capability	Use	Cost	Total Suitability
Asher	2.0	2.6	1.0	0.88	0.60	7.1
Hanssmann	2.0	1.7	1.3	0.88	0.60	6.5
Nutt	2.0	2.6	1.3	0.88	0.20	6.9
Pound	1.2	1.7	0.66	1.5	1.0	6.1
Sobin	2.0	2.1	1.0	1.3	1.0	7.4
Souder	1.2	2.6	1.0	1.3	0.60	6.7

zero-one, or profitability index model types may be useful decision aids. In a real-time study by Souder [1973b], the linear type of model was found to have high utility. This type of model was found to yield higher expected gross profit values and lower expected regret expenditures than the managers expected to achieve. However, the seven managers (in five organizations), who were subjects, all rejected the linear type model on the grounds that it achieved values which were "redundant values." That is, all managers viewed the increased values as being beyond the satisfactory levels which they actually achieved. In addition, the linear type model selected portfolios which the managers generally did not like on the basis of several intrinsic properties of the portfolios themselves.

Thus, taken together, the two studies [1973a and 1973b] indicate that, although some model types may be analytically effective, their utility for increasing the actual returns per R&D dollar spent may be low. These results are consistent with surveys (e.g., Baker and Pound [1964], Souder [1970], Souder [1972b]) which indicate that portfolio models are not widely used. The few reported cases of their usage (e.g., Disman [1962], Rosen and Souder [1965], Souder [1967b and 1972c]) indicate that the models were abandoned after brief periods of use due to a lack of continuing management interest. It is clear in these cases that the use of the models beneficially impacted the organizational decision making processes. Better interdepartmental communication, an environment of "what if" decision making analyses, and a reduced sense of uncertainty in decision making resulted (Souder [1966a, 1966b, 1967a]). However, the basic problem of developing a portfolio model that is analytically effective (yields a "best" portfolio for several different criteria), realistic, and suitable for an *organization*, remains a fundamental problem (see Souder [1968, 1973a, 1973b], and Baker [1974]).

4. NETWORK PLANNING

Once a project has been selected to be initiated, problems often occur in determining how to complete (schedule) the project within the time and resources allotted. Two techniques, CPM and PERT, were independently and concurrently developed during the 1956-1958 period for handling this problem. CPM—Critical Path Method—was first used by the DuPont Company and further developed by Mauchly Associates (see Kelly [1961], Lerda-Olberg [1966]). PERT—Project Evaluation and Review Technique—was developed by the U.S. Navy on the Polaris submarine program (see Fazar [1962], Bigelow [1962]). Both techniques are similar in that they represent a project as consisting of a network of interrelated jobs. Since their original development, a large number of modifications and second generation network techniques have developed around CPM and PERT (see Lerda-Olberg [1966]).

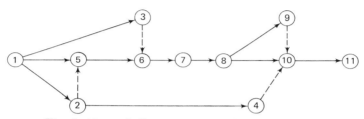

Fig. 6. Network diagram example for project A.

4.1 Network Representation

Network planning begins with a list of jobs (activities) and their estimated duration times. The network diagram is drawn using arrows to depict jobs, with the arrowheads indicating the direction of progress, as shown in Figure 6. Events, the start and completion of jobs, are points in time, and are represented by numbered nodes. The basic rules for constructing networks are as follows.

(1) No two activities (jobs) can be *identified* by the same events. This means that diagrams such as

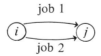

are "illegal." Instead, a correct representation is

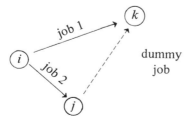

A dummy job takes no time or resources; it shows dependency only. This convention becomes vital in circumstances such as the following, where jobs 3 and 4 must follow job 2, but job 1 does not necessarily precede job 4.

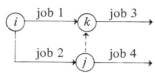

The diagram

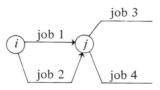

implies that, while jobs 1 and 2 may have different finish times, they both must be *completed* before jobs 3 and 4 can *start*.

(2) Precedence-successor relationships must be consistent throughout the network. For example, suppose job 6 follows jobs 4 and 2, which also follow job 3. Then the subnetwork

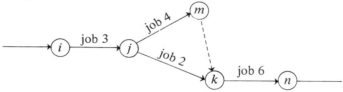

is correct *only* if job 4 must be completed *before* job 6 can *begin*. If the requirement is only that jobs 4 and 6 both *finish* before the successor job may begin, then the correct representation is:

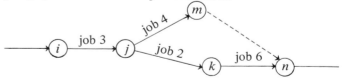

These two rules are illustrated by the network in Figure 6. Job 1–3 (the usual convention is to reference a job by its event numbers) must finish before job 6–7 begins, job 1–2 must finish before job 5–6 begins, etc. Where the ending of a predecessor job and the start of a successor job are congruent, they are taken as the same event.

4.2 Critical Path

Critical jobs are those whose delay will cause an equal delay in the completion of the project. That path through the network which consists of all such jobs is the *critical path*.

For small networks, the critical path will automatically become visible when the network is time-scaled, with all jobs placed at their earliest start positions. A time scaled version of the project A network from Figure 6 is shown for illustration in Figure 7. In larger networks, it is easier to determine the critical path by computation as the path with zero *float*. The dashed lines in Figure 7 are floats. A float is the amount of time a job could extend (float out) without delaying the occurrence time for project completion (e.g., the date corresponding to 34 time units in Figure 7). For example, job 1–2 has 8 time units of float, job 1–3 has 14 time units of float, etc. Job 2–4 has 22 time units of float if job 1–2 does not float out. However, as the job 1–2 float increases to its maximum of 8 time units (set by event 5), then job 2–4 will have only 14 time units of float remaining.

To compute the floats, one must first make a forward pass computation through the network to obtain the earliest start (*ES*) times for each job, at each node. Second, a backward pass computation is then made to obtain the latest finish (*LF*) times for each job. The total amount of float (*TF*) in each job is then computed from the difference between the duration of the job and the

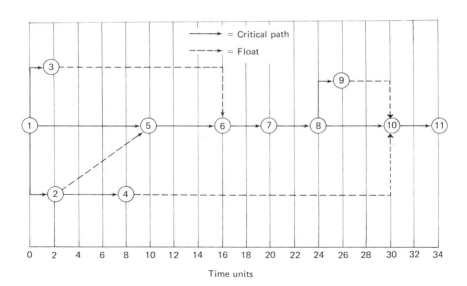

Fig. 7. Time-scaled network for project A.

time available. Specifically, the forward pass computations are obtained from

$$ES_i = \max_k \{ES_k + t_{ki}\}, \qquad i = 2, \ldots, n \text{ nodes}, \tag{3}$$

where t_{ki} is the duration of job $k - i$, $ES_1 = 0$, and ES_i denotes the early start time for all activities with predecessor node i. For example, equation (3) directs one to take the maximum value of $\{(24 + 6), (24 + 2 + 0), (8 + 0)\}$ to get $ES_{10} = 30$ (see Figure 7). That is, the maximum path length is either $ES_8 + t_{8,10}$, $ES_8 + t_{8,9} + t_{9,10}$, or $ES_4 + t_{4,10}$ (note that the durations $t_{9,10}$ and $t_{4,10}$ are both zero). The backward pass computation is analogous:

$$LF_j = \min_k \{LF_k - t_{jk}\}, \qquad j = 1, 2, \ldots, n - 1 \text{ nodes}, \tag{4}$$

where LF_j denotes the latest (allowable) finish time for all activities with successor node j, and $LF_n = ES_n$ for the terminal network node. The total float computation is:

$$TF_{ij} = LF_j - ES_i - t_{ij}. \tag{5}$$

By definition,

$$LS_{ij} = LF_j - t_{ij},$$

$$EF_{ij} = ES_i + t_{ij},$$

where LS_{ij} is the latest start and EF_{ij} is the earliest finish time for activity $i - j$. Then, alternatives to equation (5) are

$$TF_{ij} = LS_{ij} - ES_i \tag{6}$$

and

$$TF_{ij} = LF_j - EF_{ij}. \tag{7}$$

The forward, backward, and float computational results are illustrated in Table 5 for the project A network. The computational results in Table 5 are readily deduced from Figure 7. Note that total floats are assigned to jobs in the computations, but the floats do not cumulate over the activities in a particular path of several jobs in series. For example, it may be seen from Figure 7 that the *entire* path 1-2-4 cannot float out a total of the job 1-2 float plus the job 2-4 float (which is 30 time units) without delaying node 10. As pointed out above, when job 1-2 uses any of its 8 time units of float, then the float for job 2-4 must decrease accordingly. Thus, job 2-4 only has 22 less 8 equals 14 units of "free" float. The total float data, TF_{ij}, is based on an independent consideration of each job.

TABLE 5. NETWORK COMPUTATIONS FOR PROJECT A

Job[+] $(i-j)$	Duration t_{ij}	Earliest		Latest		Total Float TF_{ij}
		Start ES_i	Finish EF_{ij}	Start LS_{ij}	Finish LF_j	
1-3	2	0	2	14	16	14
1-5	10	0	10	0	10	0*
1-2	2	0	2	8	10	8
2-4	6	2	8	24	30	22
5-6	6	10	16	10	16	0*
6-7	4	16	20	16	20	0*
7-8	4	20	24	20	24	0*
8-9	2	24	26	28	30	4
8-10	6	24	30	24	30	0*
10-11	4	30	34	30	34	0*

[+]Dummy jobs not shown.
*By definition, this job is on the critical path.

4.3 Resource Leveling, Reallocation, and Time-Cost Tradeoff Procedures

An important application of float is for "leveling" resources. The resource leveling problem exists where it is desired to smooth out the profile of resource utilization within the given project duration, or to minimize project duration while meeting resource constraints. This may occur where manpower availabilities are imposed, budgets are restricted, skill categories are constrained, etc. For example, suppose jobs 1-3, 1-5, 5-6, 1-2, and 2-4 in Figure 7 each require one full-time person and only two persons are available. The two-person resource constraint can be satisfied without delaying the project completion time if the start of job 1-3 is merely delayed until time period 8 (it can be delayed up to time period 14 without delaying the project). Another feasible alternative would be to staff both jobs 1-3 and 1-2 at a lower rate; e.g., a half-man rate, and let both jobs float out by taking twice as long to complete. Resource leveling algorithms are available for large networks, e.g. Wiest [1967]. Although they are called optimization programs, only heuristic allocations are possible in most situations.   A survey of resource leveling methods is contained in Dewitte [1964] and Davis [1966, 1973].

Another important use of float is in reducing the duration of the critical path(s). Suppose we can reallocate men from jobs 1-3 and 1-2, to job 1-5, in Figure 7. The result may be that jobs 1-3 and 1-2 float out, while job 1-5 is compressed. The "optimum" trade-off is reached when either no men can be reallocated, all slacks have been absorbed, or the critical path cannot be further reduced through a reallocation of resources from a slack to a critical job. Computer programs similar to those used in leveling are available for this process (for a review see Davis [1973]). However, such reallocations may quickly run up against the resource constraints which create the need for resource leveling.

One way to reduce critical paths, after all slack to critical reallocations have been made, is to apply additional resources. The performance of some critical path jobs may be accelerated by increasing the total budget; i.e., by the allocation of additional resources from outside the project. For example, suppose a particular critical job which normally costs C_n and takes t_n time units can be completed in t_i units with C_i cost, where $t_i < t_n$ and $C_i > C_n$. Using cost increments, that is, using $\Delta C = C_i - C_n$, one can obtain a piecewise linear approximation to $C = f(t)$, which will usually be downsloping to the right (decreasing t with increasing C).

Suppose that such a time-cost function has been defined for each critical job in the network. A comparison of these critical job cost functions on the basis of the $\Delta t = (t_n - t_i)$ and ΔC data will indicate the order in which the critical jobs should receive additional resources, so as to achieve the greatest reduction in total project duration per additional cost unit. This was a major concern in the original development of CPM (Kelley [1961], Fulkerson [1961]). In the original approach, a normal point (t_n, C_n) and a crash point (t_c, C_c) were considered for critical jobs. The latter was the point beyond which the job could not be further compressed. A "slope" $(C_c - C_n)/(t_n - t_c)$ was then computed for all critical activities in the network and these were arrayed. That is, the analysis was based on the average cost per one time unit reduction achieved. The procedure calls for the compression of the activity(s) which will affect a unit reduction in project duration at *minimum increase* in total direct costs. Since a reduction in project duration *reduces* the indirect project costs, this compression process is usually continued until the sum of the opposing direct and indirect costs reaches a minimum. The latter defines an optimal project schedule in the total cost sense. Real applications of this procedure are, however, rather limited because it requires the assumption of unlimited resource availability.

The above compression procedure becomes rather complex because multiple critical paths form as the compression progresses. The (mathematically optimal) algorithms developed for this purpose by Kelley [1961] and Fulkerson [1961], are based on a network flow interpretation of the dual of the LP formulation of this problem.

Table 6 and Figures 8 and 9 show a simple but real example of manpower leveling which the author once experienced. A brief description of the jobs in the project, the assigned manpower, and the variations permitted on the project are listed in Table 6. An unleveled network plan suitable to all parties was devised as shown in Figure 8. However, before the project began, other commit-

TABLE 6. PROJECT DATA

Job	Job Description	Manpower now	Normal Job Durations	Δ Duration/man***
1	Process	2 men	6	4
2	Fixed	2 men*	7	*
3	Process	1 man	5	2
4	Analytical	outside department**	4	–
5	Development	2 men	6	1
6	Evaluation	outside contractor**	4	–
7	Costing	outside contractor**	3	–
8	Development	2 men	6	1
9	Evaluation	outside contractor**	2	–
10	Design	2 men	2	3
11	Design	2 men	5	2

*Men not transferable.

**These men are not within the control of the project manager.

***Only whole men may be transferred; these data are the changes (increase or decrease) in job durations for adding or subtracting one man.

ments arose which made only four men per time period available. The manpower requirements for the unleveled time schedule are shown in the time scaled resource profile diagram in the lower portion of Figure 8. A suitable alternative plan was the one shown in Figure 9. The four-man constraint was met by simply delaying the start of jobs 1, 5, 9, and 10, and dividing job 1 into two phases which were carried out four weeks apart. Thus, no transfer of men between jobs, so as to compress some critical job durations, was required. The "Δ Duration/man" data in Table 6 did not have to be used in this case (these data are used later, in Figure 10).

A reduction in the total project time of twenty weeks in Figure 9 is available through the time-cost schedule shown in Table 7. As an example, the total project duration can be reduced to seventeen weeks by spending $2,000 on job 11 plus $200 on job 8. This is a more cost-effective choice, for example, than the alternative of spending $3,000 on job 11 to achieve the same total project time reduction. The result, however, violates the four-man resource constraint. Starting from Figure 9, we can use the data in Table 7 to devise a seventeen day schedule which *does* meet the constraint. One such schedule involves spending the above $2,200 on jobs 11 and 8, plus $1,000 on job 6 and $500 on job 5. Note that compressing jobs 11 and 8 in Figure 9 requires the compression of jobs 6 and 5, if the manpower and completion time constraints are to be maintained. This is a more cost-effective alternative ($3,700) than the alternative of spending $2,000 on job 6 plus $3,000 on job 11. There are other time reductions and manpower trade-offs available in this example. One of the manpower

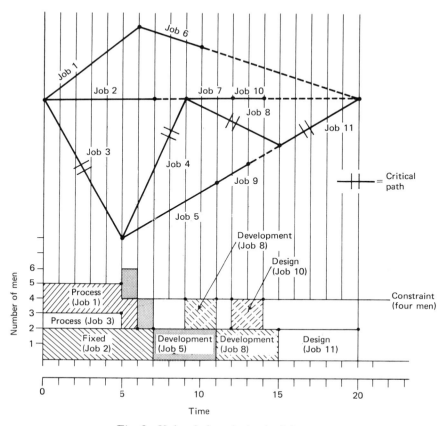

Fig. 8. Unleveled project schedule.

reallocations that can be made with the available resources is shown in Figure 10 (see Table 6 for the "Δ Durations/man" data used). The four-man constraint is, of course, violated by this schedule. It should by now be obvious to the reader that the problem of developing a cost-time "optimum" schedule, under resource constraints, may not be "easy" to solve.

4.4 Resource Allocation Algorithms

Resource allocation problems, in general, can be categorized as the determination of the schedule times for project activities which either (1) level the resource requirements subject to a constraint on the project duration, (2) mini-

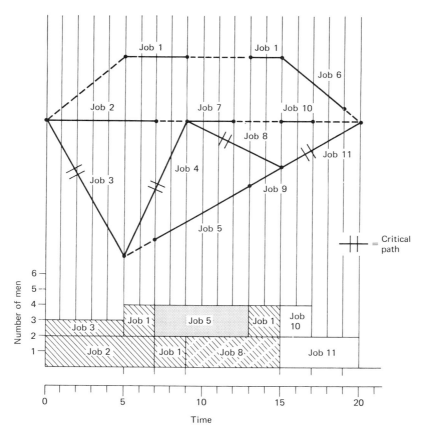

Fig. 9. Leveled project schedule.

mize the project duration subject to constraints on the availabilities of resources, or (3) minimize the total cost of the resources and the penalties due to project delay. A simulation approach to the last problem has been developed by Wiest [1967]. Most attention, however, has been devoted to the first two problems. Because of their combinatorial nature, optimal solutions, using mathematical programming, have very limited utility. The author's experience with integer and zero-one codes indicates that they are generally ineffective because they do not converge in reasonable computational times. Some branch and bound methods appear to have favorable computation times, but only for networks with less than fifty nodes (Davis [1973], Patterson and Huber [1974]).

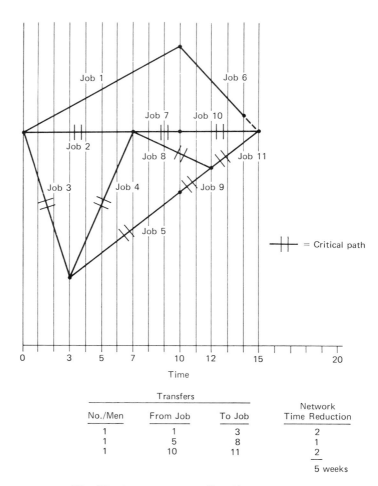

	Transfers		Network
No./Men	From Job	To Job	Time Reduction
1	1	3	2
1	5	8	1
1	10	11	2
			5 weeks

Fig. 10. A manpower reallocation.

Because of this lack of success with optimization procedures, attention has primarily been devoted to heuristic procedures which produce feasible schedules, based on some rule of thumb (heuristic) for determining the priorities among those jobs that compete for the limited resources. These procedures are classified as "serial" or "parallel" approaches, respectively, depending on whether the priorities are determined only once before activity scheduling begins or sequentially during scheduling. While most published research has dealt with parallel approaches, the relative merits of each have not as yet been determined. Davis [1966, 1973, and 1975] has studied and reviewed this problem extensively,

TABLE 7. AVAILABLE TIME-COST TRADEOFFS

	Time Reduction (weeks)	Additional Cost
Job 6	1[+]	\$1,000[+]
Job 6	2[+]	2,000[+]
Job 11	1*	1,000*
Job 11	2*	2,000*
Job 11	3*	3,000*
Job 5	1*	500*
Job 8	1*	200*

[+]The reduction is achieved through the purchase of additional outside contractors' services.
*The reduction is achieved by subcontracting portions of the work to an outside facility (manpower loadings same for remaining portions of the job).

including an evaluation of a large number of heuristics for prioritizing the activities during the scheduling process. His primary conclusion is that, while no one heuristic will always give the best schedule, the rule of scheduling the activities with *least slack first* (or the equivalent rule of minimum *latest start time*) has the best average performance.

With respect to the heuristic methods, IBM, CEIR, McDonnell Automation and Control Data Corporation, to name a few, have computer software available for handling large (1000 jobs per project), multi-resource scheduling. Many of these computer programs include features for job splitting, scheduling activities within a permissable range of resource levels, job costing, various reporting options, several different sequencing heuristics, and resource leveling. One of the few publications of the working details of such computer programs is given by Wiest [1967].

In summary, the problem of formulating the optimal resource constrained case is made difficult because explicit general criteria are lacking with respect to the "optimal" use of a resource. Furthermore, the way the restrictions on the sequencing of activities may interact with resource requirements and availabilities is difficult to predefine. Heuristic scheduling rules, computer-programmed to give "good" schedules in mechanistic fashion, will undoubtedly continue to be the basis for all practical systems for some time to come. The increased availability of more powerful time-shared computer systems should, however, produce more emphasis on the development of man-machine interactive procedures of the sort developed, for example, by Paulson [1971].

4.5 Probabilistic Considerations

Frequently, it is desirable to estimate the likelihood that a job, a set of jobs, or an entire project will not be completed by a particular date. Such considerations, which were paramount in the development of the original PERT method, can be achieved by using three time estimates for each job in the network. The three are: t_o = the optimistic time, t_m = the most likely (modal) time, and t_p = the pessimistic time. A Beta distribution is assumed to describe the hypothetical distribution of the actual job performance time (see Clark [1962]). An approximation to the mean, t_e, of the Beta distribution for these three estimates is given by $t_e = (t_o + 4t_m + t_p)/6$. The distribution is assumed to have a variance $v_t = [(t_p - t_o)/6]^2$. The t_e and v_t values may be computed for each job in the network. The expected total network completion time, T_e, is then taken as the sum of the t_e's, treated like CPM job times, for the activities comprising the longest path through the network. Confidence times, $T_{C, S}$, may then be computed for any set of critical jobs, S, by using the following relationship (which is based on the Central Limit Theorem, dealing with the sum of independent random variables):

$$T_{C, S} = \sum_{j \in S} (t_e)_j \pm K \sqrt{\sum_{j \in S} (v_t)_j}.$$

Here, K is a constant for the level of confidence ($K = 3$ for 99.7% confidence, $K = 2$ for 95% confidence, etc.). In the usual situation, an "optimum" project plan is one where $T_{C, S} \leqslant DC_S$, where DC is a desired completion time for the set of jobs, S. Network plans which do not meet this criterion may undergo slack to critical path resource reallocations, cost expediting, or more radical project replanning until this criterion is met.

It should be noted that all the above discussions are based on the assumption that the estimated completion time of the project is the target date. For most instances, this will be true. However, there are cases where the project manager may find that he can easily meet the imposed target date; e.g., the $T_{C, S}$ is well below the DC_S. Then, there is, in addition to the usual (critical-path induced) floats, an additional "free" float which results from the fact that $T_{C, S}$ is less than DC_S (Villers [1964], Clark [1962]).

4.6 Other Networking Procedures

A number of forms of networking, other than the PERT/CPM logic defined in section 4.1, are growing in importance (see Moder and Phillips [1970]). For example, it is sometimes easier to draw a network if the role of the arrows and nodes is reversed. In this case, the procedure is called *activity-on-node* networking. An extension of this procedure, which expands the PERT/CPM logic, is called *precedence diagramming* (see IBM [1967]). This procedure handles networking situations where two activities must start together, or end together, or proceed concurrently with a fixed time lag (a situation which occurs quite frequently in construction work). For example, a typical activity-on-arrow (conventional PERT/CPM) diagram is

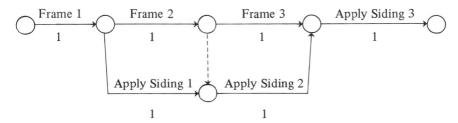

The same network can be drawn as an activity-on-node diagram:

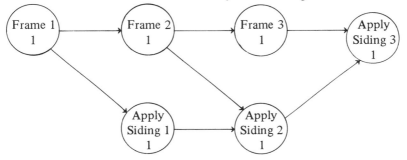

Using precedence diagramming, the network would be drawn as follows:

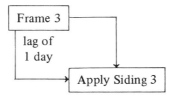

Many R&D projects are often highly nondeterministic, in that some jobs may conditionally lead to several others. For example, a chemist who synthesizes and tests a new insecticide may be aware of several outcomes such as: fail, pass, or unique result. Each of these outcomes may lead to several possible jobs. Thus, if the PERT/CPM logic is used, very large and cumbersome diagrams will result. In fact, it may not be possible to draw one single diagram to completely depict the project. These types of problems can be handled by decision point and tree diagrams in the network (see Eisner [1962]), as shown in Figure 11. Note that the floats 4-6 and 5-6 are conditional: the entire project shortens by these respective amounts, where the outcomes at node 3 are such that job 3 or job 5 are respectively elected. All other network computations follow the previously described formats, except that the computations must be discounted for the outcome probabilities. For example, in Figure 11, the expected time at node

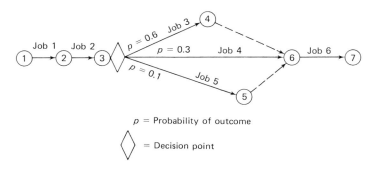

Fig. 11. Decision network.

7 would be computed as: t_e job 6 + $(.6 [t_e$ job 3] + $.3 [t_e$ job 4] + $.1 [t_e$ job 5]$)$ + t_e job 2 + t_e job 1. The GERT simulation language is specifically designed for these types of problems (e.g., see Pritsker and Happ [1966]).

4.7 Multi-Project Considerations

All the above networking concepts can be applied to the scheduling of several projects jointly administered by a single organization. For example, consider a portfolio of three R&D projects such as shown in Figure 12. In this illustration, project A must be completed before project B can start (e.g., project A produces a raw material for project B). Project X and project Y may begin and be completed any time between time a and time e, respectively. Thus, the dotted lines in Figure 12 are dummy dependencies only. They serve to indicate the time span available for all four projects. Duration times could be placed on these dummies to achieve early start and late finish project dates, if they exist. The project floats implied by these dummy jobs can be used in the same way that dummy jobs are used in single-project networks. For example, suppose the same resources are used on projects B and X. Furthermore, suppose these resource requirements exceed the availabilities because of the simultaneous demands by projects B and X. Figure 12 shows that the start of project X can be delayed until time d, while the resources are fully employed on project B. After project B is completed, the resources can be released for use on project X. Alternatively, both projects can use the resources at a reduced rate, and both projects will then float out (as long as they do not float beyond time e). Whole projects may be "cost-expedited," as described above (section 4.3). Thus, multi-project networking techniques are completely analogous to single-project networking techniques (see Wiest [1964]).

There is, however, one new aspect in multi-project scheduling: project priori-

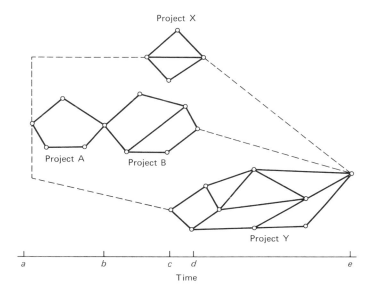

Fig. 12. A multiproject network.

ties. Suppose, in Figure 12, that project X is deemed to be the most "important" project. For example, there may be intrinsic reasons why management wishes to have it start before any other project. One such reason would be a felt competitive threat. In the RAMPS (Resource Allocation and Multi-Project Scheduling) computer algorithm developed by C-E-I-R, Inc. (Moshman, Johnson and Larsen [1963]), the project priority is used as a weighting factor in scheduling and allocating resources among competing alternative uses in multi-project networks.

In general, the iterative use of multi-project level and project level network methods provides a medium through which project and department level managers may devise integrated total plans. "Optimized" networks may be submitted by each project manager. These may then be merged into a multi-project network (Woodworth and Dane [1975]). Several multi-project network schedules may be developed, given various assumptions about priorities, resources, etc. These alternative multi-project schedules may then be examined in staff meetings attended by each project manager and the multi-project manager, e.g., the R&D director. The "best" multi-project schedule may then be selected, based on the discussions and criticisms from all parties. Several iterations of schedule development may be required between the project and multi-project level before an acceptable total or "organizational" plan is developed.

5. PROJECT CONTROL*

A major facet of any project manager's function may be said to be control. Control is that decision process which keeps project expenditures and proportionate technical achievements within planned limits. Control, therefore, consists of evaluating progress and correcting drift.

In practice, this control function is not easily separated from the planning function. First of all, control implies the existence of some plan which serves as the standard for measuring and evaluating progress. Second, the process of controlling often results in feedback which is used in replanning. Thus, planning, controlling, and replanning are interconnected activities which the project manager continually performs. Furthermore, the process of controlling is not pure control. It frequently requires some planning, such as that used in readjusting manpower and budgets within the master plan so as to correct for drift. However, let us use *planning* to refer to the processes of selecting activities, scheduling and allocating resources, and forecasting future activities. Controlling will refer to evaluating actual progress in terms of the plan and making minor readjustments within the plan so as to keep the planned activities on schedule and within the budgeted cost limits (see Souder [1968, 1969b, 1971]).

To aid project management in controlling, several types of information paradigms, ranging from simple narrative reporting to quantitative cost/time models, have been proposed or used. An example of a pure narrative type is the periodic progress report, which is common in most project organizations. This generally consists of a briefly written paragraph stating what was done and what has been accomplished (Souder [1969b]).

An effective project control model is here defined as one which yields valid indicators of the eventual fate of project by (1) informing the manager of any achievement/cost/time deviations from the plan, (2) indicating the corrective actions needed by management, and (3) communicating these to the project manager. Eventual fate here refers to the managerial assessment, at some future time, of the pass or fail status of the project. To meet these criteria, a control model must first of all merge both achievement/time and cost/time reporting. Narrative reports and cost/time models alone cannot, by their very natures, do this.

5.1   Cost/Progress Control

Let us assume that an optimal (in some sense) time-scaled network plan has been devised for the ith planning horizon. Then, let

t = the time period, $t = 1, 2, \cdots, n,$

E_t = the cumulative dollars actually expended by the end of time period $t,$

*Portions of the materials discussed herein have appeared in the *IEEE Trans. on Eng. Mgt.*, March 1968 (copyright) and *R&D Mgt.*, October 1972.

$\hat{E}_t$ = the cumulative dollars forecasted to be expended by the end of time period t,

$\Delta E_t = (\hat{E}_t - E_t)$ = the cost variance for t, (25)

ϕ_t = the cumulative actual output at the end of time period t,

$\hat{\phi}_t$ = the cumulative forecasted output at the end of time period t,

$\Delta\phi_t = (\phi_t - \hat{\phi}_t)$ = the progress variance for t, (26)

$\hat{C}_t$ = the total forecasted cost of the total actual output at the end of t,

$\Delta C_t = (\hat{C}_t - E_t)$ = the cost/progress variance for t. (27)

Output is measured as the per cent of the nodes completed in the network diagram. Then, let $\hat{\phi} = \hat{F}(\hat{E}, t)$ represent a forecast over the tth planning period. That is, $\hat{\phi}$ is the cumulative forecasted or cumulative expected output, and $\hat{\phi}$ is a function of the expenditures forecasted over time; i.e., the budget. Then, as t takes successive values from 1 to n, a tracking $\phi = F(E, t)$ can be formed so that $\{F - \hat{F}\}$ represents a cost/progress information-control system. That is, the set of comparative differences between the actual and the forecasted expenditure-output functions, as measured by several parameters, is the information feedback that triggers control action by the manager. The particular parameters chosen here are defined in equations (25), (26) and (27).

This model is illustrated in Figure 13 and Table 8. For example, at the end of five months the total actual output of the project has been determined to be .40 (40% of the nodes have been achieved), and the total actual amount expended has been determined to be $100,000. Therefore, a mark X_5 was made at the $E = 100$, $\phi = 0.4$ coordinate (ignoring for the moment the time scale). The appropriate values of the parameters $\hat{E}_5$, E_5, $\hat{\phi}_5$, ϕ_5, and $\hat{C}_5$ were entered in the "Analysis of Budget Variance," shown in Table 8, and the respective variances were computed by (25), (26) and (27). Likewise, the marks $X_1, X_2, X_3, \cdots, X_n$ were made in Figure 13 for months $1, 2, 3, \cdots, n$, and the corresponding variances were similarly computed and entered in Table 8. Thus, Figure 13 is

TABLE 8. ANALYSIS OF BUDGET VARIANCE

	Expenditure			Output			Cost/Progress	
t	E_t	$\hat{E}_t$	ΔE_t	ϕ_t	$\hat{\phi}_t$	$\Delta\phi_t$	$\hat{C}_t$	ΔC_t
1	20	20	0	0.10	0.10	0	20	0
2	50	40	−10	0.25	0.15	+0.10	70	+20
3	60	70	+10	0.35	0.25	+0.10	85	+25
4	75	90	+15	0.40	0.40	0	90	+15
5	100	120	+20	0.40	0.65	−0.25	90	−10
6	130	140	+10	0.70	0.75	−0.05	130	0
7	180	160	−20	0.70	0.85	−0.15	130	−50
8	230	180	−50	0.70	0.87	−0.17	130	−100

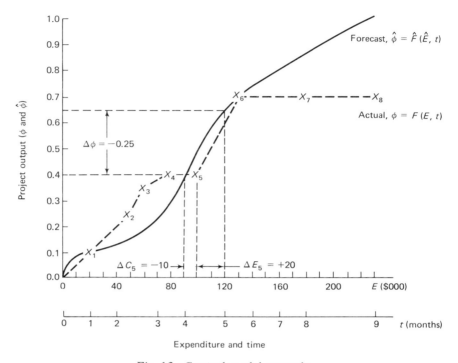

Fig. 13. Control model example.

simply another way of depicting the time-scaled (cost, time optimized) network plan, and recording actual cost and progress through it. The time and expenditure scales in Figure 13 are those from the network plan; e.g., the expenditure scale is developed by adding up the costs for each time point (or at each node). The convention of which scale, expenditure or time, to plot as the linear scale is arbitrary. However, since cost/progress is being emphasized, the expenditure was linearized here.

This model enables project management to: (1) see variances as they occur, (2) categorize their causes, (3) determine the appropriate control action to be taken; e.g., how and when to revise the plan. For example, a disproportionately high rate of expenditure for the amount achieved should always be a sufficient reason for the project manager to hold a detailed project review. The model will show all such disproportionate expenditures as negative cost/progress variances (i.e., negative numbers in the ΔC_t column of Table 8). The model indicates that a substandard achievement, even where proportional to the expenditure, should always trigger a project review. That is, in terms of Table 8, any and all negative $\Delta \phi_t$ entries should cause a review, even when accompanied by zero ΔC_t entries.

Under such circumstances, an explanation of why the rate of expenditure is below the planned level must be sought. Assuming the original plan was optimal, such positive cost variances represent a drift away from optimality, and may therefore eventually cause highly undesirable negative cost/progress variances. The data for months six through eight in Table 8 and Figure 13 can be used to illustrate this point. The cost/progress variance for month six (ΔC_6) is zero, because the substandard achievement ($\Delta \phi_6 = -0.05$) has been balanced by spending under budget ($\Delta E_6 = +10$). In this hypothetical example, suppose that the spending under budget since month three was achieved by conserving resources on this project while utilizing them on a competing project. Strictly speaking, this change calls for a reoptimization, and the generation of a new "forecast" curve in Figure 13 to reflect the altered rate of resource application on this project. However, assume that this replanning action was not taken because management felt that "lost time" now could all be regained by "crash" costing the project at a later date. Thus, suppose that in months seven and eight, crash overspending was used in an attempt to correct the substandard achievement. The results was that a proportional achievement did not occur and cost/progress variance turned increasingly negative. The point is that many projects may similarly have efficient expenditure/time schedules which may be extremely difficult to re-establish once perturbed. Effective planning over the long term depends upon good control to indicate when and how to replan from time to time.

Thus, the conclusion is that all and any positive cost variances, all and any negative progress variances, and all and any negative cost/progress variances should cause a detailed project review and project replanning.

What about overspending the budget? That is, what about negative cost variances (i.e., negative items in the ΔE_t column of Table 8)? Surprisingly enough, the model indicates that such deviations do not necessarily demand control action. For example, again considering Table 8 and Figure 13, the project manager should not be concerned about the overspending indicated by the negative cost variance at the end of the second month ($\Delta E_2 = -10$). The cost/progress variance is positive ($\Delta C_2 = +20$), indicating that the extra expenditure has "bought" more than a proportionate achievement. Note the location of X_2 in Figure 13. In other words, running over budget will not matter if the overexpenditure is "buying" proportionate achivements.

Now consider the data for the third, fourth, and fifth months in Table 8. The absolute level of achievement is slipping at an increasing rate, as shown by the entries in the $\Delta \phi_t$ column changing from +0.10, through 0, to -0.25. And the level of achievement per amount of expenditure is also slipping, as shown by entries in the ΔC_t column. Not only is the project achieving less with each passing month, but is is also achieving less per dollar with each passing month. But none of this "bad news" shows in the "budget" or cost variance, the ΔE_t column in Table 8. In fact, the project shows a favorable status in budgetary control (positive entires in the ΔE_t column) over these three months!

The conclusion is that controlling by "budget" overruns and underruns only can be seriously misleading. Cost (or budget) variances and achievement variances can balance out, as shown at the end of the sixth month in Table 8 and Figure 13. Or they may reinforce each other, as shown at the end of months seven and eight. In any event, it is the interaction of both cost and achievement variances that determine the actual status of the project. This simple fact is often obscured in project control situations. As a result, an inordinate amount of significance is generally attached to project cost overruns, while some projects running under their budgeted costs often fail to attract badly needed attention. For example, even under fixed manpower assignments, misalignments may occur because a manager may choose to underconsume his "fair share" of outside services; e.g., analytical services, in the interest of staying under budget. Or he may underconsume in the hope of reserving some funds for other "pet" projects. The above model makes the effects of such misalignments apparent.

These concepts and the application of the control model have been illustrated in several studies (see Souder [1968, 1969a, 1969b]). Standard PERT/CPM packages usually provide cost and achievement data in terms of updated estimates of project completion dates and costs (for example, see Villers [1964]). However, integrated cost/progress status reporting is usually not part of the PERT/CPM package.

6. INTEGRATED PLANNING AND CONTROL SYSTEMS

Planning premises and other informational inputs to the planning process are often highly tenuous and subject to rapid change. The technical status of the ongoing project many change rapidly (e.g., a technical breakthrough occurs), competition may introduce a similar product, the price of an essential raw material may change, etc. Changes in these planning premises can necessitate a reperformance of the planning and control functions in order to adapt to these changes. The dynamic impacts of these changes on other existing programs, or the anticipated reactions of competitors, suppliers, etc. may cause further changes which necessitate additional adaptive planning and control actions. Thus, the situation is such that an iterative planning and control cycle is performed over time. This iterative cycle is illustrated in Figure 14. In this representation, the initial perceptions received by management form the basis for the initial plan (see box I in Figure 14). The characteristic scope and details of this initial plan will depend primarily on the existing technology, and the clarity of management's perceptions of how this technology may be applied. The plan will be implemented by manipulating some discretionary variable, such as a budget (see box II of Figure 14). The results of these manipulations on certain endog-

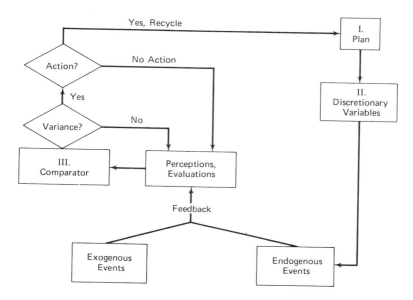

Fig. 14. Planning and control system.

enous variables (e.g., technical accomplishments) will be perceived. Changes in certain exogenous variables (e.g., the competitive situation) will also be perceived. These perceptions will then be compared with the preconceived notions and prior expectations of the perceptions (see box III of Figure 14). A decision is then needed. Is action required? If the answer is 'yes', then replanning may occur. This dynamic-adaptive planning-controlling-replanning cycle may be continuously performed over time (see Souder [1972c]).

6.1 Dynamic-Adaptive Planning and Control

Figure 15 depicts a dynamic-adaptive planning and control concept. A planning "model;" e.g., a project selection-resource allocation and network scheduling package, can iteratively be used to arrive at a satisfactory plan. After the plan is implemented, actual events may cause a change in the original predictions and estimates sufficient to warrant a replanning and iterative repetition of the planning model. That is, things have changed to the degree that we look for a new set of projects, their funding allocation, and their time schedules. This may result in the termination of some projects, a reallocation of funds among existing projects, the selection of additional projects from the list of candidates, a rescheduling of expenditures over time, or some combination of these. The planning and

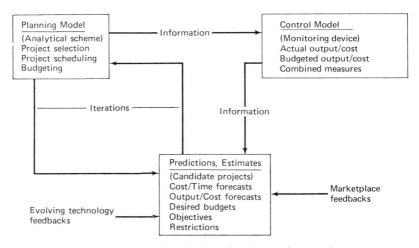

Fig. 15. Dynamic-adaptive planning and control.

control cycle thus repeats, with the planning and control models continuously re-used in these fashions as analytical aids to management.

Briefly, the planning model defines a plan-line

$$\hat{\phi}_j = \hat{F}_j(\hat{E}_j, t),$$

(see section 5.1 for a definition of the symbols) for each of $j = 1, \cdots, s$ selected and funded projects, of the set $j = 1, \cdots, n$ available for selection and funding. The control model provides an analogous track-line,

$$\phi_j = F_j(E_j, t),$$

for each of $j = 1, \cdots, s$ projects. Let $\pm \Delta f_j$ be a control limit. Then, project j is under control only when

$$\hat{F}_j - \Delta f_j \leqslant F_j \leqslant \hat{F}_j + \Delta f_j.$$

When project j is not under control, replanning is called for. Control actions; e.g., reallocations of project resources from slack to critical paths, may be taken at anytime to keep the project under control. As discussed in Section 5.1 above, control actions will be also taken on the basis of the ΔC_t and ΔE_t variances. The determination of an appropriate $\pm \Delta f_j$ depends upon the nature of the project and managerial desires. However, deviations of from 10 per cent to 20 per cent in F_j are often found in many successful project efforts (see Souder [1968 and 1969b]).

This system combines centralized and decentralized decision making. Control is decentralized in that it takes place at the lowest possible project level. The project manager keeps the project within the planned limits by making minor adjustments that are within the given budget. These are considered the proper sphere of project management, and the next level of supervision does not become involved. However, changes in total project budgets, changes in the number or types of personnel or the project, or any major replanning that affects other projects involves management at levels above project supervision. Hence, centralized decision-making is required. Thus, the planning model is the device which interfaces planning and control at the project level with planning and control at the multiproject or area level.

7. SUMMARY

Although many OR models have been developed for project and portfolio selection, the development of suitable and effective portfolio models which will be adopted by managers remains a challenge. The task is compounded by the diffuse and splintered nature of the project selection-resource allocation decision processes which exists in most organizations. These factors promote piecemeal suboptimization. Thus, index models and checklists remain the mainstay in the area of project selection aids.

Although network planning procedures have been widely adopted, their natural extensions in the form of cost/progress control and reporting has not received equal appreciation. As the concept of integrated, adaptive planning and control systems becomes more widespread, cost/progress control may become more widely used.

Major challenges for OR remain in developing useful project selection models. Considerable lattitudes remain for OR developments in the area of combined heuristic-optimal resource allocation methods for project scheduling. In the control area, important challenges remain in developing project output and achievement measures that are more meaningful than a simple count of the network jobs completed. In many projects, the degree of project goal achievement does not appear to be proportionately related to the per cent of the total project jobs completed. Also, the problems of control in networks where the job durations are random variables have not been fully resolved at the time this is being written.

REFERENCES

Ansoff, H. I., "Evaluation of Applied Research in a Business Firm," in *Technical Planning on the Corporate Level*, J. R. Bright (ed.), Harvard University Press, Cambridge, Massachusetts (1962).

Baker, N. R., "Scoring Models," in *Seminar at Airlie House*, Document 70/58, Program of Research on the Management of Research and Development, Northwestern University, Evanston, Illinois (1970).

—— and J. R. Moore, "Computational Analysis of Scoring Models for R&D Project Selection," *Management Science* **16**, No. 4: 124-134 (December 1969).

—— and W. H. Pound, "R&D Project Selection: Where We Stand," *IEEE Trans. on Eng. Management* **EM-11**, pp. 124-134 (December 1964).

——, Souder, Wm. E., Shumway, C. R., Maher, P. M., and A. H. Rubenstein, "A Budget Allocation Model for Large Hierarchical R&D Organizations," Management Sci. **23**, No. 1: 59-70 (September 1976).

——, "R&D Project Selection Models: An Assessment," *IEEE Trans. on Eng. Management* **EM21** No. 4: 165-172 (November 1974).

Bell, D. C., Chilcott, J. E., Read, A. W., and R. A. Solway, "Application of a Research Project Selection Method in the Northern Region Scientific Services Department," R&D Department, Central Electricity Generating Board (U.K.), RD/H/R2/ (1967).

Bigelow, C. G., "Bibliography on Project Planning and Control by Network Analysis," *Operations Res.* **10**, pp. 728-731 (1962).

Brockhoff, Klaus, "Some Problems and Solutions in the Selection of an R&D Portfolio," paper presented at the 1969 Conference of the International Federation of Operations Research Societies, Venice, Italy (1969).

Cetron, M. J., "Quest Status Report," *IEEE Trans. on Eng. Management* **EM-14**, No. 1: 51-62 (March 1967).

—— and L. H. Roepcke, "The Selection of R&D Program Content, *IEEE Trans. on Eng. Management* **EM-14**, pp. 4-13 (December 1967).

Clark, C. E., "The PERT Model for the Distribution of an Activity Time," *Operations Res.* **10**, pp. 405-406 (September 1962).

Cleland, D. I. and W. R. King, *Systems, Organization Analysis, Management: A Book of Readings*, McGraw-Hill, New York (1970).

Davis, Edward W., "Resource Allocation in Project Network Models—A Survey," *J. Ind. Eng.* **17**, No. 4: 33-41 (April 1966).

——, "Project Scheduling under Resource Constraints—Historical Review and Categorization of Procedures" *AIIE Trans.* **5**, No. 4: 297-313 (December 1973).

—— and J. H. Patterson, "A Comparison of Heuristic and Optimum Solutions in Resource Constrained Project Scheduling," *Management Sci.* **21**, No. 8: 944-955 (1975).

Dean, B. V. and S. S. Sengupta, "On A Method for Determining Corporate Research and Development Budgets," in *Management Science Models and Techniques* C. W. Churchman and M. Verhulst, (eds.) Pergamon Press, New York, pp. 210-225 (1960).

—— and M. J. Nishry, "Scoring and Profitability Models for Evaluating and Selecting Engineering Projects," *Operations Res.* **13**, No. 4: 13-21 (July-August 1965).

Dewitte, L., "Manpower Leveling of PER T Networks," *Data Processing for Sci./Eng.* pp. 29-37 (March-April, 1964).

Disman, Saul, "Selecting R&D Projects for Profit," *Chem. Eng.* **11**, pp. 87-90 (December 1962).

Douds, C. F., "The State of the Art in the Study of Technology Transfer," *R&D Management* **1**, No. 3: 125-131 (October 1971).

Eisner, Howard, "A Generalized Network Approach to the Planning and Control of a Research Project," *Operations Res.* **10**, pp. 115-125 (October 1962).

Fazar, W., "The Origin of PERT," *The Controller*, pp. 598-602, 618-621 (December 1962).

Fulkerson, D. R., "A Network Flow Computation for Project Cost Curves," *Management Sci.* **8**, No. 2: 51-60 (January 1961).

Gee, R. E., "A Survey of Current Project Practices," *Res. Management* **14**, No. 5: 38-45 (September 1971).

Harris, J. S., "New Product Profile Chart," *Chem and Eng. News* 39, No. 16: 110-118 (April 17, 1961).

Hart, A., "Evaluation of Research and Development Projects," *Chem. and Ind.* No. 13: 549-554 (March 27, 1965).

Hess, S. W., "A Dynamic Programming Approach to R&D Budgeting and Project Selection," *IRE Trans. on Eng. Management* EM-9 pp. 170-179 (December 1962).

IBM, "Project Control System/360 (360A-CP-06X) Program Description and Operations Manual," No. H20-0376-0, IBM Corporation, White Plains, New York (1967).

Kelley, James E., "Critical-Path Planning and Scheduling: Mathematical Basis," *Operations Res.* 9, No. 3: 296-320 (May-June 1961).

Kiefer, D. M., "Industrial Chemical Research," *Chem. and Eng. News*, 42, No. 12: 88-109 (March 23, 1964).

Lerda-Olberg, Sergio, "Bibliography on Network-Based Project Planning and Control Techniques: 1962-1965," *Operations Res.* 15, pp. 925-931 (December 1966).

Moder, J. J. and C. R. Phillips, *Project Management with CPM and PERT*, Van Nostrand Reinhold Company, New York, 2nd Ed. (1970).

Moshman, Jack, J. Johnson, and M. Larsen, *RAMPS—A Technique for Resource Allocation and Multi-Project Scheduling* C-E-I-R, Inc., Arlington, Virginia (1963).

Moore, John R., "R&D Project Selection: Theoretical and Computational Analysis of a Project Scoring Model," Ph.D. Dissertation, Purdue University, Lafayette, Indiana (June 1968).

Patterson, J. H. and W. D. Huber, "A Horizon-Varying, Zero-One Approach to Project Scheduling," *Management Sci.* 20, No. 6: 990-998 (February 1974).

Paulson, Boyd C., Jr., "Man-Computer Concepts for Project Management," Technical Report No. 148, Department of Civil Engineering, Stanford University, Stanford, California (1971).

Pritsker, A. and W. Happ, "GERT: Graphical Evaluation and Review Technique—Part I, Fundamentals," *J. Ind. Eng.* 17, No. 5: 267-274 (May 1966).

Rosen, E. M. and Wm. E. Souder, "A Method for Allocating R&D Expenditures," *IEEE Trans. on Eng. Management* EM-12, pp. 87-93 (September 1965).

Rubenstein, A. H., "Studies of Project Selection in Industry," in B. V. Dean (ed.), *Operations Research in Research and Development*, Wiley, New York, pp. 189-205 (1963).

——, "Program Summary 1967-1970," document 70/31, POROMRAD, Department of Industrial Engineering, Northwestern University, Evanston, Illinois (1970).

Shumway, C. R., Maher, P. M., Baker, N. R., Souder, Wm. E., and A. H. Rubenstein, "Diffuse Decision Making: An Empirical Examination," *Management Sci.* 21, No. 6: 697-707 (February 1975).

Souder, Wm. E., "R&D Project Selection: A Budgetary Approach," *Trans. CCDA*, pp. 25-43 (Spring 1966).

——, "Planning R&D Expenditures with the Aid of a Computer," *Budgeting* XIV, pp. 25-32 (March 1966).

——, "Solving Budgeting Problems with O.R.," *Budgeting* XIV, pp. 9-11 (July/August 1967).

——, "Selecting and Staffing R&D Projects Via Op Research," *Chem. Eng. Progress* 63, pp. 27+ (November 1967) (reprinted in Readings in *Operations Res.* W. C. House, Auerbach [1970]).

——, "Experiences with an R&D Project Control Model," *IEEE Trans. on Eng. Management* EM-15, pp. 39-49 (March 1968).

——, "Cost/Progress—A Breakthrough in Operation Budgeting," *Managerial Plan.* XVII pp. 1-9 (January/February 1969).

——, "The Validity of Subjective Probability of Success Forecasts by R&D Managers," *IEEE Trans. on Eng. Management* **EM-16**, No. 1: 34–49 (Feburary 1969).

——, "Budgeting R&D," *Bus. Horizons* **XIII**, pp. 31–38 (June 1970) (reprinted in *Readings in Business Policy*, B. P. Coleman and J. W. Bonge, MacMillan (1971); reprinted in *Product Planning*, A. E. Spitz, Auerbach, pp. 114–123 [1972]).

——, "Suitability and Validity of Project Selection Models," Ph.D. Dissertation, St. Louis University, St. Louis, Missouri (August 1970).

——, "R^2: Some Results from Studies of the Research Management Process," *Pro. AMIF*, pp. 121–130 (March 1971).

——, "A Comparative Analysis of Risky Investment Planning Algorithms," *AIIE Trans.* **4**, No. 1: 56–62 (March 1972a).

——, "A Scoring Methodology for Assessing the Suitability of Management Science Models," *Management Sci.* **18**, No. 10: 526–543 (June 1972b).

——, "An R&D Planning and Control Servosystem: A Case Study," *R&D Management* **3**, No. 1: 5–12 (October 1972c).

——, "Effectiveness of Mathematical Programming Models for Project Selection: A Computational Evaluation," *Management Sci.* **19**, No. 8: 907–923 (April 1973a).

——, "Acceptability and Utility of Project Selection Models in Development R&D," *Management Sci.* **19**, No. 12: 1384–1394 (August 1973b).

——, "Autonomy, Gratification and R&D Outputs: A Small Sample Field Study," *Management Sci.* **20**, No. 8: 1147–1156 (April 1974).

——, "Achieving Organizational Consensus With Respect to R&D Project Selection Criteria," *Management Sci.* **21**, No. 6: 669–681 (February 1975).

Sullivan, C. I., "CPI Looks at R&D Project Evaluation," *Ind. and Eng. Chem.* **53**, No. 9: 42A–46A (September 1961).

Villers, Raymond, *Research and Development: Planning and Control*, Financial Executives Research Institute, Inc., pp. 30–38 (1964).

Watters, L. D., "Research and Development Project Selection: Interdependence and Multiperiod Probabilistic Budget Constraints," Ph.D. Dissertation, Arizona State University, Tempte (1967).

Wiest, J. D., "Some Properties of Schedules for Large Projects With Limited Resources," *Operations Res.* **12**, No. 3: 395–418 (May-June 1964).

——, "A Heuristic Model for Scheduling Large Projects with Limited Resources," *Management Sci.* **13**, No. 6: B359–B377 (February 1967).

Woodworth, B. M. and C. W. Dane, "Multiproject Network Analysis with Resource Leveling: State of Art and a Governmental Application," unpublished paper, Dept. of Business Administration, Oregon State, Corvallis, Oregon (1975).

I-11

RELIABILITY

Ernest M. Scheuer
California State University, Northridge

1. INTRODUCTION

Reliability theory concerns itself with finding the probability that a stochastically failing item (component, module, system, etc.) will perform its function satisfactorily. The definition of satisfactory functioning may or may not involve a specified period of time.

It is convenient to define an indicator random variable, X, with $X = 1$ if the item is functioning and $X = 0$ otherwise. The reliability of an item can then be defined as the expected value of X or, equivalently, as $P(X = 1)$.

Example 1: An item has a probability p of being operable, and probability $1 - p$ of being nonoperable. Its reliability is

$$1 \cdot p + 0 \cdot (1 - p) = p. \tag{1}$$

Example 2: The lifetime, T, of an item has a cumulative distribution function F. If "operable" means failure-free operation for a duration t, and if one defines an indicator function, X, by

$$X(u) = \begin{cases} 0 & \text{for } u < t \\ 1 & \text{for } u \geq t, \end{cases}$$

then the reliability function is

$$\int_0^t 0 \cdot dF(u) + \int_t^\infty 1 \cdot dF(u) = 1 - F(t) \tag{2}$$

Note that the result of Example 2 follows from that of Example 1. In Example 2, the probability of the item being operable, denoted by p in Example 1, is $1 - F(t)$. Additional definitions of reliability may be found in Barlow and Proschan [1965, pp. 5-8].

We have used the word "item." It may be that the item of interest is a system formed of components. The system reliability may then have to be computed from the component reliabilities, their interrelations, and from knowledge of the system structure. The structure may be so complex that exact computation of the system reliability is a prohibitive task. In this case, one would like to be able to compute upper and lower bounds. Also, one may want to resort to computer simulation. Some of the system's components may be "backed-up" by redundancy, spare parts, repair facilities, and by the corresponding ability to replace and/or maintain components, or modules thereof, at or before failure. These latter contingencies will be treated in this chapter, and the one on Maintenance and Replacement.

Furthermore, probabilities, the form of probability distributions, or the values of pertinent parameters may not be known and must be estimated from relevant data. Unfortunately, space restrictions preclude our treating any of these *statistical* aspects of the reliability problem. (see Mann, et al. [1974]).

We begin by considering the relation between a system and its components. We examine first the *deterministic* relationship by which the functioning of the system is determined from that of its components.

2. STRUCTURAL PROPERTIES OF SYSTEMS

Consider a system having n components $c_1, \ldots, c_n$. Define binary indicator variables $x_i, i = 1, \ldots, n$ by

$$x_i = \begin{cases} 1 & \text{if } c_i \text{ is functioning} \\ 0 & \text{otherwise} \end{cases}$$

and the binary indicator variable ϕ by

$$\phi = \begin{cases} 1 & \text{if the system is functioning} \\ 0 & \text{otherwise.} \end{cases}$$

We assume sufficient knowledge of the system to be able to determine its state from that of all its components. Thus we write

$$\phi = \phi(x),$$

where $x = (x_1, \ldots, x_n)$ is the component state vector. The function $\phi(x)$ is called the *structure function* of the system.

Example 3: A series system $\overset{\bullet}{c_1}\ \overset{\bullet}{c_2} \cdots \overset{\bullet}{c_n}$ functions if and only if each of its components functions. Its structure function is

$$\phi(x) = \prod_1^n x_i = \min(x_1, \ldots, x_n) \tag{3}$$

Example 4: A *parallel* system functions if and only if at least one of its components functions. Its structure function is

$$\phi(x) = \max(x_1, \ldots, x_n) = 1 - \prod_1^n (1 - x_i) \equiv \bigvee_{i=1}^n x_i \tag{4}$$

Example 5: A k-out-of-n system functions if and only if at least k of its n components function. (Thus a series system is an n-out-of-n system, and a parallel system is a 1-out-of-n system.) Its structure function is

$$\phi(x) = \begin{cases} 1 & \text{if } \sum_1^n x_i \geqslant k \\ 0 & \text{otherwise,} \end{cases} \tag{5}$$

or

$$\phi(x) = \bigvee x_{i_1}\, x_{i_2} \cdots x_{i_k} = \max(x_{i_1}, x_{i_2}, \ldots, x_{i_k})$$

where the operation $\vee$, and the maximization is taken over all combinations $(i_1, i_2, \ldots, i_k)$ of k numbers selected from the first n integers. The structure function of a 2-out-of-3 system can be written variously as

$$\phi(x_1, x_2, x_3) = \begin{cases} 1 & \text{if } x_1 + x_2 + x_3 \geqslant 2 \\ 0 & \text{otherwise,} \end{cases}$$

or

$$\phi(x_1, x_2, x_3) = x_1 x_2 \vee x_1 x_3 \vee x_2 x_3$$
$$= 1 - (1 - x_1 x_2)(1 - x_1 x_3)(1 - x_2 x_3)$$
$$= x_1 x_2 x_3 + x_1 x_2 (1 - x_3) + x_1 (1 - x_2) x_3 + (1 - x_1) x_2 x_3.$$

2.1 Coherent Systems

Before we can introduce the concept of a *coherent system*, some notation must be established.

The symbols $(1_i, x)$ and $(0_i, x)$ refer to the vector x with its i-th position replaced, if necessary, by a 1 or a 0, respectively. That is, $(1_i, x) = (x_1, \ldots, x_{i-1},$

$1, x_{i+1}, \ldots, x_n)$ and $(0_i, \mathbf{x}) = (x_1, \ldots, x_{i-1}, 0, x_{i+1}, \ldots, x_n)$. This notation permits the statement of a theorem on the *pivotal decomposition* of a structure function, a result which allows one to express a structure function of order n (i.e., a structure function for a system having n components) in terms of structure functions of order $n - 1$.

◀ (Pivotal Decomposition Theorem)[1] For any structure function ϕ or order n

$$\phi(\mathbf{x}) = x_i \, \phi(1_i, \mathbf{x}) + (1 - x_i) \, \phi(0_i, \mathbf{x}), \tag{6}$$

for all $\mathbf{x}$ and all $i = 1, 2, \ldots, n$.

By repeatedly applying Equation (6), one obtains the representation

$$\phi(\mathbf{x}) = \sum_{\mathbf{y}} \prod_{j=1}^{n} x_j^{y_j} (1 - x_j)^{1-y_j} \, \phi(\mathbf{y}) \tag{7}$$

where the sum is taken over all 2^n vectors $\mathbf{y}$ of order n.

If the functioning of a system does not depend on the functioning of a particular component, then that component is called *irrelevant* to the system. Specifically, the i-th component is irrelevant to the system with structure function ϕ if $\phi(1_i, \mathbf{x}) = \phi(0_i, \mathbf{x})$ for all $\mathbf{x}$. If a component is not irrelevant, it is called *relevant*.

We are now in a position to define a *coherent system* as one having no irrelevant components and whose structure function is increasing[2] in each argument.

Two basic results obtain for coherent systems.

◀ For a coherent structure ϕ of order n,

$$\prod_{1}^{n} x_i \leqslant \phi(\mathbf{x}) \leqslant \bigvee_{1}^{n} x_i. \tag{8}$$

This result states that a coherent system, with components $c_1, \ldots, c_n$, is at least as good as a system having these components arranged in series, and no better than a system having the components arranged in parallel.

For vectors of binary variables we introduce the notations:

$$\mathbf{x} \vee \mathbf{y} = (x_1 \vee y_1, \ldots, x_n \vee y_n),$$

$$\mathbf{x} \cdot \mathbf{y} = (x_1 y_1, \ldots, x_n y_n).$$

Recall that for binary variables x and y, $x \vee y = \max(x, y)$ and $xy = \min(x, y)$.

◀ For any coherent structure ϕ

$$\text{(a)} \quad \phi(\mathbf{x} \vee \mathbf{y}) \geqslant \phi(\mathbf{x}) \vee \phi(\mathbf{y}), \tag{9}$$

$$\text{(b)} \quad \phi(\mathbf{x} \cdot \mathbf{y}) \leqslant \phi(\mathbf{x}) \, \phi(\mathbf{y}). \tag{10}$$

Expression (9) states that parallel replication is at least as effective at the component level as at the system level. Expression (10) states that series replication is at least as effective at the system level as at the component level. We give a simple illustration for each of these statements.

For the first statement, consider a two-component series system (Figure 1), with state vector $\mathbf{x} = (x_1, x_2)$ and another pair of components with state vector $\mathbf{y} = (y_1, y_2)$. (These latter components will be designated $1'$ and $2'$, respectively, in sketches). Parallel replication at the component level yields the schematic A, while parallel replication at the system level yields B. The structure of A will function for $\mathbf{x} = (1, 0)$, $\mathbf{y} = (0, 1)$ and for $\mathbf{x} = (0, 1)$, $\mathbf{y} = (1, 0)$, while that of B does not function for either of these pairs of state vectors. For all other pairs of state vectors $\mathbf{x}, \mathbf{y}$, the performance of A and B is identical.

The second statement can be illustrated by considering a two-component parallel system (Figure 1). With the same notation as above, series replication at the system level yields C, while replicating in series at the component level yields D (Figure 1). We observe that C is the same as A, that D is the same as B, that A is always as good as B, and therefore, that C is always at least as good as D.

In order to proceed, we need some additional terminology and notation. By $\mathbf{y} < \mathbf{x}$ is meant that $y_i \leqslant x_i$ for each i, and $y_i < x_i$ for some $i, i = 1, \ldots, n$.

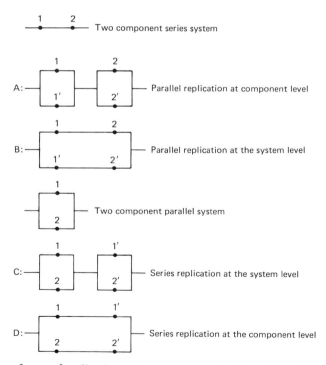

Fig. 1. Various forms of replication in two component series and parallel systems.

Consider a coherent structure function ϕ, the associated set of components $\{c_1, \ldots, c_n\}$, and the corresponding state vector $x = (x_1, \ldots, x_n)$. Define $C_0(x) = \{c_i | x_i = 0\}$ and $C_1(x) = \{c_i | x_i = 1\}$. x is called a *path vector* if $\phi(x) = 1$; $C_1(x)$ is the corresponding *path set*. x is a *minimal path vector* if it is a path vector and if for any vector y, with $y < x, \phi(y) = 0$. The corresponding $C_1(x)$ is a *minimal path set*. Note that a minimal path set is a minimal set of components whose functioning guarantees that the system functions.

x is called a *cut vector* if $\phi(x) = 0$; $C_0(x)$ is the corresponding *cut set*. x is a *minimal cut vector* if it is a cut vector and, if for any vector y with $y > x, \phi(y) = 1$. The corresponding $C_0(x)$ is a *minimal cut set*. Note that a minimal cut set is a minimal set of components whose failure causes the system to fail.

Denote the number of minimal path sets by p and the j-th minimal path set by P_j. Denote the number of minimal cut sets by k and the j-th minimal cut set by K_j.

Associated with P_j we define the *jth minimal path series structure function*, α_j, by

$$\alpha_j(x) = \prod_{c_i \in P_j} x_j. \tag{11}$$

We see that α_j is the structure function of a series arrangement of the components in the j-th minimal path set. That is, it takes the value 1 if all the components in P_j function and 0 otherwise.

Since the structure ϕ will function if and only if at least one if its minimal path structures functions, ϕ can be represented as a parallel arrangement of the minimal path structures, α_j, and we can write

$$\phi(x) = \bigvee_{j=1}^{p} \alpha_j(x) = 1 - \prod_{i=1}^{p} [1 - \alpha_j(x)]. \tag{12}$$

In the same way, we associate with K_j the *jth minimal cut parallel structure*, β_j, defined by

$$\beta_j(x) = \bigvee_{c_i \in K_j} x_i. \tag{13}$$

The function β_j, taking the value 0 if all the components in K_j fail and 1 otherwise, is the structure function of a parallel arrangement of the components of K_j.

Since the structure ϕ fails if and only if at least one of its minimal cut structures fails, we can represent ϕ as a series arrangement of the minimal cut structures, β_j, and write

$$\phi(x) = \prod_{j=1}^{k} \beta_j(x). \tag{14}$$

3. RELIABILITY OF COHERENT SYSTEMS

We now proceed beyond the deterministic properties of coherent structures and discuss their probabilistic properties—specifically their reliability. We give exact expressions for, and bounds on, system reliability, based on component reliabilities. First, we consider the situation in which the components are statistically independent of one another.

Denote the reliability of component c_i by p_i, and that of the system by h. As noted at the outset of this Chapter, $p_i = P(X_i = 1) = E(X_i)$ and $h = P[\phi(\mathbf{x}) = 1] = E[\phi(\mathbf{x})]$. If the components are independent, system reliability is a function of the component reliabilities and we will write $h = h(\mathbf{p})$. $h(\mathbf{p})$ is called the *reliability function* (of the structure ϕ). If the components are statistically dependent, then system reliability is not solely a function of $\mathbf{p}$, and we will then not write $h(\mathbf{p})$.

It follows immediately from the pivotal decomposition theorem (Equation 6) that

$$h(\mathbf{p}) = p_i h(1_i, \mathbf{p}) + (1 - p_i) h(0_i, \mathbf{p}), \tag{15}$$

and it can be shown, from Equation 15, that $h(\mathbf{p})$ is a strictly increasing function of each of its arguments p_i, for $0 < p_i < 1$.

The minimal cut and minimal path (hereafter called min cut and min path) representations of the structure function, as well as the pivotal decomposition, all provide a way to compute the reliability of a coherent system with independent components. From Equations 12 and 11 we have

$$h(\mathbf{p}) = E[\phi(\mathbf{x})] = E\left[\bigvee_{j=1}^{p} \prod_{c_j \in P_j} X_i\right]; \tag{16}$$

from Equations 14 and 13 we have

$$h(\mathbf{p}) = E\left[\prod_{j=1}^{k} \bigvee_{c_i \in K_j} X_i\right]; \tag{17}$$

and from Equation 7 we get

$$h(\mathbf{p}) = \sum_{\mathbf{y}} \phi(\mathbf{y}) \prod_{j=1}^{n} p_j^{y_j} (1 - p_j)^{1-y_j}, \tag{18}$$

the sum being taken over all 2^n vectors $\mathbf{y}$ with 0 and 1 coordinates. In expanding the right hand sides of Equations 16 and 17, one uses the fact that $X_i^2 = X_i$ and the independence of the components. In view of the latter, the expectation of a product is the product of expectations.

We can see that the calculation of system reliability can be a considerable chore, even under the simplifying assumption of independence of components. Thus, we need to consider bounds on system reliability.

3.1 Associated Random Variables

Before we can discuss bounds, we must introduce the notion of *associated* random variables, an extension of the idea of statistical dependence. Random variables, $T_1, \ldots, T_n$, not necessarily binary, are defined to be associated if, for all pairs of increasing, binary-valued functions Γ and Δ,

$$\text{cov}\ [\Gamma\ (\mathbf{T}), \Delta\ (\mathbf{T})] = E\ [\Gamma\ (\mathbf{T})\ \Delta\ (\mathbf{T})] - E\ [\Gamma\ (\mathbf{T})]\ E\ [\Delta\ (\mathbf{T})] \geq 0.$$

Associated random variables satisfy these properties:

(1) Any subset of associated random variables is associated;
(2) If two sets of associated random variables are mutually independent, then their union is a set of associated random variables;
(3) The set consisting of a single random variable is associated;
(4) Independent random variables are associated;
(5) Increasing functions of associated random variables are associated.

Property (5) states that monotonic systems, composed of associated (in particular, independent) components, are themselves associated. The min path (and min cut) structure functions of a coherent system are increasing in the component performance indicator variables $X_1, \ldots, X_n$. If these variables are associated, then the min path (and min cut) structure functions are associated. These facts are now used in connection with system reliability bounds.

3.2 Bounds on System Reliability

◀ If $X_1, \ldots, X_n$ are associated binary random variables, then

$$\text{(a)}\quad P\left(\prod_1^n X_i = 1\right) \geq \prod_1^n P(X_i = 1) \tag{19}$$

and

$$\text{(b)}\ P(\vee\ _1^n X_i = 1) \leq \vee_1^p P(X_i = 1). \tag{20}$$

Expression 19 states that a lower bound for the reliability of a series system composed of associated components is furnished by treating the components as though they were independent. Expression 20 states that an upper bound for the reliability of a parallel system composed of associated components is furnished by treating the components as though they were independent.

The crude bounds of the next Theorem follow directly from Expression (8) and Expressions (19) and (20).

◀ For a coherent system ϕ of associated components having reliabilities $p_1, \ldots, p_n$

$$\prod_1^n p_i \leq P\ [\phi(\mathbf{X}) = 1] \leq \vee_1^n p_i \tag{21}$$

Better bounds, using the min path and min cut representations of the structure, are given next.[3]

◄ Let: ϕ be a coherent structure of associated components; $\alpha_1(\underline{x}), \ldots, \alpha_p(\underline{x})$ be the min path structures of ϕ; and $\beta_1(\mathbf{x}), \ldots, \beta_k(\mathbf{x})$ be the min cut structures of ϕ. Then

$$\prod_1^k P[\beta_j(\mathbf{X}) = 1] \leqslant P[\phi(\mathbf{X}) = 1] \leqslant \vee_1^p P[\alpha_j(\mathbf{X}) = 1]. \tag{22}$$

If the components of ϕ are independent, then

$$\prod_{j=1}^k \vee_{c_j \,\epsilon\, K_j} p_i \leqslant P[\phi(\mathbf{X}) = 1] \leqslant \vee_{j=1}^p \prod_{c_i \,\epsilon\, P_j} p_i. \tag{23}$$

The bounds given in Expression 23 are more explicit, but weaker, than those of Expression 22.

3.3 Modular Decomposition

Finally, while by no means exhausting this subject, we mention that easier computation of exact system reliability, and improved lower bounds on system reliability, can be obtained by decomposing a system into disjoint subsystems or *modules* (see Bodin [1970]). The overall system reliability is computed, or bounded, via the reliability of these modules.

The reliability analysis of a complex system can be made in the following way. Decompose the system into separate functional subsystems, each subsystem into components, and each component into its individual parts. Using Expression (22) or (23), a lower bound on component reliability can be calculated from the reliability of its parts; using these expressions again, a lower bound on subsystem reliability can be calculated from the lower bounds on component reliabilities; finally, from the lower bounds on subsystem reliability, these expressions can be used to get a lower bound on system reliability. It can be shown that this procedure yields a lower bound on system reliability at least as good as that furnished by the min cut representation of the system itself.

Bodin [1970] also gives upper bounds on system reliability via a modular decomposition of the system. A general reference for Sections 2 and 3 is Barlow and Proschan [1974, Chapters 1 and 2]; cf. also the references cited therein.

4. THE TIME-TO-FAILURE AND RELATED RANDOM VARIABLES

Denote by F the cumulative distribution function (CDF) of time-to-failure of some stochastically failing item, and $1 - F$ by $\overline{F}$. ($\overline{F}$ is the survival probability or reliability function of the item). As time-to-failure is a non-negative, random variable, we shall assume $F(0-) = 0$.

The (conditional) probability that an item of age t will survive an additional time x is

$$\overline{F}(x|t) = \frac{\overline{F}(t+x)}{\overline{F}(t)}, \quad \text{for } \overline{F}(t) > 0. \tag{24}$$

The (conditional) probability of failure between times t and $t + x$, given survival to age t, is

$$F(x|t) = 1 - \overline{F}(x|t) = \frac{F(t+x) - F(t)}{\overline{F}(t)}. \tag{25}$$

The (conditional) *failure rate* function r is defined by

$$r(t) = \lim_{x \to 0} F(x|t)/x. \tag{26}$$

If F has a density f, then

$$r(t) = f(t)/\overline{F}(t). \tag{27}$$

Synonyms for the term failure rate are hazard rate, intensity rate, and force of mortality.

The following relations are easily seen to hold:

$$r(t) = -\frac{d}{dt} \log [\overline{F}(t)], \tag{28}$$

$$\overline{F}(t) = \exp \left[-\int_0^t r(x)\, dx \right], \tag{29}$$

$$f(t) = r(t) \exp \left[-\int_0^t r(x)\, dx \right]. \tag{30}$$

For small Δt, the quantity $r(t)\Delta t$ can be interpreted as the conditional probability of failure in the interval $(t, t + \Delta t)$, given survival to age t.

4.1 The Exponential Distribution

An item which does not age stochastically is one whose conditional probability of surviving an additional time x is the same regardless of its age t. That is, for all $x, t \geqslant 0$, and

$$\overline{F}(x|t) = \overline{F}(x). \tag{31}$$

This can also be written as

$$\overline{F}(t+x) = \overline{F}(t)\,\overline{F}(x). \tag{32}$$

The only continuous survival probability function satisfying this equation is

$$\overline{F}(x) = \exp(-\lambda x), \qquad \lambda > 0, \quad x \geqslant 0. \tag{33}$$

This is the exponential distribution. It, and only it, has a constant failure rate, λ. For X having the exponential distribution with failure rate λ, $E(X^n) = n!/\lambda^n$. In particular, the mean is $1/\lambda$ and the variance is $1/\lambda^2$. The density function for the exponential distribution is

$$f(x) = \begin{cases} \lambda \exp(-\lambda x), & x \geqslant 0 \\ 0, & x < 0. \end{cases} \tag{34}$$

A series system composed of n independent, exponentially distributed components, the i-th of which has failure rate λ_i, has itself an exponential distribution with failure rate $\sum \lambda_i$, and mean $1/\sum \lambda_i$. This can be seen as follows. Let T be the system time-to-failure and T_i the time-to-failure of the i-th component. Then

$$P(T > t) = P[\min(T_1, \ldots, T_n) > t] = P[T_1 > t, \ldots, T_n > t]$$
$$= \prod P[T_i > t] = \prod \exp(-\lambda_i t) = \exp\left(-\sum \lambda_i t\right).$$

A parallel system composed of n independent, exponentially distributed components does not itself have an exponential distribution. The distribution, and its mean, can be easily calculated.

$$P(T \leqslant t) = P[\max(T_1, \ldots, T_n) \leqslant t] = P[T_1 \leqslant t, \ldots, T_n \leqslant t]$$

$$= \prod_1^n P(T_i \leqslant t) = \prod_1^n [1 - \exp(-\lambda_i t)]. \tag{35}$$

$$E(T) = \sum_1^n (1/\lambda_i) - \sum_{i<j} [1/(\lambda_i + \lambda_j)] + \sum_{i<j<k} [1/(\lambda_i + \lambda_j + \lambda_k)] - \cdots \pm 1 \Big/ \sum_1^n \lambda_i. \tag{36}$$

In the special case $\lambda_1 = \cdots = \lambda_n = \lambda$ (say),

$$E(T) = \frac{1}{\lambda}\left(1 + \frac{1}{2} + \cdots + \frac{1}{n}\right). \tag{37}$$

4.2 The IFR and DFR Classes of Distributions

An item which ages stochastically can be characterized as one whose conditional survival probability function decreases with age. That is,

$$\overline{F}(x|t) \text{ decreases in } t \geqslant 0 \text{ for each } x \geqslant 0. \tag{38}$$

If F has a density, this is equivalent to the failure rate function r increasing. We say F belongs to the class of functions with increasing failure rate (or that F is IFR), if F satisfies (38).

An item which improves stochastically with age can be characterized as one whose conditional survival probability function increases with age. That is,

$$\overline{F}(x|t) \quad \text{increases in} \quad t \geq 0 \quad \text{for each} \quad x \geq 0. \tag{39}$$

If F has a density, this is equivalent to the failure rate function r decreasing. We say F belongs to the class of functions with decreasing failure rate function (or that F is DFR) if F satisfies (39).

Mixtures[4] of exponential distributions are DFR. Certain mechanical parts increase in strength as they age ("work-hardening"), and thus have a DFR distribution. The early life of some items (e.g., many forms of animal life—including humans and some electronic components) exhibit a decreasing failure rate.

The IFR class is closed under the formation of series systems. That is, a series system is IFR if all its components are IFR. The DFR class also has a similar property; i.e. a series system is DFR if all its components are DFR.

A failure rate function which is initially decreasing, followed by a period of time during which it is relatively constant, after which it increases, is sometimes seen in practice. The three phases are called, respectively "infant mortality," "useful life," and "wearout." The form of the graph of such a function has been termed "bathtub-shaped."

4.3 Some Time-to-Failure Distributions with Monotone Failure Rate

Three distributions, often used in reliability applications and having monotone failure rate function, are the Weibull, gamma, and truncated normal. We define them and give a few of their properties.

The CDF of the *Weibull* distribution, with scale parameter λ and shape parameter α, can be written as

$$F(t) = 1 - \exp\left[-(\lambda t)^\alpha\right], \quad \text{for} \quad t \geq 0, \quad \text{and} \quad \lambda, \alpha > 0. \tag{40}$$

Its failure rate function is

$$r(t) = \alpha\lambda(\lambda t)^{\alpha - 1}, \quad \text{for} \quad t > 0. \tag{41}$$

Thus, the Weibull distribution is IFR for $\alpha \geq 1$, DFR for $0 < \alpha \leq 1$, and it coincides with the exponential distribution for $\alpha = 1$.

The mean and variance of the Weibull distribution are

$$(1/\lambda)^{1/\alpha} \; \Gamma\left(\frac{1}{\alpha} + 1\right) \quad \text{and} \quad (1/\lambda)^{2/\alpha} \left[\Gamma\left(\frac{2}{\alpha} + 1\right) - \Gamma^2\left(\frac{1}{\alpha} + 1\right)\right],$$

respectively.

The density of the *gamma* distribution, with scale parameter λ and shape parameter α, is given by

$$g(t) = \frac{\lambda^\alpha t^{\alpha - 1}}{\Gamma(\alpha)} \exp(-\lambda t), \qquad \text{for } t \geqslant 0 \text{ and with } \lambda, \alpha > 0. \qquad (42)$$

For positive integral values of α, the CDF of the gamma distribution can be written as

$$G(t) = 1 - \sum_{i=0}^{\alpha - 1} \frac{(\lambda t)^i}{i!} \exp(-\lambda t), \qquad \text{for } t \geqslant 0. \qquad (43)$$

(Note that this gives the gamma CDF in terms of the CDF of the Poisson distribution).

Also, for 2α being a positive integer (say $m = 2\alpha$), $F(2\lambda t)$ is the CDF of the chi-square distribution, with m degrees of freedom. More generally, the gamma CDF has been tabulated by Pearson [1934] and by Harter [1964]. The sum of n independent exponentially distributed random variables, each with failure rate λ, has the gamma distribution with scale parameter λ and shape parameter n. The mean and variance of the gamma distribution are α / λ and α / λ^2, respectively.

The reciprocal of the failure rate function for the gamma distribution can be written

$$1/r(t) = \int_0^\infty (1 + u/t)^{\alpha - 1} \exp(-\lambda u) \, du. \qquad (43)$$

From this it follows that the gamma distribution is DFR for $0 < \alpha \leqslant 1$, IFR for $\alpha \geqslant 1$, and coincides with the exponential distribution for $\alpha = 1$.

The density of the *truncated normal* distribution is

$$f(t) = \frac{1}{a\sigma\sqrt{2\pi}} \exp[-(t - \mu)^2 / (2\sigma^2)], \qquad t \geqslant 0, \quad \sigma > 0 \qquad (44)$$

where

$$a = \int_0^\infty \frac{1}{\sigma\sqrt{2\pi}} \exp[-(t - \mu)^2 / (2\sigma^2)] \, dt.$$

The constant a is a normalizing constant which makes $\int_0^\infty f(t) \, dt = 1$. If μ is more than three times σ, a is essentially equal to 1, and may, for the most practical purposes, be omitted, thereby making (44) the usual (untruncated) normal density with mean μ and variance σ^2.

The truncated normal distribution is IFR. The demonstration of this fact ordinarily proceeds via properties of a class of functions called the Pólya frequency functions of order 2 (PF$_2$ for short). We will not pursue this here, and the interested reader may consult Barlow and Proschan [1965, 1974], or Karlin [1968].

4.4   Other Classes of Distribution Functions

While one might think that a coherent structure composed of components with IFR lifetimes would, itself, have an IFR life distribution, this turns out not to be the case. Birnbaum, Esary, and Marshall [1966] have shown that the smallest class of distribution functions F, containing the class of all exponential distributions and closed under the formulation of coherent structures, is the one for which $-(1/t) \log \overline{F}(t)$ increases with $t \geqslant 0$. If F has a density, this is equivalent

to $-(1/t) \displaystyle\int_0^t r(x) \, dx$ increasing with $t \geqslant 0$ and, for this reason, this class is called

the class of distribution functions with increasing failure rate average, or the IFRA class. Note, however, that a distribution function F need not possess a failure rate function in order to be in the IFRA class.

As an IFR distribution is also IFRA, and an exponential distribution is IFR, coherent structures composed of exponential or IFR components have an IFRA lifetime.

By analogy, the DFRA class of distribution functions is that for which $-(1/t) \log \overline{F}(t)$ decreases in $t \geqslant 0$. While the DFRA class is not closed under the formulation of coherent structures, it is closed under the mixture operation[4] and under the formation of series system. The DFRA class of distribution has, to date, not found significant application in the field of reliability.

We next discuss four additional classes of distribution functions: the New Better Than Used (NBU), New Worse Than Used (NWU), New Better Than Used in Expectation (NBUE), and New Worse Than Used in Expectation (NWUE) classes. These arise, in a natural way, in the consideration of replacement policies. Definitions follow.

A distribution F is NBU (NWU) if

$$\overline{F}(x + y) \leqslant (\geqslant) \overline{F}(x) \overline{F}(y), \qquad \text{for} \quad x, y \geqslant 0. \tag{45}$$

This is equivalent to requiring that the conditional probability $\overline{F}(y|x) = \overline{F}(x + y)/\overline{F}(x)$, that an item of age x will survive an additional time y is less (greater) than the probability $\overline{F}(y)$ that a new item will survive a time y. Equality holds in (45) for, and only for, an exponential distribution.

A distribution is NBUE (NWUE) if

(a) F has finite (finite or infinite) mean μ, and

(b) $\displaystyle\int_t^\infty \overline{F}(x) \, dx \leqslant (\geqslant) \mu \overline{F}(t)$ for $t \geqslant 0$. $\qquad$ (46)

This is equivalent to requiring that the mean residual lifetime of an item of age

$t, \displaystyle\int_t^\infty [\overline{F}(x)/\overline{F}(t)] \, dx$, is less (greater) than the mean lifetime μ of a new item.

The following chain of strict inclusions holds for the various classes of distributions mentioned in this Chapter:

$$\text{IFR} \subset \text{IFRA} \subset \text{NBU} \subset \text{NBUE};\tag{47}$$

and

$$\text{DFR} \subset \text{DFRA} \subset \text{NWU} \subset \text{NWUE}.\tag{48}$$

4.5 Renewal Processes

Consider a continuing process in which an item is immediately replaced, upon failure, by a new item with the same life distribution as its predecessor, and in which all lifetimes are independent. Let $F(t)$ be the common lifetime CDF, and let $F^{(k)}(t)$ denote the k-fold convolution of $F(t)$ with itself. For CDF's of nonnegative random variables,

$$F^{(1)}(t) = F(t),$$

$$F^{(k)}(t) = \int_0^t F^{(k-1)}(t - x)\, dF(x).\tag{49}$$

$F^{(k)}(t)$ is the distribution of $X_1 + \cdots + X_k$, where $X_1, \ldots, X_k$ are independent, and have common CDF, $F(t)$. Suppose $S_1, S_2, \ldots$ are the successive replacement times (so that the successive operating times are $S_1, S_2 - S_1, S_3 - S_2, \ldots$). Let $N(t)$ denote the number of replacements made in $[0, t]$; $N(t)$ is a non-negative integer valued random variable with

$$P[N(t) = 0] = P[X_1 > t] = \overline{F}(t),\tag{50}$$

$$P[N(t) = k] = P[X_1 + \cdots + X_k \leq t \text{ and } X_1 + \cdots + X_{k+1} > t]$$

$$= F^{(k)}(t) - F^{(k+1)}(t), k \geq 1.\tag{51}$$

The stochastic process $\{N(t): t \geq 0\}$ is called a *renewal counting process*. The expected value of $N(t)$ is denoted by $M(t)$ and is called the *renewal function*. It is easy to see that

$$M(t) = \sum_{k=0}^{\infty} kP\,[N(t) = k] = \sum_{k=1}^{\infty} F^{(k)}(t).\tag{52}$$

The *Poisson process with rate* λ can be defined as the renewal counting process for exponential lifetimes having failure rate λ. If $F(t)$ is the exponential distribution with failure rate λ, then the k-fold convolution $F^{(k)}(t)$ is the gamma distribution with shape parameter λ and scale parameter k. Using this fact and (43), one sees that

$$P[N(t) = k] = (\lambda t)^k \exp(-\lambda t)/k!;\tag{53}$$

i.e., $N(t)$ has a Poisson distribution with mean λt. Thus, for the exponential distribution with failure rate λ,

$$M(t) = \lambda t. \tag{54}$$

Renewal analysis for the (untruncated) normal distribution does not yield such simple formulas as (53) and (54), but is numerically quite tractable, since the k-fold convolution of a normal distribution with mean μ and variance σ^2 is the normal distribution with mean $k\mu$ and variance $k\sigma^2$. The renewal function for the Weibull distribution has been discussed by Leadbetter and Smith [1963] and by Lomnicki [1966].

If $N(t)$ counts the number of renewals of a stochastically failing item with CDF F having mean μ and variance σ^2, then $N(t)$ has asympototically (in t) the normal distribution, with mean t/μ and variance $\sigma^2 t/\mu^3$. Other important asymptotic results concerning $N(t)$ and $M(t)$ follow.

◄
$$\lim_{t \to \infty} N(t)/t \to 1/\mu \quad (a.s.).^5 \tag{55}$$

◄ *Blackwell's Theorem:* If F is a nonlattice[6] distribution function with mean μ,

$$\lim_{t \to \infty} [M(t + h) - M(t)] = h/\mu. \tag{56}$$

◄ *The Key Renewal Theorem:* If g is of bounded variation on $[0, \infty]$, and F is nonlattice with mean μ,

$$\lim_{t \to \infty} \int_0^t g(t - u)\, dM(u) = \frac{1}{\mu} \int_0^\infty g(u)\,du. \tag{57}$$

◄ *The Elementary Renewal Theorem:*

$$\lim_{t \to \infty} M(t)/t = 1/\mu. \tag{58}$$

Additional material concerning renewal theory can be found in Cox [1962], Smith [1958], and in the chapter by Smith on stochastic processes (Volume I, chapter 3-1). Applications of renewal theory to reliability and maintenance are to be found in Barlow and Proschan [1965, 1974] and in Gnedenko, *et al.* [1969]. We also mention a few in the sequel.

5. SOME RELIABILITY BOUNDS

We present some bounds on reliability, $\overline{F}(t)$, under various assumptions concerning the family to which F belongs, as well as bounds applicable in renewal analysis, and in the reliability of series, parallel, and, more generally, coherent systems.

5.1   Bounds on $\overline{F}(t)$

The first bound compares IFRA and DFRA survival probabilities having a prescribed quantile with the survival probability of an exponential distribution having the same quantile.

◄ Let F be IFRA(DFRA), with p-th quantile ξ_p (i.e., $F(\xi_p) = p$), and let $\alpha = -[\log(1 - p)]/\xi_p$.

Then

$$\overline{F}(t) \begin{cases} \geqslant (\leqslant) \exp(-\alpha t) & \text{for } 0 \leqslant t \leqslant \xi_p, \\ \leqslant (\geqslant) \exp(-\alpha t) & \text{for } t \geqslant \xi_p. \end{cases} \tag{59}$$

Next, we give lower and upper bounds on IFRA survival probabilities.

◄ Let F be IFRA with mean μ_1. Then, for fixed $t > 0$,

$$\overline{F}(t) \leqslant \begin{cases} 1, & \text{for } t \leqslant \mu_1 \\ \exp(-wt), & \text{for } t > \mu_1, \end{cases} \tag{60}$$

where $w > 0$ is a function of t which satisfies

$$1 - w\mu_1 = \exp(-wt). \tag{61}$$

◄ Let F be IFRA with r-th moment μ_r,

$$\left(\mu_r = \int_0^\infty t^r \, dF(t) = r \int_0^\infty t^{r-1} \overline{F}(t) \, dt \right).$$

Then

$$\overline{F}(t) \geqslant \begin{cases} \min\left[\exp(-b_t t), \exp(-ct) \right], & \text{for } t < \mu_r^{1/r} \\ 0, & \text{for } t > \mu_r^{1/r}, \end{cases} \tag{62}$$

where b_t satisfies the equation

$$t^r [1 - \exp(-b_t t)] + \int_t^\infty b_t x^r \exp(-b_t x) \, dx = \mu_r \tag{63}$$

and

$$c = (\mu_r/r!)^{1/r} \tag{64}$$

The next bound compares IFR survival probabilities having a prescribed r-th moment with a corresponding exponential survival probability.

◄ Let F be a continuous IFR distribution with prescribed r-th moment μ_r, and let $\lambda_r = \mu_r/r!, r \geqslant 1$. Then

$$\overline{F}(t) \geqslant \begin{cases} \exp\left[-t/\lambda_r^{1/r}\right], & \text{for } t < \mu_r^{1/r} \\ 0, & \text{for } t \geqslant \mu_r^{1/r} \end{cases} \tag{65}$$

This is a sharp bound.

If one knew any of the moments of F, it seems most reasonable to suppose that μ_1, the mean, would be known. This is the case $r = 1$ of (65) and yields the important result:

◄   Let F be IFR with mean μ_1. Then

$$\overline{F}(t) \geqslant \begin{cases} \exp\left(-t/\mu_1\right), & \text{for } t < \mu_1 \\ 0, & \text{for } t \geqslant \mu_1. \end{cases} \tag{66}$$

This is a sharp bound. Application of (66) will be made in the sequel.

Finally, we mention an upper bound on DFR survival probabilities.

◄   Let F be DFR with mean μ_1. Then

$$\overline{F}(t) \leqslant \begin{cases} \exp\left(-t/\mu_1\right), & \text{for } t \leqslant \mu_1 \\ \mu_1/(te), & \text{for } t \geqslant \mu_1. \end{cases} \tag{67}$$

This bound is sharp.

Proofs of these bounds are given by Barlow and Proschan [1965 and 1970]. They also give other related results including bounds on moments, a tabulation of the IFRA lower bound of (62) for $\mu_1 = 1$, and a graph comparing the IFRA lower bound of (62) with the IFR lower bound of (66) for $t < \mu_1 = 1$. (As might be expected, since the IFR assumption is more restrictive than the IFRA assumption, the IFR lower bound exceeds the IFRA lower bound). For other results, see Barlow and Marshall [1964, 1965, 1967] and Barlow [1965].

5.2   Bounds in Renewal Analysis

If an item has life distribution F, and if it is replaced instantly upon failure by an independent, new item having the same life distribution, how many replacement items should be stocked so as to insure, with probability $1 - \alpha$, that there will be no interruption of service during the interval $[0, t]$? (This has been termed "the spare parts" problem). The number of replacements that will be required was denoted $N(t)$ in Section 4.5.

If F is the exponential distribution with mean μ, then it follows from (53) that for $n = 1, 2, \ldots$

$$P[N(t) > n] = \sum_{j=n+1}^{\infty} (t/\mu)^j \left[\exp\left(-t/\mu\right)\right]/j!. \tag{68}$$

These are Poisson probabilities which are widely tabulated; e.g. by Molina [1942] or General Electric Co. [1962].

The probability of a shortage, given that n spare items are stocked, is given by (68). Thus, the solution to the spare parts problem is the smallest integer n^*, satisfying $P[N(t) > n^*] \leq \alpha$.

If, instead of assuming that F is exponential, we assume merely that F is IFR with mean μ, it follows from (66) that

$$P[N(t) > n] \leq \sum_{j=n+1}^{\infty} (t/\mu)^j [\exp(-t/\mu)]/j! \quad \text{for } 0 \leq t < \mu \quad (69)$$

This tells us that the Poisson distribution gives a conservative estimate for the probability of more than n failures in $[0, t]$, for $t < \mu$ when F is IFR with mean μ.

Other bounds, valid for all $t \geq 0$ and for other classes of distribution, are given in the following result (Barlow and Proschan [1974]):

◄ Let F be continuous with $F(0) = 0$, and let $R(t) = -\log \overline{F}(t)$.

(a) If F is NBU (NWU), then

$$P[N(t) > n] \leq (\geq) \sum_{j=n+1}^{\infty} [R(t)]^j [\exp(-R(t))]/j! \quad \text{for } t \geq 0, n = 1, 2, \ldots$$

(70)

(b) If F is IFR (DFR), then

$$P[N(t) > n] \geq (\leq) \sum_{j=n+1}^{\infty} [nR(t/n)]^j [\exp(-nR(t/n))]/j$$

$$\text{for } t \geq 0, n = 1, 2, \ldots \quad (71)$$

An application of (70) can be made to the Weibull distribution (40) for $\alpha \geq 1$. For $\alpha \geq 1$, the Weibull is IFR and hence, also NBU. As $R(t) = (\lambda t)^\alpha$, we have from (70)

$$P[N(t) > n] \leq \sum_{j=n+1}^{\infty} [(\lambda t)^\alpha]^j [\exp(-(\lambda t)^\alpha)]/j \quad \text{for } t \geq 0, n = 1, 2, \ldots$$

(72)

The exact computation of $P[N(t) > n]$ for the Weibull can only be done numerically, so this bound, in terms of the Poisson distribution with rate $(\lambda t)^\alpha$, may be quite useful.

Finally, we present a number of bounds on $M(t) = E[N(t)]$, the renewal function.

◄ Let F be NBU (NWU). Then

$$M(h) \leqslant (\geqslant) M(t + h) - M(t). \tag{73}$$

◄ Let the underlying distribution F of a renewal process have finite mean μ. (a) Then

$$M(t) \geqslant (t/\mu) - 1 \quad \text{for} \quad t \geqslant 0 \tag{74}$$

(b) If F has finite mean μ and is NBUE (NWUE), then

$$M(t) \leqslant (\geqslant) t/\mu. \tag{75}$$

Thus, if F is NBUE (74) and (75) can be combined to yield

$$(t/\mu) - 1 \leqslant M(t) \leqslant t/\mu \quad \text{for} \quad t \geqslant 0. \tag{76}$$

It follows that if F is NBUE with mean μ, its renewal function can be approximated by $(t/\mu) - (1/2)$ and the error of approximation will be at most $1/2$ for all $t \geqslant 0$. Since $M(t)$ is, in general, hard to compute, the bounds of (76) can be quite useful.

5.3   Reliability Bounds for Coherent Systems

Consider a coherent system with reliability function h, and consisting of n independent components with IFR distributions $F_1, \ldots, F_n$, having known means $\mu_1, \ldots, \mu_n$. We seek a lower bound on the system reliability function at time t; i.e., on $h(\overline{F}_1(t), \ldots, \overline{F}_n(t))$. Since h is an increasing function of each of its arguments, and using the lower bound (66), we conclude

$$h(\overline{F}_1(t), \ldots, \overline{F}_n(t)) \geqslant h(\exp(-t/\mu_1), \ldots, \exp(-t/\mu_n))$$

$$\text{for} \quad t < \min(\mu_1, \ldots, \mu_n). \tag{77}$$

We do not actually need to know the system's reliability function, and we need only assume association, not independence, of the components in order to get a conservative lower bound on a system's reliability. Using (19) and (66), and denoting the system's structure function by ϕ, we obtain

$$h(\overline{F}_1(t), \ldots, \overline{F}_n(t)) = P[\phi(X_1(t), \ldots, X_n(t)) = 1]$$

$$\geqslant \prod_1^n P[X_i(t) = 1] \geqslant \prod_1^n \exp(-t/\mu_i)$$

$$= \exp\left(-t \sum_1^n (1/\mu_i)\right) \quad \text{for} \quad t < \min(\mu_1, \ldots, \mu_n). \tag{78}$$

The lower bound $\exp\left(-t \sum_1^n (1/\mu_i)\right)$ is one which also arises in the reliability estimation procedure called the "parts count" method. If a system consists of K different component types, with k_i of type i which has mean lifetime μ_i, the system reliability at time t is estimated as $\exp\left(-t\sum_1^K (k_i/\mu_i)\right)$. This estimate would be exactly correct if all the components were independent, connected in series, and had exponential lifetimes with components of type i having given lifetime μ_i, $i = 1, \ldots, K$. As we have just seen, the parts count method yields a conservative lower bound on system reliability for $t < \min(\mu_1, \ldots, \mu_K)$ if the system is coherent and the components are associated with IFR life distributions with components of type i having given means μ_i, $i = 1, \ldots, K$.

5.4 Mean Life of Series and Parallel Systems

The results of this section are excerpted from Marshall and Proschan [1970] and Barlow and Proschan [1974]. We will state two general results and then give applications of them to the subject of this section. Distributions F_i and G_i that are mentioned satisfy $F_i(0) = G_i(0) = 0$.

◄ Let

$$\int_0^t \bar{F}_i(x)\,dx \geq \int_0^t \bar{G}_i(x)\,dx \qquad \text{for all } t \geq 0, \text{ and } i = 1, \ldots, n \quad (79)$$

Then

$$\int_0^t \prod_1^n \bar{F}_i(x)\,dx \geq \int_0^t \prod_1^n \bar{G}_i(x)\,dx \qquad \text{for all } t \geq 0 \quad (80)$$

Since $\int_0^\infty \prod_1^n \bar{F}_i(x)\,dx$ is the mean life of a series system of independent components in which the i-th component has life distribution F_i, and similarly for $\int_0^\infty \prod_1^n \bar{G}_i(x)\,dx$, the above result tells us that if (79) is satisfied, the mean life of a series system of independent components is larger when the components have distributions $F_1, \ldots, F_n$ than when they have distributions $G_1, \ldots, G_n$.

The next result applies to parallel systems.

◄ Let

$$\int_t^\infty \bar{F}_i(x)\,dx \leq \int_t^\infty \bar{G}_i(x)\,dx \qquad \text{for all } t \geq 0 \text{ and } i = 1, \ldots, n. \quad (81)$$

Then

$$\int_t^\infty \left[1 - \prod_1^n F_i(x)\right] dx \leq \int_t^\infty \left[1 - \prod_1^n G_i(x)\right] dx \qquad \text{for all } t \geq 0. \quad (82)$$

Since $\int_0^\infty \left[1 - \prod_1^n F_i(x)\right] dx$ is the mean life of a parallel system of independent components in which the i-th component has distribution F_i, and similarly for $\int_0^\infty \left[1 - \prod_1^n G_i(x)\right] dx$, the above result tells us that if (81) is satisfied, the mean life of a parallel system of independent components is smaller when the components have distributions $F_1, \ldots, F_n$ than when they have distributions $G_1, \ldots, G_n$.

We next list four conditions under any one of which (79) and (81) hold, and therefore, also the conclusions stated after (80) and (81):

(1) F_i is IFRA, $\overline{G}_i(t) = \exp(-\lambda_i t)$;
(2) $\overline{F}_i(t) = \exp(-\lambda_i t)$, G_i is DFRA;
(3) F_i is a gamma distribution with shape parameter α_i;
    G_i is a gamma distribution with shape paramter $\beta_i \leq \alpha_i$;
(4) F_i is a Weibull distribution with shape parameter α_i;
    F_i is a Weibull distribution with shape parameter $\beta_i \leq \alpha_i$.

In all of (1)-(4), the distributions F_i and G_i must have the same mean.

Using the results stated just past expression (34), in (36) and (37), and conditions (1) or (2) above, we can state a number of interesting conclusions. We use $\mu_s(\mu_p)$ to denote the mean life of a series (parallel) system.

◄ Let n independent IFRA components have means $1/\lambda_1, \ldots, 1/\lambda_n$, respectively. Then

$$\mu_s \geq 1 \bigg/ \sum_1^n \lambda_i \tag{83}$$

and

$$\mu_p \leq (\text{right hand side of (36)}). \tag{84}$$

If $\lambda_1 = \ldots = \lambda_n = \lambda(\text{say})$, then

$$\mu_p \leq \frac{1}{\lambda}\left(1 + \frac{1}{2} + \cdots + \frac{1}{n}\right). \tag{85}$$

◄ Let n independent DFRA components have means $1/\lambda_1, \ldots, 1/\lambda_n$, respectively. Then

$$\mu_s \leqslant 1 \Big/ \sum_1^n \lambda_i \tag{86}$$

and

$$\mu_p \geqslant (\text{right hand side of (36)}). \tag{87}$$

If $\lambda_1 = \cdots = \lambda_n = \lambda$ (say), then

$$\lambda_p \geqslant \frac{1}{\lambda}\left(1 + \frac{1}{2} + \cdots + \frac{1}{n}\right). \tag{88}$$

The results (83) through (88) are actually valid under the more general assumption that the components are associated and with the i-th component having a marginal distribution with mean $1/\lambda_i$. Independence is a stronger assumption than is really needed.

6. INTERVAL RELIABILITY AND AVAILABILITY

6.1 Interval Reliability

Consider an item with life distribution F having mean μ. When the item fails, it is replaced instantly by another item having the same life distribution; all lives are independent. We seek the probability $p_t(u)$ that the item is working at time t and continues to work without failure for an additional interval of duration u.

It can be shown (cf., e.g., Gnedenko, et al. [1969] or Barlow and Proschan [1974]) that

$$p_t(u) = \overline{F}(t + u) + \int_0^t \overline{F}(t - x + u)\, dM(x), \tag{89}$$

where $M(x)$ is the renewal function corresponding to F.

Barlow and Proschan [1974] show that, if F is NBU (NWU), then

$$p_t(u) \leqslant (\geqslant)\, \overline{F}(u). \tag{90}$$

Using the Key Renewal Theorem (57), it can be shown that as t increases, the probability $p_t(u)$ no longer depends on t. The result is

$$p(u) = \lim_{t \to \infty} p_t(u) = \frac{1}{\mu} \int_u^\infty \overline{F}(x)\, dx. \tag{91}$$

It follows immediately from the definition of the classes that, if F is NBUE (NWUE), then

$$p(u) \leqslant (\geqslant)\, \overline{F}(u). \tag{92}$$

A random variable, $\gamma(t)$, the remaining life of an item in service at time t, which arises in renewal theory, also has survival probability $p_t(u)$. That is,

$$P[\gamma(t) > u] = p_t(u), \tag{93}$$

where

$$\gamma(t) = S_{N(t)+1} - t. \tag{94}$$

$N(t)$ is the number of renewals made in $[0, t]$ and S_n is the time at which the n-th renewal is made. Additional results are given by Barlow and Marshall [1967].

6.2 Availability

Once again, consider an item with life distribution F having mean μ. When the item fails, it is replaced by another item having the same life distribution. Now, however, we no longer assume that replacements are instantaneous but require a time which has distribution G with mean v. *Availability at time* t, $A(t)$, is defined to be the probability that, at time t, an item is in operation.

Let T_i be the duration of the i-th period in which the item is functioning and D_i be the duration of the i-th repair or replacement period. (D stands for "downtime.") While it is not necessary to assume that T_i and D_i are independent, we do require that the sequence $\{T_i + D_i\}_{i=1,2,\ldots}$ be mutually independent. Let H denote the common distribution of $T_i + D_i$, $i = 1, 2, \ldots$ and let M_H be the renewal function corresponding to H. Then it can be shown (e.g., Gnedenko, et al. [1969]) that

$$A(t) = \overline{F}(t) + \int_0^t \overline{F}(t - u)\, dM_H(u). \tag{95}$$

By application of the Key Renewal Theorem (57) it can be shown that, as t increases, $A(t)$ no longer depends on t. The limiting value of $A(t)$, denoted by A and called *limiting availability*, is

$$A = \lim_{t \to \infty} A(t) = \frac{E(x)}{E(x) + E(D)} = \frac{\mu}{\mu + v}. \tag{96}$$

Note that A does not depend on the distributions of operating time or downtime, only on the means of these quantities.

Barlow and Proschan [1974] discuss two interesting models for system availability. In the first, a coherent system ϕ of n independent component positions is considered. The distribution of the lifetime of the item in position i is F_i, with mean μ_i, and the distribution of downtime for position i is G_i, with mean v_i. Let h be the reliability function of the structure ϕ and $A(t)$, $A(A_i(t), A_i)$ be the availability at time t and limiting availability for the system (for the i-th component), respectively. Suppose that, while repair or replacement of any failed component is going on, all other components remain in operation. Then

$$A(t) = h(A_1(t), \ldots, A_n(t)),$$ (97)

and

$$A = h(A_1, \ldots, A_n)$$

$$= h\left(\frac{\mu_1}{\mu_1 + \nu_1}, \ldots, \frac{\mu_n}{\mu_n + \nu_n}\right).$$ (98)

In the second model, a series system is considered. Thus, the system fails when a component fails. Additionally, when a failed component is undergoing repair or replacement, all other components are in "suspended animation." They resume operation when the failed component is restored and, at that instant, are as good as they were when the system failed—not "as good as new." The further assumption is made that two or more components cannot fail at the same time. This is the case if all failure distributions are continuous.

Let $U(t)$ $(D(t))$ denote system operating time (downtime) accumulated by time t. Note that $U(t) + D(t) = t$. The following results obtain

◄
$$\lim_{t \to \infty} \frac{U(t)}{t} = \left(1 + \sum_{1}^{n} \nu_j/\mu_j\right)^{-1} \quad \text{(a.s.)}$$ (99)

◄
$$A_{av} = \lim_{t \to \infty} \frac{E[U(t)]}{t} = \left(1 + \sum_{1}^{n} \nu_j/\mu_j\right)^{-1}.$$ (100)

"A_{av}" denotes average availability.

◄ The average of system operating times converges a.s. to

$$\mu = \left(\sum_{1}^{n} 1/\mu_i\right)^{-1}.$$

◄ The average of system downtimes converges almost surely to

$$\nu = \mu \sum_{1}^{n} \nu_i/\mu_i.$$

FOOTNOTES

1. Results in this Chapter are stated without proof. It has been convenient to indicate a number of important results (i.e., those that might elsewhere be

labeled "theorem") by the symbol ◄. However, the absence of this symbol preceding the statement of a result should not suggest its unimportance. References are frequently cited, but where none are, or where additional information is sought, the reader should first consult Barlow and Proschan's monograph [1965] or their textbook [1974]. I want to express my appreciation to Professors Barlow and Proschan for making the manuscript of their 1974 book available to me prior to its publication. My preparation of this Chapter depended crucially upon this material, as even a quick comparison will indicate.

2. Throughout this Chapter, the terms increasing and decreasing are used in their nonstrict sense; i.e., to mean nondecreasing and nonincreasing, respectively.

3. While one would think that the lower bound in expressions (22) or (23) (based as they are on the min path representation of the structure ϕ) would always be better than the trivial lower bound in expression (21) (which uses no information at all about ϕ), this is not true. For example, for a three-out-of-four system composed of independent components each with reliability p, the trivial bound is actually better than the min cut lower bound. There is a crossover, however, and it is conjectured that, generally, the min cut lower bound is always better for p "not too small."

4. A mixture of a finite of countable number of distributions $F_1, F_2, \ldots$ is a life distribution $F(t) = \sum p_i F_i(t)$, where the p_i are all nonnegative and $\sum p_i = 1$. More generally, let $\{F_\alpha\}$ denote a family of distribution functions indexed by a parameter α, which itself has a distribution function $G(\alpha)$. Then the resulting mixture of the family of distribution $\{F_\alpha\}$ is given by

$$F(t) = \int_{-\infty}^{\infty} F_\alpha(t) \, dG(\alpha).$$

5. "a.s." stands for almost surely; i.e., with probability 1.

6. A random variable X has a lattice distribution if there exists $h > 0$, such that $P[X = nh, n = 0, 1, 2, \ldots] = 1$.

7. Consider two exponential components in parallel, one having failure rate 1, the other having failure rate $1/2$. One can calculate that the failure rate of this system is not increasing. However, it is increasing on the average.

8. See footnote 4.

REFERENCES

Barlow, R. E., "Bounds on Integrals with Applications to Reliability Problems," *Ann. Math. Stat.* **36**, pp. 565–574 (1965).

—— and F. Proschan, *Mathematical Theory of Reliability*, Wiley, New York (1965).

——, *Statistical Theory of Reliability and Life Testing: Probability Models*, Holt, Rinehart and Winston, New York (1974).

—— and A. W. Marshall, "Bounds for Distributions with Monotone Hazard Rate, I & II," *Ann. Math. Stat.* **35**, pp. 1234–1274 (1964).

——, "Tables of Bounds for Distributions with Monotone Hazard Rate," *J. Amer. Stat. Assoc.* **60**, pp. 872–890 (1965).

——, "Bounds on Interval Probabilities for Restricted Families of Distributions," in Proceedings of the Fifth Berkeley Symposium on Mathematical Statistics and Probability, **III**, pp. 229–257, University of California Press, Berkeley (1967).

Birnbaum, Z. W., J. D. Esary, and A. W. Marshall, "Stochastic Characterizations of Wearout for Components and Systems," *Ann. Math. Stat.* **37**, pp. 816–825 (1966).

Bodin, L., "Approximations to System Reliability Using a Modular Decomposition," *Technometrics* **12**, No. 2: 335–344 (1970).

Cox, D. R., *Renewal Theory*, Wiley, New York (1962).

General Electric Company, *Tables of the Individual and Cumulative Terms of the Poisson Distribution*, Van Nostrand, Princeton (1962).

Gnedenko, B. V. Yu, K. Belyayev, and A. D. Solovyev, *Mathematical Methods of Reliability Theory*, Academic Press, New York (1969).

Harter, H. L., "New Tables of the Incomplete Gamma Function Ratio and of Percentage Points of the Chi-Square and Beta Distribution," U.S. Government Printing Office, Washington, D.C. (1964).

Karlin, S., *Total Positivity*, Stanford University Press, Stanford (1968).

Leadbetter, M. R. and W. A. Smith," On the Renewal Function for the Weibull Distribution," *Technometrics* **5**, pp. 393–396 (1963).

Lomnicki, Z. A., "A Note on the Weibull Renewal Process," *Biometrika* **53**, pp. 375–381 (1961).

Mann, N. R., R. E. Schafer, and N. Singpurwalla, "Methods for Statistical Analysis of Reliability and Life Data," Wiley, New York (1974).

Marshall, A. W. and F. Proschan, "Mean Life of Series and Parallel Systems," *Appl. Prob.* **7**, pp. 165–174 (1970).

Molina, C. E., *Poisson's Exponential Binomial Limit*, Van Nostrand, New York (1942).

Pearson, K., *Tables of the Incomplete Gamma Function*, Cambridge University Press, Cambridge (1934).

Smith, W. L., "Renewal Theory and its Ramifications," *J. Roy. Stat. Soc.* Series B, **20**, pp. 243–302 (1958).

I-12

MAINTENANCE AND REPLACEMENT

Andrew K. S. Jardine
University of Windsor

1. INTRODUCTION

Problem situations, concerned with controlling the condition of "equipment," can be termed problems of maintenance and replacement. Figure 1 gives a classification of such problems, where it is seen that one deals with either deterministic or stochastic models for problems which fall into the areas of replacement, inspection, overhaul and repair or organizational structure.

Deterministic problems are ones where there is no uncertainty when the control action (be it topping up a gearbox with oil or replacing a component) takes place, or what the consequences will be of the action. Stochastic problems, on the other hand, are ones where uncertainty can be associated with the timing and/or consequence of the action.

Before proceeding to discuss some specific problems within the four areas identified in Figure 1, it should be realized that, when one attempts to obtain a best solution to the problem, the objective to be met should be clear. For example, it is futile to determine a maintenance policy which enables system availability to be maximized if the organization would rather have profitability maximized. In some circumstances, the optimal maintenance policy may be identical to meet each objective, but this certainly is not always the case. A survey of models applicable to maintenance and replacement problems is provided by Pierskalla and Voelker [1976].

Fig. 1. Maintenance and replacement problem classification.

2. REPLACEMENT

Replacement of an item, be it a component or complex equipment, means that the 'as new' condition is achieved on completion of the action. Thus, strictly, the term renewal ought to be used, although replacement is common usage.

Deterministic replacement problems refer to the replacement of items whose performance deteriorates deterministically over time. For example, with certain parts of a boiler plant, such as an air-heater, the cost of operating the plant increases, in part, due to soot deposits building up on the heat transfer surfaces of the heater. This increase in operating cost may follow a modified exponential curve of the form $A\text{-}Be^{-kt}$, and no uncertainty is then associated with the operating cost at time t after replacement.

If the problem is of a short-term nature; i.e., replacements are made frequently, and the time horizon for optimization is long, then the optimizing criteria will be in terms of *total costs* (or benefits or other appropriate criterion) *per unit time*. If these assumptions are not realistic, then optimization over a finite time horizon is necessary, and dynamic programming may be a useful tool for purposes of analysis.

2.1 Replacement of Equipment Whose Performance Deteriorates Deterministically

The Short-Term Deterministic Replacement Problem—Infinite Planning Horizon. The general case is one where the cost of operating the equipment increases with time. To reduce this cost, a replacement can be made. This replacement costs money, and the objective is to determine the optimal interval between replacements, such that total costs/unit time are minimized. Defining $C(t_r)$ as this total cost/unit time when replacement occurs with equipment of age t_r, then:

$$C(t_r) = \frac{\int_0^{t_r} c(t)\,dt + C_r}{t_r},$$

where $c(t)$ is the instantaneous operating cost/unit time at time t since replacement (assumed monotone increasing); and C_r is the net cost of replacement.

The optimal value of t_r is obtained by setting $C'(t_r) = 0$, and solving for t_r. As Dean [1961] (pp. 337–338) points out, the optimal value of t_r occurs when $C(t_r) = c(t_r)$; i.e., when the average total cost to date equals the current instantaneous operating cost.

The Long-Term Deterministic Replacement Problem—Infinite Planning Horizon. In long-term replacement problems it is assumed that the interval between replacements will be measured in terms of years rather than weeks or months, as is the case for short-term problems, and thus, account has to be taken of the time-value of money. The usual problem is to determine a replacement policy, such that total discounted net benefits derived from operating and replacing equipment are maximized, or that total discounted costs are minimized. A benefit maximization model is given in Jardine ([1973] pp. 63–68). The following cost minimization model was presented by Churchman, Ackoff, and Arnoff [1957] (pp. 484–488).

Referring to Figure 2 and defining the following parameters: A is the net acquisition cost of the new equipment; C_i is the operating cost in the ith period from new assumed monotone increasing, and is payable at the start of the period; r is the present worth factor equal to $[1/(1 + d)]$ where d is the period interest (discount) rate; n is the age in periods when the equipment is replaced and $C(n)$ is the total discounted cost of operating and replacing equipment (with identical equipment) over an infinite period, with replacements occurring at intervals of n periods.

Specifying the objective as determination of the optimal value of n to minimize $C(n)$ we obtain:

$$C(n) = C_1(n) + C_2(n)r^n + C_3(n)r^{2n} + \ldots,$$

where $C_1(n)$ is the total discounted cost of the first cycle of operation, and $C_2(n)$, $C_3(n) \ldots$ are similarly defined for the second, third, $\ldots$ cycles (all discounted to the start of the respective cycles).

Since $C_1(n) = C_2(n) = C_3(n) = \cdots = c(n)$, say, we have the sum to infinity of

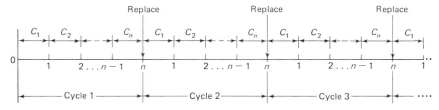

Fig. 2. Long-term deterministic replacement problem.

a geometric progression. Since $r < 1$, we obtain

$$C(n) = \frac{c(n)}{1 - r^n}$$

with

$$c(n) = A + \sum_{i=1}^{n} C_i r^{i-1}.$$

Obtaining the optimal value of n through differential calculus results in the following policy being identified: Replace with identical equipment if the next period's operating cost is greater than the weighted average of previous costs; otherwise, continue operating present equipment.

The weighted average cost up to and including period n, is obtained from the formula:

$$\left[A + \sum_{i=1}^{n} C_i r^{i-1} \right] \bigg/ \left[1 + \sum_{i=1}^{n-1} r^i \right]$$

Thus, if C_{n+1} is greater than the above weighted average, then replacement after period n would be in order.

Technological Improvement. If an alternative equipment becomes available to do the work of an equipment currently being operated, the problem, then, is to determine whether or not to continue using the current equipment or change over to the new equipment. Churchman, Ackoff, and Arnoff [1957] (pp. 489–491) show that the optimal decision is to change over when the cost of the next period of operation of the current equipment exceeds the weighted average cost of the new equipment at its optimal replacement age.

Some Limitations of the Long-Term Deterministic Replacement Models. Although the models outlined above will give an indication of the optimal policy, account usually has to be taken of tax allowance or grants which may be available for the purchase of capital equipment. A paper extending the model disdussed above (the long-term deterministic replacement problem) to take into account tax and grant considerations is that of Eilon, et al. [1966]. Essentially, modifications to cash flows due to tax allowances and grants are incorporated into the model by identifying where they occur within the operating cycle.

As far as technological improvement is concerned, the major problem is not construction or solution of a model, but determination of the trends in costs resulting from such improvement. A dynamic programming model for the technological improvement case, catering for exponential trends in income, operating cost, and replacement cost, is presented by Bellman and Dreyfus [1962] (pp. 117–123).

2.2 Replacement of Equipment that Fails Stochastically

Replacement of an item on failure usually incurs a greater immediate cost than would be the case if the item had been replaced before failure; i.e., on a preventive basis. For this reason it seems sensible to decide whether or not a policy of preventive replacement is worthwhile and, if so, when the preventive replacements should be made. The intervals between replacements (either failure or preventive) tend to be 'short' and so no account needs to be taken of the time value of money. The optimizing criterion will be the expected total cost per unit time (provided cost is the appropriate measure).

Statistical Preliminaries. The purpose of this sub-section is to briefly introduce some statistical notation which is used in replacement studies of stochastically failing equipment:

$f(t)$ = probability density function of the time to failure of the equipment.

$F(t) = \displaystyle\int_0^t f(x)\,dx$. $F(t)$ is termed the cumulative distribution function, and gives the probability of failure occurring before time t.

$R(t) = 1 - F(t)$. $R(t)$ is termed the reliability function (sometimes survival function), and gives the probability of failure occurring after time t.

$r(t) = f(t)/[1 - F(t)]$. $r(t)$ is termed the hazard function or instantaneous failure rate. $r(t)\,dt$ gives the conditional probability of failure occurring in interval $(t, t + dt)$, given that the equipment has survived to time t. Further comments about $r(t)$ are given in this Handbook (Chapter I-11).

Details of the algebraic form of these functions for all common life distributions are given by Hastings and Peacock [1974].

Constant Interval Policy. The constant interval policy is illustrated on Figure 3. Thus, it is seen that preventive replacements occur at constant intervals of length t_p, with failure replacements occurring as necessary. We define the parameters as follows:

C_p: total cost of a preventive replacement.

C_f: total cost of a failure replacement.

$C(t_p)$: the expected total cost per unit time if preventive replacements occur at intervals of length t_p.

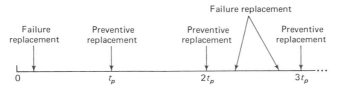

Fig. 3. Constant interval preventive replacement policy.

Then,

$$C(t_p) = \frac{\text{Expected total cost/cycle}}{\text{Cycle length}} = \frac{H(t_p)\,C_f + C_p}{t_p},$$

where, $H(t_p)$ is the expected number of failures in interval $(0, t_p)$. It is termed the renewal function in renewal theory.

The optimizing value of t_p is obtained by setting $C'(t_p) = 0$. This gives (see Barlow and Prochan [1965] p. 95):

$$t_p h(t_p) - H(t_p) = \frac{C_p}{C_f},$$

where, $h(t_p)$ is the derivative of $H(t_p)$, and termed the renewal density.

Procedures for deriving $H(t)$ and $h(t)$ are given by Cox [1962]. (See also in this Handbook the Chapter I-11.) The renewal theory approach to determination of $H(t)$ may require the use of Laplace transforms. Owing to the difficulties associated with inverting the transforms for some failure distributions, a discrete approximation procedure may be used. One such approach is to solve the following recurrence relation (for fuller details see Jardine [1973] pp. 82–85):

$$H(T) = \sum_{i=0}^{T-1} [1 + H(T - i - 1)] \int_{i}^{i+1} f(t)\, dt; T \geqslant 1,$$

with $H(0) = 0$, and where $H(T)$ is the expected number of failures in T periods.

As Churchman, et al. [1957] (pp. 506–507) point out, the optimal solution of the discrete approach to the constant interval policy is to make a preventive replacement at the end of the Tth period if the cost of failure replacements in the Tth period is greater than the expected total cost per period up to the end of the Tth period.

Group Replacement (or Block Replacement). It is sometimes worthwhile to replace identical items in groups, rather than singly, because of economies of scale. An obvious example is the replacement of street lamps. In this case, the policy to be adopted is to perform group replacements at constant intervals of length t_p, with failure replacement being made as necessary. The model is almost identical to that for the constant interval policy. The difference is that N items are considered rather than one. Thus we obtain

$$C(t_p) = \frac{NC'_g + NH(t_p)C_f}{t_p},$$

where $C(t_p)$, $H(t_p)$, C_f and N are as defined previously. C_g is the cost of replacing one item under group replacement conditions.

Age-Based Policy. An obvious limitation of the easily implementable constant interval policy is the risk that a preventive replacement is made shortly after a failure replacement. To remove this deficiency the age-based policy may be adopted. This is one where preventive replacement of an item only occurs when it has reached a specified age, say t_p. In this case, there are two possible cycles of operation, as illustrated in Figure 4. t_p is the age at which preventive replacement is made; $M(t_p)$ is the mean time to failure of the item if preventive replacements occur at age t_p and equals

$$\frac{\displaystyle\int_0^{t_p} tf(t)\, dt}{1 - R(t_p)};$$

C_p, C_f is the total cost of preventive and failure replacement, respectively, and $C(t_p)$ is the expected total cost/unit time if preventive replacement occurs when equipment is of age t_p. Then,

$$C(t_p) = \frac{C_p R(t_p) + C_f(1 - R(t_p))}{t_p R(t_p) + M(t_p)(1 - R(t_p))}.$$

Note: The ratio of two expectations is being taken here. This is acceptable since Smith [1955] has shown that

$$\lim_{t \to \infty} \frac{K(t)}{t} = \frac{\text{Expected cost/cycle}}{\text{Expected cycle length}},$$

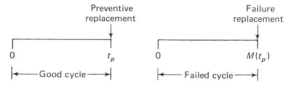

Fig. 4. Possible operating cycles for an age-based policy.

where $K(t)$ is the cumulative expected cost due to a series of cycles in an interval $(0, t)$, and $K(t)/t$ is the expected cost per unit time. The optimal value of t_p is obtained from setting $C'(t_p) = 0$ and obtaining

$$r(t_p) \int_0^{t_p} R(t)\, dt - F(t_p) = \frac{C_p}{C_f - C_p}.$$

A necessary and sufficient condition for an age-based policy to be preferable to simple replacement on failure was obtained by Woodman [1969]. It is that

$$\frac{C_p}{C_f} < 1 - \frac{M_R(a)}{M_R(0)} \qquad \text{for some} \quad a > 0,$$

where C_p and C_f are the total costs associated with preventive and failure replacements, respectively. $M_R(t)$ is defined as the mean residual life, and is the expectation of the time to failure of components which have already been in use for a time t.

$$M_R(t) = \frac{\displaystyle\int_0^\infty xf(t+x)\, dx}{R(t)}.$$

This necessary and sufficient condition implies that: (a) the total cost of a failure replacement must be greater than the total cost associated with preventive replacement; and (b) the instantaneous failure rate, $r(t)$, must be increasing. As Woodman points out, if one restricts attention to items having an increasing instantaneous failure rate, the necessary and sufficient condition becomes

$$\frac{C_p}{C_f} < 1 - \frac{M_R(\infty)}{M_R(0)}.$$

Glasser's Graphs. Glasser [1969] produced two most useful graphs, shown in Figures 5 and 6. Given that the failure distribution of an item can be adequately described by a Weibull distribution, and the cost ratio $k = (C_f/C_p)$ and the average service life in standard deviation units (v) are known, the optimal preventive replacement interval or age can be obtained from the appropriate graph. This is done as follows: given k and v, the chart shows the optimal value of t_p in standard deviation units away from the mean, denoted as z. Once z is obtained from the graph, t_p is obtained from

$$t_p = E(t) + z\sigma(t),$$

where $E(t)$ is the mean time-to-failure, and $\sigma(t)$ is the standard deviation of the failure times. Jorgenson, et al. [1967] also give graphs similar to Figure 6, from which the optimal preventive replacement age can be obtained, given that the

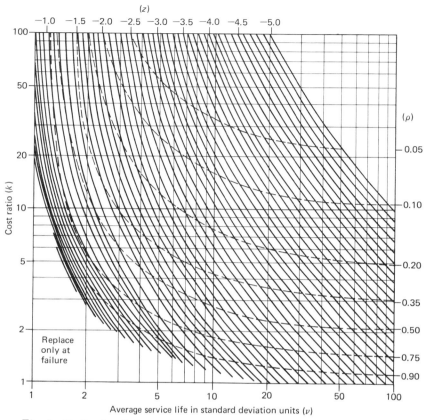

Fig. 5. Optimal policies under block replacement: Weibull distribution.

failure distribution can be described by the Weibull, normal, lognormal, or gamma distribution.

Note 1: Also given in Figures 5 and 6 are curves of a standardized cost ratio, ρ, referred to by Glasser in his paper. The value of ρ at the intersection of the appropriate k and v values gives the cost of the optimal policy as a decimal fraction of the cost of a 'replace only on·failure' policy.

Note 2: The Weibull distribution has found wide applicability in maintenance and replacement studies, since it is easy to fit to raw data through Weibull probability paper (see King [1971]). The Weibull distribution is a family of curves, dependent upon its shaping parameter, β.

The probability density function of the Weibull distribution is:

$$f(t) = \frac{\beta}{\eta}\left(\frac{t - t_o}{\eta}\right)^{\beta-1} \exp -\left(\frac{t - t_o}{\eta}\right)^{\beta}; \quad \text{for } t \geqslant t_o,$$

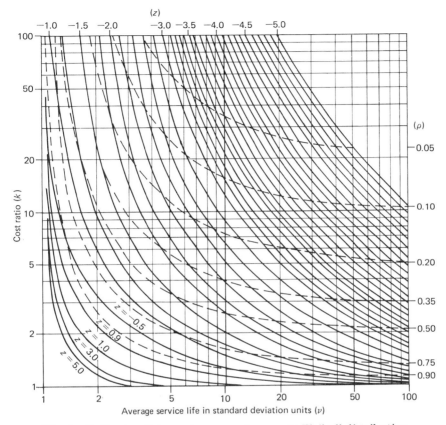

Fig. 6. Optimal policies under age replacement: Weibull distribution.

where $\eta > 0$ is a scale parameter (sometimes termed characteristic life), $\beta > 0$ is a shape parameter, and t_o is a location parameter (often equal to 0, and assumed so in the graphs provided by Glasser).

Figure 7 illustrates the form of the Weibull distribution for various β values (when $\beta \doteq 3.4$ the Weibull approximates the normal, when $\beta = 1$ it is equal to the negative exponential).

Idle Time Policy. If it is possible that, when an item fails it can be left in the failed state (i.e., idle) until the next planned replacement time, but that a cost is incurred due to the failed item remaining idle, then Woodman [1967a] constructs a model to determine the optimal time, t_i, below which idle time should be incurred. This optimal time is obtained by solving the following

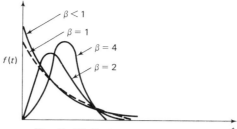

Fig. 7. Weibull distribution.

equation for t_i:

$$\frac{C_f}{C_i} = \int_0^{t_i} R(t)\,dt,$$

where C_f is the total cost of a failure replacement, and C_i is the total cost/unit time associated with a failed item remaining in position. The optimal policy is (a) replace the items when a planned replacement opportunity occurs and; (b) replace failed items unless there is less than a time t_i to go to the next replacement opportunity; otherwise do nothing. This policy is optimal provided $C_f < C_i M_R(0)$.

Optional Replacement Policy. In certain work situations equipment may cease to operate, not because of its own failure, but because some other part of the production process has stopped, say due to failure or lack of raw materials. When such an incident arises there may be the opportunity to make a preventive replacement. Should this be done or not? Woodman [1967b] discusses this problem and develops a model which can be used to determine control limits which enables a decision to be taken on whether or not to take advantage of the opportunity to make a preventive replacement. The policy is illustrated in Figure 8. An approximation to the optimal control limit is given in Woodman [1969].

An extension of Woodman's work to incorporate the possibility of preventive replacement occurring at fixed intervals, rather than only at downtime opportunities, is covered by Duncan and Scholnick [1973].

3. INSPECTION

The basic purpose behind an inspection is to determine the condition of equipment. The major decisions required are (a) the depth, or thoroughness, of inspection, (b) the indicators to be used to describe equipment condition (such

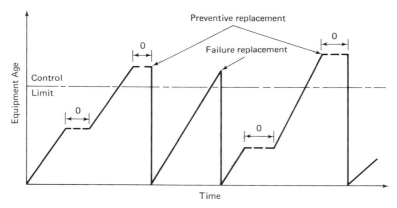

0: Opportunity for preventive replacement

Fig. 8. The optional replacement policy problem.

as bearing wear, gauge readings, product quality), and (c) the timing of the inspection. In practice, most problems in the area of inspection fall into one of three categories dependent upon equipment usage.

3.1 Inspection Frequencies for Equipment which Is in Continuous Operation and Subject to Breakdown

Equipment that breaks down from time to time requires materials and tradesmen to repair it. Also, while the equipment is being repaired, there is a loss in production output. In order to reduce the number of breakdowns we can, from time to time, inspect the equipment and rectify any minor defects which may eventually cause complete breakdown. These inspections cost money in terms of materials, wages, and loss of production due to scheduled downtime.

The optimal inspection policy is one where the total costs associated with the inspection are balanced against the benefits. The specific objective may be maximization of profit, minimization of costs, or minimization of downtime. White, et al. [1969] deal with a profit maximization situation where the model is

$$P(n) = V \left(1 - \frac{\lambda(n)}{\mu} - \frac{n}{i} \right) - \frac{R\lambda(n)}{\mu} - \frac{In}{i},$$

where $P(n)$ is the profit per unit time, derived from operating the equipment when the numbers of inspections (and minor maintenance) per unit time is n; V is the profit value of machine output per unit time (if no stoppages occur); $\lambda(n)$ is the mean number of breakdowns per unit time if the inspection frequency is n; $1/\mu$ is the mean time to effect a repair (distribution assumed negative exponential); $1/i$ is the mean time needed to effect an inspection (distribution of inspection times assumed negative exponential, and independent of the frequency); R is the repair cost per unit time; and I is the inspection cost per unit time. The optimal inspection frequency is then obtained from:

$$\frac{d\lambda(n)}{dn} = -\frac{\mu}{i}\left(\frac{V+I}{V+R}\right).$$

3.2 Inspection Intervals for Equipment Used Only in Emergency Conditions

Equipment such as fire extinguishers and many military weapons are stored for use in an emergency. If the equipment can deteriorate while in storage there is the risk that when it is called into use it will not function. To reduce the probability that equipment will be inoperable when required, inspections can be made, and, if equipment is found to be in a failed state, it can be repaired or replaced, thus returning it to the 'as new' condition. Inspection and repair or replacement takes time, and the problem in this situation is to determine the best interval between inspections to maximize the proportion of time that the equipment is in the available state.

Under the assumption that at the end of an inspection, or repair if it has been found to be failed at an inspection, the equipment is in the as new condition. Jardine [1973] (pp. 110-112) shows that availability per unit time $A(t_i)$ is given by:

$$A(t_i) = \frac{t_i R(t_i) + \displaystyle\int_0^{t_i} t f(t)\, dt}{t_i + T_i + T_r(1 - R(t_i))}\ ,$$

where t_i is the interval between inspections, and T_i and T_r are the mean times required to effect inspection and repair, respectively. A useful review of work done in this class of inspection problem (termed preparedness models) is given by McCall [1965], and expanded in Jorgenson, et al. [1967].

3.3 Inspection Intervals for Equipment Subject to Important Degradation in Performance

The third category of inspection problem relates to equipment for which the 'failed' (i.e., unacceptable) state is likely to be in terms of degraded performance, rather than complete breakdown. This failure might result in the production of goods outside tolerance limits, and the state of the equipment, good or failed, can only be determined by an inspection, for example by checking the quality of the machine output. When failure is detected, then the equipment is returned to the 'as new' condition by "repair." The problem is to determine an optimal inspection schedule to minimize the total costs per unit time associated with inspection, repair, and undetection of a failed equipment. Barlow and Prochan [1965] (pp. 107–117), deal with such a problem, and White [1967] effectively extends that work to include the possibility of one of a variety of maintenance actions being taken at the inspection, depending on the condition of the equipment. A solution procedure which is rapid and gives a good solution to the problem dealt with by Barlow and Prochan (obtaining the optimal solution to their model can lead to computational difficulties) is obtained by Munford and Shahani [1972].

4. OVERHAUL AND REPAIR

In this section, an overhaul is taken to be a restorative maintenance action which is taken before equipment has reached a defined failed state, while a repair is made after the failed state has occurred. Neither action necessarily returns the equipment to the as new condition. (Note that the failed state does not necessarily mean that equipment has 'broken-down', in the usual sense that it ceases completely to function, but it may be in a failed state because items, say, are being produced outside specific tolerance limits, or there may be certain risks associated with continued use of certain equipment, such as some aircraft components).

The main decisions associated with overhaul and repair are determination of

(a) The interval between overhauls. Note that this could be infinity, which means that no overhauls (i.e., a form of preventive maintenance) are carried out, but only repairs are made (i.e., breakdown maintenance); and

(b) The degree to which equipment should be overhauled or repaired; i.e., just how close to the 'as new' condition does the equipment get as a result of the maintenance action. (Note that in the limit both overhaul and repair could be equivalent to replacement.)

Figure 9 illustrates the 'usual' consequences of overhauls and repairs. Thus, it is seen that they both improve the condition of the equipment, although there is a gradual deterioration over time until replacement of the complete equipment occurs.

Several models of overhaul and repair problems are formulated in Jardine [1973] (pp. 117–129), using dynamic programming.

The concept of repair limits for equipment subject to failure is developed by Hastings [1969]. Figure 10 illustrates the problem. A repair limit is a limit on the amount of money which can be spent on the repair of an equipment at a single repair. When an equipment fails, the necessary repair work is costed. If the cost exceeds the repair limit, the equipment is replaced; otherwise it is repaired.

The model takes account of the cost of repair (if it is undertaken) and the

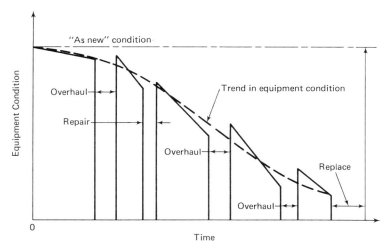

Fig. 9. Overhaul and repair consequences.

resulting expected life of the equipment, and compares this with the cost and failure characteristics of the equipment (if it is replaced). From the analysis, repair limits for equipment of different ages are determined. Thus, if equipment requires a repair, the decision on whether or not to repair can be determined from the repair limit; i.e., the maximum amount of money which should be spent repairing equipment of a given age. An application of the use of such limits to assist in replacement decisions for Army vehicles is reported by Hastings [1970].

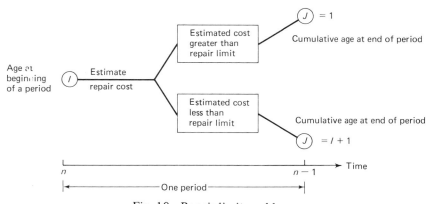

Fig. 10. Repair limit problem.

5. ORGANIZATIONAL STRUCTURE

There are two interrelated problem areas fundamental to the structure of the maintenance organization:

(1) determination of what facilities (e.g., manpower and equipment) there should be within the organization; and

(2) determination of how these facilities should be used, taking into account the possible use of contractors (i.e., outside resources).

Within an organization, there are generally some maintenance facilities available such as workshops, stores, and manpower. In addition, there is usually some form of contact between the organization and contractors who are capable of performing some or all of the maintenance work required by the organization.

Maintenance work can be performed either by company personnel or contractors, on company premises, or in contractors' workshops. Just which of these four alternatives is chosen at any particular time will depend upon: the nature of the maintenance work required, the maintenance facilities available within the company, the maintenance resources available outside the company, the maintenance workload and its variation with time, and the costs associated with each alternative.

In determining the best composition of maintenance facilities within the company, the nature, amount, and variation of the demand for maintenance work, and the availability of outside resources, must be considered. Increases in the range of maintenance equipment, such as lathes, increases the capital tied up in plant and buildings and requires an increase in manpower. If the workload varies, it may be difficult to strike a balance between overload of the facilities and idle capacity.

Increases in the in-plant facilities, however, will reduce the necessity to depend on outside resources such as general engineering workshops. In this case, a balance is required between the cost associated with using in-plant facilities and costs of using outside resources. A difficult costing problem arises, since not only the cost charged by the outside resource has to be considered. There may also be some sort of cost associated with the control of the work carried out. For example, by using outside resources, there is the possibility of greater downtime occurring on production equipment. So, the problem emerges of associating a cost with this downtime.

Also, within this area, there is the problem of determining the size of the maintenance crew. The major conflicts arising here are that:

(1) as crew size increases, so does its cost.

(2) as crew size increases, the time which machines are idle awaiting a crewman decreases.

(3) downtime may be reduced, since larger crews can be used to repair equipment. (If they can all work at the same time.)

Problems within the area of organizational structure are frequently analyzed through queueing theory or simulation. Morse [1963] looks at the problem of determining the optimal size of a repair crew through queueing theory, and an interesting case study in this area is reported by Carruthers, et al. [1970], relating to crew size optimization in an open-cast coal mine.

If there is the possibility of a repair crew being responsible for the repair of a number of machines, the problem exists of determining what this number should be. Machine interference is the term used to describe the problem, since incoming machine breakdowns may have to remain in a queue until the repair crew is free from attending to earlier breakdowns. Cox and Smith [1961] deal in detail with a variety of problems associated with machine interference.

Little work seems to be reported into the problem of determining the optimal level of maintenance resources (in terms of manpower and equipment), taking into account the possible use of contractors. Jardine [1973] (pp. 163–166) presents a model, from which this optimal balance can be obtained, to minimize the total cost per unit time associated with fixed and variable costs, provided it can be assumed that all incoming work within a unit of time is completed by the end of the time period. The possibility of carrying over work from one week to another is discussed by White [1973].

6. THE FUTURE

For too long maintenance, and the associated problem of replacement, have been regarded as a necessary evil, and although this philosophy has not been completely eliminated, there is, today, a growing awareness that scientifically controlled maintenance can become a positive profit contributing activity within an organization. The increasing complexity of equipment, and with it a parallel increase in the problems involved in the maintenance function not solvable by conventional subjective methods, is mainly responsible for this new philosophy.

In 1970, the government of the United Kingdom was responsible for coining a new word—terotechnology (based on the Greek root tereo—to take care of)—and setting up a Committee for Terotechnology to focus attention on the importance of the maintenance function. Terotechnology is defined as:

> ... a combination of management, financial, engineering and other practices applied to physical assets in pursuit of economic life-cycle costs; it is concerned with the specification and design for reliability and maintainability of plant, machinery, equipment, buildings and structures, with their installation, commissioning, maintenance, modification and replacement, and with feedback of information on design, performance and costs.

It must surely be clear that OR concepts and techniques will play an increasingly significant role in arriving at decisions relating to the maintenance and replacement of equipment.

REFERENCES

Barlow, R. E. and F. Prochan, *Mathematical Theory of Reliability*, Wiley, New York, pp. 107–117 (1965).

Bellman, R. E. and S. E., Dreyfus, *Applied Dynamic Programming*, Princeton University Press, Princeton, New Jersey/Oxford University Press, London (1962).

Churchman, C. W., R. L. Ackoff, and E. L. Arnoff, *Introduction to Operations Research*, Wiley, New York, (1957).

Carruthers, A. J., I. MacGow, and G. C. Hackemer, "A study of the optimum size of plant maintenance gangs," in *Operational Research in Maintenance*, A. K. S. Jardine, (ed.), Manchester University Press, Manchester/Barnes and Noble, New York (1970).

Cox, D. R., *Renewal Theory*, Methuen, London/Wiley, New York pp. 45–55 (1962).

—— and W. L. Smith, *Queues*, Methuen, London/Wiley, New York, pp. 91–109 (1961).

Dean, B. V., *Replacement theory in Progress in Operations Research, Volume 1*, R. L. Ackoff (ed.), Wiley, New York (1961).

Duncan, J., and L. S. Scholnick, "Interrupt and opportunistic replacement strategies for systems of deteriorating components," *Operational Res. Quart.* **24**, No. 2: 271–283 (1973).

Eilon, S., J. R. King, and D. E. Hutchinson, "A study in equipment replacement," *Operational Res. Quart.* **17**, Number 1: 59–71 (1966).

Glasser, G. J., "Planned replacement; some theory and its application," *J. Quality Tech.* **1**, pp. 110–119 (1969).

Hastings, N. A. J., "The repair limit replacement method," *Operational Res. Quart.* **20**, Number 3: 337–349 (1969).

——, "Equipment replacement and the repair limit method," in *Operational Research in Maintenance*, A. K. S. Jardine, (ed.), Manchester University Press, Manchester/Barnes and Noble, New York (1970).

—— and J. B. Peacock, *Statistical Distributions*, Butterworth, London/Halsted Press (Wiley), New York (1974).

Jardine, A. K. S., *Maintenance, Replacement and Reliability*, Pitman, London/Halsted Press (Wiley), New York (1973).

Jorgenson, D. W., J. J. McCall, and R. Radnor, *Optimal Replacement Policy*, North-Holland, Amsterdam (1967) (Originally issued as RAND Report R-437-PR).

King, J. R., *Probability Charts for Decision Making*, Industrial Press, New York (1971).

McCall, J. J., "Maintenance policies for stochastically failing equipment; a survey," *Management Sci.* **11**, Number 5: 493–524 (1963).

Morse, P. M., *Queues, Inventories & Maintenance*, Wiley, N.Y., 168–170 (1963).

Munford, A. G. and A. K. Shahani, "A nearly optimal inspection policy," *Operational Res. Quart.* **23**, Number 3: 373–379 (1972).

Pierskalla, W. P. and J. A. Voelker, "A survey of maintenance models: the control and surveillance of deteriorating systems," *Nav. Res. Log. Quart.* **23**, No. 3: 353–388 (1976).

Smith, W. L., "Regenerative stochastic processes," *Proc. Roy. Stat. Soc., A*, **232** (1955).

White, D. J., "Setting maintenance inspection intervals using dynamic programming," *J. Ind. Eng.* **18**, Number 6: 376–381 (1967).

——, "An example of loosely coupled stages in dynamic programming," *Management Sci.* **19**, Number 7: 739–746 (1973).

——, W. A. Donaldson, and N. L. Lawrie, *Operational Research Techniques, Volume 1*, Business Books, London pp. 189–192 (1969).

Woodman, R. C., "Replacement strategies," *Operational Res. Quart.* **18**, Number 2: 193–195 (1967a).

——, "Replacement policies for components that deteriorate," *Operational Res. Quart.* **18**, Number 3: 267–280 (1967b).

——, "Replacement rules for single and multi-component equipment," *J. Roy. Stat. Soc.*, Series C **18**, Number 1: 31–40 (1969).

SECTION II
Applications of Operations Research to Selected Societal and Industrial Systems

II-1

URBAN SERVICE SYSTEMS

E. S. Savas
Gus W. Grammas
Columbia University

1. INTRODUCTION

Governments in the United States spend one-third of the gross national product and employ one out of every six civilian workers. Eighty per cent of government employees work for state and local governments; their numbers doubled between 1955 and 1970.

Despite this massive investment, the public mood is one of dissatisfaction with government services. Expectations do not match performance. Despite increasing expenditures for education, police, welfare, job training, housing, transportation, sanitation, and health services, for example, citizens in urban areas complain about low reading scores, crime, poverty, unemployment, slums, pollution, congestion, dirty streets, and astronomical medical bills. Citizens feel that government, particularly local government—which is in the unenviable position of being observable at close hand—is inefficient and ineffective. The disparity between inputs to and outputs from government looms large in the public eye. Political pressure is being applied to improve the performance of government agencies, and productivity has become an issue at the local level, as candidates promise improved delivery of services.

Faced with this pressure, local governments are responding. Traditional methods for increasing productivity—capital investment in technology—have been rediscovered and applied, however belatedly; not surprisingly, improvements have resulted. Now the newer tools of systems analysis, management science, and computers are being introduced, sometimes overenthusiastically, but increasingly with discrimination and sophistication. Although local governments may be five to ten years behind industry in the application of such techniques, the gap is closing as the public sector begins to compete effectively with the private sector for talented personnel, after a dearth that goes back to the depression.

This chapter reviews some of the important applications of operations research (OR) to urban service delivery, and identifies the problems and challenges which confront the OR practitioner in this arena.

2. EMERGENCY SERVICES

One of the most visible and vital services that an urban center provides its citizens is the "emergency" service. Only recently, however, have the operational problems of this type of service benefited from systematic analysis using OR tools (see, e.g., the review articles by Chaiken and Larson [1972] and by Blum [1972]). An urban emergency service can be defined as any system having the following three properties: 1) incidents occur in the urban center which give rise to requests for service, and the times and places at which these incidents occur cannot be specifically predicted in advance; 2) in response to each request, one or more emergency service units are dispatched to the scene of the incident although, in some cases, these requests may be monitored in order to establish priority of dispatch (e.g., New York City's 911 emergency telephone number); and 3) an important characteristic of the quality of service is the time elapsed before an emergency unit arrives at the incident. This section will be primarily concerned with the three major emergency services: police, fire, and ambulance. The analyses and comments made, however, apply to other emergency service units such as certain tow trucks, bomb disposal units, and emergency repair trucks for gas, electric, and water services.

Although all emergency services share the above properties, they may differ according to three important characteristics: cruising vs. fixed location of service units at time of dispatch, ability to determine the urgency of the incoming request for service, and certain non-emergency activities which must also be carried out. These differing characteristics are important for both administrative and analytical purposes.

Some emergency units, such as fire engines and ambulances, are usually stationed at fixed locations while others, such as police patrol cars, are cruising. In principle, then, it is possible to vary the location, size, and shape of police patrol sectors, while the response areas of fire units depend primarily upon the (fixed) locations of fire stations. The distinction between cruising and fixed location units begins to break down during periods of high demand, when units may be dispatched directly from one incident to the next or while en route from a previous incident to their home locations. At these times, moreover, the system operation is not very sensitive to the distribution of initial locations.

Emergency services also differ in their ability to determine the urgency of the incoming requests for service. The percentage of non-urgent calls to an emergency service varies from about thirty percent for ambulances, to forty percent for fire alarms (in New York), to seventy-five percent for police departments. This ability to establish priorities of calls determines the options available to a dispatcher during periods of high demand. If priorities can be established, the dispatcher may decide to send no units, or hold the call in queue and await the availability of a unit near the scene, or place the call in queue (even when a unit is available) if he expects to receive a call of higher priority. However, if priorities cannot be established, the dispatcher must send at least one unit to each incident so that its priority can be determined.

Some emergency services are also required to perform certain non-emergency activities. For example, police cars carry on routine patrol which is believed to deter particular types of crime (although even this plausible contention is subject to verification). Thus, a police dispatcher may place some calls in queue in order to preserve the deterrent patrol.

Emergency service systems operate in a complex environment which includes often conflicting mixtures of objectives, and sometimes harsh administrative, legal, and political constraints. Typically, each system seeks to provide minimal service delays, while trying to establish a reasonable workload for its personnel and still stay within its budget.

In general terms, the basic operational problems are to determine an optimal allocation of the existing resources of men and equipment, and to determine the number of men and units required to satisfy some ill-defined objectives. As one might expect, it is almost impossible to find globally optimal solutions to the operational problems of these services. In recent years, however, OR techniques have been applied to these problems with some success. This section will focus on the techniques that are available, the types of solutions which have been generated, and, most importantly, on the improvement of service that can be achieved by quantitative, analytical study.

The cost of providing for emergency services is considerable. In 1971, for example, New York City budgeted approximately one billion dollars for the police and fire departments alone. As an industry, emergency services may be one of the most labor-intensive, undercapitalized in the country, with employee salaries and fringe benefits consuming a large percentage of the budget for each service (as high as 90 to 98 percent in some cases). At present salary levels, for instance, the cost of manning a two-man police patrol car around the clock ranges from $100,000 to $200,000 annually and the comparable cost for one fully staffed fire engine is about $500,000 annually. Thus, any solution to operational problems which requires increased manpower must be examined very carefully.

As OR techniques have been employed, certain significant points have arisen. First of all, changes in procedures and/or deployment often affect the performance of emergency service systems in counterintuitive ways; for example, in order to minimize overall average travel time for fire engines, it may be necessary to send a unit other than the closest one to an incident. Second, use of more formal analytical methods, rather than operational "rules of thumb," can improve performance significantly; for example, using queueing models, rather than traditional workload formulas, can better determine the minimum number of units to have on duty. Finally, simple changes in procedure often produce more significant improvements than either expensive new hardware systems or increases in manpower; for example, dispersing ambulances throughout an area can result in significantly less overall response time. These points are discussed more fully below.

The primary areas for analysis of emergency service systems are 1) determining the number of units to have on duty in each area, 2) designing the response areas, and 3) locating the units and facilities. Typical changes which may be recommended include selective queueing of low priority calls, varying the number of units on duty by time and place, dispatching units other than the closest ones to certain incidents, relocating units as unavailabilities begin to develop, and, in the case of police, assigning cars to overlapping patrol sectors. With the implementation of such recommendations it is often possible to reduce queueing and travel time delays, improve the balance of workload among units, and enhance the amount of preventive patrol where needed.

The first important factor in determining the performance of an emergency service system is the number of units on duty in each area of the city. Traditionally, the two most commonly used methods for selecting the number of units were based on land use (geography) patterns and workload formulas. Methods based on geographical factors are, typically, used in order to meet certain standards and regulations. For example, in order for a district to be classified as "high-value" for fire insurance purposes, no point in the district should be more than one mile from an engine company and 1.25 miles from a ladder company. As a general rule, however, geographical methods cannot determine whether an adequate number of units are on duty, because of time between receipt of a call for service and the arrival of emergency units depends on many factors in addition to geography. Methods based on workload (or hazard) formulas subjectively combine virtually all factors that are thought to be relevant for allocating units. This produces a "hazard score" for each area, and the units are distributed among the areas in direct proportion to their hazard scores. A common formula for computing an area's score for police purposes relies on a weighted sum of factors (such as number of arrests, number of street miles, etc.), where the weights are subjective indicators of relative importance. In general, however, the simple form of workload formulas does not adequately describe the complex, highly nonlinear, stochastic relationships between system variables. Furthermore, because there is no theoretical basis for such workload formulas, it is difficult to determine how to improve the formulas.

2.1 Use of Queueing Models

In recent years, OR models have been used to determine the number of units on duty. From a mathematical modeling viewpoint, urban emergency service systems have two distinct features: (1) probabilistic demands and service requirements over time, and (2) probabilistic distribution of incidents and response units over the space of the city. The first feature, corresponding to the systems' congestion problems, is naturally analyzed by queueing models and the second feature, corresponding to the systems' spatial characteristics, gives rise to travel time models. In addition, more sophisticated modeling tools, such as simulation and dynamic programming, can be used to analyze both features simultaneously and then produce a general allocation algorithm.

The primary objective of the queueing analysis is to determine the minimum number of units required so that the probability of an important call encountering a queue, or the expected waiting time in queue, is below some specified threshold. Due to the stochastic nature of the arrival and service times, no response system with a finite number of units can guarantee that every call will result in an immediate dispatch. As a simple application of the single-server queueing model, imagine a response area with exactly one emergency unit (server) assigned to it, and where no other unit may respond. Using the standard formulas for the single-server queue, a maximum value for the probability of a queue or the average waiting time in queue for any sector is selected, and then the sectors would be selected small enough to assure that the threshold is not exceeded. The total number of sectors designed in this way then determines the number of units needed. No emergency service system, however, actually operates in this fashion since, at fixed manpower levels, other arrangements lead to fewer delays and, at fixed performance levels, other arrangements require fewer total response units.

Typically, applications to real emergency services require a multi-server queueing model. For example, Larson [1972a] describes the use of the queueing model (M/M/S) to determine the number of operators to have on duty each hour to answer N. Y. City's 911 emergency telephone number. The service level specification requires that sufficiently many operators be assigned, so that the fraction of calls delayed T or more time units will be P or less. Time is measured in service time units so that, for instance, if the average service time per call is 80 seconds, then 160 seconds would be two service-time units. Also required as input is a prediction of the average number of calls to be received each hour; in fact, successful application of the queueing model is limited by the accuracy of this prediction.   As an illustration of the use of this model (applying the standard formulas for the multi-server queue), suppose that $T = 0.25$, $P = .05$, the average service time is 80 seconds, and that for a given hour of operation the estimate is that 840 calls will be received. The minimum number of operators, S, required for this case is 24; if T is lowered to 0., then the required S is 26. The M/M/S queueing model assumes that calls arrive in a Poisson manner, that the service time is exponentially distributed, that the S servers have identical characteristics, and that the service discipline is first-come, first-served (FCFS). Larson points out that even though the second and third assumptions are not met, a detailed simulation model was not necessary to achieve large improvements in the system operating characteristics; the multi-server queueing model was implemented and it performed satisfactorily, in spite of the fact that not all the assumptions were met.

Queueing models have been used to analyze each of the emergency services. For police service, McEwen [1966] discusses the use of the multi-server model for the allocation of police patrol cars in St. Louis, and Larson ([1972b] p. 153) uses priority queueing models to reduce delays associated with important incoming calls for service. For fire service, Chaiken [1971] develops a queueing model for determining the number of units on duty when more than one unit may be dispatched in response to a call. For ambulance service, Stevenson [1972] uses a steady-state version of the M/M/S model to determine the required number of ambulances in a region; Bell and Allen [1969] develop queueing theory models for determining the number of ambulances required to respond immediately to 95 (or 99) percent of service requests; Hall [1972] models the Detroit ambulance as a multifunction stochastic service system with semi-Markov arrivals and state-dependent service times.

2.2 Travel Time Models

Although queueing delays dominate the response time during the periods of system saturation, travel times usually comprise the greatest fraction of total response time during normal operating periods. Models are, therefore, required which relate travel time to the number of units on duty, geographical characteristics, arrival rates of calls, and service times at incidents. In periods of light or moderate demand, the travel time models can replace traditional geographical factors in determining the number of units to have on duty, provided that the units are spatially dispersed throughout the region. If the units are located at only one facility, such as the "base case" for ambulance service described by Savas [1969b] , then travel time from facility to incident does not depend on the number of units on duty but only on the geographical factors describing the region.

Under certain assumptions, particular geometrical models (sometimes called "inverse square-root laws") can be used for determining the relationship between travel distance (or time) and the spatial distribution pattern of the units. Larson and Stevenson [1972] show that if units are positioned in such a way as to minimize average travel distance, the mean travel distance is $0.47/\sqrt{r}$, where r is the average number of units per square mile. For police service, Larson [1972b] discusses a similar model for travel distance, when the units are randomly located. For fire service, Kolesar and Blum [1973] derive the results for the travel distance of the n th-arriving unit, when more than one are dispatched and, even more importantly, show that in certain cases it may be possible to find an empirical relationship directly between mean travel time and the average density of available units (in which case the travel distance models are not needed). The travel distance models, using empirical data relating travel time to travel distance and the given spatial distribution of units, provide an estimate of the travel time distribution which, in turn, allows one to estimate the probability that travel time exceeds a specified limit (Kolesar [1975], Kolesar, et al. [1975]).

The travel time models can be used in conjunction with the queueing models, in order to determine the number of units to have on duty. Given N total units on duty, the queueing model is used to obtain the probability that n units will be available for dispatch, and the geometrical model gives the travel time distribution for this circumstance. Two constraints are employed: the first specifies a limit on some measure of queueing (probability of a queue forming, expected waiting time, etc.) and the second sets a limit on an appropriate measure of travel time (e.g. average travel time). It is then possible to determine the smallest number of units, N, meeting both constraints.

The queueing and travel time models discussed above are usually not sufficient, by themselves, to determine the number of units needed. This is due to the fact that easily quantifiable measures, such as probability of encountering a queue and average travel time, do not necessarily have a clear relationship to the true performance of an emergency service system. For example, the actual benefits which result from decreasing response time may be difficult to quantify. Nevertheless, a careful and realistic use of such measures can often provide reliable substitutes for more fundamental measures (such as number of lives saved, property damage averted, etc.). Such a situation is discussed by Carter and Ignall [1970], where a simulation-queueing model, using the measures of travel time and response workload, is employed to determine the extent to which an added fire unit provides relief to overworked units in a particular area. Typically, an administrator will want to employ several of the performance measures simultaneously in order to arrive at reasonable allocations. In order to incorporate such factors as workload and preventive patrol into the queueing and travel time models, more sophisticated modeling tools, such as simulation and dynamic programming, are needed to produce a general allocation algorithm. Carter and Ignall [1970] used simulation models for fire service, and Larson [1972b] developed a dynamic programming algorithm for the allocation of police patrol cars to commands, incorporating a wide variety of measures. In one of the earliest modeling studies of emergency services, a simulation model was used in a comprehensive analysis of ambulance service in a large city Savas [1969b]. Simulation experiments provided the insights and the impetus for a series of major changes that resulted in substantial service improvements. The changes included organizational centralization of the service; geographical decentralization of ambulances among new, dispersed satellite stations; screening of calls to reduce demand; transfer of dispatching responsibility; and technological innovations in dispatching and control.

2.3 Response Areas

The design of response areas is another important factor in determining the performance of an emergency service system. A response area indicates where a particular patrol unit, fire engine, or ambulance is to have primary responsibility. In designing such an area, there are several (often conflicting) objectives such as minimization of response time, equalization of workload, demographic homogeneity of each area, and administrative convenience. Obviously, no single mathematical technique can take into account all of the relevant factors, but models have been developed, in recent years, which provide useful insights into the design problem.

Traditionally, response areas have been designed as squares or circles, with the objective to keep at a minimum the time required for an emergency unit to travel to the scene of a reported incident. Travel speeds, however, may depend on the direction of travel, so, quantitative techniques have recently been used to predict the travel time characteristics of any proposed response area design. For instance, under the assumption that each police patrol unit responds only within its area, Larson [1972b] has shown that average intrasector travel time is minimized when the average time required to travel east-west equals the average north-south travel time. In Manhattan, where the north-south speed is about 4 times as great as the east-west speed, this implies that the response areas should be 4 times as long in their north-south direction. Such an area design can be expected to reduce average travel time by approximately 20% over that obtained by the usual square or circular design. For another example, fire departments have traditionally designed response areas (districts) so that the dispatched units are the ones closest to the fire; thus, all points on the dividing line between two districts are equally close to some pair of companies. Carter, Chaiken, and Ignall [1972] have shown, however, that even interpreting "closest" to mean "shortest travel time" does not produce optimal dividing lines, and that overall average travel time is minimized by following a policy that often requires sending a unit other than the closest one. That is, it may be preferable to incur an immediate travel time penalty so that the overall system is left in a state which best anticipates future demands. These authors have also shown that the boundaries which minimize overall average response times will frequently also reduce workload imbalance (i.e., the difference in the fraction of time worked by the busiest unit and by the least busy unit). On a much simpler scale, Keeney [1972] presented a simple and intuitive procedure for determining the boundaries of service districts, using the criterion that each facility serves all points to which it is closest in either distance or travel time.

2.4 Facility Location

The location of units and facilities is the final important factor in determining the performance of an emergency service system. The problems of location include: which site to select for an additional facility, where to place a new facility when consolidating two or more existing facilities, "pre-positioning" (i.e., where to locate units at the start of a tour), and "repositioning" (i.e., how, and under what circumstances, to change the location of units during a tour to correct for unavailabilities as they develop). Traditionally, the facility location problem has been treated in economic terms which ignore the probabilistic aspects of the operations. Recently, Toregas, et al. [1971] viewed the location of emergency facilities as a set covering problem, with each set being composed of the potential facility sites within a specified time or distance of each demand point. If costs are the same for all facility locations, a linear programming (LP) model is developed to minimize the total number of service facilities required to meet the (maximum) response time or distance standards.

To the extent that probabilistic analytical methods have been used for locating emergency service units, the application has been limited to a small number of units or to a small number of potential sites for the units. Typically, these methods determine the travel time properties of all possible combinations of locations, or utilize simple algorithms which assist in searching for the optimal locations. Savas [1969b] explored the implications of dispatching ambulances from two fixed locations (as an alternative to the previous single site) by considering every possible division of n units between the two locations, and by using a simulation model to estimate average response times. Larson and Stevenson [1972] also considered only two sites, but the location of one of them was permitted to be arbitrary. A steepest-descent search routine enabled them to find the location of the second site which minimized average travel time. More importantly, however, the results suggest that the optimal location of a new site is rather insensitive to the precise locations of existing units. In locating ambulances so as to minimize mean response time, Swoveland, et al. [1973], used a digital simulation to gather information on system characteristics under various ambulance assignments and dispatch rules, and then utilized the simulation output to construct an analytical approximation to the mean response time. The resulting combinatorial optimization problem was then solved, using a probabilistic branch and bound algorithm.

More extensive analytical work has been completed concerning the repositioning of units during the course of a tour. Larson [1972b] has shown that any local repositioning (among nearby sectors) of police patrol units is advantageous in terms of travel distance only if patrol is concentrated near the boundaries of the appropriate sectors. For repositioning of fire units, Kolesar and Walker [1974] utilize the idea of "coverage." A point is said to be covered if at least one available engine company (or ladder company) is within T minutes of the location. If one or more neighborhoods are expected to be uncovered for an undesirable amount of time, a heuristic algorithm (for a mathematical programming formulation of the problem) determines which vacant firehouses to fill and then, which available units to relocate to them. The results of testing indicate that the proposed algorithm, while not "optimal," is a significant improvement over existing methods, and appears to compute very reasonable relocations using little computer time and memory. This computer-based method will become part of a real-time, command-and-control system.

2.5   Computer Simulation Models

Increasing use has recently been made of computer simulation models for evaluating proposed changes in allocation procedures. Typically, an agency administrator is faced with a number of proposed changes in his allocation policy simultaneously (e.g., adopt priority queueing schemes, add units at certain times of day, select new locations for some units, change response areas or patrol patterns, and modify the procedures for relocating units.) In addition, certain technological innovations (e.g. automatic car locator systems) may have been proposed to accomplish some of the same objectives. Thus, an administrator will require a realistic cost-benefit analysis for each proposal before making a choice among the alternatives.

Such a cost-benefit analysis usually requires a computer simulation model which can provide information about the effect of a proposed policy change on a wide range of variables: response times to particular types of calls, workload of units, queueing delays, availability of units, etc. The simulation studies by Savas [1969b] and Carter and Ignall [1970] have been discussed previously. Fitzsimmons [1973] develops a computer model for predicting the entire response time distribution for an actual operating system. This is coupled with a pattern search routine to find the deployment of ambulances that minimizes mean response time. In applying this methodology in Los Angeles, Fitzsimmons found that an additional benefit was a substantial smoothing of workload among the ambulance crews. Larson [1972b] developed a simulation model to study the best use of automatic vehicle locator systems in police departments. His analysis showed that superimposing an automatic vehicle locator system on a patrol force assigned to non-overlapping sectors causes an average travel time reduction of about 10 to 20 percent.

Current use of OR models in evaluating the performance of emergency service systems has shown which aspects of performance are likely to improve or be degraded as a result of a specific policy change. Recent studies by Larson [1973, 1975], Jarvis [1973], and Hoey [1973], indicate quite clearly that sophisticated quantitative models can play an important role in the analysis of emergency service systems. In the future, it is expected that models will improve in their utility and sophistication and, more importantly, that agency administrators will make increasing use of them.

3. ENVIRONMENTAL PROTECTION

Environmental protection problems are usually divided into those of solid waste collection and disposal, water resources, and air quality. The intimate relationships between these problems, however, is well recognized. For example, the incineration of solid waste is a major contributor to air pollution and the dumping of solid waste in water degrades our water resources. It should be noted, however, that the discharge of wastes does not necessarily result in "pollution"; pollution occurs only when discharges are of such duration and concentration that they have deleterious consequences for the users of land, water, or air. Traditionally, environmental problems were thought to be primarily in the domain of the sanitary engineer. Only recently have the tools of OR and systems analysis been brought to bear on these problems.

One of the earliest comprehensive quantitative analyses of urban waste management was that of the Regional Plan Association (Anderson [1968]). This study focused on the following aspects of the problem: projecting waste generation, calculating the costs and uncertainties of alternative management policies, and outlining the information needed for a systematic approach to waste management. More recently, Coulter [1970] and Clough [1973] discuss the role of OR in the waste problem. In particular, Coulter [1970] criticizes certain studies which conclude that much can be done to control pollution, but as a prerequisite for effective action, the government must be reorganized; he advocates an approach which adapts to the constraints imposed by the present government systems. Clough [1973] describes the increasingly involved role of the OR analyst in environmental problems. He sees the major areas of involvement as: 1) identifying pollution conditions, developing better methods of monitoring and measuring, and estimating pollution costs; 2) devising methods for pollution control, such as incentives to assure self-regulation and standards of performance to be pursued; 3) participating in cost-benefit analyses of large-scale environmental control schemes; and 4) developing fundamental theories and complex models of the social and economic processes of environmental control.

There are essentially two types of quantitative approaches (models) for controlling the discharge of wastes. One approach is to legislate the manner and the maximum amount of waste that a polluter can discharge. This typically leads to optimization models which attempt to find the least-cost solution satisfying a given goal (see Parvin and Grammas [1976a]). Another approach is to impose charges (taxes) on the amount of discharge, in order to change the waste production pattern of the polluter. This typically leads to mathematical models for determining the (social) costs of removing these discharges. Such an "economic" approach is advocated by Freeman and Haveman [1972] and by Freeman, et al. [1973].

OR models have also been used to model the physical system of an environmental problem (e.g., diffusion models for air quality control) and to find least cost solutions for providing some minimum level of service (e.g., network models for refuse collection).

3.1 Solid Waste

Solid waste collection and disposal problems are among the most diffuse of environmental problems. Essentially, solid waste is composed of all materials which are unwanted and cannot be readily disposed of into the liquid or gaseous waste systems. The management decisions are concerned with planning and operating facilities and equipment within an existing institutional (and policy) framework. Typically, the generation of solid waste, in its current or projected varieties and quantities, is taken as a given input to the system, and attention is focused on collecting, transporting, storing, treating, and disposing of this waste. In addition, methods for reclaiming useful materials and burning garbage for fuel are considered part of the solid waste management system.

The decision-making process is theoretically composed of two stages. The first stage is to specify the kind of service desired, and the second stage is to determine methods for obtaining that service at least cost. Typically, however, the decision-maker finds himself in the position of exploring the costs of obtaining various levels of service and then selecting the "desired" level subjectively. Service quality decisions include frequency of pick-up, kinds of waste which will be picked up, and any required separation by the user. Various descriptive and predictive models can be used to estimate the costs involved in changing service quality. Cost minimization models attempt to determine 1) the number and type of facilities (landfills, incinerators, transfer stations) and their location, and 2) the size and type of collection vehicles and the routing of these vehicles, as well as the number of men in the crew.

From a modeling point of view, a solid waste system has four components: 1) the generation of waste, 2) the fixed facilities used for transfer, treatment, and disposal, 3) the vehicles used for transporting the waste, and 4) the men who operate the system. Most mathematical models of the system are optimization models with minimum cost as the objective; the main exception is the predictive type of model for waste generation. Liebman [1972] presents a recent survey of optimization models for solid waste problems.

Waste generation projections are required for many waste management decisions. Green [1969] uses the techniques of linear regression analysis to produce an equation relating the overall density of waste material to the proportion, by weight, of paper in the refuse. A typical refuse-treatment plant requires a refuse density estimate for its orderly operation. In an interesting statistical study, Quon, et al [1968] examined household generation rates before and after a shift from once-per-week to twice-per-week collection. The result was a very significant increase in the generation rate after the change, and this increased rate persisted even after a year. Such a phenomenon is still not well understood.

Facility and site selection problems are readily analyzed by optimization models. Typically, these are mixed integer programming models of the form (see Liebman [1972], and also chapter I-8 Facility Location and Layout):

$$\text{Minimize} \quad \sum_i \sum_j (T_{ij} + D_j)X_{ij} + \sum_j F_j Y_j$$

$$\text{Subject to} \quad \sum_j X_{ij} = a_i \quad \text{for each source} \quad i$$

$$b_j Y_j - \sum_i X_{ij} \geqslant 0 \text{ for each site} \quad j$$

$$Y_j \quad \text{is an integer, either} \quad 0 \text{ or } 1,$$

where Y_j is equal to 1 if a facility is built at site j and zero otherwise; F_j is the fixed cost of constructing such a facility; D_j is the cost of each ton of waste which passes through an incinerator at site j; T_{ij} is the cost of shipping a ton of waste from source (collection area) i to site j; a_i is the amount of waste generated at collection area i; b_j is the capacity at site j; and X_{ij} is the amount of waste to be shipped from collection area i to site j. The objective function is the total cost; the first set of constraints require that the total amount of waste generated in each collection area be collected, and the second set of constraints require that if a facility is built, the amount flowing into it may not exceed its capacity. This type of model has been extended by ReVelle, et al. [1970b] and by Marks and Liebman [1971] to determine, in addition, the appropriate locations for transfer facilities. For an economic analysis of transfer stations (and vehicle relays) the reader is referred to Green and Nice [1969].

The problem of collection vehicle routing requires dividing the collection region into individual areas, and then routing a vehicle from a depot to its area, through its area, and back to the depot. The objective in routing is to provide the required level of service (frequency of collection) with minimum cost. Early attempts at modeling the routing problem took the form of the classic "traveling salesman" and "chinese postman" problem (see Liebman

[1972]). Recently, other OR techniques have been applied to the routing problem. Coyle and Martin [1969] discuss a model for collection which is a function of varied housing layouts, collection times, team sizes, and the distance of the collection points from the disposal point. They develop a computational method which allocates collection operatives to vehicles and designs routes which together minimize the total collection cost. Bodner, et al. [1970] use simulation methods to obtain a best route; the computer model examines a large number of possible routes and then selects the least-cost alternative. Beltrami and Bodin [1973] use network and graph theory to design routes which minimize total travel time, and to determine the minimum number of vehicles required for a specified level of service. It is important to note that vehicle routes are clearly dependent upon facility locations. Ideally, a location-routing model is required; in practice, however, routing is a short-term decision, while location of facilities is a long-term one.

The problem of manpower scheduling requires that the workload be equitably distributed, and that the appropriate number of workers be employed. Altman, et al. [1971] use a nonlinear programming model to determine the manpower requirements for household refuse collection. Work shifts are matched to curbside refuse demands so as to minimize weekly missed collections, subject to union regulations and to manpower and vehicle constraints. Bodin, et al. [1971] use heuristic algorithms to solve the same type of problem. In a similar vein, Ignall, et al. [1972] use an LP model for assigning crews to shifts so as to achieve a balance between payroll cost and missed refuse collections while satisfying the constraints due to available equipment and policies for granting days off. However, Savas [1974, 1977] shows that, within a single metropolitan area, the organizational form of refuse collection can affect costs by a factor of three, which dwarfs the kinds of improvements that can be expected from routing and scheduling efforts.

Economic analyses typically provide the tools for investigating the feasibility of recycling solid waste, either for resource (materials) recovery or fuel (energy) recovery. In a recent study, the Management and Behavioral Science Center [1971] discusses a system of incentives (taxes) to: 1) minimize the amount of solid waste generated, 2) minimize the cost and maximize the effectiveness of collection, treatment, and disposal of solid waste, 3) maximize the percentage of solid waste that can be economically separated and reused, and 4) minimize the negative impact of solid waste disposal on all ecological systems. Abert, et al. [1974] show that recycling offers the potential for an environmentally and economically superior alternative to many current municipal disposal practices. Resource recovery is not yet a self-supporting enterprise, but, given a market for recovered materials, it can compete with the present alternatives available to urban communities. Presently, studies are underway to make Denver's garbage the main source of fuel at the Coors Brewery in Golden, Colorado and to construct a 225-acre island (Recap Island) in lower New York Bay for recycling garbage into fuel and converting solid waste into usable products.

3.2. Water Resources

OR techniques have been used in analyzing water resources systems. (See; e.g., review articles by Marks [1972, 1975] and by Haimes [1972].) In general, the main problem of a water resources system is the allocation of a scarce resource, in sufficient quality and quantity, among often conflicting alternative uses. The problem of water quality is directly related to a conflict between developmental and environmental objectives. In order to establish policies for limiting the deterioration of water quality, a thorough consideration of the complex technical, economic, and social implications of waste management is of critical importance. The problem of water quantity involves achieving a reasonable distribution of water among its various users. In some cases, the concern is that there is too much in a particular place, as in flooded agricultural lands, or too little at a particular location for a particular use.

There are essentially three main issues in water quality management: 1) determining an appropriate level of water quality; 2) determining how this level of quality is to be achieved at least cost; and 3) establishing a plan for implementation. An analysis of the first problem requires that preferences for water use be defined explicitly in terms of physical parameters that can be determined or, at least, estimated. It is in the analysis of the second and third problems that OR has had its greatest impact. In recent years, mathematical models have been developed which evaluate the alternative means for improving water quality. Such alternatives include: waste treatment at a source, "piping" to points on the water body which are less sensitive, flow augmentation and stream aeration, and imposing economic penalties such as taxation to reduce resource consumption by those sources which create excessive wastes.

Mathematical modeling of water resources systems typically leads to complex multivariate models. This is due to the fact that water quality cannot be measured by a single variable, such as the amount of dissolved oxygen. Water characteristics are defined by a number of factors such as amount and type of suspended and organic material, temperature, biological oxygen demand, and the amount of chlorides, phosphates, nitrates, algae, etc. For example, Haimes [1972] describes a general (non-linear) multivariate mathematical model for determining the optimal policy (economic penalties) for achieving the desired water quality, while minimizing the total cost to an environmental protection agency.

There are essentially two classes of mathematical models for the analysis of water quality. The first type of model is a physical model that describes the cause and effect relationship between waste discharge and water quality in a particular environment. For example, Loucks and Lynn [1966] use a Markov chain approach to model the stochastic nature of streamflow (which dilutes wastes) and then evaluate various water release strategies. The second type of model is a mathematical programming model to find the least-cost mix of alternatives open to a regional authority that satisfies a given goal. Marks [1972] presents a series of increasingly complex (linear to nonlinear) programming models which attempt to find the least-cost solution. The decision variable, x_j, is the amount of waste removed at source j, and the objective is to mininize the total cost of removal, $\sum f_j(x_j)$, subject to conditions that at least some level of water quality is maintained. Note that quality is specified only at a discrete set of points, and that there is no time aspect to the formulation (i.e., the problem is viewed as a steady state one rather than reflecting the stochastic nature of stream flow, waste flows, and physical parameters). Loucks, ReVelle, and Lynn [1967] assume a linear form for $f_j(x_j)$ and the constraints. The models they develop can be used not only in determining system costs for various quality standards, but also for measuring cost sensitivity to changes in wastewater flows and in the location of treatment facilities. Marks points out that two major problems in water quality management still remain unsolved: the problem of locating regional treatment facilities that minimize the cost of meeting quality goals, and the problem of finding measures for allocating those costs.

An alternative approach to water quality control is the use of effluent charges or incentives (taxes) to change the waste production pattern of the polluter. Kneese and Bower [1968] advocate such an economic approach, which allows the polluter to make the most efficient decision about controlling his pollution production. It is interesting to note, however, that the Delaware River Basin Commission chose (see Marks [1972]) to use the mathematical programming models for regulation and enforcement of water quality standards, rather than to try the economic approach, because it felt strongly about taking a more traditional approach.

The field of urban water quantity (supply) management deals with the effects of urbanization and development on water resources. The design of hydraulic systems for transporting water and processing it for different uses has been examined by de Neufville [1970] and by de Neufville, et al. [1971]. These papers propose a method for cost-effectiveness studies of civil engineering works, and illustrate it by a case study of the application of this method to the planning and design of New York City's third water supply tunnel. This approach tries to bridge the dichotomy of objectives that often exists between the policy levels of government and the engineering agencies. Possibly the major contribution of this method lies in its recognition of objectives rather than, as in usual practice, standards.

OR models have also played a significant role in the actual operations of water supply systems. Reservoirs, for example, are used to fulfill different objectives such as power generation, flood protection, water supply, and recreation, all of which require different modes of operation. The central problem of how much water should be stored and released in the system when the inputs are stochastic has been addressed by ReVelle, et al. [1969, 1970a], where chance-constrained LP and a linear decision rule are used to design the operating policy for a reservoir.

3.3 Air Quality

As with water, air is a natural resource whose degradation in recent years has been the subject of much scientific analysis. Man pollutes his atmosphere primarily by the burning of fuels to produce energy, by the incineration of wastes, and by the emission of gaseous by-products from industrial processes. Although the problem of atmospheric pollution is world-wide, it is primarily a problem of urban centers where pollutants are concentrated in relatively small geographical areas with high population density. For example, the reader is referred to Eisenbud [1970] for a survey of air pollution problems and current air pollution control programs in New York City and to Parvin and Grammas [1976b] for a discussion of the trade-offs existing between technological abatement and locational adjustment. It is clear that systematic analysis and planning are required to manage the air resources of a metropolitan region.

The ultimate goals of an air pollution control program relate to the medical, aesthetic, and economic effects of air pollution. Practically speaking, however, there is insufficient knowledge at present to permit a firm, quantitative link between these ultimate factors and the level of air pollution; control standards are difficult to express in such terms. Nevertheless, recent work in this direction is encouraging. For example, Rabow [1973] outlines a systematic approach for determining the costs of loss in health or well-being due to air pollution, and illustrates this approach by describing a scheme for determining the cost of excess mortality due to air pollution. In time, it is reasonable to expect that goals will be stated in terms of maximum permissible annual dosages of particular pollutants. Meanwhile, however, the goals must be expressed in terms of a secondary factor, namely air quality, which lends itself to relatively unambiguous and quantitative specification and measurement (e.g., air quality standards for the concentration of sulfur dioxide can be expressed as follows: the annual arithmetic mean should not exceed .03 ppm and the maximum 24-hour average should not exceed 0.14 ppm).

The planning of suitable policies for abatement of air pollution, in both the near term and the long term, is a complex technical problem. The technical problem, however, is embedded within a larger legal and sociopolitical context, as is to be expected of any matter of such serious public import. Typically, abatement plans can be formulated with respect to types of permissible fuels, combustion equipment, exhaust controls, type of emission source, location of emission sources, and scheduling of emissions.

A quantitative analytic approach can be applied to air pollution abatement planning involving the following classical series of steps: 1) define the desired goals in quantitative terms, 2) propose a comprehensive spectrum of alternative abatement policies, 3) establish the criteria by which the alternative policies (or combinations of policies) are to be evaluated, and 4) evaluate the alternative strategies in rigorous, quantitative terms from a cost/benefit viewpoint. One of the earliest comprehensive scientific studies of air pollution (American Association for the Advancement of Science [1965]) examined the economic implications of air pollution, the variety of public policies for abatement, and the formation of public attitudes which in turn affect the formation of these public policies. Savas [1967] presented a conceptual outline of a suitable simulation system to facilitate planning by urban air pollution control agencies and identified the elements of such a system. This simulation system can be used for both long- and short-term planning, and has the potential to be used for real-time prediction of air quality as well. When viewed from the point of view of feedback control systems, the identifiable inputs, outputs, means of measurement, and means of control can be assembled into a set of strategies for controlling urban air pollution. The control actions taken against the emitting sources (which are monitored by the system) are determined by the extent to which air quality deviates from the established code standards. Moreover, if the effects of future weather conditions can be predicted, control action can be taken in an anticipatory mode rather than a corrective one.

In another approach to the problems of air pollution, Ellis and Keeney [1972], described how the tools of decision analysis can aid a public official in choosing an air pollution control program. They discuss a set of objectives and measures of effectiveness which are used to describe the consequences of each of the alternative courses of action. Of great importance here, is the notion of obtaining a politically viable solution.

There are fundamentally two types of mathematical models for the analysis of air quality. The first type of model describes the physical environment for air pollution. For example, Larsen [1969] indicated that the log-normal family of probability distributions (a two-parameter family) provides an excellent fit to empirically observed cumulative frequency distributions for daily concentrations of sulfur dioxide, and Naden, et al. [1973] described the use of set theory and diffusion models for the remote surveillance of air pollution sources. The second type of model is the mathematical programming model for use in choosing between alternative abatement strategies. Kohn [1971] presented a LP model whose basic assumption is that there is a maximum allowable annual emission flow for each pollutant in an airshed. The solution of the model for the St. Louis airshed was examined in order to evaluate claims that it was economically infeasible to impose restrictions on the sulfur content of coal for the purposes of air pollution control. Kohn found that such a regulation was justified for certain types of stokers but not others and, moreover, that furnaces with a heating efficiency of 75% or less should be converted to natural gas. In general, however, the use of mathematical programming models in air pollution control appears to be limited. Most analysts involved with mathematical models for air pollution have focused either on data analysis and data management, or diffusion and meterological modeling.

An alternative approach to air quality control is, of course, the imposition of charges (taxes) at the source of emission to discourage pollution. Such an approach is taken by Cesario [1973], for example, who considered the problem of establishing the appropriate (social) charges or tolls to be levied against each highway user commensurate with the social costs he inflicts on others.

4. STREET SERVICES

Although not as critical as the emergency services and environmental protection, the "street services" that an urban community performs contribute greatly to the quality of life of the citizens. Moreover, if these street services are perceived to be inadequate, severe political repercussions can result (Savas [1973]). The major street services are snow removal, parking, street cleaning, street maintenance, and traffic control. All of these services are designed to keep streets clean and convenient to use.

On February 9, 1969 a major snowstorm produced a serious snow emergency and a political crisis in New York City. An analysis of the problem (Savas [1973]) focused on four basic questions: 1) How much snow falls on New York City? 2) How much work has to be done to clean it up? 3) What is the capacity for performing this work? 4) What improvements are needed to correct any imbalance between work load and work capacity? A low-cost snow emergency plan was prepared, calling for some additional equipment, better deployment, and a strategy for more rapid mobilization. Cook and Alprin [1976] indicate that cities can significantly improve their snow and ice removal operations by also improving the routing of salt spreader trucks.

The availability and quality of parking plays an important role in the service provided by an urban transportation system. Moreover, the design of the parking system can significantly influence the quality of the environment, particularly the ambient air quality and the noise levels in high-density areas. The main problems concern location of parking facilities, capacity and type of facilities, policies of operation (e.g., pricing policies, hours of operation), and staging of construction. Bennett, Ellis, and Rassam [1972] discuss a simulation model for evaluating any particular parking program. A main component of this model is a linear program which minimizes the joint disutility for all parkers (arriving parkers are allocated among alternative facilities), subject to capacity constraints for each facility and subject to the satisfaction of all demands. The outputs from the model are 1) the number of parkers with a given final destination who use each parking facility, 2) the number of available parking spaces in each facility, and 3) the resulting revenues.

The presence of parked cars along the curb in urban areas in violation of existing parking regulations adversely affects traffic flow and the delivery of essential services such as fire protection, waste collection, and street cleaning. A systems analysis of parking regulations, violations, and enforcement activities was conducted in New York City (Savas and Berenyi [1971]). DeStefano and Levis [1972] present a simple analytical model to evaluate the degradation of the street cleaning operation by mechanical brooms, as a result of illegally parked cars on both metered and non-metered streets. Compliance with parking regulations is defined by $C = (N - I)/N$, where N is the total number of parking spaces on a block-side and I is the number of illegally parked cars. It is shown that high compliance levels (85 percent) are necessary to sweep 70 to 75 percent of a curb (a minimal definition of "clean"). Tartarone and Levis [1973] develop a finite-state Markov chain model that relates parking regulation enforcement policies to expected levels of compliance. They describe the effects of deterministic and random policies and analyze a class of implementable policies that yield satisfactory results. These results are used to determine schedules and routes for enforcement officers that increase their effectiveness.

Adequate maintenance of city streets is required for safety, ease of traffic flow, and aesthetics. The three main categories of work are total construction, resurfacing of existing pavement, and emergency repairs (pothole repairs and patching). Two recent cost-benefit analyses by Parker and Renold [1971] and by Naphtali [1971] examine the tradeoffs between these categories. The optimum allocation of maintenance funds takes into account capital and expense budget constraints, and limitations on the capacity of contractors and in-house forces.

With respect to their primary purpose, transportation, city streets are used for parking and movement of vehicles. The problem of congestion is serious and has been addressed by OR methods and on-line traffic-control computers. Macrocontrol is used for implementing a control strategy over a relatively large area on a time scale of minutes or hours. Microcontrol is applied on a second-by-second basis to a limited number of intersections.

The problem can be viewed as one of allocation: assigning green-light phases so as to maximize some measures of vehicular movement. Mixed-integer LP has been used to design progression systems, but such systems are predicated on the assumption that the streets are relatively empty. Therefore, clever operation of traffic lights alone decreases delays by no more than ten percent or so. Route control, in which a set of roads is viewed as a traffic store-and-forward network, approaches the problem more realistically and offers the opportunity for additional improvements. Gazis [1972] presents a detailed review of traffic control theory and applications.

5. OTHER LOCAL SERVICES

Local governments are responsible for more than emergency services, environmental protection, and street services, of course. Education is the costliest local service, and much OR work has been focussed on school system planning, enrollment projections, site selection, scheduling, pupil assignment, school lunchroom operations, school-bus routing, and desegregation. OR applications in education are discussed in Chapter II-3 of this *Handbook*.

Criminal justice systems are not uniquely urban, nor even restricted to local government. Indeed, many of the problems of the criminal justice system in the United States derive from the fragmented nature of the system. Federal, state, and local law enforcement agencies interact with various prosecutors, a variety of court jurisdictions, miscellaneous facilities ostensibly intended for correction and rehabilitation, and agencies responsible for parole and probation. Blumstein and Larson [1969] constructed a system flow model of the entire criminal justice process, while others have simulated court subsystems (Taylor, et al. [1968], Jennings [1971a, 1971b]).

The field of social services, with value-laden, hard-to-quantify performance criteria, poses a challenge to OR analysts. Spindler [1970] discusses the various issues that arise with respect to child welfare services. He states program goals and identifies the variables that must be included in models of the system if they are to be useful. He emphasizes the curse of the urban analyst—the unavailability of data.

Fisher and Purnell [1973] studied the geographic migration of the welfare population in metropolitan Chicago. Their findings fail to support the widely accepted "calculative migration" hypothesis, which asserts that low-income families move to Chicago in order to obtain more generous welfare benefits. They found that most migrants who receive the aid in question resided in the state at least five years before obtaining such assistance. Greenberg [1971] examined the potential impact of income maintenance programs in New York and predicted that male heads of households would reduce their working hours if the proposed family assistance plan were implemented.

Hess, et al. [1965] pioneered in the computer-assisted creation of political district boundaries. Mills [1967] applied LP, together with a heuristic component, to the problem of establishing electoral boundaries for Bristol County Borough. However, there is no evidence that the results were actually used. In New York City, a heuristic algorithm was used to show the savings in election costs that could be achieved by creating more efficient election districts (Savas

[1971a]); a simple manual approach based on the computer algorithm was implemented at a saving of more than one million dollars annually [Savas, et al., 1972].

Municipal budgeting has also been subjected to modelling efforts (Crecine [1967]; Governmental problem solving . . . , [1967]; however, another important function of local government has been quite neglected: recreation. Cesario [1969] reviewed the work of predicting recreation travel flows and estimating economic benefits of outdoor recreation, while Fisher and Krutilla [1972] studied the optimal capacity of recreation facilities, but those works did not address issues pertinent to planning or operating urban parks. Despite Cicchetti's article [1971], little has been done to determine the demand for urban recreation by different segments of the population, to establish the desired mix and location of different recreation facilities, or to relate usage to operating costs and maintenance needs, and thereby to program and schedule recreational events and activities by time and place within urban areas.

Municipal zoning decisions usually elicit intense political forces, and would not appear to be susceptible to OR methods. However, a model was developed to simulate the process by which zoning ordinances are changed in Pittsburgh (Davis and Reuter [1972]). It was tested by allowing a computer to decide all 125 zoning changes that were proposed during a two-year period. The computer arrived at the same conclusions as the decision-making bodies in about 90 per cent of the cases.

A word is in order about urban development models. While there has been considerable effort expended on the construction of models which show the interaction of factors involved in urban growth and development (Lowry [1964], Harris [1965], Kilbridge, et al. [1969]) and notably the work of Forrester [1968] on urban dynamics, these efforts seem to have had little practical impact to date, outside of Forrester's stimulation of much academic debate reminiscent of the angel-pinhead discussions earlier in this millenium (Chan [1972]).

6. CITIZEN FEEDBACK

One can look beyond individual public services to examine their attributes in a more aggregate context. For example, Savas [1969a, 1970] found it fruitful to view municipal service delivery as a feedback control process in which goal-setting, administrative actuation, disturbances, system dynamics, and information feedback take on appropriate new interpretations in the context of city government. He pointed out that social indicators can be estimated from citizen complaints and from objective measurements, and used to generate error signals in a municipal control system. Krendel [1971] analyzed this system from a control engineering viewpoint, and examined complaint-processing procedures in a city government in order to estimate the parameters which describe the dynamic characteristics of the system (Krendel [1970]).

The subject of citizen feedback is attracting increased attention as its important role in societal decision-making and in goal achievement is recognized (Stevens [1970], Krieger [1971]). A pilot system of citizen feedback was developed for the governor of Puerto Rico in order to improve government functioning (Little, et al. [1971a, 1971b]). It distinguished between various kinds of information flow. Citizen feed*forward* is the projection of information by government to the citizens for the purpose of eliciting *involvement feedback*, that is, opinions, suggestions, and participation. Involvement feedback augments service feedback, which is comprised of complaints, requests, and inquiries. Citizen feedback components and systems were studied in the context of live problems in Massachusetts (Little,et al. [1972]). "Participatory technology," based on computers and telecommunications, was used to facilitate citizen feedback on an experimental basis in various settings (Etzioni [1972], Johnson and Ward [1972], Lucas and Yin [1973]). The application of systematic citizen surveys to measure the performance of local government (Webb and Hatry [1973]) is increasing, and has been used to evaluate individual services (Blair and Schwartz [1972], Hatry [1974]). In addition, Yin, et al. [1973] have examined alternative forms of citizen participation in the delivery of social services, looking at such involvement as a means of reforming and improving the administration of social programs—not as a social reform.

7. PROBLEMS IN APPLYING URBAN OR

The preceding sections have catalogued the use of OR in problems of urban service delivery. A variety of operational problems have been addressed successfully. However, the use of OR at the strategic level to solve urban problems has been less successful—a shortcoming that OR shares with all other disciplines. The results have been particularly disappointing when measured against the early expectations of some uncritical enthusiasts, that "the urban problem" would be conquered by the modern management armamentarium of OR, the systems approach, planning-programming-budgeting systems, and the like.

In order to understand the reasons for the modesty of the impact of OR at the strategic level, it is necessary to examine the barriers to implementation and the nature of the larger systems within which urban service systems are nested (Halbrecht, et al. [1972], Hoos [1972], Savas [1975]). Only then can one properly perceive the new challenges and new opportunities which confront "urban OR." Some of the implementation difficulties encountered by the urban analyst are similar to those found in other application areas, but are exacerbated in the urban setting. Others are common to public-sector problems (Spindler [1970]). Still others are peculiar to local government, and not only in the U.S. (Ward [1970]). What follows is a compilation of these problems.

1. One man's system is another man's subsystem. The complexities of urban problems make it difficult for an analyst to define a problem area that is large enough to be meaningful but small enough to be tractable. Any preferred solution is therefore vulnerable to the criticism that it has ignored issues which arise in the next larger system.

2. To undertake an OR study of a problem is a political act; that is, to select a particular area for study reflects someone's judgment that there is something wrong in that area. This decision is inevitably threatening to at least one bureaucracy, and gratifying to at least one other. The analyst is therefore exposed to bureaucratic crossfire if he attempts to do something significant.

3. The OR analyst, while comfortable with the abstract concepts of resource allocation and scheduling, finds himself disconcertingly enmeshed in the unfamiliar political process of which group gets what, when, and where—which is, after all, what allocation and scheduling of public resources is all about.

4. Getting to the moon was relatively easy, for there are no constituents on the moon. The decisions about lunar landing sites were based entirely on technical considerations: the public did not care where the astronauts set down, whether in the Sea of Tranquility or on the Heights of Assininity. However, the public cares a great deal about where a waste disposal site is to be located or where an airport is to be built, and, therefore, the technical analysis generated by OR plays a relatively minor role in such decisions. An algorithm which seems to prove that the "best" place for a drug-treatment center is just down the block from a councilman's home, proves instead that the algorithm is a poor one and that the analyst will be ignored, at best.

5. A common lament by analysts is that decision making in the public sector is too political and not sufficiently rational. What this reveals is that the analyst doesn't understand the objective function of the decision maker. The decision maker includes terms in his (implicit) objective function which reflect factors that the analyst is either unaware of or unable to handle.

6. The OR analyst is a would-be agent of change: his conclusions never recommend maintenance of the status quo, they almost always recommend change. But change in the urban context usually means changing institutional relationships, work patterns, and relative power of people, and such changes, while lightly recommended, are difficult to effect. Furthermore, the role of change agent in this setting is a hazardous one; Socrates, an early analyst who questioned current ways of thinking, was prosecuted by a public official and given poison by a civil servant.

7. The OR tradition has fostered a view of decision-making that is inap-

propriate for urban problem solving. Whereas the analyst sees himself as presenting to the decision-maker the consequences of alternative decisions, in reality, governmental decision-making rarely consists of a neat, crisp, binary selection. Rather, it is usually a vague, prolonged, diffuse, and pluralistic process. Therefore, if a "decision" is ever to ensue from an analytic study, the technician must become an active force pushing for resolution along an unmarked front—an unaccustomed and uncomfortable role for many analysts. Kash [1968] eloquently describes public-sector decision making:

[I] t is important to recall that decision-making . . . is a process. Phrases like the "decision-making process" and the "process of policy formulation" are not mere incantation: they refer to the continuous flow of decisions, large and small, that make up the seamless web of policy formation and administrative action in . . . government. The dynamic flux of the policy process makes the job of the advisor particularly difficult. It means that there is no orderly procedure whereby the advisor can state his views or explain his research and then retire from the scene confident that his advice will receive systematic consideration. There are numerous distractions and competing demands on the decisionmaker's time and span of attention. Decisions once made can become unmade a week later. The advisor may face a difficult task to secure a full hearing for his views in the first place, and then must struggle to keep attention focused on his recommendations for a long enough period to assure action of some kind. Continuity is thus an essential attribute of effective communication of policy oriented research. A corollary of this is that the advice cannot simply be given to the top levels if favorable decision and effective implementation of advice is desired. Consider the case of a high level decisionmaker accepting the recommendation of an advisory group and making a "policy" decision designed to implement the advice. Unless the subordinates carry out the decision effectively the whole intent can be defeated. Comprehension of the basis for the decision reached at the higher level can be a vital factor in winning the consent and enthusiasm of those who must execute the decision and, in doing so, make a myriad of other decisions which can determine the success or failure of the original decision.

8. The irrelevance of technical elegance is obvious to political leaders and government executives, but not to the legions of analysts, who, armed with mathematical tools or computer programs, earnestly seek urban problems upon which to use them. As Russell Ackoff once said, "I'd rather be operated upon by a skilled surgeon with a rusty penknife than by a salesman of fine surgical instruments using his latest wares."

9. Optimization, a classic concept in OR, takes on a very different meaning in urban problem solving, where, exasperatingly, it often appears that there is *no* feasible solution. Optimization in this setting usually consists of trying to determine which constraint can be forced back, at minimal political cost, sufficiently so as to create one feasible, and hence, optimal point.

10. Problems not perceived by the public are problems not acted upon. Perception of a problem by an intellectual elite, such as OR analysts, is not sufficient · to induce action. The public does not yet reward long-range political decisions which prevent problems from arising, nor does it punish its representatives for failure to act when the price of inaction is a deficit to be paid in the future.

11. Predictive models for urban phenomena are poor. It is difficult to forecast the effect of a disturbance on a system, and it is difficult to calculate the kind and quality of anticipatory corrective action that should be taken to counteract that effect.

12. The urban complex exhibits counterproductive behavior; that is, the ultimate result of an action often turns out to be quite the opposite of that which is intended. For example, consider the elaborate bureaucratic system of checks and balances designed to assure fair value in a city's purchases. The procedures were constructed to protect against graft and corruption when contracting for supplies, equipment, and services. However, the consequence for some cities is an inordinately long delay in securing bids and paying bills, with the result that many potential vendors refuse to do business with the city, and those who do have to charge higher prices in order to make up for the additional expense of dealing with the city. Thus, a strategy designed to *increase* competition and *reduce* the cost of goods has the perverse effect of *reducing* competition and *increasing* the cost of goods (Savas [1970]).

13. Too many operations researchers come to work late and leave early. This refers not to their daily work habits but to the narrow view of their role. They should be involved much earlier in problem definition and in learning about the subtleties of the constraints and the objectives, and they should remain involved much later throughout the implementation process. In urban problems, the analytical phase occupies only a small portion of the total effort; the dominant phases are problem definition, data collection, and implementation.

14. The OR analyst concerned with implementation of his findings—as of course he has to be—should be aware of five classic defenses used by bureaucrats to resist a recommendation for change:

(a) "But we've always done it this way!"
(b) "It can't be done that way."
(c) "We tried that in 1948 and it didn't work."
(d) "Well, we're really doing that already, sort of."
(e) "Yes, I guess you can do it, but even if you did, it wouldn't do any good."

8. NEW DIRECTIONS FOR URBAN OR

Urban OR has focussed primarily on *problems* and *programs*, but improvement of the quality of urban life and the management of urban services requires *structural* or *institutional* reforms (Gordon [1973], Rosenbloom and Russell [1971], Brewer [1973]). Designing optimal patrol routes for city police forces seems somehow inconsequential in the face of the startling finding that of 31,000 policemen in the New York City Police Department, only 1,000 are on patrol at any given time (Burnham [1974]). How much effort should be expended to improve the productivity of municipal refuse collection by optimal scheduling, routing, and disposal-site selection, when it has been demonstrated that private firms collect refuse at only one-third the cost of the municipal agency (Savas [1974]) (and do so without benefit of OR)? The monopoly nature of some municipal services goes far to explain their poor performance (Savas [1971b]) and suggests the obvious—but politically explosive—remedy of introducing competition into the delivery of local services (Savas [1974, 1977]).

While admirable OR work has been done to model and to operate family planning systems (for example, the work of Urban [1974] and others), OR helps undo such work in other ways: modern marketing methods are being used to promote the fad of bottle feeding instead of breast feeding, even in underdeveloped nations which have high birth rates. Because lactation inhibits ovulation, a natural contraceptive process is thus being undermined; it is estimated that prolonged lactation in a highly fertile community could prevent up to 20 percent of births (Wade [1974]).

OR has solved large classes of problems involving job scheduling and work assignment, but when employee motivation is vitiated by a rigid civil service system (Savas and Ginsburg [1973]), it is of little avail to update the parameters in a model in order to reflect dwindling productivity.

The very notion of effectiveness in urban services has only recently begun to receive analytical attention (Hatry [1974]). This is a necessary starting point; to evaluate police services one must go beyond simple measures such as response times, for example, and look at victimization rates as well. Similiarly, while city agencies proudly report how many tons of refuse they collect, they usually fail to report how many tons are left behind. Only recently has the novel but sensible question been asked: How clean is our city? (Blair and Schwartz [1972])

Public agencies typically point to the demand for service and seek resources to *satisfy* that demand. Increasingly, it is to be hoped, they will employ OR to utilize those resources efficiently. But there is little motivation to *reduce* the demand. A fertile area for exploration is the use of pricing and market mechanisms to change the pattern and reduce the level of demand (Mushkin [1972])—whether for rush-hour traffic or for peak-period demand for water. The suggestion by Savas [1969a], to use registered nurses to screen unnecessary requests for ambulances, resulted in a 10% reduction of ambulance trips; two nurses caused the same reduction in average response time as could be achieved by ten ambulances, at much lower cost (Lee [1971]).

One of the most fundamental issues affecting urban services has to do with the structure of local government. In most metropolitan areas there is a gross incongruity between the natural geographic boundaries of a service function and the legal boundaries of the jurisdiction nominally charged with attending to that function. It is necessary to sort out these functions. Which level of government should provide which services to whom, and how should they be paid for? Issues of revenue sharing, regionalism, and neighborhood government, among others, are involved. Poverty and welfare are best handled nationally, while transportation, pollution, water supply, and waste disposal are clearly regional in character. However, street cleaning, street repair, and refuse collection have primarily a local impact and can be handled at the neighborhood level. New tiers of government—regional and neighborhood—are needed to supplement or replace the obsolete units of government extant since colonial times in some of our urban areas.

In all these challenges involving institutional change, OR has an important role to play. Above all, it is needed to help design adaptive systems that will enable our urban society to survive with its deeply held human goals intact. To do so, OR will have to ally itself with other disciplines in "the science of the systems age" (Ackoff [1973]).

REFERENCES

Abert, J. G., H. Alter, and J. F. Bernheisel, "The Economics of Resource Recovery from Municipal Solid Waste," *Science* **183**, pp. 1052–1058 (March 15, 1974).

Ackoff, R., "Science in the Systems Age: Beyond IE, OR, and MS," *Operations Res.* **21**, No. 3: 661–671 (1973).

Altman, S. M., E. J. Beltrami, S. S. Rappaport, and G. K. Schoepfle, "Nonlinear Programming Model of Crew Assignments for Household Refuse Collection," *IEEE Trans. Systems, Man, and Cybernetics* **SMC-1**, No. 3: 289–291 (1971).

American Association for the Advancement of Science, "Air Conservation", *A.A.A.S.* (1965).

Anderson, R. T. (ed.), *Waste Management: Generation and Disposal of Solid, Liquid, and Gaseous Wastes in the New York Region*, Regional Plan Association, New York (1968).

Bell, C. E. and D. Allen, "Optimal Planning of an Emergency Ambulance Service", *Socio-Econ. Plan. Sci.* **3**, pp. 95–101 (1969).

Beltrami, E. J. and L. D. Bodin, "Networks and Vehicle Routing for Municipal Waste Collection", *J. Networks* **4**, pp. 65–94 (1973).

Bennett, J. C., R. H. Ellis, and P. R. Rassam, "A Guide to Parking Systems Analysis", U. S. Department of Transportation/Federal Highway Administration No. 5001–00049 (October 1972).

Blair, L. H. and A. I. Schwartz, *How Clean is Our City?*, Urban Institute, Washington, D. C. (1972).

Blum, E. H., "Deployment Research of the New York City Fire Project," *Urban Anal.* **1**, pp. 63–94 (1972).

Blumstein, A. and R. Larson, "Models of a Total Criminal Justice System," *Operations Res.* **17**, No. 2: 199–232 (1969).

Bodin, L. D., A. C. Tucker, S. M. Altman, and E. J. Beltrami, "Heuristics in Manpower Scheduling", Urban Science and Engineering Technical Report No. 71-7, State University of New York at Stony Brook (March 1971).

Bodner, R. M., E. A. Cassell, and P. J. Andros, "Optimal Routing of Refuse Collection Vehicles," *J. Sanitary Eng. Div., ASCE* **96**, No. SA4: 893–904 (1970).

Brewer, G. D., *The Politician, the Bureaucrat, and the Consultant*, Basic Books, New York (1973).

Burnham, D., "1,000 of the City's 31,000 Policemen Are Out in Radio Cars At Any One Time," *New York Times*, p. 1 (February 18, 1974).

Carter, G. M., J. M. Chaiken, and E. Ignall, "Response Areas for Two Emergency Units," *Operations Res.* **20**, No. 3: 571–594 (1972).

———, and E. J. Ignall, "A Simulation Model of Fire Department Operations: Design and Preliminary Results," *IEEE Trans. Systems Sci. and Cybernetics* **SSC-6**, No. 4: 282–293 (1970).

Cesario, F. J., "Operations Research in Outdoor Recreation," *J. Leisure Res.* **1**, pp. 33-51 (1969).

———, "Optimal Road Pricing for Air Pollution Control," *The Regional Sci. Assoc. Pap.* **30**, pp. 97-110 (1973).

Chaiken, J. M., "Number of Emergency Units Busy at Alarms Which Require Multiple Servers," New York City–Rand Institute, R-531-NYC/HUD (March 1971).

——— and R. C. Larson, "Methods for Allocating Urban Emergency Units: A Survey," *Management Sci.* **19**, No. 4, Part II: 110–130 (1972).

Chan, K. (ed.), "Urban Dynamics: Extensions and Reflections," *IEEE Trans. Systems, Man, and Cybernetics* **SMC-2**, No. 2: 121–220 (1972).

Cicchetti, C. J., "Some Economic Issues in Planning Urban Recreation Facilities," *Land Econ.* **47**, 14–23 (1971).

Clough, D. J., "Environmental Pollution," in *Operational Research '72*, M. Ross (ed.), North-Holland Publishing Company, Amsterdam (1973).

Cook, T. M. and B. S. Alprin, "Snow and Ice Removal in an Urban Environment," *Management Science* **23**, No. 3: 227–234 (1976).

Coulter, J. B., "The Role of Government and Systems Analysis in Waste Management," in *The Challenge to Systems Analysis: Public Policy and Social Change*, G. J. Kelleher (ed), John Wiley & Sons, New York (1970).

Coyle, R. G. and M. J. C. Martin, "Case Study: The Cost Minimization of Refuse Collection Operations," *Operational Res. Quart.* **20**, Special Conference Issue, 43–56 (1969).

Crecine, J. P., "A Computer Simulation Model of Municipal Budgeting," *Management Sci.* **13**, No. 11: 786–815 (1967).

Davis, O. and F. Rueter, "A Simulation of Municipal Zoning Decisions," *Management Sci.* **19**, No. 4: P39–P78 (1972).

de Neufville, R., "Cost-Effectiveness Analysis of Civil Engineering Systems: New York City's Primary Water Supply," *Operations Res.* **18**, No 5: 785–804 (1970).

———, J. Schaake and J. H. Stafford, "Systems Analysis of Water Distribution Networks," *J. Sanitary Eng. Div., ASCE* **97**, No. SA6: 835–842 (1971).

DeStefano, L. T. and A. H. Levis, "A Model for the Effect of Illegally Parked Cars on Street Cleaning," *J. Environ. Syst.* **2**, No. 2: 109–129 (1972).

Eisenbud, M., "Environmental Protection in the City of New York," *Science* **170**, 706–712 (November 13, 1970).

Ellis, H. M. and R. L. Keeney, "A Rational Approach for Government Decisions Concerning Air Pollution," in *Analysis of Public Systems*, A. Drake, R. Keeney, and P. Morse (eds.), M.I.T. Press, Cambridge, Massachusetts (1972).

Etzioni, A., "Minerva and Electronic Town Hall," *Policy Sci.* **3**, 457–474 (1972).

Fisher, A. and J. V. Krutilla, "Determination of Optimal Capacity of Resource-Based Recreational Facilities," *Natural Resource J.* **12**, 417–444 (1972).

Fisher, I. N. and S. W. Purnell, "The Connection Between Migration and Welfare Dependency in the Chicago Metropolitan Area," Rand Corp. Report R-1388-IISP, Santa Monica, California (1973).

Fitzsimmons, J., "A methodology for Emergency Ambulance Deployment," *Management Sci.* **19**, No. 6: 627–636 (1973).

Forrester, J. W., *Urban Dynamics*, M.I.T. Press, Cambridge, Massachusetts (1968).

Freeman, A. M. and R. H. Haveman, "Residual Charges for Pollution Control: A Policy Evaluation," *Science* **177**, 322–329 (July 28, 1972).

——, ——, and A. V. Kneese, *The Economics of Environmental Policy*, John Wiley & Sons, New York (1973).

Gazis, D. C., "Traffic Flow and Control: Theory and Applications," *Am. Scientist* **60**, 414–424 (1972).

Gordon, D. R., *City Limits: Barriers to Change in Urban Government*, Charterhouse, New York (1973).

Governmental Problem Solving: A Computer Simulation of Municipal Budgeting, Rand McNally, Chicago (1967).

Green, J. A., "Predicting Future Quantities of Refuse," Local Government Operational Research Unit Report No. T.20 (August 1969).

——, and R. W. Nice, "The Economics of Transfer Stations and Vehicle Relays as Methods of Refuse Collection," Local Government Operational Research Unit Report No. T.19 (July 1969).

Greenberg, D. H., "The Potential Impact of the Family Assistance Plan on New York City," New York City-Rand Institute Rept. R-658-NYC, New York (1971).

Haimes, Y. Y., "Pollution and Ecology," in *Systems Approach and the City*, M. D. Mesarovic and A. Reisman (eds.), North-Holland Publishing Company, Amsterdam (1972).

Halbrecht, H., E.S. Savas, G. Hoffman, H. F. Ayres, M. Radnor, and F. Edelman, "Through a Glass Darkly," *Interfaces* **2**, No. 4: 1–17 (1972).

Hall, W. K., "Management Science Approaches to the Determination of Urban Ambulance Requirements," *Socio-Econ. Plan. Sci.* **5**, 491–499 (1971).

——, "The Application of Multifunction Stochastic Service Systems in Allocating Ambulances to an Urban Area," *Operations Res.* **20**, No. 3: 558–570 (1972).

Harris, B. (ed.), "Urban Development Models: New Tools for Planning," *J. Am. Inst. Planners* **31**, No. 2 (1965).

Hatry, H. P., "Measuring the Quality of Public Services," in *Improving the Quality of Urban Management*, W. Hawley and D. Rogers (eds), Sage Publications, Inc., Beverly Hills, California (1974).

Hess, S. W., J. B. Weaver, H. J. Siegfeldt, J. N. Whelan, and P. A. Zitlau, "Nonpartisan Political Redistricting by Computer," *Operations Res.* **13**, No. 6: 998–1006 (1965).

Hoey, J. M., "Planning for an Effective Hospital Administered Emergency Ambulance Service in the City of Boston," M.I.T. Operations Research Center Report No. RR-01-73 (September 1973).

Hoos, I. R., *Systems Analysis in Public Policy: A Critique*, University of California Press, Berkeley, California (1972).

Ignall, E., P. Kolesar, and W. Walker, "Linear Programming Models of Crew Assignments for Refuse Collection," *IEEE Trans. Systems, Man, and Cybernetics* **SMC-2**, No. 5: 664–666 (1972).

Jarvis, J. P., "Optimal Dispatch Policies for Urban Server Systems," M.I.T. Operations Research Center Report No. TR-02-73 (September 1973).

Jennings, J. B., "Quantitative Models of Criminal Courts," Rand Corp. Report P-4641, Santa Monica, California (1971).

———, "The Flow of Arrested Adult Defendants Through the Manhattan Criminal Court in 1968 and 1969," New York City-Rand Institute Report R-638-NYC, New York (1971).

Johnson, N. and E. Ward, "Citizen Information Systems: Using Technology to Extend the Dialogue Between Citizens and Their Government," *Management Sci.* 19, No. 4: P21–P36 (1972).

Kash, D. E., "Research and Development of the University," *Science* 160, 1313–1318 (June 21, 1968).

Keeney, R. L., "A method for Districting Among Facilities," *Operations Res.* 20, No. 3: 613–618 (1972).

Kilbridge, M. D., R. P. O'Block, and P. V. Teplitz, "A Conceptual Framework for Urban Planning Models," *Management Sci.* 15, No. 6: B246–B266 (1969).

Kneese, A. V. and B. T. Bower, *Managing Water Quality: Economics, Technology Institutions*, Johns Hopkins Press, Baltimore, Maryland (1968).

Kohn, R. E., "Application of Linear Programming to a Controversy on Air Pollution Control," *Management Sci.* 17, No. 10: B609-B621 (1971).

Kolesar, P., "A Model for Predicting Average Fire Engine Travel Times," *Operations Res.* 23, No. 4: 603–613 (1975).

Kolesar, P. and E. H. Blum, "Square Root Laws for Fire Engine Response Distances," *Management Sci.* 19, No. 12: 1368–1378 (1973).

———, and W. E. Walker, "An Algorithm for the Dynamic Relocation of Fire Companies," *Operations Res.* 22, No. 2: 249–274 (1974).

———, W. E. Walker, and J. Hauser, "Determining the Relation Between Fire Engine Travel Times and Travel Distances in New York," *Operations Res.* 23, No. 4: 614–627 (1975).

Krendel, E. S., "A Case Study of Citizen Complaints as Social Indicators," *IEEE Trans. Systems Sci. and Cybernetics* SSC-6, No. 4: 265–272 (1970).

———, "Social Indicators and Urban Systems Dynamics," *Socio-Econ. Plan. Sci.* 5, 387–393 (1971).

Krieger, M. H., "Social Reporting for a City: A Perspective and Some Problems," New York City-Rand Institute, P-4651 (1971).

Larsen, R. I., "A New Mathematical Model of Air Pollutant Concentration Averaging Time and Frequency," *J. Air Pollution Control Assoc.* 19, No. 1 (1969).

Larson, R. C., "Improving the Effectiveness of New York City's 911," in *Analysis of Public Systems*, A. Drake, R. Keeney, and P. Morse (eds.), M.I.T. Press, Cambridge, Massachusetts (1972).

———, *Urban Police Patrol Analysis*, M.I.T. Press, Cambridge, Massachusetts (1972).

———, "Illustrative Police Sector Redesign in District 4 in Boston," M.I.T. Operations Research Center Report No. PP-01-73 (November 1973).

———, "Approximating the Performance of Urban Emergency Service Systems," *Operations Res.* 23, No. 5: 845–868 (1975).

———, and K. A. Stevenson, "On Insensitivities in Urban Redistricting and Facility Location," *Operations Res.* 20, No. 3: 595–612 (1972).

Lee, V., "Nurses Screening 911 Calls to Save Ambulance Runs," *New York Daily News* (January 2, 1971).

Liebman, J. C., "Systems Approaches to Solid Waste Collection Problems," in *Systems Approach to Environmental Pollution*, G. K. Chacko (ed.), Operations Research Society of America, Arlington, Va. (1972).

Little, J. D. C., T. B. Sheridan, C. H. Stevens, and P. Tropp, "Citizen Feedback Components and Systems," M.I.T. Operations Research Center Report No. 76 (June 1972).

——, C. H. Stevens, and P. Tropp, "Citizen Feedback System: The Puerto Rico Model," *Nat. Civic Rev.* **60,** 191–203 (1971).

——, and N. Gusdorf, "Puerto Rico's Citizen Feedback System," M.I.T. Operations Research Center Report No. 59 (April 1971).

Loucks, D. P. and W. R. Lynn, "Probabilistic Models for Predicting Stream Quality," *Water Resources Res.* **2,** No. 3 (1966).

——, C. S. ReVelle, and W. R. Lynn, "Linear Programming Models for Programming Models for Water Pollution Control," *Management Sci.* **14,** No. 4: B166–B181 (1967).

Lowry, I. S., "A Model of Metropolis," Rand Corp. Report RM-4035-RC, Santa Monica, California (1964).

Lucas, W. A. and R. K. Yin, "Serving Local Needs with Telecommunications," Rand Corp. Report R-1345-MF, Santa Monica, California (1973).

Management and Behavioral Science Center, "A Systems Approach to the Problems of Solid Waste and Litter," Wharton School of Finance and Commerce, University of Pennsylvania (September 1971).

Marks, D. H., "Operations Research and Water Quality Management," *Urban Anal.* **1,** No. 1: 29–44 (1972).

Marks, D. H., "Models in Water Resources," in *A Guide to Models in Governmental Planning and Operations*, S. I. Gass and R. L. Sisson (eds.), Sauger Books, Potomac, Maryland (1975).

——, and J. C. Liebman, "Location Models: Solid Waste Collection Example," *J. Urban Plan. and Dev., ASCE* **97,** No. UP1: 15–30 (1971).

McEwen, T., Project Director, "Allocation of Patrol Manpower Resources in the Saint Louis Police Department," **I, II,** (1966).

Mills, G., "The Determination of Local Government Electoral Boundaries," *Operational Res. Quart.* **18,** No. 3: 243–255 (1967).

Mushkin, S. (ed.), *Public Prices for Public Products*, Urban Institute, Washington, D. C. (1972).

Naden, R. A., J. V. Leeds, and P. E. Pfeiffer, "Use of the Reciprocity Theorem and Mapping Theorems in Locating Anomalous Air Pollution Sources," *IEEE Trans. Systems, Man, and Cybernetics* **SMC-3,** No. 2: 147–154 (1973).

Naphtali, L. M., "Maintenance Planning System for the Department of Highways," City of New York, Office of the Mayor (November 16, 1971).

Parker, C. and J. Renold, "Value for Money in Highway Maintenance: Report of a Feasibility Study," Local Government Operational Research Unit Report No. C.98 (July 1971).

Parvin, M. and G. W. Grammas, "Optimization Models for Environmental Pollution Control: A Synthesis," *Journal of Environmental Economics and Management* **3,** No. 2: 113–128 (1976).

——, "Technological Abatement vs. Locational Adjustment: A Time-Space Dilemma," in M. Chatterji and P. Van Rompuy (eds.), *Energy, Regional Science and Public Policy*, Springer-Verlag, New York (1976).

Quon, J. E., M. Tanaka, and A. Charnes, "Refuse Quantities and the Frequency of Service," *J. Sanitary Eng. Div., ASCE* **94,** No. SA2: 403–420 (1968).

Rabow, G., "Cost of Polution," *IEEE Trans. Systems, Man, and Cybernetics* **SMC-3,** No. 3: 275–276 (1973).

ReVelle, C. S., E. Joeres, and W. Kirby, "The Linear Decision Rule in Reservoir Management and Design: 1. Development of the Stochastic Model," *Water Resources Res.* **5,** No 4: 767–777 (1969).

——, and W. Kirby, "The Linear Decision Rule in Reservoir Management and Design: 2. Performance Optimization," *Water Resources Res.* **6**, No. 4: 1033–1044 (1970).

——, D. H. Marks, and J. C. Liebman, "An Analysis of Private and Public Sector Location Models," *Management Sci.* **16**, No. 11: 692–707 (1970).

Rosenbloom, R. S. and J. R. Russell, *New Tools for Urban Management*, Harvard University, Boston (1971).

Savas, E. S., "Computers in Urban Air Pollution Control Systems," *Socio-Econ. Plan. Sci.* **1**, 157–183 (1967).

——, "City Hall and Cybernetics," in *Cybernetics and the Management of Large Systems*, E. M. Dewan (ed.), Spartan Books, New York (1969).

——, "Simulation and Cost-Effectiveness Analysis of New York's Emergency Ambulance Service," *Management Sci.* **15**, No. 12: B608–B627 (1969).

——, Cybernetics in City Hall," *Science* **168**, 1066–1071 (May 29, 1970).

——, "A Computerized System for Forming Efficient Election Districts," *Operations Res.* **19**, No. 1: 135–155 (1971).

——, "Municipal Monopoly," *Harpers Magazine*, 55–60 (December 1971).

——, "The Political Properties of Crystalline H_2O: Planning for Snow Emergencies in New York," *Management Sci.* **20**, No. 2: 137–145 (1973).

——, "Municipal Monopolies vs. Competition in Delivering Urban Services," in *Improving the Quality of Urban Management*, W. Hawley and D. Rogers (eds.), Sage Publications, Inc., Beverly Hills, California (1974).

——, "New Directions for Urban Analysis," *Interfaces* **6**, No. 1 (1975).

——, *The Organization and Efficiency of Solid Waste Collection*, Lexington Books, Lexington, Massachusetts (1977).

——, and J. Berenyi, "Systems Analysis of Parking Regulations, Violations and Enforcement Activities," Office of the Mayor, City of New York (1971).

——, and S. Ginsburg, "The Civil Service: A Meritless System?," *The Public Interest*, No. 32: 70–85 (Summer 1973).

——, H. Lipton, and L. Burkholz, "Implementation of an OR Approach for Forming Efficient Election Districts," *Operations Res.* **20**, No. 1: 46–48 (1972).

Spindler, A., "Social and Rehabilitation Services: A Challenge to Operations Research," *Operations Res.* **18**, No. 6: 1112–1124 (1970).

Stevens, C. H., "Science, Government, and Citizen Feedback," *Operations Res.* **18**, No. 4: 577–591 (1970).

Stevenson, K. A., "Emergency Ambulance Transportation," in *Analysis of Public Systems*, A. Drake, R. Keeney, and P. Morse (eds.), M.I.T. Press, Cambridge, Massachusetts (1972).

Swoveland, C., I. Uyeno, I. Vertinsky, and R. Vickson, "Ambulance Location: A Probabilistic Enumeration Approach," *Management Sci.* **20**, No. 4 Part II: 686–698 (1973).

Tartarone, S. and A. H. Levis, "Enforcement Policies for Parking Regulations," *IEEE Trans. Systems, Man, and Cybernetics* **SMC-3**, No. 6: 604–610 (1973).

Taylor, J. G., J. A. Navarro, and R. H. Cohen, "Simulation Applied to a Court System," *IEEE Trans. on Systems Sci. and Cybernetics* **SSC-4**, No. 4: 376–379 (1968).

Toregas, C., R. Swain, C. ReVelle, and L. Bergman, "The Location of Emergency Service Facilities," *Operations Res.* **19**, No. 6: 1363–1373 (1971).

Urban, G. L., "A Model for Managing a Family Planning System," *Operations Res.* **22**, No. 2: 205–233 (1974).

Wade, N., "Bottle-Feeding: Adverse Effects of A Western Technology," *Science* **184**, 45–48 (1974).

Ward, R. A., "Operations Research in British Local Government," in *Proceedings of the*

Fifth International Conference on Operational Research, J. Lawrence (ed.), Tavistock Publications, Ltd., London (1970).

Webb, K. and H. P. Hatry, "Obtaining Citizen Feedback," The Urban Institute, Washington, D. C. (1973).

Yin, R. K., W. A. Lucas, P. L. Szanton, and J. A. Spindler, "Citizen Organizations: Increasing Client Control Over Services," Rand Corp. Report R-1196-HEW, Santa Monica, California (1973).

II-2

THE HEALTH SERVICES

Robert B. Fetter
Yale University

INTRODUCTION

Applications of operations research (OR) in health care may be viewed as having occurred at two levels. Most of the initial work in the field concentrated on micro-analytic studies, usually within hospitals. Thus, work can be found, for example, dealing with scheduling in outpatient clinics; determination of appropriate inventory control methods for linens, drugs, and other consumables; the development of operating policies for blood banking; analysis of the utilization of inpatient facilities; and studies of the relative effectiveness of alternative methods for delivery of specific services.

More recently, OR has come to be applied—usually as "systems analysis"—to macro-analytic studies. In this context, one finds work concerned with the design and operation of hospitals, regional planning of facilities for delivery of health care, manpower planning studies, both national and international, information systems, and quality control in health care.

The material that follows will discuss the past, present, and future of work in these two broad areas as OR in health care, even though the labeling of the work by its authors may alternatively be management science or systems analysis. Material which will not be discussed falls mainly in two categories. First, the general area of biomedical engineering, including patient monitoring, laboratory systems, radiological analysis, equipment design, and the like which, while often concerned with 'systems' and employing some of the techniques utilized in OR, is not included. Second, studies in the epidemiology of diseases, effectiveness of treatment, nutrition, clean water, as well as automation in clinical practice, diagnostic models, and the like, are not included here as separate areas of interest. The major criterion for inclusion has been work on problems of concern in the *management of the health care delivery process* and not on the techniques for the delivery of care, *per se*. Certainly, decision-making with respect to diagnosis and treatment (that is, patient management) is often an area of interest to those in OR, and is included when it is of concern as a part of those already mentioned (for example, in quality control or the design of hospitals). But it is not included separately, just as 'planning' is not a separate area, and for the same reasons. These kinds of labels are pervasive when one is dealing with the problems of health care delivery, and while they could be treated separately, it seems more effective to classify and discuss the problem areas as indicated above.

No attempt will be made here to define and describe the OR approach in health care. The general approach has been dealt with elsewhere in the companion volume, "Operations Research Handbook: Foundations and Fundamentals," and it would be redundant here. The reader of work in applications is assumed to be familiar with approach and techniques, at least at a level sufficient for understanding the descriptive material which follows.

1.1 Problems in Health Care

No attempt is made here to delineate all problems of health care delivery, but only to give some background of the health care environment and 'system' so as to place in context the diverse applications described later. Health care delivery may be described as the process by which an individual's state of health is monitored, imbalances in that state and deviations from the desired state are detected, decisions are taken as to the application of available health care resources (patient management), the resources are applied, and the individual is returned to a state of health (homeostasis) as nearly consonant with his original state as the disease and resource availability allow.

As can be seen, this definition focuses on first, the individual as the central actor in the process, and second, the available resource structure as the agent. The quantity and quality of health care delivered in any incident of care is a function of the interaction of these two. The occurrence of individual incidents, their detection, and the availability of resources to deal with such incidents, describe a dynamic, complex system which is not well understood and is subject to various and variously effective management policies and practices in a diversity of settings throughout the world. In reviewing the need for better management in the health services, it has often been recognized that there exist in most environments overlapping, conflicting, and often competing organizations within the system.

Further, effective control over costs has not been obtained, and in most systems there exists a diversity of relatively independent funding mechanisms. Finally, knowledge concerning the demand for services, as well as decision mechanisms for allocating resources to meet known needs, do not exist in large measure.

Thus, the opportunity for OR applications is great, but the problems are large, complex, and very often not well understood. Most work done to date has been in the micro-analytic area, but most interest and the greatest challenges and opportunities exist in the macro-analytic areas. In the following, some of the major problems of interest, from the OR point of view, are described.

(1) Perhaps the most pervasive and persistent problem, but one which has seen little OR work is that of the regional organization of health services. Here one is dealing with such questions as demand prediction, scale and location of facilities, alternative design and organization of these facilities, staffing, criteria for delivery of care, funding and payment mechanisms, and in fact, simultaneously, a vast range of problems each of which is important in its own right.

(2) A problem of great importance, with little in the way of substantive applications to report, is that of allocating resources (of an economy) to the health care sector in competition with the requirements and goals of other sectors. Here, we would be mainly concerned with providing information for policy and strategy by predicting the consequences of alternative allocations under various sets of assumptions.

(3) Program planning within the health sector is a system problem of great interest. Here, one is interested in the dynamics of various programs (e.g., clean water, nutrition, family planning, inoculation, and the like) as they interact in consuming resources over time and generating benefits.

(4) Manpower planning can be viewed from a national and international level, as well as from a local and regional level. The mix of manpower required is a function of the set of services to be delivered over time. The provision of manpower is a function of a set of training facilities, incentives, and disincentives for entering, leaving, or transferring among training programs, as well as faculty requirements and effects of migration. The dynamics of this interaction in producing a prediction of manpower availability and utilization is an interesting and formidable analytical problem.

(5) Measuring and controlling the quality of health care delivered in any setting is increasingly a challenging problem whose solution is urgently needed. A major difficulty is that there exists no general agreement on the approach which ought to be taken toward measurement in the first place.

(6) Cost prediction and control has received a great deal of attention, but operational systems are scarce and, as yet, not very effective. A large body of both normative and descriptive literature attests to efforts in this area, and it is a distinct challenge to OR to develop operational methods for management in health care enterprises.

(7) Outpatient services have been the subject of many OR studies but still present many problems, due to changes in the nature of such services, as well as changes in delivery methods. With greater understanding of the actual and potential role of outpatient services has come the need for new and better approaches to the analysis of their efficiency and effectiveness.

(8) Emergency services, including transport and referral, have received considerable attention by operations researchers, but problems of consequence remain. The scope and organization of such facilities, their relationship to other delivery facilities, screening, staffing, and a host of other operating problems are all present in this setting.

(9) Radiology, pathology, and laboratory services are increasingly important in both diagnosis and treatment. The provision of these services economically and efficiently present interesting problems in facilities planning, staffing, introduction of technology, and use of computers in data handling and analysis.

(10) From an economic point of view, inpatient services present perhaps the greatest challenge to OR. Such services account for a large proportion of total expenditures in any health delivery system, and their rationalization in a diversity of settings is a critical problem. Various actual and potential structures, differing in scope and methods of care, exist. Planning appropriate facilities in each setting where they are required provides many opportunities for OR applications.

(11) The operation of facilities and services within hospitals provides opportunities for applications of inventory theory. Supplies of all kinds, linen service, and blood banking are a few of the areas which have received attention.

(12) Menu planning has been approached, utilizing mathematical programming as well as heuristic methods.

(13) The design and implementation of information systems in the health care setting, from both the patient and financial management point of view, opens up many opportunities for OR applications. Grave doubts have been expressed as to the technical and economic feasibility of heavily computerized systems in hospitals, but it seems reasonable that advances in technology and reduction in costs have been such as to argue strongly for progress toward such systems.

With this brief survey of problems, we now turn to a review of some of the work done so far. In this review, the goal is to highlight areas of application with examples. It is not possible to cover all work done, nor is it reasonable in most instances to provide, at this stage, qualitative evaluations of such work. A comprehensive bibliography, covering both applications and literature on problem background and settings, is included for the interested reader. If one has interest in a specific problem, it is suggested that he consult *Abstracts of Hospital Management Studies* [Cooperative Information Center, various dates]. A major section of this publication is devoted to Management Science and Operations Research. Background and institutional information may be located easily by subject.

2. OPERATIONS RESEARCH STUDIES IN THE HEALTH SERVICES

As stated earlier, the basic organization of OR work in health is in terms of macro and micro-analytic studies. The focus of the studies included is on management problems in the health services, and it should be recognized that the dividing line between micro-macro, as well as that defining managerial orientation, is both arbitrary and fuzzy. The bibliography gives a reasonably complete listing of reported work in the various areas described here, but no attempt is made to encapsulate all of this work. (A very comprehensive review of such work is included in Stimson and Stimson [1972].) Rather, studies typical for their class are described briefly, or else the major thrust of the class is given without any attempt to attribute the work specifically to a particular report. In this way, it is hoped to give the reader the flavor for both research and applications, with the references relied upon for substantive detail. Historically, micro-analytic studies were the rule in early applications, and they are reported here first.

2.1 Outpatient Service

Among the earliest OR studies made in health care were applications of queuing theory to problems in the design and scheduling of outpatient clinics (Bailey [1952], Welch [1952b, 1964], Welch & Bailey [1952]). General guidelines were established by these studies, concerning appointment intervals, scheduling of doctors and other personnel, and policies and allowances for nonappointive patients. Given a number of circumstances, however, simulation models have played an increasingly important role in such studies (Fetter & Mills [1973], Fetter & Thompson [1966], Hoffman & Rockart [1969], Hoffman & Barnett [1970], Rockart & Hoffman [1969], Soriano [1966], Williams, et al. [1967]).

The outpatient facility does not lend itself to analytical queuing theory directly for a number of reasons:

(1) Demands are both scheduled and nonscheduled and, in fact, scheduling plays an important role in the provision of service as well as the demand.

(2) Patient mix is not, in general, stable from period to period, and may vary within relatively short intervals.

(3) In many settings, outpatient facilities operate at various levels of capability, with referral and reappointment systems to handle successively more complex patients.

(4) Such facilities often share resources with inpatient or other health care facilities making prediction of utilization a rather different problem than that assumed by the theory.

Beyond the problem of planning facilities and determining policies for scheduling and operation of these facilities, the problems of manpower provision are of great importance. Some recent research has focused attention on the potential use of paraprofessional personnel in outpatient clinics (Golladay, et al. [1971]), and most of the simulation analyses currently underway include provision for dealing with the manpower planning problem.

2.2 Inpatient Services

Here we find a host of applications, ranging from the highly specific to work of a rather general nature. The earliest major work was that conducted at Johns Hopkins in the period from 1955–1965, and included studies on prediction and control of inpatient census (Connor [1960], Young [1965]), staffing techniques (Flagle, et al. [1960], Wolfe & Young [1965a, 1965b]), disease screening (Flagle [1965]), and implementation of the concept of progressive patient care (Flagle, et al. [1960a, 1963]). At Yale, work was conducted over this same period on prediction of requirements for maternity facilities (Thompson & Fetter [1963]), scheduling the use of surgical facilities (Fetter & Thompson [1965], Kavet [1967], Kavet & Thompson [1967]), the economics of multiple occupancy facilities (Thompson & Fetter [1969]), and more recently, analyses of the utilization of progressive patient care facilities (Fetter & Thompson [1969, 1973]). All of these studies, and the many more cited in the bibliography, focused on attempts to make more effective the delivery of care as defined and produced in existing institutions. They addressed, primarily, problems of acute care, and usually dealt with a subsystem or one aspect of the service spectrum.

This is not meant to detract from the importance of work of this kind in its attempts to understand better and rationalize care delivery to inpatients, but to emphasize the fact that in large measure, even in these relatively well-structured settings, a great potential for OR work exists, as will be discussed later.

Within any hospital, many activities exist which are candidates for treatment in the same manner as their counterparts in business firms. This work tends to be closer to the more traditional industrial engineering approach than representative of OR work in general. A sampling of literature in 1973 reveals the following areas of interest. Such activities as pharmacies, laundries, and maintenance are clear examples. Dietary services have been the subject of several interesting research efforts (Balintfy [1966a], Balintfy & Nebel [1966], Gue & Liggett [1966], Eckstein [1970]). A comprehensive set of applications has been reported by the study group at Georgia Institute of Technology (Smalley & Freeman [1966]).

In the area of long term care, not much work has been done, but it seems clear that alternatives to acute care facilities must be found for many classes of patients. The serious questions of substitution and complementarity with respect to current modes of inpatient care are primary subjects for OR studies.

2.3 Medical Information Systems

The purposes of information systems in health care can be classified on the one hand as medical or administrative, and on the other as research or operational. This can be portrayed as follows:

	Medical	*Administrative*
Research	1	2
Operational	3	4

An information system which embraces all four areas could certainly be termed a "total" system, but its attainment raises serious questions of feasibility. Most efforts have been addressed to area 4, and include fairly standard business applications of payroll, billing, stores control, and the like. Some attempts have been made to implement and much research has been done on systems in area 2, but success thus far has been limited.

Many prototype systems have been developed and are in use in area 3 in such entities as clinical laboratories, outpatient departments, pharmacies, and the like, but no general patterns seem to be emerging. Area 4 has received some attention, with several prototype systems under development (Control Data [1971], IBM [1970], Lockheed [1969]). The role of information systems in areas 1 and 4 on an integrated basis seems to offer great promise, but is faced with significant problems both technical and economic (Ball [1971], Lair [1969], Lamson, et al. [1970], Lawton [1970], James [1969], Saunders [1969]).

2.4 Emergency Services

Here, a great deal or OR work has been accomplished and significant efforts are in progress. The two most important areas which have been studied are coronary care (Kao [1972], Thomas [1968]) and casualty services (Handyside & Morris [1967], Newell [1954]). A problem of great importance in the study of emergency services organization and operation is the relationship between such services and more routine ambulatory care services. In practice, this relation is often poorly defined and detracts from the effectiveness of both kinds of service.

OR has a great deal to contribute in research aimed at dealing more effectively with trauma. Here, it is clear that significant advances in medical care are intimately related to the logistical issues involved. Facilities required are varied and expensive, timing of delivery is often crucial, the site at which trauma has its onset could be anywhere but is often predictable if extensive (major highways, for example). The concatenation of these factors gives rise to an area in which modeling and analysis is essential to the development of more effective delivery.

3. NATIONAL AND REGIONAL PLANNING OF HEALTH CARE DELIVERY

At the level of national planning, while the need for analytical work is widely recognized (Hilleboe, et al. [1972]), actual applications of OR are not widespread. The process is viewed as one in which hard data are lacking and where political, administrative, and resource constraints inhibit rationality. The use of many OR models is reported, however, in both the USSR (Popov [1971]) and Sweden (Hilleboe, et al. [1972]) at the national level; and the PAHO-CENDES approach (Ahumada, et al. [1965]), employed in several Latin American settings, relies on an underlying mathematical programming model.

A resource allocation model in public health planning (Feldstein, et al. [1973]) has been employed in the Republic of Korea for tuberculosis control, and states the problem of health planning in terms of a mathematical program. This approach has been implemented in a number of settings by personnel of the World Health Organization and is continually being refined through these applications.

The integration of curative and preventive services at local, regional, and national levels has received some attention (WHO [1967, 1971b, 1971c]), and is largely confined to specific diseases and/or specific population groups. Regional planning of both services and training facilities has received limited attention, but is an area with considerable potential for OR work.

3.1 Manpower Planning

In this area, only relatively simple models have been utilized for projecting manpower requirements usually based on observed usage rates (Kissick [1967a] , WHO [1971d]). Straightforward forecasting models as a means of predicting supply of and demand for health personnel do not really get at the basic problems in manpower planning, and some efforts are underway to provide planners with analytical tools to increase their understanding of the effect of change in systems parameters (Fetter & Mills [1972]). A persistent question of interest, for example, concerns the effects of substitutions among various types of manpower in the provision of health services (a mathematical programming approach has been tried; Golloday, et al. [1971]).

3.2 Control of Health Care Delivery Systems

Questions of both administrative and medical control arise here. The former are in response to the rapidly escalating cost of providing health care, while the latter are due largely to the increased perception of the consumer's role in health care delivery. In the administrative area, systems for budgeting and control through cost-benefit analysis have been proposed or are under study (Crystal & Brewster [1966] , Kissick [1967c] , Packer [1968] , Wiseman [1963]).

With the advent of Medicare, a legal requirement for utilization review was imposed on providers of inpatient care, in order to assure delivery of appropriate care to the user of government financing. The usual form of such review consists of a procedure for selecting cases for retrospective review, in which the case selection process is tied to length of stay. For example, one might select all cases with a length of stay greater than some given number of days. These cases are submitted to both institutional as well as regional peer review boards in the hope that through an evaluation and feedback process, quality control, with respect to patient care management, can be effected.

Various studies have been done on the decision processes involved in both case selection (McClain & Riedel [1973], Riedel, Fetter, et al. [1972], Wolfe [1967]) and in determining the appropriateness of care (Donabedian [1966, 1968, 1969], Herring [1970], Riedel, Brenner, et al. [1972]). Most of this work is aimed at beginning to build a control structure, based on understanding resource consumption in health care as a function of patient state. Little work has been accomplished thus far on concurrent review and evaluation.

3.3 Patient Screening

In this area, methodologies based on the use of computers and decision theory have been studied. Both screening for particular diseases (Flagle [1965], Lincoln & Parker [1967]) and multi-phasic screening (Collen [1970]) have been employed in the attempt to improve health care delivery by concentrating on prevention of illness and maintenance of health as the basic strategy, rather than treatment of acute illness.

4. FUTURE CONTRIBUTIONS OF OPERATIONS RESEARCH

In what areas is it likely that OR practitioners can make the greatest contribution to health care? The answer at this point seems quite clear, whether one is concerned with delivery in a developed or less-developed setting. The design and implementation of delivery systems which address the basic issues of health care, and are economically and technically feasible and effective, presents the greatest challenge today. Embedded in such designs is a host of problems for which analytical methods have much to offer. Whether or not they will be employed is strictly a function of the ability of the OR professional to implement his expertise in an area fraught with an extraordinary number of constraints.

In the developed settings such as the U.S. and the U.K. tradition and institutional constraints are such that change in any guise is enormously difficult. In the less-developed settings, politics and poverty combine to very often render ineffective the most rational and well-meaning efforts. The point is not to introduce despair, but to emphasize that the more traditional staff role of the OR analyst is not likely to pay off in substantive results in the health care field. Further, the traditional methodologies, while useful in a limited sense, do not really encompass the enormously complex problems of health care planning.

To indicate the scope of this problem, the model which follows has been formulated. It represents an attempt to provide a broad perspective on the health care delivery planning problem, while at the same time providing a flexible, general-purpose, labeling scheme, so that a wide variety of specific problems could be analyzed using the model's structure.

5. RESOURCE ALLOCATION MODELS FOR HEALTH CARE

In analyzing health care delivery systems from the point of view of design or modification, the basic problem faced is one of allocating scarce resources among the alternatives available for treatment. The problems to be addressed range from fairly simple questions of comparing alternative treatments for a single important disease condition, to dealing comprehensively with the health problems of a diverse population employing a variety of facilities.

A simple example of the analysis required could be found in the case of designing a program for treatment of a population for some particular disease. The prevalence of the disease would be measured and predicted, the alternative treatments and their resource costs defined, the effect of treatment estimated in terms of some set of measures, the dynamics of the disease and its treatment described. Such a situation could be modelled as follows:

$$e_{prt}P_{prt} - \left[Y_{prt} + \sum_{h=0}^{t} g_{prh} X_{prm,t-h} \right] = 0, \tag{1}$$

in which

e_{prt} is the expected incidence of the disease in population type p, region r, at time t;

P_{prt} is the size of population type p, region r, at time t;

Y_{prt} is the size of the eligible population of type p, region r, at time t;

X_{prmt} is the number of cases it is decided to treat employing method m; and

g_{prh} is the effect on incidence of treatment over some horizon from the treatment period, to h periods later.

Thus, this relation projects the incidence as a function of expected incidence and population projections, and then dynamically feeds back the effect of treatment decisions considered within the model as they affect incidence.

$$\sum_{mp} a_{km} X_{mprt} \leqslant A_{krt}, \tag{2}$$

in which

a_{km} is the amount of resource k required to treat the disease employing method m;

A_{krt} is the availability of resource k in period t, region r.

This relation allows resource availability to constrain the employment of the alternative treatment methods.

$$\sum_m d_{bmprt} X_{mprt} - B^+_{bprt} + B^-_{bprt} = B_{bprt} \tag{3}$$

in which

d_{bmprt} is a measure of the amount of benefit b obtained in population type p, region r by treating the disease using method m in period t;

B_{bprt} is the desired level of attainment of benefit b; and

B^+_{bprt}, B^-_{bprt} measure departures from this desired level.

This relation expresses benefits in terms of some desired level of attainment (goal), as a consequence of treatment. Thus, for example, reduction in mortality could be designated separately in each region for each population type.

Finally, the relation

$$Z = \text{MIN} \sum_{bprt} [w^+_{bprt} B^+_{bprt} + w^-_{bprt} B^-_{bprt}]$$

would allow the specification of weights associated with each "goal," and the "optimization" of the model according to this function. One of the relations of type 3 could easily describe the cost of treatment, and a single cost minimization formulation could be accomplished. It is, however, much more likely that one would want to employ a multidimensional goal structure and a set of judgments as to the relative desirability of such goals in this kind of analysis.

Expanding the point of view taken in this kind of model to include a set of diseases, would require adding a disease type subscript (d) to the variables and parameters. Additionally, one would very likely wish to include a specification of facilities available or to be made available as a separate resource type, so that facilities utilization could be made explicit. This would be especially true in cases in which the planning problem was concerned with incremental alterations in existing health care facilities.

In any case, the important point to be made here is that modelling to address problems in health care delivery should be comprehensive and informative, but relatively straightforward and consistent in structure. Planners and policy makers in this area need and deserve information to guide their decision-making. Modelling and analysis should be concerned with this task of information support in response to such needs.

6. THE FUTURE OF HEALTH CARE DELIVERY

It seems safe to predict that health care delivery, in the U.S. at least, will be subjected to enormous pressure for change in the future. The demands are growing rapidly, disease and states of health are subject to an extraordinary knowledge explosion, and observable costs of providing care have been rising uncontrollably. This combination results in both challenge and opportunity. OR work will certainly continue in virtually all of the areas cited earlier. An expansion of microanalytic work will almost certainly take place in response to these pressures. At the same time, it is important in these applications to recognize the problems of planning and change which are bound to occur in the larger systems of which these are a part.

Health care is certain to be an industry in which OR can make a substantial contribution. The extent and value of this contribution will depend in large measure on the professional capability which our practitioners exhibit.

BIBLIOGRAPHY

Abel-Smith, B., "An International Study of Health Expenditures and its Relevance for Health Planning", WHO Public Health Paper No. 32, Geneva (1967).

Ahumada, J., et al., "Health Planning: Problems of concept and method," Pan American Health Organization, Washington, D.C. (1965).

Alper, P., P. H. Armitage and C. S. Smith, "Educational Models, Manpower Planning and Control," *Operational Res. Quart.*, 18, No. 2: 93–103 (1967).

Arrow, K. J., "Uncertainty and the Welfare Economics of Medical Care," *Am. Econ. Rev.* 53, pp. 941–973 (1963).

Badger, K. H., "Queuing Theory: Predicting Optional Obstetric Service Utilization on Medical Hill," University of California, Graduate Program in Hospital Administration (1967).

Bailey, N. T. J., "Operational Research in Medicine," *Operational Res. Quart.* 3, pp. 24–29. (June 1952a).

———, "A Study of Queues and Appointment Systems in Hospital Out-patient Departments, With Special Reference to Waiting-times," *J. Roy. Stat. Soc.*, Series B., No. 14: 185–199 (1952b).

———, "Queuing for Medical Care," *Appl. Stat.* 3, pp. 137–145 (November 1954).

———, "Statistics in Hospital Planning and Design," *Appl. Stat.* 5, pp. 146–157 (November 1956).

———, "Operational Research in Hospital Planning and Design," *Operational Res. Quart.* 8, pp. 149–157 (September 1957).

———, *The Mathematical Approach to Biology and Medicine*, Wiley, New York (1967).

Baligh, H. H. and D. J. Laughhunn, "An Economic and Linear Model of the Hospital," *Health Services Res.* 4, pp. 293–303 (Winter 1969).

Balintfy, J. L., "A Stochastic Model for the Analysis and Prediction of Admissions and Discharges in Hospitals," in C. W. Churchman and M. Verhulst (Eds.) *Management Sciences: Models and Techniques*," Vol. 2, Pergamon Press, New York, pp. 288–299 (1960).

———, "Linear Programming Models for Menu Planning," in H. E. Smalley and J. R. Freeman (Eds.), *Hospital Industrial Engineering*, Reinhold, New York, pp. 402–415 (1966a).

——, "A Hospital Census Predictor Model," in H. E. Smalley and J. R. Freeman (Eds.), *Hospital Industrial Engineering*, Reinhold, New York, pp. 312–316 (1966b).

—— and E. C. Nebel, "Experiments with Computer-Assisted Menu Planning," *J.A.H.A.* **40**, pp. 88–96 (June 1966).

Ball, M. J., "An Overview of Total Medical Information Systems," *Meth. Info. in Med.* **10**, pp. 73–82 (April 1971).

Barker, J., "Computers in Hospitals," *The Hospital* **67**, pp. 279–282 (August 1971).

Barnett, G. O., "Computers in Patient Care," New England J. Med. **279**, pp. 1321–1327 (December 1968).

——, "The Use of Computers in Clinical Data Management: The Ten Commandments," in Committee on Computer Systems in Medicine, American Medical Association (Ed.), *Symposium on Computer Systems in Medicine*, Chicago, American Medical Association, pp. 85–89 (1971).

—— and P. A. Castleman, "A Time-sharing Computer System for Patient-care Activities," *Computers and Biomed. Res.* **1**, pp. 41–51 (March 1967).

—— and R. A. Greenes, "Interface Aspects of a Hospital Information System," *Ann. N.Y. Acad. Sci.* **161**, pp. 756–768 (September 1969).

—— and P. B. Hofmann, "Computer Technology and Patient Care: Experiences of a Hospital Research Effort, *Inquiry* **5**, pp. 51–57 (September 1968).

Barnoon, S. and H. Wolfe, "Scheduling a Multiple Operating Room System: A Simulation Approach," *Health Services Res.* **3**, pp. 272–285 (Winter 1968).

Barr, A., "Measuring Nursing Care" in G. McLachlan (Ed)., *Problems and Progress in Medical Care*, Oxford University Press, London (1964).

Bartlett, M. S., "Monte Carlo Studies in Ecology and Epidemiology, IV, Proceedings of the 4th Berkeley Symposium on Mathematics," *Stat. and Prob.* IV, (1961), pp. 39–55.

Bartscht, K. G., "Hospital Staffing Methodologies–Concepts, Development, and Uses," *J. Ind. Eng.* **18**, pp. 708–717 (December 1967).

—— and E. F. Rothenbuhler, "Man-minute Computations form the Basis for New Staffing Methodology," *Hospitals, J.A.H.A.* **40**, pp. 62–66 (March 1966).

—— and F. H. Bayha, "Time Analyzed for Alternative Food Flow Systems," *Hospitals, J.A.H.A.* **40**, pp. 88–92 (March 1966).

—— and M. A. Estrella, "Range of Required Skills Detailed in Study of the Pharmacy Function," *Hospitals, J.A.H.A.* **40**, pp. 94–98 (March 1966).

—— and R. M. Grimes, "Linen Production Methods Analyzed in the Laundry," *Hospitals, J.A.H.A.* **40**, pp. 107–110 (March 1966).

Baruch, J. J., "Hospital Research and Administration With a Digital Computer," *Circulation Res.* **11**, pp. 629–636 (September 1962).

Battelle-Northwest, *Systems Programs for Hospitals*, Battelle-Northwest, Richland, Washington, 1969.

Battistelia, R. M. and T. E. Chester, "Role of Management in Health Services in Britain and United States," *Lancet*, pp. 626–630 (March 1972).

Bisphram, K., W. W. Holland, and J. Stringer, "Planning for Health," *The Hospital* (March 1971).

Bithell, J. F., "A Class of Discrete-time Models for the Study of Hospital Admission Systems," *Operations Res.* **17**, pp. 48–69 (January–February 1969).

—— and H. B. Devlin, "Prediction of Discharge of Inpatients," *Health Services Res.* **3**, pp. 174–184 (Fall 1968).

Blanco-White, M. J. and M. C. Pike, "Appointment Systems in Outpatients' Clinics and the Effect of Patients' Unpunctuality," *Med. Care* **2**, pp. 133–145 (1964).

Blumberg, M. S., "Systems Analysis and Health Manpower: Medical Manpower Continuing Crisis," *J.A.M.A.* **201**, pp. 856–860 (1967).

Bodenham, K. E. and F. Wellman, "Foundations for Health Services Management: A Scicon Report for the Scottish Home and Health Department on the Requirements for a Health Service Information System," Oxford University Press, London (1972; for the Nuffield Provincial Hospital Trust).

Bogatyrev, J. D., "O Kriterijah Effectivnosti Dlja Matematiceskogo Modelirovani ja Razlicnyh Vidov Medicinskoj Pomosci Naseleni ju," ("Evaluation Criteria for the Mathematical Modelling of Various Forms of Medical Care"), *Sovetsk, Zdravoohr* **5**, pp. 8–13 (1969).

Boodman, D. M., "Scientific Inventory Control," *Hosp. Progress* **48**, pp. 78+ (November 1967).

Bove, J. R. and D. K. McKay, "Computer Approach to Hospital Blood Bank Inventory Control," *Transfusion* **9**, pp. 143–150 (May–June 1969).

Brown, P. T. S., "Computers in Hospitals" in J. Rose (Ed.), *Computers in Medicine*, J. & A. Churchill, London, pp. 108–119 (1969).

Bruce, R. A. and S. R. Yarnall, "Computer-Aided Diagnosis and Diagnosis of Cardiovascular Disorder," *J. Chronic Dis.* **19**, pp. 473–484 (1966).

Buchanan, J. M., "Automated Hospital Information Systems," *Military Med.* **131**, pp. 1510–1512 (December 1966).

Budd, P. J., "AHIS–Automated Hospital Information System," Information Bulletin IB 30-70-2, Veterans Administration, Department of Data Management, Washington, D.C. (1970).

Caceres, C. A. and A. E. Rilke, "The Digital Computer as an Aid in the Diagnosis of Cardiovascular Disease," *Trans. N.Y. Acad. Sci.* **23**, pp. 240–244 (January 1961).

Carpenter, R. J., "A Review of Developed and Developing Routine Computer Applications in Medicine," WHO Documents, HS/ADP/66.1 and HS/ADP/66.1 Add. 1, Geneva (1966).

Catassi, C. A. and E. L. Peterson, "The Blood Inventory Control System–Helping Blood Bank Management Through Computerized Inventory Control," *Transfusion* **7**, pp. 60–69 (January-February 1967).

Catherer, A. and M. D. Warren, (Eds.), "Management and the Health Services," Pergamon Press, Oxford (1971).

Catliff, G. C., "Critical Path Analysis as an Aid to Hospital Planning," *Brit. Hosp. Soc. Serv. J.*, pp. 1204–1206 (1964).

Chacko, G. K., (Ed.), *The Recognition of Systems in Health Services*, Operations Research Society of America, Arlington, Virginia (1969).

Clark, E. L. and W. W. Diggs, "Quantifying Patient Care Needs," *Hospitals, J.A.H.A.* **45**, pp. 96–100 (September 1971).

Collen, M. F., "General Requirements for a Medical Information System (MIS)" in M. F. Collen (Ed.), "Medical Information Systems, U.S. Department of Health Education, and Welfare, Health Services and Mental Health Administration," Washington, D.C., pp. 1–16 (1970).

——, et al., "Automated Multiphasic Screening and Diagnosis," Am. J. Public Health **54**, pp. 741–750 (May 1964).

Connor, R. J., "A Hospital Inpatient Classification System," Doctoral Dissertation, Department of Industrial Engineering, The Johns Hopkins University (1960).

Connor, R. J., "A Work Sampling Study of Variations in Nursing Work Load," *Hospitals, J.A.H.A.* **35**, pp. 40+ (May 1961).

Connors, M. M., "A Stochastic Elective Admissions Scheduling Algorithm," *Health Services Res.* **5**, pp. 308–319 (Winter 1970).

Control Data Corporation, "Integrated Medical Systems," Pub. No. X0010103, CDC Corp., La Jolla, California (1971).

Cooperative Information Center for Hospital Management Studies, "Abstracts of Hospital Management Studies Quarterly and Annual Cumulative," (various dates), University of Michigan, Ann Arbor, Michigan.

Cross, K. W. and J. L. Roberts, "Management Control in Medical Care," *The Hospital* **66**, pp. 45–47 (February 1970).

——, ——, and J. Droar, "Electronic Processing of Hospital Records" G. McLachlan and R. A. Shegog, Eds., *Computers in the Service of Medicine, Vol. 1,* Oxford University Press, London pp. 23–39 (1969).

Crystal, R. A. and A. W. Brewster, "Cost Benefit and Cost Effectiveness Analysis in the Health Field," *Inquiry* **3**, pp. 3–13 (1966).

—— and ——, "Improving the Use of Hospital Maternity Beds," *Operational Res. Quart.* **16**, pp. 65–76 (1965).

Cvetanovic, B., B. Grab, and K. Uemura, "Epidemiological Model of Typhoid Fever and its Use in the Planning and Evaluation of an Anti-Typhoid Immunization and Sanitation Programmes," Bulletin, World Health Organization **45**, pp. 53–75 (1971).

Davies, J. O. F., et al., *Towards a Measure of Medical Care: Operational Research in the Health Services*, Oxford University Press, London (1962).

Davis, L. S., et al., "Computer-stored Medical Record", *Computers and Biomed. Res.* **1**, pp. 452–469 (May 1968).

Deboeck, G., "User Oriented Modelling for Health Planning and Programming," IIASA Conference on Systems Aspects of Health Planning, Baden, Austria (August 1974).

DeLand, E. C. and B. D. Waxman, "Review of Hospital Information Systems," Report No. P-4337, The Rand Corporation, Santa Monica, California (1970).

Denison, R. A., R. Wild, and M. J. C. Martin, *A Bibliography of Operational Research in Hospitals and the Health Services*, University of Bradford, Management Center, Bradford, England (1969).

Dennis, L. C., II., and J. L. Balintfy, "A Linear Programming Analysis of Institutional Management Policies." Paper presented at Joint Meeting of the Operations Research Society of America and the Institute of Management Sciences, May, 1968, San Francisco.

Dixon, R. A., "A Model of a Hospital's Patient Medical Information System," *Methods of Info. in Med.* **9**, pp. 88–97 (April 1970).

Donabedian, A., "Evaluating the Quality of Medical Care," *Milbank Memorial Fund Quart.*, Part 2, Vol. 44, July (1966), pp. 166–206.

Donabedian, A., "Promoting Quality Through Evaluating the Process of Patient Care," *Medical Care* **6**, pp. 181–202 (May–June 1968).

——, "Medical Care Appraisal–Quality and Utilization," in A Guide to Medical Care Administration, Vol. 2, American Public Health Association (1969).

Douville, G., "La Technique de la Simulation Appliquée au Block Operatoire," Administration et Santé, **3** pp. 5–15 (Hiver) (1968).

Dowling, W. L., "The Application of Linear Programming to Decision-Making in Hospitals," *Hosp. Admin.* **16**, pp. 66–75 (Summer 1971).

Dunn, H. D. and A. Hindle, "Decision Making in the Hospital Environment," Paper presented at the 31st Conference of the Operations Research Society of America, New York (May 1967).

Dunn, R. G., "Scheduling Elective Admissions," *Health Services Res.* **21**, pp. 181–215 (Summer 1967).

Eckstein, E., "Is the 'Diet Problem' Identical to the 'Menu Planning Problem?," *Management Sci.* **16**, pp. 527–528 (May 1970).

Edgecumbe, R. H., "The CASH Approach to Hospital Management Engineering," *Hospitals, J.A.H.A.* **39**, pp. 70–74 (March 1965).

Elston, R. C. and J. C. Pickrel, "A Statistical Approach to Ordering and Usage Policies for a Hospital Blood Bank," *Transfusion* **3**, pp. 41–47 (January–February 1963).

—— and ——, "Guides to Inventory Levels for a Hospital Blood Bank Determined by Electronic Computer Simulation," *Transfusion* **5**, pp. 465–470 (September–October 1965).

Elveback, L. and A. Varma, "Simulation of Mathematical Models for Public Health Problems", Public Health Repts. **80,** No. 12: 1067–1076 (1965).

Esogbue, A. O., "Experiments on Scheduling Disciplines in Surgery: A Simulated Queuing Approach," Technical Memorandum No. 168, Case Western Reserve University, Department of Operations Research (1969).

Fagnani, F., "Introduction a la Recherche Operationnelle en Santé Publique", Bulletin du l'Institut National de la Santé et de la Recherche Médicale, Vol. 23, pp. 837–856 (1968).

Fairey, M. J., "Information Systems in Hospital Administration", in M. E. Abrams, Ed., *Medical Computing*, American Elsevier, New York, pp. 384–389 (1970).

Fanshel, S. and J. F. Bush, "A Health Status Index," *Operations Res.* (December 1970).

Feldstein, M. S., *Economic Analysis for Health Service Efficiency*, North Holland Publishing, Amsterdam (1967).

——, "Economic Analysis, Operational Research, and the National Health Service," *Oxford Econ. Pap.* **15,** pp. 19–31 (March 1963).

——, "Effects of Differences in Hospital Bed Scarcity on Type of Use", Brit. Med. J. **2,** pp. 561–564 (August 1964).

——, "An Aggregate Planning Model of the Health Care Sector," *Med. Care* **5,** pp. 369–381 (November–December 1967).

——, M. A. Piot, and T. K. Sundaresan, "A Resource Allocation Model for Public Health Planning," *WHO Bull. Supplement* (1973).

Feldstein, P. J. and J. J. German, "Predicting Hospital Utilization: An Evaluation of Three Approaches.", *Inquiry* **2,** pp. 13–36 (June 1965).

Fetter, R. B. and R. Mills, "HOSPSIM: A Simulation Modeling Language for Health Care Systems," WP25, *Simulation*, pp. 73–80 (March 1973).

—— and ——, "A Language to Aid in Manpower Planning," Puter Associates, New Haven, Connecticut (1972).

——, and J. D. Thompson, "The Simulation of Hospital Systems," *Operations Res.* **13,** pp. 689–711 (September–October 1965).

—— and ——, "Patients' Waiting Time and Doctors' Idle Time in the Outpatient Setting," *Health Services Res.* **1,** pp. 66–90 Summer (1966).

—— and ——, "A Decision Model for the Design and Operation of a Progressive Patient Care Hospital," *Med. Care* **7,** pp. 450–462 (November–December 1969).

—— and ——, "A Planning Model for the Delivery of Health Services," in A. Reisman and M. Kiley (Eds.), *Health Care Delivery Planning*, Gordon & Breach, New York (1973).

Fetter, R. B., "Interactive Modelling of Health Care Delivery Systems," Proceedings of the Colloquium on Systems Theory and Scientific Management of Public Utilities, University of Montreal (January 1975).

Flagle, C. D., "Operatic..s Research in a Hospital," in C. D. Flagle, W. H. Huggins, and R. H. Roy (Eds.), *Operations Research and Systems Engineering*, Johns Hopkins Press, Baltimore (1960).

——, "Operations Research in the Health Services", *Operations Res.* **10,** pp. 591–603 (September–October 1962).

——, Operations Research in Community Services, in D. B. Hertz and R. T. Eddison (Eds.), *Progress in Operations Research, Vol. 2*, Wiley, New York (1964).

——, "A Decision Theoretical Comparison of Three Methods of Screening for a Single Disease," Proceedings of the 5th Berkeley Symposium on Mathematics, Statistics and Probability, Vol. 5, pp. 887–898 (1965).

——, "A Decade of Operations Research in Health," in F. Swicky and A. G. Wilson (Eds.), *New Methods of Thought and Procedure*, Springer-Verlag, New York, pp. 33–41 (1967).

——, "Technological Development in the Health Services," *Health Services Res.* **4,** pp. 6–13 (Spring 1969a).

——, "Communication and Control in Comprehensive Patient Care and Health Planning", *Ann. N. Y. Acad. Sci.* **161**, pp. 714–729 (September 1969b).

——, "The Role of Simulation in the Health Services," *Am. J. Public Health* **60**, pp. 2386–2394 (December 1970).

—— and J. P. Young, "Application of Operations Research and Industrial Engineering to Problems of Health Services, Hospitals, and Public Health," *J. Ind. Eng.* **17**, pp. 609–614 (November 1966).

——, et al., "Optimal Organization and Facility for a Nursing Unit," Progress Report, Dec. 1957–Dec. 1959, Johns Hopkins Hospital, Operations Research Division, Baltimore (1960a).

——, et al., "The Problems of Organization for Hospital Inpatient Care," in C. W. Churchman and M. Verhulst (Eds.), *Management Sciences: Models and Techniques*, Vol. 2, Pergamon Press, New York, pp. 275–287 (1960b).

——, et al., "The Progressive Patient Care Hospital: Estimating Bed Needs," Public Health Service Publication No. 930-C-2, U. S. Government Printing Office, Washington, D.C. (1963).

Frankfurter, G. M., et al., "A Regional Computer-Based Blood Inventory Information System," *Transfusion* **10**, pp. 203–214 (July–August 1970).

Freibrun, R. B., "Two Years Invested in Planning New Loyola Information System," Modern Hospital, Vol. 112, February (1969), pp. 99–100.

Fretheim, H. E. and E. E. Nussbaum, "A Computer Based Medical Information System," Control Data Corporation, Medical Systems Research Laboratory Report, Burlington, Vermont (1971).

Friend, J. K. and W. N. Jessop, *Local Government and Strategic Choice: An Operational Research Approach to the Processes of Public Planning*, Tavistock Publications, London (1969).

Fries, B. E., "The Application of Operations Research to the Hospital Complex", Technical Report No. 92, Cornell University, Department of Operations Research, Ithaca, New York (1969).

Fuchs, V. R., "The Basic Forces Influencing Costs of Medical Care." In U.S. Department of Health, Education, and Welfare, Report of the National Conference on Medical Costs, June 27–28, U. S. Government Printing Office, Washington, D.C., pp. 16–31 (1967).

Gargov, K., V. Colakov, and D. Borisov, "Zdraveopazvane i Novijat Nacin na Planirane i Rokovodstovo na Narodnoto Stopanstvo," ("The Health Services and New Methods of Planning and Managing the National Economy") *Hig. Zdraveop. (Sofija)* **4**, pp. 309–315 (1969).

Geisler, R., "The THOMAS Medical Information System," *Datamation* **16**, June (1970), pp. 133–136.

General Electric Company, "MEDINET Nursing Staff Allocation," General Electric, Watertown, Mass. (1969).

Gillette, P. J., P. W. Rathbun, and H. B. Wolfe, "Hospital Information Systems," Parts 1 and 2, *Hospitals, J.A.H.A.*, **44**, pp. 76–78 (August 1970), **44**, pp. 45–48 (September 1970).

Gocka, E. F., "A Survey of Medical Information Systems", paper presented at the 11th American Meeting of the Institute of Management Sciences, Los Angeles (October 1970).

Goldman, J. and H. A. Knappenberger, "How to Determine the Optimum Number of Operating Rooms", *Mod. Hosp.* **111**, pp. 114+ (September 1968).

Golladay, F. L., K. R. Smith, and M. Miller, "Allied Health Manpower Strategies: Estimates of the Potential Gains From Efficient Task Delegation," Research Report #5, University of Wisconsin, Health Economics Research Center, Madison, Wisconsin (October 1971).

Gordon, B. L., "Medical Data Repository: Resources; Development: Utilization," in Committee on Computer Systems in Medicine (Ed.), *Symposium on Computer Systems in Medicine*, American Medical Association, Chicago, pp. 12–21 (1971).

Gorry, G. A., "Problem Solving Strategies in a System for Computer-Aid Diagnosis", Working Paper No. 267–68, Massachusetts Institute of Technology, Sloan School, Cambridge, Massachusetts (1967).

Gouveia, W. A., "Computer Applications in the Hospital Pharmacy," *Hospitals, J.A.H.A.* **45**, pp. 80–83 (January 1971).

Greenes, R. A. and V. W. Sidel, "The Use of Computer Mapping in Health Research," *Health Services Res.* **2**, pp. 243–258 (1967).

Grooms, H. R. and T. Au, "The Simulation of Hospital Patient Treatment Systems," in Proceedings of the Third Conference on Applications of Simulation, Los Angeles (December 8–10, 1969).

Grundy, F. and W. Reinke, "Health Practice Research and Formalized Managerial Methods," *WHO Publications*, Geneva (1972).

Gue, R. L., "Operations Research in Health and Hospital Administration," *Hosp. Admin.* **10**, pp. 6–25 Fall (1965).

——, "An Introduction to the Systems Approach in the Dietary Department," *Hospitals, J.A.H.A.* **43**, pp. 100–101 (September 1969).

——, and J. C. Liggett, "Mathematical Programming Models for Hospital Menu Planning," *J. Ind. Eng.* **17**, pp. 395–400 (August 1966).

Gupta, I., J. Zoreda, and N. Kramer, "Hospital Manpower Planning by Use of Queuing Theory," *Health Services Res.* **6**, pp. 76–82 (Spring 1971).

Halpert, H. P., W. J. Horvath, and J. P. Young, "An Administrator's Handbook on the Application of Operations Research to the Management of Mental Health Systems", Pub. No. 1003, National Clearinghouse for Mental Health Information, U.S. Government Printing Office, Washington, D.C. (1970).

Hammon, G. L. and S. E. Jacobs, "Shared Computer Systems," Parts 1 and 2, *Hospitals, J.A.H.A.* **44**, pp. 50–53; (May 1970) **44**, pp. 16 (1970).

Handyside, A. J. and D. Morris, "Simulation of Emergency Bed Occupancy," *Health Services Res.* **2**, pp. 287–297 (Fall–Winter 1967).

Harrington, J. H., "Operations Research—A Relatively New Approach to Managing Man's Environment," *New England J. Med.* **275**, pp. 1342–1350 (December 1966).

Harvey, N. A., "Cybernetic Applications in Medicine," *N. Y. State J. Med.* **65**, pp. 765–772, 871–875, 995–1002 (1965).

Hearn, C. R. and J. M. Bishop, "Computer Model Simulating Medical Care in Hospital," *Brit. Med. J.* **3**, pp. 396–399 (August 1970).

Herring, C., "Ohio Hospitals' Quality Control and Staff Utilization Program," *Hosp. Progress* **51**, pp. 38–44 (July 1970).

Hershey, J. C., W. J. Abernathy, and N. Baloff, "A Variable Nurse Staffing Model," Research Paper No. 45, Stanford University, Graduate School of Business, Stanford, California (1971).

Hilleboe, H. E., A. Barkhuus, W. C. Thomas, "Approaches to National Health Planning," WHO Public Health Paper No. 46 (1972).

Hills, P. M., "Towards a Hospital Information System," in M. E. Abrams (Ed.), *Medical Computing*, American Elservier, New York (1970).

Hirsch, R. L., E. Brodheim, and F. E. Ginsberg, "A Computer-Based Blood Inventory and Information System for Hospital Blood Banks as Part of a Regional Blood-Management Program," *Transfusion* **10**, pp. 194–202 (July–August 1970).

Hofmann, P. B. and W. A. Gouveia, "Computers: Great Future, Perilous Present," *Mod. Hosp.* **111**, pp. 98+ (July 1968).

—— and J. F. Rockart, "Implications of the No-show Rate for Scheduling OPD Appointments," *Hosp. Prog.* **50**, pp. 35–40 (August 1969).

—— and G. O. Barnett, "Planning for an Automated Clinic Appointment System", *Hosp. Topics* **48**, pp. 37–42 (October 1970).

Högman, C. F. and O. Ramgren, "Computer System for Blood Transfusion Service," *Transfusion* **10**, pp. 121–132 (May–June 1970).

Horvath, W. J., "The Systems Approach to the National Health Problem," *Management Sci.* **12**, pp. B-391–392 (1966).

——, "British Experience With Operations Research in the Health Services," in K. L. White (Ed.), *Medical Care Research*, Pergamon Press, New York, pp. 55–64 (1965).

——, "Operations Research in Medical and Hospital Practice," in P. M. Morse (Ed.), *Operations Research for Public Systems*, The MIT Press, Cambridge, Massachusetts, pp. 127–157 (1967).

——, "Organizational and Management Problems in the Delivery of Medical Care," *Management Sci.* **14**, pp. 275–279 (February 1968).

Howell, J. T., "Systems Opportunities in Modern Medical Organizations," *World Hosp.* **5**, pp. 153–156 (July 1969).

Howland, D., "Approaches to the Systems Problem," *Nursing Res.* **12**, pp. 172–174 (Summer 1963a).

——, "A Hospital System Model," *Nursing Res.* **12**, pp. 232–236 (Fall 1963b).

——, "A Model for Hospital System Planning," in G. Kreweras and G. Morlat (Eds.), "Proceedings of the Third International Conference on Operational Research, English Universities Press, London, pp. 204–211 (1964).

——, "Approach to Nurse-Monitor Research," *Am. J. Nursing* **66**, pp. 556–558 (March 1966).

——, "Toward a Community Health-System Model," *Bio-Med. Computing* **1**, pp. 11–29 (1970).

Hurlburt, E. L. and A. R. Jones, "Blood Band Inventory Control," *Transfusion* **4**, pp. 126–133 (March–April 1964).

Ingbar, M. L., "Organization of Health Services: Challenge to Operations Research," in G. K. Chacko (Ed.), *The Recognition of Systems in Health Services*, Operations Research Society of America, Arlington, Virginia, pp. 5–27 (1969).

Inquiry, Special Issue—"The Computer and Hospital Information Systems," **5**, (September 1968).

International Business Machines Corporation, "Medical Information Systems Program (MISP)," Version 2, Application Description Manual, IBM Corp., White Plains, New York (1970).

——, "HIS-MISP: Hospital Information System—Medical Information System Programs," Mimeographed, IBM Corp., White Plains, New York (undated).

Jackson, R. R. P., J. D. Welch, and J. Fry, "Appointment Systems in Hospitals and General Practice," *Operations Res. Quart.* **15**, pp. 219–237 (1964).

James, F. D., "The Development and Implementation of a Computer-Based Hospital Information System," in G. McLachlan and R. A. Shegog, (Eds.), *Computers in the Service of Medicine, Vol. 2*, Oxford University Press, London, pp. 155–167 (1969).

Jelinek, R. C., "A New Approach to the Analysis of Nursing Activities," *Hospitals, J. A. H. A.* **40**, pp. 89–91 (October 1966).

——, "A Structural Model for the Patient Care Operation," *Health Services Res.* **2**, pp. 226–242 (Fall–Winter 1967).

——, "An Operational Analysis of the Patient Care Function," *Inquiry* **6**, pp. 53–58 (June 1969).

Jennings, J. B., "An Analysis of Hospital Blood Bank Whole Blood Inventory Control Policies," *Transfusion* **8**, pp. 335–342 (November–December 1968).

——, "Information Needs for Hospital Blood Bank Inventory Control," *Transfusion* **9**, pp. 214–216 (July–August 1969).

Kant, V., "*Matematiceskie i ekonomiczeskie metody v zdravoohranenii*," (The Use of Mathematical and Economic Methods in the Health Services) Kisinev.

Kao, E. P. C., "A Semi-Markov Model to Predict Recovery Progress of Coronary Patients," *Health Services Res.* **7**, No. 3: 191–208 (1972).

——, "A Semi-Markovian Population Model with Applications to Hospital Planning," *IEEE Trans. on Syst., Man, and Cybernetics* **SMC-3**, No. 4: 327–336 (1972).

Kast, F. E. and J. E. Rosenzweig, "Hospital Administration and Systems Concepts," *Hosp. Admin*, **11**, pp. 17–33 (Fall 1966).

Kavet, J., "The Application of Computer Simulation Techniques to the Surgical Sybsystem," Unpublished Master's Essay, Yale University, School of Medicine, New Haven, Connecticut (1967).

—— and J. D. Thompson, "Computers Can Tell You What Will Happen Before It Happens," *Mod. Hosp.* **109**, pp. 102–105 (December 1967).

Kendall, D. G., "Mathematical Models of the Spread of Infection," Mathematics Research Council *Mathematics and Computer Science in Biology and Medicine*, London, pp. 213–225 (1945).

Kennedy, F. D., "Development of a Community Health Service System Simulation Model," in A. Reisman and M. Kiley (Eds.), *Health Care Delivery Planning*, Gordon and Breach, New York (1973).

Kiley, J. M., et al., "A Computer-based Medical Record," *J. A. M. A.* **205**, pp. 571–576 (August 1968).

Kilpatrick, K. E. and L. E. Freund, "A Simulation of Tank Oxygen Inventory at a Community General Hospital," *Health Services Res.* **2**, pp. 298–305 (Fall–Winter 1967).

Kirk, J. F., A. Murray, and J. M. Neilson, "Automation of Hospital Medical Records—Data Processing," *Health Bull.* **28**, pp. 49–52 (January 1970).

Kissick, W. L., Forecasting Health Manpower Needs," *Hospitals, J. A. H. A.* **41**, pp. 47–51 (September 1967a).

——, "How Imagination and Innovation Can Help Bridge Manpower Gaps," *Hospitals, J. A. H. A.* **41**, pp. 76+ (October 1967b).

——, "Planning, Programming and Budgeting in Health," *Med. Care* **V**, pp. 201–207 (1967c).

Klarman, H. E., "Increase in the Cost of Physician and Hospital Services," *Inquiry* **7**, pp. 22–36 (March 1970).

——, "Some Technical Problems in Areawide Planning for Hospital Care," *J. Chronic Dis.* **17**, pp. 735–747 (1964).

Kleczkowski, B. M., *Planning and Evaluation of the Community Health Care Programmes: Model of a General Optimizing Method*, Sante Publ., Bucharest, Vol. 3, pp. 259–278 (1971).

Kolesar, P., "A Markovian Model for Hospital Admission Scheduling," *Management Sci.* **16**, pp. 384–396 (February 1970).

Krismer, J. R., "Comprehensive Health Operating and Information Systems," *Trans. Am. Acad. Ophthalmology and Otolaryngology* **75**, pp. 1126–1131 (September–October 1971).

Lair, B. M., "Computerizing Total Hospital Activities—A Pioneer Report," *Comput. and Autom.* **18**, pp. 30–32 (July 1969).

Lamson, B. G., et al., "The First Decade of Effort: Progress Toward a Hospital Information System at the UCLA Hospital, Los Angeles, California," *Methods Info. in Med.* **9**, pp. 73-80 (April 1970).

Lawton, M. D., "Systems Design for a Management-oriented Hospital Information System," in M. E. Abrams (Ed.), *Medical Computing*, American Elsevier, New York, pp. 358-373 (1970).

Lechat, M. F. and C. D. Flagle, "Statistical Decision Theory and the Selection of Diagnostic and Therapeutic Strategies in Public Health," Proceedings of the Third International Conference on Operational Research, Oslo (1963).

—— and C. D. Flagle, "Allocation of Medical and Associated Resources to the Control of Leprosy," in N. N. Barish and M. Verhulst (Eds.), *Management Sciences in the Emerging Countries*, Pergamon Press, Oxford, Great Britain Chapter 9 (1965).

Leighton, E., "CHD: California's Computerized Information System for Hospitals," *Hosp. Forum* **13**, pp. 6+ (May 1970).

Levy, R. P. and M. R. Cammarn, "Information Systems Applications in Medicine," in C. A. Cuadra (Ed.), *Annual Review of Information Science and Technology, Vol. 3*, Encyclopaedia Britannica, Chicago, pp. 397-428 (1968).

——, ——, and M. J. Smith, "Computer Handling of Ambulatory Clinic Records," *J. A. M. A.* **190**, pp. 1033-1037 (December 1968).

Lincoln, T. L. and R. D. Parker, "Medical Diagnosis Using Bayes' Theorem," *Health Services Res.* **2**, pp. 34-45 (1967).

Lipkin, M., R. L. Engle, Jr., et al., "Digital Computer as an Aid to Differential Diagnosis. Use in Hematological Diagnosis," *Arch. Internal Med.* **108**, pp. 57-72 (1961).

Lockheed Missiles & Space Company, "Proposal for a Mayo Clinic Medical Information System: Systems Analysis and Design Phase," LMSC, Sunnyvale, California (1966).

——, "Analysis of a Clinical Information System: University of Saskatchewan Hospital," LMSC, Hospital Systems Study Group, Sunnyvale, California (1967).

——, "Resumé of Capabilities and Interests in Medical Information Systems," Mimeographed, LMSC, Sunnyvale, California (1968).

——, "Analysis of Information Needs of Nursing Stations," Technical Report No. LMSC-682684, LMSC, Sunnyvale, California (1969).

Long, M. and P. J. Feldstein, "The Economics of Hospital Systems: Peak Loads and Regional Coordination," *Am. Econ. Rev.* **b-2**, pp. 119-128 (1967).

Lubin, J. W., D. L. Drossness, and L. G. Wylie, "Highway Network Minimum Path Selection Applied to Health Facility Planning," *Public Health Rep.* **80**, pp. 771-777. (1965).

——, I. M. Reed, G. L. Worstell, and D. L. Drossness, "How Distance Affects Physician Activity," *Mod. Hosp.* **107**, pp. 80-82ff (1966).

Luck, G. M., "Hospital Operation Policies at the Commissioning Stage," Institute for Operations Research, Health Report, No. 3 (1969).

——, J. Luckman, B. W. Smith, and J. Stringer, *Patients, Hospitals and Operational Research*, Tavistock, London (1971).

Luckman, J., "Management Policies for Large Ward Units," Institute for Operations Research, Health Report No. 1, (1969).

——, "Planning Surgery—A Computer Simulation," Institute for Operations Research, Health Report No. 2 (1972).

Mahler, H. T. and M. A. Piot, "Essais d'Application de la Recherche Operationnelle Dans la Lutte Anti-Tuberculeuse," *Bull. de l'Institut National de la Santé et de la Recherche Médicale* **21**, pp. 855-882 (1966).

Masouredis, S. P., et al., "Development of an Automated Blood Inventory and Information System for a Regional Transfusion Service," *Transfusion* **10**, pp. 182-193 (July–August 1970).

Michael, J. M., J. Spatofore, and E. R. Williams, "A Basic Information System for Health Planning, *Public Health Rep.* **83,** No. 1: 21–28 (1968).

Mills, R. E. and R. B. Fetter, "CML: A Conversational Modeling Language," Technical Report No. 53, Yale University, Department of Administrative Sciences (1972).

McCarn, D. B. and D. G. Moriarty, "Computers in Medicine," *Hospitals, J. A. H. A.* **45,** pp. 37–39 (January 1971).

McClain, J. O. and D. C. Riedel, "Screening for Utilization Review: On the Use of Explicit Criteria and Non-Physicians in Case Selection," *Am. J. Public Health* **63,** No. 3: 247–251 (1973).

McLachlan, G., (Ed.), *Operational Research in the Health Services, a Symposium*, Oxford University Press, London, 1962 (For the Nuffield Provincial Hospital Trust.)

—— and R. A. Shegog, (Eds.), *Computers in the Service of Medicine. Essays on Current Research and Applications, Vol. 1-2*, Oxford University Press, London, 1968 (For the Nuffield Provincial Hospital Trust.)

——, "Health Operations Research and Systems Analysis Literature," in A. Sheldon, F. Baker and C. P. McLaughlin (Eds.), *Systems and Medical Care*, MIT Press, Cambridge, Massachusetts, pp. 27–48 (1970).

McNerney, W. J., "Why Does Medical Care Cost So Much?," *New England J. Med.* **282,** pp. 1458–1465 (June 1970).

Nasta, M. D., J. K. Beddow, and R. A. Shapiro, "A Deterministic Input-Output Model to Facilitate Management of a Hospital System," *J. Operations Res. Soc. Japan* **15,** pp. 19–33 (March 1972).

Navarro, V., "Systems Analysis in the Health Field," *Socio-Econ. Plan. Sci.* **3,** pp. 179–189 (August 1969).

——, R. Parker, and K. White, "A Stochastic and Deterministic Model of Medical Care Utilization," *Health Services Res.* **5,** No. 4: 342–357 (1970).

Newell, D. J., Provision of Emergency Beds in Hospitals," *Brit. J. Preventive and Social Med.* **8,** pp. 77–80 (April 1954).

——, "Immediate Admissions to Hospital," in G. Kreweras and G. Morlat (Eds.), *Proceedings of the Third International Conference on Operational Research*, English Universities Press, London, pp. 224–233 (1964a).

——, "Problems in Estimating the Demand for Hospital Beds," *J. Chronic Dis.* **17,** pp. 749–759 (September 1964b).

——, "Hospital Bed Usage," *Brit. J. Hosp. Med.* **3,** pp. 915–917 (June 1970).

Newhouse, J. P., "Toward a Theory of Nonprofit Institutions: An Economic Model of a Hospital," *Am. Econ. Rev.* **60,** pp. 64–74 (March 1970).

Ockenden, J. M. and K. E. Bodenham, *Focus on Medical Computer Development*, Oxford University Press, London (1970).

O'Connel, B. P. and A. H. McFarlane, "A Medical Care Information System: An Approach to the Computerization of Ambulatory Patient Records," *Med. Care* **8,** pp. 82–87 (January–February 1970).

O'Hara, M. and A. M. Josephson, "Regional Automated Data-Processing System for Blood Banks," *Transfusion* **10,** pp. 215–220 (July–August 1970).

O'Malley, C. D., "Application of Systems Engineering in Nursing," *Am. J. Nursing* **69,** pp. 2155–2160 (October 1969).

Overall, J. E. and E. M. Williams, "A Computer Procedure for Diagnosis of Thyroid Function," in K. Enslein (Ed.), *Data Acquisition and Processing in Biology and Medicine, Vol. 2*, Pergamon Press, London (1962).

Packer, A. H., "Applying Cost-Effectiveness Concepts to the Community Health System," *ORSA J.* **16,** pp. 343–350 (1968).

Pan American Health Organization, "Regional Advisory Committee on Computers in Health, First Meeting," Scientific Publication No. 211, Washington (1970).

Park, K. S. and J. R. Freeman, "Community Health Resources Allocation With Linear Programming Methods," Technical Report No. 2, University of Florida, Health Systems Research Division (1969).

Pegels, C. C. and A. E. Jelmert, "An Evaluation of Blood-Inventory Policies: A Markov Chain Application," *Operations Res*. 18, pp. 1087–1098 (November–December 1970).

Piot, M. and T. K. Sundaresan, "A Linear Programme Decision Model for Tuberculosis Control," Progress Report on the First Test-Runs. WHO/TB/Techn. Information/ 67.55, WHO, Geneva (1967).

Polkin, B. N., V. J. Anderson and A. G. Kononov, "Optymalnoe Raspledelenie Priorosta Cisla Koek v Lecebnyh Ucrezdenijah po Specialnostjam i Territorii s Primeneniem Elektronnovycislitelnyh Masin," ("Optimal Distribution of Growth in Number of Hospital Beds by Speciality and Territory Using Electronic Computers"). *Sovetsk, Zdravoohr*. 10, pp. 24–35 (1969).

Popov, G. A., Principles of Health Planning in the USSR," *WHO Public Health Papers No. 43*, Geneva (1971).

Rath, G. J., O. G. Kennedy, and R. E. Lapp, "Developing a Composite Hospital Simulation Model," Report DDC-69-8-1, Northwestern University, The Technological Institute, Design and Development Center, Evanston, Ill., (1969).

Reed, R., Jr. and W. E. Stanley, "Optimizing Control of Hospital Inventories," *J. Ind. Eng*. 16, pp. 48–51 (January–February 1965).

Rice, D. P., "Measurement and Application of Illness Costs," *Public Health Rep*. 84, No. 2 (1969).

Riedel, D. C., Brenner, M. H., et al., "Psychiatric Utilization Review As Patient Care Evaluation," *Am. J. Public Health* 62, No. 9: 1222–1228 (1972).

——, R. B. Fetter, et al., "Basic Utilization Review Program (BURP)," Technical Report WP21, Yale University, Health Services Research (1972).

—— and T. B. Fitzpatrick, *Patterns of Patient Care*, University of Michigan Press, Ann Arbor, Michigan (1964).

——, ——, and R. P. Leifer, "Prediction of Hospital Length of Stay," *Health Services Res*. 1, pp. 287–300 (Winter 1966).

——, ——, and P. Wing, "Computer Simulation of Hospital Patient Scheduling Systems," *Health Services Res*. 3, pp. 130–141 (Summer 1968).

Rockart, J. F. and P. B. Hofmann, "Physician and Patient Behavior Under Different Scheduling Systems in a Hospital Outpatient Department," *Med. Care* 7, pp. 463–470 (November–December 1969).

Rockwell, T. H., R. A. Barnum, and W. C. Giffin, "Inventory Analysis as Applied to Hospital Whole Blood Supply and Demand," *J. Ind. Eng*. 13, pp. 109–114 (March–April 1962).

Romania, Ministry of Health, *Studies and Methods of Operational Research in Public Health*, Bucharest, (1969).

Rösch, G., "Operational Research in the Medical Field in France," WHO Document No. EURO 0408/11, Copenhagen (1969).

Rosen, D., "Medical Care Information System of the Veterans Administration," *Public Health Reps*. 83, pp. 363–371 (May 1968).

Saunders, M. G., "The Computer and Total Medical Information Processing–A Present Fiction," *Canadian Hosp*. 46, pp. 64–67 (October 1969).

Schwartz, M. D., "Status of Hospital Information Systems," *Hosp. Progress* 51, pp. 53–60 (June 1970).

Scheff, T. J., "Decision Rules, Types of Errors and Their Consequences for Medical Diagnosis," *Behavioral Sci*. 8, pp. 97–107 (1963).

Shegog, R. F. A., "Reviewing Some Applications for Computers to Medicine," in G. Mc-Lachlan (Ed.), *Problems and Progress in Medical Care, Third Series*, Oxford University Press, London, pp. 146–170 (1968).

Sheldon, A., F. Baker, and C. P. McLaughlin (Eds.), *Systems and Medical Care*, MIT Press, Cambridge, Massachusetts (1970).

Siegel, S. J., "Developing an Information System for a Hospital," *Public Health Rep.* **83**, pp. 359–362 (May 1968).

Silver, A. and Alice M. Silver, "An Empirical Inventory Control System for Hospital Blood Banks," *Hospitals, J. A. H. A.* **38**, pp. 56+ (August 1964).

Singman, D., et al., "Computerized Blood Bank Control," *J. A. M. A.* **194**, pp. 113–116 (November 1965).

Smalley, H. E., "Hospital Systems Research," *Hosp. Admin.* **11**, pp. 42–50 (Winter 1966).

—— and J. R. Freeman, *Hospital Industrial Engineering*, Reinhold, New York (1966).

——, et al., "Inventory Policies," *Hosp. Management* **97**, pp. 92–97 (March 1964).

Smallwood, R. D., et al., "A Medical Service Requirement Model for Health System Design," Proceedings of the IEEE (Special Issue on Automated Health Services) (1969).

Smallwood, R. D., E. J. Sondik, and F. L. Offensend, "Toward An Integrated Methodology for the Analysis of Health Care Systems," *Operations Res.* **19**, pp. 1300–1322 (October 1971).

Smith, B. W. and Luck, G. M., "Networks for the Commissioning of Walsgrave Hospital, Coventry," Institute for Operations Research, Health Report No. 4 (1970).

Soriano, A., "Comparison of Two Scheduling Systems," *Operations Res.* **14**, pp. 388–397 (May–June 1966).

Souder, J. J., "Computers Can Bring a New Rationality Into Hospital Design," *Mod. Hosp.* **110**, pp. 80–86 (March 1968).

——, et al., *Planning for Hospitals*, American Hospital Association, Chicago (1964).

Stimson, D. H., "Utility Measurement in Public Health Decision Making," *Management Sci.* **16**, pp. 17–30 (October 1969).

——, "Health Agency Decision-Making: An Operations Research Perspective," in M. F. Arnold, L. V. Blankenship, and J. M. Hess (Eds.) *Administering Health Systems: Issues and Perspectives*, Aldine-Atherton, New York, pp. 398–433 (1971).

—— and R. H. Stimson, "Operations Research in Hospitals," Hospital Research & Educational Trust, Chicago, Ill., (1972).

Stringer J., "Operations Research for 'Multi-Organizations,'" *Operational Res. Quart.* **18**, No. 2: 105–120 (1967).

——, "Operational Research in Planning and Designing Medical Facilities in the United Kingdom," WHO Document EURO 0408/12, Copenhagen (1969).

Strand, L., "Moznosti Aplikace Metody Monte Carlo ve Zdravotnickych Zarizenih," ("The Use of the Monte Carlo Method in Planning the Work of Medical Institutions"), *Cs. Zdvar.* **4–5**, pp. 193–198 (1969).

Teitz, M. B., assisted by Polly Bart, "Models of Patient Flows in a Hospital System: A Preliminary Analysis," Internal Working Paper, University of California, Department of City and Regional Planning, Berkeley, California (1968).

Thomas, W. H., "A Model for the Prediction of Demand for Nursing Services," Paper presented at the 27th National Meeting of the Operations Research Society of America, Boston (May 1965).

——, "A Model for Predicting Recovery Progress of Coronary Patients," *Health Services Res.* **3**, pp. 185–213 (1968).

——, et al., "A Model of a Hospital Information System," Research Report No. 4, State University of New York at Buffalo, Department of Industrial Engineering (1965).

Thompson, J. D., "On Reasonable Costs of Hospital Services," *Milbank Memorial Fund Quart., Part 2*, **46**, pp. 33–41 (Januray 1968).

—— and R. B. Fetter, "The Economics of the Maternity Service," *Yale J. Biol. and Med.* **36**, pp. 91–103 (August 1963).

—— and ——, "Research Helps Calculate OB Bed Needs," *Mod. Hosp.* **102**, pp. 98–101. (January 1964).

—— and ——, "The Application of Simulation to Hospital Planning, in "Proceedings on Simulation in Business and Public Health." First Annual Conference of American Statistical Association (New York Chapter Area) and Public Health Association of New York City (1966).

—— and ——, "Economics of Occupancy with Varying Mixes of Private and Other Patient Accommodations: A Simulation," Health Services Res. pp. 42–52 (Spring 1969).

——, ——, and D. C. Riedel, "CUPISS, A Multipurpose Regional, Medical Information System Based on Three Inputs for Each Patient." Mimeographed, Yale University, Department of EPH, New Haven, Connecticut (1969).

——, O. W. Avant, and E. D. Spiker, "How Queuing Theory Works for the Hospital," *Mod. Hosp.* **94**, pp. 75–78 (March 1960).

——, et al., "Predicting Requirements for Maternity Facilities," *Hospitals, J. A. H. A.* **37**, pp. 45+ (February 1963).

——, "The Use of Computers in Hospitals," Report No. PB 195 629, National Technical Information Service, National Center for Health Services Research and Development, Springfield, Virginia (1969).

Tsao, R. F., "A Second Order Exponential Model for Multidimensional Dichotomous Contingency Tables, with Applications in Medical Diagnosis," Report No. 320-2014, IBM Corporation, Scientific Center, Cambridge, Massachusetts (1967).

Vallbona, C., "Applications of Computers for Hospital Usage," *J. Chronic Dis.* **19**, pp. 461–472 (April 1966).

VanBrunt, E. E., "The Kaiser-Permanente Medical Information System," in M. F. Collen (Ed.), *Medical Information Systems*, U. S. Department of Health, Education and Welfare, Health Services and Mental Health Administration, Washington, D. C., pp. 87–101 (1970).

Venediktov, D. D., "Problema Rosstanovki i Ispolzovanija Mediciniskih Kadrov." ("The Distribution and Use of Medical Staff") *Sovetsk, Zdravoohr.* **8**, pp. 3–9 (1967).

Waaler, H., A. Gesser, and S. Anderson, "The Use of Mathematical Models in the Study of the Epidemiology of Tuberculosis," *Am. J. Public Health* **52**, pp. 1002–1013 (1962).

Warner, D. M. and J. Prawda, "A Mathematical Programming Model for Scheduling Nursing Personnel in a Hospital," Mimeographed, University of Michigan, Bureau of Hospital Administration, Ann Arbor, Michigan (1971).

Warner, H. R., A. F. Toronto, et al., "A Mathematical Approach to Medical Diagnosis," *J. A. M. A.* **177**, pp. 75–81 (1961).

Weinerman, E. R., "Research on Comparative Health Services Systems," *Med. Care* **19**, No. 3 (1972).

Weir, R. D., G. B. Fowler, and I. Dingwall-Fordyce, "The Prediction and Simulation of Surgical Admission." in G. McLachlan and R. A. Shegog (Eds.), *Computers in the Service of Medicine, Vol. 2*, Oxford University Press, London, pp. 141–154 (1969).

Welch, J. D., "Hospital Applications," *Operation Res. Quart.* **3**, pp. 8–10 (March 1952a).

——, "Some Research Into the Organization and Design of Hospital Outpatient Departments," *J. Roy. Sanitary Inst.* **72**, pp. 298–311 (July 1952b).

——, "Appointment Systems in Hospital Outpatient Departments," *Operational Res. Quart.* **15**, pp. 224–231 (September 1964).

—— and N. T. J. Bailey, "Appointment Systems in Hospital Outpatient Department," *Lancet* 1, pp. 1105-1108 (May 1952).

Whitston, C. W., "An Analysis of the Problems of Scheduling Surgery, Parts 1 and 2," *Hosp. Management* 99, pp. 58+ (April 1965); 99, pp. 45-49 (May 1965).

Williams, W. J., R. P. Covert, and J. D. Steele, "Simulation Modeling of a Teaching Hospital Outpatient Clinic," *Hospitals, J. A. H. A.* 41, pp. 71-75 (November 1967).

Wilson, H. H. and M. R. Schulmeister, "Medical Systems Engineering," *Inquiry* 5, pp. 35-41 (September 1968).

Wiseman, J., "Cost-Benefit Analysis and Health Service Policy," in A. T. Peacock and D. J. Robertson (Eds.), *Public Expenditure: Appraisal and Control*, Oliver & Boyd, Edinburgh, pp. 128-145 (1963).

Wolfe, H., "Computerized Screening Device for Selecting Cases for Utilization Review," *Med. Care* 5, pp. 44-51 (1967).

——, M. Iskander, and T. Raffin, "A Study of Obstetrical Facilities," in G. K. Chacko (Ed.), "The Recognition of Systems in Health Services," Operations Research Society of America, Arlington, Virginia, pp. 369-392 (1969).

—— and J. P. Young, "Staffing the Nursing Unit: Controlled Variable Staffing," *Nursing Res.* 14, pp. 236-245 (Summer (1965a).

—— and ——, "Staffing the Nursing Unit: The Multiple Assignment Technique," *Nursing Res.* 14, pp. 299-303. (Fall 1965b).

World Health Organization, Regional Office for Europe, "Methods of Evaluating Public Health Programmes," Report on a Symposium, EURO 0375, Report on a Symposium, Kiel, (November 1967). WHO, Copenhagen (1968).

——, Regional Office for Europe, "Health Operational Research," URO 0408, Report on a Seminar, Bucharest (September 1963). WHO, Copenhagen (1969).

——, Regional Office for Europe, "The Regional Office's Activities in the Field of Medical Computing," EURO 3093, Report on a Working Group, Bratislava (February 1970). WHO, Copenhagen (1970a).

——, Regional Office for Europe, "The Use of Operational Research in Health Services," EURO 0408(1), Report on a Meeting, Copenhagen (February 1970). WHO, Copenhagen (1970b).

——, "Development of a Methodology for Economic Assessment of Parasitic Disease Control Programmes," Report of Working Group PD/71.8, WHO Geneva (1971a).

——, "A Manual of Concepts and Procedures," Health Projection Formulation, WHO Document PSA/71.1, Rev. 1, Project System Analysis, WHO, Geneva (1971b).

——, "Statistical Indicators for the Planning and Evaluation of Public Health Programmes," WHO Technical Repor-Series No. 472, Report of a WHO Scientific Group, WHO, Geneva (1971c).

——, "The Development of Studies in Health Manpower," WHO Technical Report Series No. 481, Report of a WHO Scientific Group, WHO, Geneva (1971d).

Young, J. P., "Stabilization of Inpatient Bed Occupancy Through Control of Admissions," *Hospitals, J. A. H. A.* 39, pp. 41-48 (October 1965).

——, "Administrative Control of Multiple-Channel Queuing Systems With Parallel Input Streams," *Operations Res.* 14, pp. 145-156 (January–February 1966a).

——, "Information Nexus Guides Information System," *Mod. Hosp.* 106, pp. 101-105 (February 1966b).

——, "A Conceptual Framework for Hospital Administrative Decisions Systems," *Health Services Res.* 3, pp. 79-95 (Summer 1968).

——, "No Easy Solutions," in G. K. Chacko (Ed.), *The Recognition of Systems in Health Services*, Operations Research Society of America, Arlington, Virginia, pp. 395-398 (1969).

II-3

EDUCATIONAL PROCESSES

Alexander M. Mood

1. ANALYSIS OF THE EDUCATION PROCESS

In Part 1 of this chapter, we shall confine our attention to analysis of the education process itself. Operations research has, of course, many contributions to make toward analyzing various other operations carried out by educational organizations. For example, there are many nice programming and scheduling problems having to do with the most efficient use of teachers and of teaching facilities; schools have sizable information systems which will surely become larger in the future as more emphasis is placed on following the progress of each child and tailoring his curriculum to his needs; schools are replete with queues at registration desks, cafeterias, athletic events, gymnasium facilities, and the like; and finally, the routing of school buses is not an insignificant task. These problems as well as others in this field, are the subjects of other chapters of this handbook. Part 2 of this chapter, which is little more than a slightly annotated bibliography, will refer to a number of examples of such applications.

Operations analysis of the public school system refers to a quantitative description of the system as a production operation, with a view to better understanding how one might manipulate the system to make it more effective. The rationale for such analysis is that educational processes are analogous to other production processes; they transform input material (partially educated individuals) into output products (better educated individuals), using capital equipment (school buildings, laboratories, buses, libraries, athletic fields, etc.) and personnel (administrators, teachers, counselors, coaches, etc.) and processes (curricular and extracurricular programs). A believable quantitative model accurately relating these various school factors to educational outcomes could be particularly valuable to educational administrators and policy-makers who are managing the system, allocating resources within the system, and deciding how much of the nation's resources should be devoted to education. It could also provide a basic framework by means of which a great many isolated experiments in education could be related to the system at large and to each other. It could bring some precision to discussions of the pros and cons of proposed educational policies. It could bring a larger measure of science to educational methodology, and a larger measure of scientific management to educational administration. The earliest sophisticated discussion of this approach to education is probably that of Kershaw and McKean [1959].

1.1   Inputs and Outputs

A rather broad conceptualization of a global model of the educational system has been developed at the U.S. Office of Education (Mood [1969]). It is far too elaborate to be realizable at this time, but will serve as a general introduction to what is involved in developing such a model. At a highly aggregated level, the conceptulization rests on the following six major inputs to a student's educational progress:

The student's own abilities and attitudes.
The support of his education by his family.
The endorsement of educational endeavor by his peers.
Community support of education.
Properties of the educational system.
Society's posture with respect to education.

Figure 1 provides a very gross view of the arrangement of these inputs. In it, the oval representing young persons is sliced to represent individuals; the darkened slice represents a student, in that it overlaps the school system oval; the student is also a member of a family and of the community and of society at large. The community consists of a variety of other persons, organizations, and facilities not shown by the diagram; many of them are important to learning in the large sense; some (e.g., a museum) are relevant to formal education.

These very broad determinants of a student's educational accomplishment need to be broken down into components before an attempt is made to create quantitative measures for them. An example of such a specification is provided by the following outline:

Components of family support of a student.

Provision of a physically and psychologically comfortable home.
Pressure on the student to perform well at school.

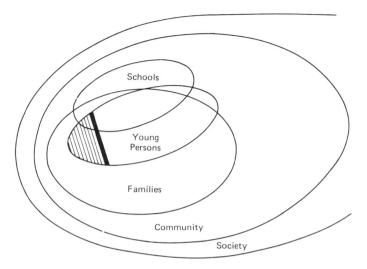

Fig. 1. Major inputs to a student's educational process.

Pressure on the school to educate the student well.
Provision of educational know-how.

Components of peer support of a student.

Positive attitude toward educational achievement.
High educational expectations for themselves.
Assist student with his school work.

Components of community support.

Healthy social climate.
Belief in the value of education.
Participation in school activities.
Financial support.
Provision of community cultural and recreational resources.

Components of society's support.

Freedom to pursue knowledge.
Laws and policy regarding school organization, school governance, curriculum,
    personnel, and attendance.
Provision of resources for education.

Components of the school system.

Teachers
    Belief in educability of the pupils.

Competence in organizing and managing classroom.

Knowledge of field in which teaching.

Knowledge of educational technology.

Ability to communicate with students.

Ability to motivate students.

Administrations

Selection of goals appropriate to the needs of students and society.

Competence in creating effective organizations of teachers and students for reaching these goals.

Competence in monitoring programs and in making suitable modification of them when achievement of goals is threatened.

Ability to maintain clear communication between school and society.

Curriculum and other aspects of school program

Relation to social and economic opportunities.

Appropriateness to student capabilities and desires.

Adaptability to needs of individual students.

Health and food programs.

Extracurricular and recreational programs.

Facilities

Amount and quality of classrooms, laboratories, libraries, etc.

Availability of learning equipment (books, records, projectors, computers, TV, musical instruments, works of art, sports equipment, etc.).

Adequacy of space, grounds, and athletic fields.

Variety and quality of community cultural and recreational facilities used by school.

Components of educational state of the students.

Achievement of skills and knowledge

Communications.

Mathematics and computer languages.

Natural sciences.

Social sciences.

Humanities.

Arts.

Personal development

Social competence.

Sense of responsibility.

Self-confidence.

Creativeness.

Ethics.

Ambition.

Ability to concentrate.

Judgment.

These last fourteen components (of the educational state of a student) are outputs as well as inputs. We may think of them as being inputs at the beginning of a school year and as being outputs at the end of the year. The other five major determinants may then be regarded as operating on the input state of the student to transform it during the course of the year to the output state.

1.2 Measures

Having arrived at a set of components such as those listed above, one can then begin to assemble a set of items by means of which each component might be quantified. For example, the set of items associated with a given component might be combined with appropriate weights to form an index number that will serve as a measure of the component.

Going back for illustration to the components of family support, the first was provision of a comfortable home. Items that might serve to indicate the level of that component are:

Quality of food.
Quality of clothing.
Quality of residence.
Adequacy of space (uncrowded).
Both parents living at home?
Parents reasonably congenial?
Parents deal reasonably fair with children?
Quiet place to study?
Family has reasonably good relations with neighbors?
Absence of serious emotional disturbances that might distract student from
  school work?
Student required to augment family income?

In measuring such items one would not give any credit to luxury. That is, quality of food would mainly refer to balanced nutrition; quality of clothing would reach the top of the scale if clothing were warm, clean, and no embarrassment to the child.

For another illustration, the second component of family support refers to pressure to perform well. Some items that might give good indication of such pressure are:

Rewards for good grades.
Distress at low grades.
Parents apprise themselves of homework requirements and insist that it be
  done.
Parents enforce regular attendance at school.
Parents influence students to undertake ambitious educational programs.

Parents influence students toward careers that demand outstanding educational performance.

An item such as the second might be measured on a simple qualitative scale using categories as: severe discipline for low grades, real hostility generated on part of parents toward student, withdrawal of significant rights and privileges, minor penalties, reasoned disapproval, little concern, entirely satisfied with barely passing grades.

None of the six aggregated inputs and none of their primary components has a direct measure. Each of them must, therefore, be quantified by means of an appropriate index number or other measure. A few are already well in hand; for example, various tests for achievement in different subject-matter fields have been designed and validated by educators; sociologists have developed indexes of social and economic status. Some of the other components can be readily indicated by easily available economic and financial data. Nevertheless, there remains a sizable development task. There must be assembled for each unquantified component a list of items, out of which can be constructed a test or questionnaire that will provide the basis for a satisfactory measurement of the component.

The measures will often be only indicators because the components are so complex or abstract that no comprehensive list of their elements is possible. It may be worthwhile to distinguish between indexes and indicators. The Cost of Living Index (maintained by the U.S. Bureau of Labor Statistics) is made up of quite a long list of prices of items that provide a very complete representation of things families must purchase. One could use instead a simple indicator made up of, say, prices of only four items: bread, rent, automobiles, and hospital room rates. With properly chosen weights, the indicator will have very high correlation with the complete index. That is the distinction; an indicator does not pretend to be a comprehensive measure, but it does give reasonable promise that it would have high correlation with a comprehensive measure if one existed. Often, the 'reasonable promise' will rest only on the judgment of reasonable persons; it will not be possible to verify that a high correlation exists.

It is essential, if education is to develop a widely applicable body of quantitative theory, that there be agreement among educational researchers about the construction of each index or indicator. Although many indicators will be quite arbitrary and far less satisfactory than the indexes used by economists, they must necessarily have the same standing in the field of education that the Cost of Living Index, Gross National Product, Wholesale Price Index, etc., have in the field of economics. When we do have such generally accepted measures, then research workers will be able to calibrate the subjects (students, teachers, parents, school administrators, curricula, etc.) of their experiments and surveys the same way, and there will begin to be some real verification of the results of others when replication is attempted. Educational research will begin to build some quantitative structure.

Of course, wide agreement about formulation of measures does not mean that they must have their specifications fixed forever. They can be revised periodically (just as economic indexes are) to reflect the evolution of society and of educational goals and practices.

To be taken seriously, the model must be reasonably complete. Omission of significant inputs or outputs may disastrously distort relations between those that are retained, and hence give gravely misleading guidance about how outputs depend on inputs. This is a particularly troublesome matter with respect to the outputs; educators have developed measures of cognitive skills and knowledge (the first six components of the educational state of the student listed above), but they have developed no such measures for the personal development components. The result is that educational research on policy and administration tend to give most attention to the measured components and tend to neglect those that do not yet have measuring instruments, even though there is wide agreement that the personal development components are fully as important as the cognitive components.

1.3 Regression Models

In the distant future it is to be hoped that there will have been developed a very comprehensive structural model of the educational process, which will consist of a large number of simultaneous equations relating inputs to outputs, inputs to each other, and outputs to each other. It might be reminiscent of the massive model of the U.S. economy that has been developed at the Brookings Institute by Duesenberry [1965] and others, which involves over 100 equations. We are a very long way from such a model now for lack of agreement on definition of variables, lack of understanding of relationships between variables, and lack of data for exploring such relationships. As a result, we can point to only very primitive models, usually consisting of a single regression equation which attempts to relate scores on an achievement test to a few independent variables chosen to represent home and school influences.

In terms of the general inputs and outputs described already, a general regression model might be put in the form where $S_1 = f(S_0, P, F, L, C, Y)$, where S_0 is the initial state of the student and is a vector consisting of fourteen components; S_1 is the output state of the student and is the same vector; P, F, L, C, Y are indicators or index numbers representing, respectively the major determinants: peers, family, school, community, and society; the function f is linear in the regression coefficients. These five measures will ordinarily be linear regression functions of their components which will, in turn, ordinarily be linear regression functions of the items chosen to specify them.   The function f will normally consist of a sum of powers and products of its variables, multiplied by regression coefficients, although when S has only one component it is often convenient to use a device called *criterion scaling* to force the function to be linear in its variables (see Mood [1969] and Beaton [1969]).

These models are usually constructed using the major determinants as independent variables rather than orthogonal variables derived from the components by factor analysis.   The reason is that a given orthogonal variable is frequently composed of a variety of components in a way that defies intuitive understanding of what the variable represents.   This model is intended not just for research workers but for educational administrators and for laymen who sit on school boards and in legislative bodies.   If they are to understand the quantitative findings of this model and to use them in their deliberations about educational operations and budgets, then it is extremely important that the terms used to describe the findings be altogether meaningful to laymen.   Esoteric jargon could destroy much of the utility of the model.

1.4   Partitioning of Variance

The major inputs affecting learning appear to be confounded to an extraordinary degree.   Thus far, at any rate, efforts to disentangle their effects have had little success, and it is altogether possible that they may never be separated.   Certainly, there is so much interaction between home and school in learning that we can hardly expect to fully separate their effects.

Let us suppose that index numbers for the major inputs have been developed, and that we are examining a set A of achievement data in fifth grade arithmetic by means of a linear regression on five indexes of the five major inputs; the regression would have the form:

$$A = aP + bF + cL + dC + eY,$$

in which the lower-case letters are the regression coefficients.   Application of the regression will reduce the raw variance V of the achievement scores to $(1 - R^2)V$, where R^2 is the multiple correlation coefficient.

As indicated above, the five indexes will turn out to be highly correlated with each other.   The result is, therefore, that any four of the five will remove nearly as much variance as all five.   In fact, any three will not do much worse than any four.

A device for measuring the extent to which the five indexes are uniquely associated with achievement and jointly associated with achievement is a special partition of variance into unique and common parts (see Coleman [1966], Mood [1971] and Newton and Spurrell [1967]).   The idea is best presented with only two independent variables.   Let V be the variance of the achievement scores A. Let the regression on P alone remove the fraction R_P^2 of the variance, and let the regression on F alone remove the fraction R_F^2 of the variance. Finally, let the regression on P and F jointly, that is, $A = aP + bF$, remove the fraction R_{PF}^2 of the variance. This last fraction can be split into three parts as follows: $R_{PF}^2 - R_P^2$ is the fraction of V uniquely associated with F, $R_{PF}^2 - R_F^2$ is the fraction associated with P, and the remainder

$$R_{PF}^2 - (R_{PF}^2 - R_P^2) - (P_{PF}^2 - R_F^2) = R_P^2 + R_F^2 - R_{PF}^2$$

is the proportion that may be associated with either P or F; it is often called the commonality of P and F.

In general, with n independent variables, one can define a similar partition into $2^n - 1$ parts. If we now use the integers $1, 2, \ldots, n$ to denote the variables (instead of $P, F, L, \ldots$), then a simple device for writing down formulas for the part of a variance common to a subset—say $2, 4, 7$, out of 8 variables—is to expand the product

$$-(1 - \chi_2)(1 - \chi_4)(1 - \chi_7)\chi_1\chi_3\chi_5\chi_6\chi_8,$$

and replace the resulting terms by R^2, with the same subscripts as appear on the χ's in the term. Thus, for four variables, the unique proportion of the variance associated with the second variable is

$$U_2 \sim -(1 - \chi_2)\chi_1\chi_3\chi_4 = R_{1234}^2 - R_{134}^2,$$

and the part that may be associated with either 1 or 3 is

$$E_{13} \sim -(1 - \chi_1)(1 - \chi_3)\chi_2\chi_4 = -R_{1234}^2 + R_{124}^2 + R_{234}^2 - R_{24}^2.$$

In using this rule to write the formula for the part that may be associated with all the independent variables, the -1 is deleted after expansion of the appropriate product

$$-(1 - \chi_1)(1 - \chi_2)(1 - \chi_3)\cdots(1 - \chi_n).$$

After examining a few numerical results, we shall be in a better position to examine the question of why researchers have preferred the partitioning of variance technique to the estimation of regression coefficients for exploring relationships between inputs and outputs.

1.5 Illustrative Results

An opportunity to implement a model of this kind on a large scale arose with the passage by Congress of the Civil Rights Act of 1964. Section 402 of the Act required the Commissioner of Education to survey the "lack of availability of equal educational opportunities for individuals by reason of race, color, religion, or national origin." The survey was carried out in 1965, and a final report was published by Coleman, et al. [1966]. The survey produced a large and comprehensive set of school, student, family, and community data from 600,000 students in 4,000 public schools. Teachers, principals, and superintendents, as well as students, filled out personal questionnaires. Students and teachers took tests. The results given below are selected from an elaborate study by Mayeske and others [1972, 1973], which was carried out after the survey report was published. The study combined four achievement scores into a composite achievement criterion, and formed index numbers from questionnaire items by maximizing the correlation between the criterion and the index. The items were criterion scaled to linearize the regression function.

When one examines the variance of achievement scores in a large nationwide sample, he finds that about one-third of the variance lies between schools, and about two-thirds lies between students in the same school. The illustrative numerical results given below refer only to the one-third of the variance between schools. Thus they refer to a regression of school averages of achievement against school averages of the indexes representing the major determinants. Table 1 gives the proportion of variance removed (squared multiple correlation coefficient) by two determinants individually (the peer index P and the school index L) in the first two lines and together in the third line. Then, in the last three lines there are proportions of variance uniquely associated with P and L, and the proportion that may be associated with either P or L. In the right-hand column we observe that 82 percent of the variance in achievement between schools is removed by a regression on the peer index alone, and that 79 percent is removed by the school index alone. Putting both indexes into the regression raises the percent of variance removed to 86 percent. Hence, the proportions of variance uniquely attributable to P and L are quite small; the bulk of the variance removed can be associated with either the peers or the school characteristics.

Table 2 shows the relative importance of teachers as opposed to other school characteristics. In it, the school index L was split into two indexes, T and O, with T being the index of teacher quality and O including all other aspects of

TABLE 1. PROPORTIONS OF VARIANCE IN ACHIEVEMENT BETWEEN SCHOOLS ASSOCIATED WITH PEER QUALITY P AND SCHOOL QUALITY L

	Third grade	Sixth grade	Ninth grade	Twelfth grade
R_P^2	0.5254	0.7884	0.8207	0.8221
R_L^2	0.4901	0.7322	0.7601	0.7865
R_{PL}^2	0.5646	0.8296	0.8662	0.8617
Unique for P	0.0745	0.0974	0.1061	0.0752
Unique for L	0.0392	0.0412	0.0455	0.0396
Either P or L	0.4509	0.6910	0.7146	0.7469

school quality, such as class size, age of school building, laboratories, libraries, textbooks, audio-visual and other equipment, curriculum, administration, adequacy of grounds and athletic fields, extracurricular activities, etc. The first seven lines of Table 2 give the squared multiple correlation coefficients for the individual regressions against P, T, and O; then for them two at a time; then for all three together.

The most striking result is seen in the second and third lines and in comparing them with the second line of the first table. Essentially the whole school effect can be associated with the teacher quality index; the other part of the school index takes out much less variance on its own, and, comparing the third and last lines of Table 2, we see that the major part of its regression effect overlaps both the teacher- and the peer-regression effects.

1.6 Proportions of Variance Versus Regression Coefficients

The use of proportions of variance removed by variables rather than their regression coefficients to assess their importance is a mark of the primitiveness of the models. Analysts could calculate the regression coefficient for a major variable such as peer effect, and then translate that into coefficients associated with the individual indicators which make up the peer effect index; but those coefficients would be relatively meaningless, because the indicators by no means form a complete set and are serving as proxies for others that might appear in a complete set. Hopefully, the proportion of variance associated with a given

TABLE 2. PROPORTIONS OF VARIANCE IN ACHIEVEMENT BETWEEN SCHOOLS ASSOCIATED WITH PEER QUALITY P, TEACHER QUALITY T, AND OTHER SCHOOL CHARACTERISTICS O

	Third grade	Sixth grade	Ninth grade	Twelfth grade
R_P^2	0.5254	0.7884	0.8207	0.8221
R_T^2	0.4751	0.7145	0.7195	0.7441
R_O^2	0.1129	0.1588	0.2543	0.3178
R_{PT}^2	0.5569	0.8197	0.8449	0.8399
R_{PO}^2	0.5336	0.8028	0.8495	0.8444
R_{TO}^2	0.4901	0.7322	0.7601	0.7865
R_{PTO}^2	0.5646	0.8296	0.8662	0.8617
Unique for P	0.0745	0.0974	0.1061	0.0752
Unique for T	0.0310	0.0268	0.0167	0.0173
Unique for O	0.0077	0.0099	0.0213	0.0218
Either P or T	0.3462	0.5466	0.4891	0.4514
Either P or O	0.0073	0.0058	0.0193	0.0206
Either T or O	0.0005	0.0045	0.0075	0.0005
P or T or O	0.0974	0.1386	0.2062	0.2749

factor via its set of indicators will be less vulnerable to change when, in the future, other investigators use other sets of indicators for the factor.

There is a further problem with regression coefficients that arises from the high correlation between variables. Such correlation tends to generate instability in regression coefficients. Beaton has shown (in a paper not yet published) that there is less instability in the multiple correlation coefficient associated with a collection of such correlated variables.

It should be pointed out that commonalities can be negative despite the fact that all those in Tables 1 and 2 are positive. That occurs when two independent variables are negatively correlated but both positively correlated with the dependent variable. To use an example by Beaton—ability to play football is positively correlated with both speed and weight of players, but speed and weight are themselves negatively correlated and would have a negative commonality in a regression of ability on speed and weight. The interpretation of the negative commonality is that the explanatory power of one is much improved by inclusion of the other in the regression. To put it another way, speed will reduce error variance of the football ability regression more if added to a set of independent variables which includes weight than it would if added to a set which does not include weight.

1.7 Structural Models

The long run goal of these research efforts is construction of a reasonably comprehensive causal model which will connect well-defined, accurately measured variables in a set of believable causal relationships similar to the simultaneous equation models used by econometricians such as Johnson [1963] and Goldberger [1964]. A very general specification of such a model has been developed by Jöreskog [1971].

The first steps in this direction have been taken by Levin [1970], Michelson [1970 and 1972], and Adelman and Parti [1972]. A selection from Michelson's work will illustrate the nature of this kind of effort. For investigating a portion of the equal educational opportunity survey data, he uses the following three equation system, developed by Levin:

$$A = b_1 S + c_1 G + \sum_i d_{1i} X_i$$

$$S = a_2 A + \sum_i d_{2i} X_i$$

$$G = a_3 A + \sum_i d_{3i} X_i,$$

where A is achievement score, S is a measure of the student's attitude toward his own capabilities and chances for success, and G is a measure of the student's desire for good grades in school. The rationale of the model is that the first equation is not enough because, inevitably, one's attitude S towards himself depends to some degree on one's success in school as measured by scholastic achievement, A; hence the second equation. Similarly, while aspirations G for good grades must affect A, the reverse must also be true; hence the third equation is necessary.

These three variables are the endogenous variables in the language of econometricians. The X's are student background characteristics and school characteristics; they are the exogenous variables. The lower case letters are coefficients to be estimated from the data. The expectation of the model is that estimation of the effect of A on S and G by means of the second and third equations, and then substitution of these two in the first equation to get a "reduced form" for A, depending only on the X's, will give a much more realistic appraisal of the dependence of A on the exogenous variables.

In Table 3 below the two methods are compared. The exogenous variables are named on the left; their coefficients as determined from the simple regression

$$A = b_0 + \sum_i b_i X_i$$

are given in the first column of figures; their coefficients as determined by the reduced form, using the 3 equation system, are given in the second column. In both cases, there was a long list of possible exogenous variables, and only

TABLE 3. ACHIEVEMENT AS A LINEAR FUNCTION OF INDEPENDENT VARIABLES

Independent (exogenous) variables	Coefficients for:	
	Simple regression	Reduced form
Sex	.8	.8
Age	−7.5	−6.8
Size of family	−.5	−.6
Family possessions	1.4	1.3
Father's education	.3	.4
Identity of person serving as mother		−.5
Identity of person acting as father		−.4
Kindergarten attendance	2.1	2.1
Mother has job		−.3
Teacher's test score		.3
Quality of teacher's college		7.7
Teacher's experience	.4	.8
Teacher's preference for another school		1.0
Race discrepancy between teacher and pupils	−2.7	
Teacher turnover		−.2
Size of school library	.3	.5
School has auditorium, cafeteria, gymnasium	.7	

those were retained which made a significant contribution, as determined by a rule specifying a significant reduction in the residual sum of squares. The two methods turned out to differ much more in the two sets of exogenous variables selected, than in the coefficients of those variables that appeared in both sets. This three equation structural model is representative of the most sophisticated models currently available for representing the educational process.

There are no objective criteria for determining the validity of a causal model, the superiority of one causal model over another, or even the superiority of a causal model over a simple regression. However, common sense would lead most research workers to put more faith in the three equation model, which tries to use good judgment about how the variables relate to each other. As between several such models, preference would similarly depend on judgments about which one appeared to use the most reasonable assumptions in its construction. Only long experience in constructing and testing such models can generate great confidence in their validity. As of this date, there is little such experience, and we can only surmise that the present state-of-the-art of models of the educational process is primitive.

REFERENCES

1. Adelman, I. and M. Parti, "The Determinants of Student Achievement," Research Bulletin, Rutgers University, New Brunswick, New Jersey (1972).
2. Beaton, A. E., "Criterion Scaling of Questionnaire Items," *Socio-Econ. Plan. Sci.* 2, pp. 355–362 (1969).
3. Coleman, J. S. et al., *Equality of Educational Opportunity*, U.S. Government Printing Office (FS 5.238: 38001) Washington, D.C. (1966).
4. Dusenberry, J. S. et al., *The Brookings Econometric Model of the United States*, Rand McNally, Chicago (1965).
5. Goldberger, A. S., *Econometric Theory*, Wiley, New York (1964).
6. Johnson, J., *Econometric Methods*, McGraw-Hill, New York (1963).
7. Jöreskog, K. G. et al., *A General Program for Analysis of Covariance Structures Including Generalized MANOVA*, Educational Testing Service, Princeton, New Jersey (1971).
8. Kershaw, J. A. and R. N. McKean, *Systems Analysis and Education*, The Rand Corporation, Santa Monica, California (1959).
9. Levin, H. M., "A New Model of School Effectiveness," *Do Teachers Make A Difference?*," pp. 55–78, U.S. Government Printing Office (HE 5.258: 58042) Washington, D.C. (1970).
10. Mayeske, G. W. et al., *A Study of Our Nation's Schools*, U.S. Government Printing Office (HE 5.210: 10085) Washington, D.C. (1972).
11. ——, *A Study of the Achievement of Our Nation's Students*, U.S. Government Printing Office (1780–1055) Washington, D.C. (1973).
12. ——, *A Study of the Attitude Toward Life of Our Nation's Students*, U.S. Government Printing Office (1780–01146) Washington, D.C. (1973).
13. Michelson, S., "The Association of Teacher Resourceness with Children's Characteristics," *Do Teachers Make a Difference?*," pp. 120–168, U.S. Government Printing Office (HE 5.258: 58042) Washington, D.C. (1970).

14. ——, "Equal School Resource Allocation," *J. Human Resources,* 7, pp. 283–306 (1972).
15. Mood, A. M., "Macro-Analysis of the American Educational System," *Operations Res.* 17, pp. 770–784 (1969).
16. ——, "Partitioning Variance in Multiple Regression Analyses as a Tool for Developing Learning Models," *Am. Educ. Res. J.,* 8, pp. 191–202 (1971).
17. Newton, R. G. and D. J. Spurrell, "A Development of Multiple Regression for Analysis of Routine Data," *Applied Statistics,* 16, pp. 51–64 (1967).

2. ANNOTATED BIBLIOGRAPHY

This second part of the chapter is essentially a bibliography, providing selected references to other aspects of operations analysis of education. It is organized under the following headings:

Education as a Sector of the Economy
Stochastic Models of Learning
Enrollment and Cohort Analysis
Manpower Models
Effective Use of Resources
Design of Facilities
Racial Balance

2.1 Education as a Sector of the Economy

There is extensive literature in the field of economics which treats education as a sector of the economy, and builds models of the economy in which education plays a significant role. To try to cover it in this handbook would give it too large a portion of the book, yet it cannot be omitted altogether. I have comprised a bibliography, including a few of the classical works, together with a few of the more recent papers (from which one can get a good indication of the state of the art). I have also cited the Hüfner [1969] bibliography, which provides very comprehensive coverage of this field.

Theodore W. Schultz [1960] is generally regarded as the originator of the basic theoretical developments that treat education as capital in the economic sense and hence, treat schooling as not an expense, but an investment in productive capital. A number of investigations (e.g. Miller [1960] have estimated the value of the investment by measuring the additional wages or salary received by persons with additional education. Becker's classical study recognized that some of the additional personal income often attributed to education should rather be attributed to superior ability; that is, more able people do well in school and hence, tend to get more education. One would expect them to earn more income than less able people, even without any additional education.

This general economic approach is widely used as a basis for evaluation of

Federal programs designed to assist various segments of the population by means of education or training. I have included several examples of such evaluations and also Mincer's pioneering paper on the evaluation of training.

R. L. Ackoff, "Toward Strategic Planning of Education," *Efficiency in Resource Utilization in Education*, OECD, Paris (1969).

> Presents a sophisticated conceptual model of the whole society as a context for examining the role of education in society. It is an elaboration of an earlier model developed by W. J. Platt (cited below). The model has not been specified in detail nor applied to any data.

G. S. Becker, *Human Capital*, Columbia Univ. Press, N.Y. (1964).

D. M. Bellante, "A Multivariate Analysis of a Vocational Rehabilitation Program," *J. Human Resources*, 7, 226–241 (1972).

> Develops cost-benefit relationships for many subgroups of persons who participated in the program.

M. Blaug, "The Private and Social Returns on Investment in Education: Some Results for Great Britain," *J. Human Resources*, 3, 330–346 (1967).

> Valuable analysis for its inclusion of social returns.

A. Daniere and J. Mechling, "Direct Marginal Productivity of College Education in Relation to College Aptitude of Students and Production Costs of Institutions," *J. Human Resources*, 5, 51–70 (1970).

> Estimates present value of earnings flows of students of different aptitude attending institutions of different quality.

E. E. Denison, "Measuring the Contribution of Education to Economic Growth," *The Residual Factor and Economic Growth*, 13–55, OECD, Paris (1964).

> Estimates the contribution by considering it to be the residual, after all the more conventional factors have been taken into account.

R. S. Eckaus, *Estimating the Returns to Education*, Carnegie Commission on Higher Education, Berkeley, California (1973).

> Uses hourly pay rates instead of annual income and deals with occupations individually rather than in the aggregate.

G. Hanoch, "An Economic Analysis of Earnings and Schooling," *J. Human Resources*, 3, 310–329 (1967).

> Estimates marginal rate of return attributable to one year of schooling, using 1960 Census data.

W. L. Hansen and B. A. Weisbrod, "The Distribution of Costs and Direct Benefits of Public Higher Education: The Case of California," *J. Human Resources*, 4, 176–191 (1969).

> Examines the distribution of public funds for higher education to various income groups.

K. Hüfner, "Economics of Higher-Education and Educational Planning: A Bibliography," *Socio-Eco. Plan. Sci.*, 2, 25–101 (1969).

> Contains 1333 items organized under the headings: Bibliographies, General Surveys, Surveys Related to Particular Countries or Institutions, Organization, The University as an Enterprise, Cost Analysis, Financing, Public Financing, Private Financing, Socio-Economic Determinants, Concept of Human Capital, Return from Educational Expenditures, Education and Economic Growth, National Planning and Manpower, Demand for Particular Manpower, Other.

H. P. Miller, "Annual and Lifetime Income in Relation to Education: 1937–1959," *Amer. Eco. Rev.*, 50, 962–986 (1960).

J. Mincer, "On-The-Job Training: Costs, Returns and Implications, *J. Political Economy*, 7 (Supplement), 50–59 (1962).

J. Mincer, "Investment in Human Capital and Personal Income Distribution," *J. Political Economy*, 66, 281–302 (1958).

W. J. Platt, *Educational Policy for Economic Growth*, Stanford Research Institute, Menlo Park, Calif. (1961).

T. I. Ribich, *Education and Poverty*, Brookings Institution, Washington, D.C. (1968).
Applies cost-benefit analysis to several job-retraining and compensatory education programs undertaken by the Federal government as anti-poverty measures.

T. W. Schultz, "Capital Formation by Education," *J. Political Economy*, 68, 571–583 (1960).

T. W. Schultz, "Rise in the Capital Stock Represented by Education in the U.S., 1900-1957," *Economics of Higher Education*, S. J. Mushkin, editor, 93–101, Dep't HEW, U.S. Government Printing Office, Washington (1962).

T. W. Schultz, *The Economic Value of Education*, Columbia Univ. Press, N.Y., 1962.

A. K. Sen, "Education, Vintage, and Learning by Doing," *J. Human Resources*, 1, 3–21 (1966).
Estimates economic returns to what is learned on the job.

G. G. Somers and E. W. Stromdorfer, "A Cost-Effectiveness Analysis of the In-School and Summer Neighborhood Youth Corps Program," *J. Human Resources*, 7, 446–459 (1972).
An evaluation of the nationwide program.

R. G. Spiegelman, "A Benefit-Cost Model to Evaluate Educational Programs," *Socio-Eco. Plan. Sci.*, 1, 443–460, 1968.
Develops a 13 equation model which includes both private and social costs and benefits, the model is applied to the Title I Program (of the Elementary and Secondary Education Act) in San Francisco.

B. A. Weisbrod, "Education and Investment in Human Capital," *J. Political Economy*, 7 (Supplement), 106–123 (1962).

2.2 Stochastic Model of Learning

Another field which is altogether too large to be included in this bibliography, began some twenty years ago with some simple probabilistic models of the number of repetitions necessary for a person to retain something in his memory. The Bush and Mosteller [1955] book was the first organized presentation of such models. The field has blossomed to the extent that it has had its own journal for ten years (Journal of Mathematical Psychology), and those who wish to become familiar with recent work in the field might best begin by perusing the later volumes of that journal.

R. R. Bush and W. K. Estes, *Studies in Mathematical Learning Theory*, Stanford Univ. Press, Stanford, Calif. (1959).

R. R. Bush and F. Mosteller, *Stochastic Models of Learning*, Wiley, N.Y. (1955).

R. D. Luce, R. R. Bush and E. Galanter (Eds.), *Handbook of Mathematical Psychology*, Vols. I, II, and III, Wiley (1963-1965).

Journal of Mathematical Psychology, Vols. 1-10 (1964-1973).

2.3 Enrollment and Cohort Analysis

Since all educational planning, operations, and administration depend critically on the number and varieties of students to be educated, a great deal of attention has been given to the development of models for projecting enrollments and for predicting how students will move from one educational category to another. Regression models are widely used—particularly autoregression models which, for example, predict next year's junior enrollment on the basis of this year's sophomore enrollment. Also widely used are *flow models*, which regard those completing some stage of education as flowing into later stages, and which are mathematically specified by equations which conserve the flow. Thus, high school graduates flow into college, trade schools, military forces, employment, or unemployment. Since most education is on an annual cycle, an alternative *Markov-type* model is also widely used. It regards students as being situated in a variety of states, and as changing those states instantaneously at the completion of a school year in accordance with a transition matrix analogous to the probability matrix of a Markov stochastic process. The elements of the matrix in educational models are regarded, not as probabilities, but simply as the proportions of students transferring from a given state to a succeeding state; hence, the description Markov-type rather than Markov.

P. H. Armitage, C. S. Smith and P. Alper, *Decision Models for Educational Planning*, Allen Lane, London (1969).

P. H. Armitage, C. M. Phillips and J. Davies, "Towards a Model of the Upper School System," *J. Roy. Stat. Soc.*, 133, 166–205 (1970).

A. Baisuck and W. A. Wallace, "A Computer Simulation Approach to Enrollment in Higher Education," *Socio-Eco. Plan. Sci.*, 4, 365–381 (1970).
   Applies a Markov-type model to Rensselaer Polytechnic Institute data.

K. R. Balachandran and D. Gerwin, "Variable-Work Models for Predicting Course Enrollment, *Operations Res.*, 21, 823–834 (1973).
   Several Markov-type models are developed and applied to data.

C. Bell, "Can Mathematical Models Contribute to Efficiency in Higher Education?" *Papers on Efficiency in the Management of Higher Education*, Carnegie Commission on Higher Education, 43–60, Berkeley, Calif. (1972).

A. M. Cartter, "The Supply of and Demand for College Teachers," *J. Human Resources*, 1, 22–38 (1966).
   First prediction of the Ph.D. glut.

D. J. Clough and W. P. McReynolds, "State Transition Model of an Educational System Incorporating a Constraint Theory of Supply and Demand," *Ontario J. Educ. Res.*, 9, 53–65 (1966).

J. Conlisk, "The Determinants of School Enrollment and School Performance," *J. Human Resources*, 4, 140–157 (1969).
   Uses 1960 Census data to relate educational performance in public schools to sex, race, rural-urban, parents' income, and parents' education by regression analysis.

A. J. Corazzini, D. J. Dugan, and H. H. Grabowski, "Determinants and Distributional Aspects of Enrollment in U.S. Higher Education," *J. Human Resources*, 7, 39–59 (1972).

Uses regression analysis to examine the extent to which college attendance depends on family income.

H. Correa, *Quantitative Methodologies of Educational Planning*, International Textbook Co., N.Y. (1969).

Thorough exposition of flow models to plan educational programs and facilities to meet manpower needs for economic growth.

H. Correa and J. Tinbergen, "Quantitative Adoption of Education to Accelerated Growth," Kyklos, 15 (1962).

An early specification of a simple flow model.

J. S. Dyer, "Assessing Effects of Changes in the Cost of Higher Education on Student Enrollment." *Socio-Eco. Plan. Sci.*, 5, 307–316 (1971).

K. A. Fox and J. K. Sengupta, "The Specification of Econometric Models for Planning Educational Systems," *Kyklos*, 21, 665–694 (1968).

General discussion of input-output, Markov-type and linear programming models.

J. Gani, "Formulae for Projecting Enrollments and Degrees Awarded in Universities," *J. Royal Statistical Soc.*, A126, 400–409 (1963).

Markov-type model.

D. S. P. Hopkins, "On the Use of Large-Scale Simulation Models for University Planning," *Rev. of Educ. Res.*, 41, 467–478 (1971).

Questions utility on grounds that extensive resources must be devoted to estimating fleeting parameters.

K. Marshall and R. M. Oliver, "A Constant-Work Model for Student Attendance and Enrollment," *Operations Res.*, 18, 193–206 (1970).

Develops a model for interpreting college attendance data, using the idea of a fixed number of course units to be completed for a degree and a probability of successfully completing a unit.

K. T. Marshall, "A Comparison of Two Personnel Prediction Models," *Operations Res.*, 21, 810–822 (1973).

Compares a Markov-type model with a cohort model using UC Berkeley data.

Mathematical Models in Educational Planning, OECD, Paris (1967).

S. Masters, "The Effect of Family Income on Children's Education," *J. Human Resources*, 4, 158–176 (1969).

Regression analysis of 1960 Census data.

C. A. Moser and P. Redfern, "A Computable Model of the Educational System in England and Wales," *Proceedings of the 35th International Statistical Institute*, Belgrade (1966).

C. B. Nam, A. L. Rhodes and R. E. Herriot, "School Retention by Race, Religion and Socio-economic Status," *J. Human Resources*, 3, 171–190 (1968).

Regression analysis of 1965 Current Population Survey (U.S. Census) data.

R. M. Oliver and D. S. P. Hopkins, "An Equilibrium Flow Model of a University Campus," *Operations Res.*, 20, 249–264 (1972).

Develops a simple 8 cohort flow model to relate student admissions and enrollments to the final demand for educated students. The model is applied to data from the University of Calif., Berkeley.

L. Orr, "The Dependence of Transition Proportions in the Educational System on Observed Social Factors and School Characteristics," *J. Roy. Stat. Soc.* 135, 74–95 (1972).

K. Simon, *Projections of Educational Statistics*, U.S. Office of Education, Dep't of HEW, an annual publication.

Each year the Office of Education issues detailed ten-year projections of enrollments of various categories of students (kindergarten through Ph.D.), and of degrees awarded in various fields. Those are based on elaborate regression models which are specified in detail in an appendix to the publication.

R. Stone, "A Model of the Educational System," *Minerva*, 3, 172–186 (1965).

    Very general specification of Markov-type model.

R. Stone, "Input-Output and Demographic Accounting: A Tool for Educational Planning," *Minerva*, 4, 363–380 (1966).

    General dynamic Markov-type planning model.

R. Stone, G. Stone and J. Gunton, "An Example of Demographic Accounting: The School Ages," *Minerva*, 6, 185–212 (1968).

    Application of R. Stone's model to British data.

E. K. Zabrowski, "The Dynamod Model of Student and Teacher Population Growth," *Socio-Eco. Plan. Sci.*, 2, 455–464 (1968).

    Dynamod in a computerized Markov-type model which sequentially calculates the states of 140 student and teacher groups over selected intervals of time.

2.4 Manpower Models

There is no good dividing line between this category of papers and the preceding one because many cohort analysis models are related to supplying various categories of educated manpower. The papers listed here simply have their primary emphasis on manpower considerations.

I. Adelman, "A Linear Programming Model of Educational Planning," *The Theory and Design of Economic Development*, I. Adelman and E. Thornbecke (eds.), 385–411, Johns Hopkins Univ. Press, Baltimore (1966).

    Programs educational system to maximize economic growth. Model is applied to data from Argentina.

P. Alper, P. H. Armitage and C. S. Smith, "Educational Models, Manpower, Planning, and Control *Operational Res. Quart.*, 18, 93–103 (1967).

    Discussion of Markov-type model and problem of relating it to nationwide sprectrum of manpower requirements.

W. Balinsky and A. Reisman, "Some Manpower Planning Models Based on Levels of Educational Attainment," *Management Sci.*, 18, B691–B705 (1972).

    Develops manpower flow models, which track people through educational and employment sectors with the objective of minimizing costs resulting from oversupplies or undersupplies of categories of trained manpower.

K. H. Bolt, W. L. Koltun and O. H. Levine, "Doctoral Feedback into Higher Education," *Science*, 148, 918 (1965).

S. Bowles, *Planning Educational Systems for Economic Growth*, Harvard Univ. Press, Cambridge (1969).

    Careful development of an LP model for the government of Nigeria.

P. M. LeVasseur, "A Study of Inter-Relationships between Education, Manpower, and Economy," *Socio-Eco. Plan. Sci.*, 2, 269–295 (1969).

    Describes a computerized flow model which links education, manpower, and economic planning at the national need.

S. N. Levine, "Economic Growth and the Development of Educational Facilities," *Socio-Eco. Plan. Sci.*, 1, 27–32 (1967).

    Simulation model to relate manpower needs to overall growth of the educational plant.

A. Reisman, "The Generation of Doctorates and Their Feedback into Higher Education," *Socio-Eco. Plan. Sci.*, 2, 473–486 (1969).

    A 200 equation simulation model developed to study manpower policies.

G. Skorov, "Manpower Approach to Educational Planning," *Economic and Social Aspects of Educational Planning*, UNESCO, Paris (1964).

Manpower planning in the U.S.S.R.

J. Tinbergen and H. C. Bos, "A Planning Model for Educational Requirements of Economic Growth," *The Residual Factor and Economic Growth*, 147–169, OECD, Paris (1964).

Cohort analysis of requirements for manpower having various levels of education.

2.5 Effective Use of Resources

Most of the papers in this section have to do with efficient allocation of educational resources to various educational activities. A few refer to the other societal problem of how much resources should be allocated to education; but that issue is mainly the concern of the general field of economics of education illustrated in the first section of this bibliography (some manpower models also have as their primary focus the determination of how much resources education should be given). Also included here, are a few papers on how to do a particular activity efficiently.

C. C. Abt, "Design for an Educational System Cost-Effectiveness Model," *Socio-Eco. Plan. Sci.*, 2, 399–415 (1968).

Develops a set of simulations suitable in the aggregate for evaluation of Title I Programs (Elementary and Secondary Education Act of 1964).

R. Besel, "A Linear Model for the Allocation of Instructional Resources," *Socio-Eco. Plan. Sci.*, 6, 501–506 (1972).

LP allocation in terms of required achievement levels assuming students require various amounts of resources, depending on aptitude.

J. E. Bruno, "A Mathematical Programming Approach to School Finance," *Socio-Eco. Plan. Sci.*, 3, 1–12 (1969).

An LP model which places educational finance in a system constrained by political, social, and economic considerations.

J. E. Bruno, "Using LP Salary Evaluation Models in Collective Bargaining Negotiations with Teacher Unions," *Socio-Eco. Plan. Sci.*, 3, 103–117 (1969).

Model is designed to serve meeting a variety of union demands at minimum cost.

J. E. Bruno, "The Use of Monte Carlo Techniques for Determining Optimal Size of Substitute Teacher Pools in Large Urban School Districts," *Socio-Eco. Plan. Sci.*, 4, 415–428 (1970).

Investigates possibility of replacing occasional substitute teachers by a pool of full-time substitute teachers.

J. Burkhead, T. G. Fox and J. W. Holland, *Input and Output in a Large City High School*, Syracuse Univ. Press, Syracuse, N.Y. (1967).

LP model applied to Chicago and Atlanta High School districts to study achievement as a function of budget.

R. M. Durstine, "In Quest of Useful Models for Educational Systems," *Socio-Eco. Plan. Sci.*, 2, 417–437 (1968).

Flow models are examined as a means for describing the performance of an educational system.

J. S. Dyer, "A Procedure for Selecting Educational Goal Areas for Emphasis," *Operations Res.*, 21, 835–845 (1973).

Develop a practical utility function process.

D. Gerwin, "A Process Model of Budgeting in a Public School System," *Manag. Sci.*, 15, 338–361 (1969).
Develops a very comprehensive simulation model of the school district budgeting process and applies it to the Pittsburgh school system.

R. W. Judy and J. B. Levine, *A New Tool for Educational Administration*, Univ. of Toronto Press (1965).
Detailed input-output model (called CAMPUS) to assist individual institutions of higher education in their planning.

R. A. Kaufman, R. E. Corrigan and D. W. Johnson, "Towards Educational Responsiveness to Society's Needs," *Socio-Eco. Plan. Sci.*, 3, 151–157 (1969).
Outlines a model using the individual's utility to society as a basis for educational planning.

F. Kodoma, "An Approach to the Analysis of Vocational Education and Training Requirements," *Management Sci.*, 17, B178–B191 (1970).
Allocates time to curricular elements to minimize the expected number of accidents and errors on the job.

H. E. Koenig, and M. G. Keeney, "A Prototype Planning and Resource Allocation Program for Higher Education," *Socio-Eco. Plan. Sci.*, 2, 201–215 (1968).
State-space description of a university's utilization of resources in its various programs.

S. M. Lee and E. R. Clayton, "A Goal Programming Model for Academic Resource Allocation," *Management Sci.*, 18, B395, B408 (1972).
Allocates resources using an LP model, with the criterion being an index of slack variables weighted by importance. Model is applied to data from Virginia Polytechnic Institute.

R. I. Lerman, "Some Determinants of Youth School Activity," *J. Human Resources*, 7, 366–379 (1972).
Uses regression analysis on Census data to study effect of family characteristics on education and employment of various categories of youths.

H. M. Levin, "A Cost-Effectiveness Analysis of Teacher Selection," *J. Human Resources*, 5, 24–33 (1970).
Uses a simple production function to compare various criteria for teacher selection.

J. F. McNamara, "A Regional Planning Model for Occupational Education," *Socio-Eco. Plan. Sci.*, 5, 317–339 (1971).
Uses an LP model to study the allocation of vocational education funds to programs in Pennsylvania.

R. M. Newton and W. H. Thomas, "Design of School Bus Routes by Computer," *Socio-Eco. Plan. Sci.*, 3, 75–85 (1969).
Develops a procedure by partitioning the optimum route that would be followed by a traveling salesman with a huge bus.

J. D. Owen, "The Distribution of Educational Resources in Large American Cities," *J. Human Resources*, 7, 26–38 (1972).
Uses regression analysis to examine allocation of resources to poor and nonwhite neighborhoods.

T. Ploughman, W. Darnton and W. Heuser, "An Assignment Program to Establish School Attendance Area Boundaries and Forecast Construction Need," *Socio-Eco. Plan. Sci.*, 1, 243–258 (1967).
Simulation model is developed to project growth of school system over a number of years as applied to Oakland County Michigan.

A. Reisman and M. I. Taft, "A Systems Approach to the Evaluation and Budgeting of Educational Programs," *Socio-Eco. Plan. Sci.*, 3, 245–277 (1969).
Allocates on the basis of an aggregate utility made up of utilities of individual programs.

B. K. Sinha, S. K. Gupta, and R. L. Sisson, "Towards Aggregate Models of Educational Systems," *Socio-Eco. Plan. Sci.*, 3, 25–36 (1969).

    Describes (1) a student flow model and (2) a student achievement model based on resource inputs.

R. L. Sisson, "Can We Model the Education Process?" *Socio-Eco. Plan. Sci.*, 2, 109–119 (1968).

    General discussion of problem of relating educational outputs to resource inputs.

M. Szekely, M. Stankard and R. L. Sisson, "Design of a Planning Model for an Urban School District," *Socio-Eco. Plan. Sci.*, 1, 231–242 (1967).

    Develops a simulation model for planning the activities of a school district.

2.6 Design of Facilities

These papers might have been included in the preceding section but made up a large enough cluster to warrant separating them out.

R. H. Crandall, "A Constrained Choice Model for Student Housing," *Management Sci.*, 16, 112–120 (1969).

    An LP model is used to determine the optimum mix of student housing including off-campus housing, to minimize cost to the college.

C. M. Eastman and K. D. Kortanek, "Modeling School Facility Requirements in New Communities," *Management Sci.*, 16, B784–B799 (1969).

    Uses an LP model to relate growing stock of residential housing and residential transfer rates to requirements for public school facilities.

R. J. Graves and W. H. Thomas, "A Classroom-Allocation Model for Campus Planning," *Socio-Eco. Plan. Sci.*, 5, 191–204 (1971).

    Uses an LP model to design a campus fulfilling certain space requirements at minimum cost. Model is applied to SUNY Buffalo data.

T. W. Maver, "Spatial Environment in Comprehensive Schools," *Operational Res. Quart.*, 23, 305–322 (1972).

    Describes computer programs developed to aid architectural design of schools when an important goal is flexibility of space utilization.

R. J. O'Brien, "Model for Planning the Location and Size of Urban Schools," *Socio-Eco. Plan. Sci.*, 2, 141–153 (1969).

    Develops a set of submodels which may be combined to serve user's utility function.

R. L. Smith, "Accommodating Student Demand for Courses by Varying the Classroom-Size Mix, *Operations Res.*, 19, 862–874 (1971).

    Develop processes for assigning course sections to available classrooms under the criterion that as few students as possible fail to get a desired course because there is not room for them.

2.7 Racial Balance

The problem of integrating school systems has stimulated some quantitative analysis of how it might be done most economically.

P. Belford and H. D. Ratlift, "A Network-Flow Model of Racially Balancing Schools," *Operations Res.*, 20, 619–628 (1972).

Develops a flow model for achieving racial balance under the criterion that the number of student miles traveled be a minimum. The model is applied to the Gainsville, Florida High School District.

S. Clarke and S. Surkis, "An OR Approach to Racial Desegregation in School System," *Socio-Eco. Plan. Sci.*, 1, 259–272 (1968).

Uses an LP model to assign students to school to satisfy specified ethnic compositions and minimize aggregate travel time. Model is applied to Brooklyn, N. Y. data.

L. B. Heckman and H. M. Taylor, "School Rezoning to Achieve Racial Balance," *Socio-Eco. Plan Sci.*, 3, 127–133 (1969).

Uses an LP model to determine boundaries of school attendance areas which will achieve balance with minimum travel.

E. Koenigsberg, "Mathematical Analysis Applied to School Attendance Areas," *Socio-Eco. Plan. Sci.*, 1, 465–475 (1968).

General LP formulation of student assignment problem to achieve integration using various objective functions.

S. N. Levine, "A Model of Racially Changing Neighborhoods," *Socio-Eco. Plan. Sci.*, 1, 477–479 (1968).

Develops 2 parameter model suitable for representing changing composition of ethnically mixed neighborhoods.

II-4

TRANSPORTATION SYSTEMS

Brian F. O'Neil
University of Miami

Anthony J. Catanese
University of Wisconsin—Milwaukee

David Hinds
Transportation Administration—Dade County

INTRODUCTION

> TRANSPORTATION: The movement of people and goods within a society as a means to certain ends.

As is illustrated by this brief definition, transportation is a very broad subject area, involving many different aspects. Topics ranging from rush hour flow models to lessen automobile congestion, to large scale transshipment models, can all be appropriately called topics of transportation. Problems associated with a single mode or problems of an intermodel nature, are all studied by transportation researchers.

Sometimes, people may take for granted the existance of an efficient transportation system while not realizing its importance. However, when one considers that approximately 20% of the G.N.P. of the United States can be attributed directly to transportation (Kriebel [1970]), or that 35-40% of all developed urban land is used for transportation (Creighton [1970]), the importance is quickly recognized. People, in general, become aware when something goes wrong, such as a traffic jam, a missed airplane connection, or a lost shipment.

As is true in most societies, when enough criticism has been registered, then steps are taken to relieve the situation.

As a result of the growing complexity of transportation systems and the ensuing problems, there has been an increasing interest in transportation in many nations of the world. For example, many people, in varying capacities, many different cities, and many different nations are now studying the problems of mass transportation. These people are well aware of the need for good mass transit systems, and they have been able to identify the benefits that can be attributed to a well designed system, such as a more efficient use of the increasingly scarce energy resources and the possible revival and restoration of downtown areas.

Greater attention is now being given to the movement of goods. Many business enterprises are now looking at the physical distribution of their products from a "systems point of view," and are taking advantage of the inherent relationships associated with the elements of the system. The results achieved by considering the physical distribution function from a systems point of view often show up quite dramatically in considerable cost savings.

One very important point is that transportation is not a separate entity, but is intimately related with other systems—transportation is a means to an end. For example, transportation of goods is only a part of the overall physical distribution system of an enterprise. The subsystems involved in this case include inventory control, order processing, production, information, and control systems. The complex network of streets and highways, mass transit, rapid transit, and automobiles make up the elements of the urban transportation system. It is not enough to say that the urban transportation system merely performs a function necessary for the existence of other urban systems (economic, social, political, physical, and recreational systems). The important point is that planning must necessarily include a comprehensive view of how transportation fits in with the total system.

In these brief introductory remarks an attempt has been made to demonstrate not only the importance of transportation and the increasing recognition of this importance, but also the wide diversity of transportation topics that can be included in a discussion of the application of OR. Throughout this chapter, the terms "public" and "private" sector will be used. The public sector of transportation is taken to include public highway networks, public transit systems, and private personal transit either within or between cities. The private sector involves industrial distribution systems and any other privately-owned systems, albeit government regulated, for the transit of goods.

The basic structure of this chapter evolves around a fairly well defined, generic process which can be used in the analysis and design of most transportation system problems. The generic process follows very closely the general concepts of proper systems analysis. The steps involved in this generic process, as illustrated in Figure 1, are:

1. Traffic Demand Forecasting
2. Traffic Facilities Analysis and Allocation
3. Specification of Problems to be Solved and Formulation of Alternative Solutions
4. Evaluation of Alternative Solutions
5. Development of Prototypes and Final Testing
6. Implementation

The remainder of the chapter will closely follow this flow chart.

As stated previously, this process can be used for the analysis and design of most transportation problems, whether they involve the public or private sector. Obviously, some steps will receive more or less attention, depending upon the particular problem being analyzed.

1. TRAFFIC DEMAND FORECASTING

Traffic demand forecasting essentially entails predicting future demand that will be placed on the transportation system in consideration. The demand, would, in general, consist of eight components: source, destination, volume, mode, link, commodity type, schedule, and timing. The commodity may be goods or people. Examples taken from both the public and private sectors of transportation illustrate the meaning of each of these components in Table 1.

Transportation decisions are made on the basis of the expected action of large groups of people. Industry is basically concerned with demands which affect the industry's flow of goods, while urban governments must plan for the movements of commuters, shoppers and, in general, the demands for movement that produces the flow of people. Demand may be forecast as close as one day in advance for manpower scheduling, or as far as twenty years in advance for planning a rapid transit system.

Industry responds to an aggregate demand for goods. Control of the source of shipment, mode, link, and schedule is generally held by the organization involved. On the other hand, personal transit is initiated by a desire to travel from one point in the city to another; choice of all the components of travel is made by the commuter himself, within constrained choice sets. There are, of course, some exceptions to the general rule.

Essentially, urban governments exercise no direct demand controls except in isolated situations, such as a ban on certain types of vehicles in certain areas. They do have indirect controls, such as the design and scheduling of public transit systems and zoning laws to shape land use patterns. While both of these factors can have a significant effect on transit patterns, it is important to note that where, when, and how a person travels is not subject to direct government con-

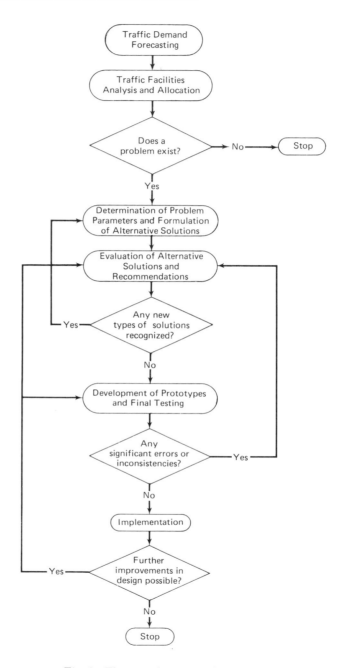

Fig. 1. The generic process flowchart.

TABLE 1

	Public Sector	Private Sector
Source/	Residential/"bedroom"	Wholesale/Retail Outlets
Destination	Communities	Factories, Warehouses, Distribution
(Where)	Employment, Shopping, Recreational, and Government Centers	Centers, Raw Materials supply points
Link	Expressways	Interstate Highways
(Where)	Roads & Streets	State Roads
	Transit Guideways	Air Corridors
	Railroad Tracks	Shipping Lanes/Railroad Tracks
Commodity	Workers (Blue or White collar)	Great number of different types and sizes
Type	Shoppers, School children	of products.
(What)	Aged, Handicapped	
Mode	Car, Bus, Rapid Transit	Private/Leased Truck
(How)	Walk, Bike	Common Carrier
	People-movers	Train, Air, Ship
Volume	ADT (Avg. Daily Traffic	Weight–Any quantity "AQ"
(How much)	through a corridor)	TL/LTL–Truckload/Less Than Truck Load
	Peak Flow Rates	CL/LCL–Carload/Less Than Car Load
Schedule	Work Schedules	Vehicle Scheduling/Dispatcher
(When)	Housewive's shopping Schedule	
	School Schedule	
	Special Events' Schedule	
Timing	Rush-Hour Traffic	Shipment Due Date
(When)	On/Off Season	Seasonal Trends

trol. These are essentially random variables, thus placing a greater forecasting burden on the urban transportation planner.

Demands are not only probabilistic, but are also difficult to obtain at any one point in time, due to the large population that must be surveyed. This acquisition problem is best illustrated by the costliness of data collection procedures. These include origin-destination and market research studies, which may run into hundreds of thousands of dollars (Mouchahoir [1972]). In very extensive studies such as these, the quality of data is sometimes suspect, due to lack of immediate control over data collectors.

Multiple regression is used in many areas to forecast traffic demand. One example is cited in the air cargo industry (Bluestone [1970], Verleger [1972]), where future air cargo volumes have been predicted by using a multiple regression equation combining G.N.P., national inventory levels, cargo capacities, and an industry growth factor, to name a few. Parameters of the regression equation are generated using historical data and the standard regression least squares technique. In the Chicago Area Transportation Study (CATS [1962]), trips per household were estimated rather successfully with regression on the basis of car ownership and net residential density.

Nonlinear, curve-fitting techniques were also used in CATS. Polynomials and Gaussian-shaped curves were used to estimate bus trips per person and automobile registrations per person as a nonlinear function of time.

Factor analysis is a more sophisticated statistical technique used less frequently than those previously mentioned. Factor analysis is used to combine a large number of variables into a smaller number of groups with highly inter-correlated variables making up each group. It is sometimes used as a prerequisite for regression analysis in that reducing a large number of variables can make a regression analysis more meaningful. One application was made by Garrison and Marble [1965], in an attempt to isolate generalized patterns in the transportation networks and commodity flow patterns of various countries. Mouchahoir [1972] used factor analysis to make efficient the input for urban traffic demand modes.

Computer simulation programs are also available for forecasting future demands of transportation systems. A discussion of some of the major comprehensive systems will be made in the evaluation state. One simulation used mainly as a forecasting tool is Lockheed's "Air Apparent" (Parrish [1970]). The main purpose of Air Apparent is to forecast air carrier equipment needs as far as ten years into the future. This is accomplished using a ten year accumulation of data from United States airlines.

Originally used as a marketing tool, this simulation model is capable of predicting many characteristics such as route systems required, traffic growth and fares, passenger, baggage, cargo and aircraft handling facilities required, and total system cost, to name but a few. A simulation technique is most appropriate for this particular situation, because Lockheed has attempted to predict requirements for a great number of different airlines drawing from essentially the same demand population.

Consider that, normally, a particular airline will forecast its own requirements from its point of view, in which it is competing against the entire airline industry. Perhaps only a few major competitors are singled out specifically. Lockheed apparently accomplishes this task for almost every commercial U.S. airline, coordinating a number of microscopic views (each from the point of view of the individual airline), into a total macroscopic picture, and then breaking back the aggregate estimate down to the level of the individual airline again for forecasting purposes. Thus, Air Apparent can combine a detailed overview of the related characteristics of all the airlines as individuals. This is a rather unique achievement, and may be a worthwhile undertaking for other national transportation systems such as the trucking, railroad, or maritime.

There are a number of techniques used to predict components of traffic demand for urban traffic. Sometimes called trip distribution models, these include growth-factor models, preferencing models, the Intervening Opportunities Model, the Competing Opportunities Model, and the Gravity Model (Creighton [1970]).

These models propose different theories as to how the source, destination, volume, and type components of demand are related to other variables. These other variables include current values for the same variables used to predict future values for them, projected growth rates, current employment densities, shopping and recreational area locations, zone to zone spatial and temporal separation, "attractiveness factors," to name a few.

Source and destination components are represented by the establishment of specific zones within the city. The volume component is usually expressed as either number of person-trips or number of vehicle-trips. A generally accepted classification of trip types is: home, work, recreational, social, school, convenience shopping, goods shopping, and passenger-service.

Growth factor methods determine future distribution of trips from zone to zone by using existing trip origins and destinations or trip interchanges, and expanding these to the forecast year by utilizing a growth factor. This factor is some measure of the anticipated change in population and/or land-use patterns for the zone in question.

A number of growth-factor methods have been postulated. These include uniform-factor methods, average factor methods, the judgement-applied methods, and the Detroit method. However, the most sophisticated and widely-used growth-factor method developed so far is the Fratar Method (Fratar [1954]).

The basic premise of the Fratar Method is that the distribution of trips from any zone i to any zone j at some time in the future is proportional to the current total trips out of zone i modified by the growth factor of the zone j to which these trips are attracted.

The general formulation of the Fratar Method is:

$$T_{ij(i)} = t_{ij} F_j F_i \sum_x t_{ix} \Big/ \Big(\sum_x t_{ix} F_x \Big),$$

where:

$T_{ij(i)}$ is the forecasted trips between zone i and zone j, due to the growth at zone i.

$T_{ij(j)}$ due to growth at zone j; this term, used in the equation below, is defined by the equation above by interchanging the subscripts i and j.

T_{ij} is the total trip volume forecast from zone i to zone j.

t_{ij} is the current trip interchange between zone i and zone j.

F_x is the growth factor for zone x, where x ranges over the zones defined by the study.

Then,

$$T_{ij} = \frac{T_{ij(i)} + T_{ij(j)}}{2}$$

Because the results of the model do not normally satisfy the logical constraint that

$$\sum_{\text{all } j} T_{ij} = F_i \sum_{\text{all } j} t_{ij},$$

and iterative procedure known as "successive approximations" must be employed to satisfy this constraint.

The Intervening Opportunities Model was developed by Stouffer [1940], and applied to the CATS Study [1962]. A more recent discussion was made by Clark and Peters [1965]. The basis for the model is that the number of persons traveling outward a distance X from some point is proportional to the number of "opportunities" at the distance X, and inversely proportional to the number of intervening opportunities. The variable "opportunities" could mean available employment locations for work trips, city or county parks for recreational trips, or shopping centers for shopping trips.

The Intervening Opportunities Model was formulated as follows:

$$T_{ij} = O_i \left[e^{-LD} - e^{-L(D+D_j)} \right],$$

where:

T_{ij} is the trips from zone i to zone j.
O_i trip origins in zone i.
D trip destinations (or opportunities) considered to be prior (or intervening) to zone j.
D_j trip destinations in zone j.
L some measure of the probability that a random destination will satisfy the needs of a particular trip. It is an empirically derived function that describes the rate decay with increasing trip destinations and increasing length of trip.
e logarithmic base (=2.71828 . . .).

The Intervening Opportunities Model requires calibration with respect to the L parameters.

The concept underlying the Competing Opportunities Model (Tomazinis [1962]), is that opportunities, within equal travel-time, distance, or cost bands, are measured from the origin of the trip. They actually "compete" for trips; each opportunity having an equal chance of attracting a trip.

The Preferencing Model, developed by Kirby [1970], is another opportunity trip distribution model. The assumption is that each trip origin rates trip destinations in order of preference, and that each destination rates trip origins in order of preference. An optimal pairing can be either "origin-optimal" or destination-optimal," and must satisfy certain stability conditions. Kirby showed, by applying the techniques to data from Launceston, Tasmania, that the Preferencing Model is feasible for urban applications.

The Gravity Model (Voorhees [1955]), the most widely used and documented of the trip distribution models, attempts to explain trips from zone i to zone j, assuming that the trips from i to j are proportional to some "attractiveness factor" for zone j, and inversely proportional to the spatial or temporal separation from zone i and zone j, raised to some exponent.

The Gravity Model can be formulated as follows:

$$T_{ij} = \frac{P_i A_j F_{ij} K_{ij}}{\sum\limits_{\text{all } j} A_j F_{ij} K_{ij}},$$

where:

T_{ij} trips produced in zone i and attracted to zone j.

P_i trips produced in zone i.

A_j trips attracted to zone j.

F_{ij} empirically-derived travel-time factor, which is a function of the spatial separation between zones; $F_{ij} = d_{ij}^{-b}$. Where d_{ij} is the distance and b more accurately written as b_{ij}, is dependent on the distance, varies with d_{ij} and is normally computed using a linear regression estimate.

K_{ij} specific zone to zone correction factor for special social or economic effects, which is estimated from trip distribution tables to adjust predicted values to observed values.

The Gravity Model must be calibrated with respect to the F and K parameters. It has been said that the Gravity Model's success stems mainly from its simplicity, and from the small number of factors to be calibrated combined with its accuracy at the aggregate level. An interesting article by Heggie [1969] has induced some lively debate as to whether the gravity Model is a valid distribution predictor for disaggregated areas as well. It is interesting to note that the alternative Heggie suggests is a qualitative technique, involving the analysis of empirical evidence concerning volumes, personal income, population movements, and travel costs. He cites three applications of his technique in which fairly good accuracy was attained.

The Gravity, Intervening Opportunities, Competing Opportunities Models, and the Fratar Method were compared in a valuable study by Heanue and Pyers [1966]. These four were applied to trip distribution data for Washington D.C. for 1948 and 1955. It was determined that the Gravity Model was slightly more accurate, overall, than the Intervening Opportunities Model. (Although eliminating the socioeconomic factor K_{ij} from the Gravity Model made the model less accurate than the Intervening Opportunities model, indicating that the extensive parameter calibration of the Gravity Model may have caused the difference.) Both models appeared to be equal in reliability and utility, while the Intervening Opportunities Model was obviously easier to calibrate. The Fratar

Method was fairly useful for stable areas. However, in zones where the land-use patterns were changing over the test period, the Fratar Method proved to be quite inadequate. The Competing Opportunities Model was never really compared, in that meaningful calibration was impossible for the zonal structure of Washington D.C. The great many small zones made the establishment of cost-bands extremely difficult. This is a rather significant deficiency, since many urban land-use studies employ quite detailed zonal structures.

The newly-developed "entropy-maximization" derivation of the Gravity Model is most recent innovation in the field of trip distribution models. For a more detailed discussion of trip distribution models and the latest derivations, see Potts and Oliver [1972].

2. TRAFFIC FACILITIES ANALYSIS AND ALLOCATION

This step in the generic process involves a careful analysis of the present transportation system under study. The main purpose is to allocate present and predicted demands to the current fixed system. In essence, this step enables the analyst to decide whether or not a change in the system's configuration or capacities is necessary to handle the future demand which will be placed on the system.

A clear distinction is made, at this point, between public and private applications. Because control of mode, link, and source is generally held by the organizing entity (business enterprise) in the private sector, allocation of forecasted demand to the current fixed system is made according to the decision of the management. In the public sector, however, all crucial components of demand are random variables under the control of the traveler himself, and thus allocation of forecasted demand in the public sector is again a forecasting problem. Essentially, the allocation is a forecast dependent upon future demand which is itself a forecast.

A number of OR models have been developed to provide the analyst with the means for allocating in the most efficient way, or forecasting the most probable way in which forecasted traffic demand will be allocated to the transportation system under consideration.

In the private sector, there exist widely used models for studying inventory control, production scheduling, vehicle scheduling, modal selection, and facility location; in essence, all the elements of a physical distribution system. These elements are treated in other chapters of this Handbook. It is important to note, however, that using these models requires that assumptions be made concerning the whole system. The use of these models, individually, yields only sub-optimal solutions (i.e., solutions for only a segment of the total problem). To avoid such an eventuality, large scale computer simulation models have been constructed, that are capable of incorporating all elements of a physical distribution system into one model. Such a model will be discussed in the evaluation section.

A specific application of an OR model in the private sector is in the area of *modal selection*. Modal selection models generally represent the decision process, from a total cost point of view. The trade-offs are made between costs and levels of service. Costs associated with a particular mode include initial investment, and operating and maintenance costs. Levels of service include transit times, cargo-carrying capacity, and reliability.

As is often the case in transportation applications, the value of some of these costs is very difficult to assess. Consider that lower transit times, such as the difference between air and rail, may allow lower inventory levels, while still maintaining the same level of reliability ("reliability" in this case could mean the percent of times a customer's order cannot be filled from available inventory, applied to a situation where the demand is probabilistic). The benefits associated with a lower inventory level are related to opportunity and obsolesence costs. The value of these costs is often a matter of judgement.

An interesting modal selection model was developed by McQuie [1971]. The relationship of 28 operating and design characteristics to cargo vehicle productivity are estimated. Although many modal selection models are designed for computer solutions, McQuie's model is an empirical set of equations designed to be hand-solved. Another modal selection model of interest is one by Eatherly [1972].

As stated previously, techniques for *allocation of demand* in the public sector are essentially predictive models. Some of these, called traffic assignment models, determine how traffic will utilize existing or proposed highway facilities. Some models that will be discussed in this chapter are minimum path techniques, such as tree-building algorithms and the "all-or-nothing" assignment model, and minimum network cost techniques, such as the "out-of-kilter" algorithm. Other allocation models, known as modal split models, attempt to determine the proportion of travelers selecting each of the available modes.

The allocation of traffic demand to a transportation network has been accomplished under two different philosophies (Wardrop [1952]). The first, described as a "user-optimized" pattern, proposes that the system will reach an equilibrium when no driver can improve his travel time by switching to a different route. The second, known as a "system-optimized" pattern, assumes that the average trip-time is a minimum.

Cheapest route (or minimum path) algorithms assume that the traveler will choose the cheapest (or near cheapest) route available (user-optimized system).

Tree-building algorithms solve the minimum path problem by building a tree out from the home node to all other nodes in increasing order of cost. Dreyfus [1969] has written a good critique of minimum-path models, indicating some of the pitfalls that may be encountered. Turn-penalities may be added to the algorithms to simulate the real-world difficulties in turning, and also to eliminate the possibility of "stair-case" type route assignments. There are additional costs assigned when a path traverses two consecutive links whose physical alignment necessitates a change in travel directions. The assumption of user-optimization may not be valid. Consider the many rational and even irrational reasons travelers may have for choosing their routes (Wachs [1967]). Thus, the link costs themselves would tend to be a random variable dependent on the traveler's attitude.

Another problem is that the link costs, in reality, are flow-dependent. Travel time on a major artery increases greatly during the rush hour, making secondary routes more desirable at that time. This problem can be handled using the capacity restraint technique, which is an iterative process that allows the link costs to increases as the accumulated traffic flow exceeds the link flow capacity (CATS).

With respect to the assignment using cheapest-route methods, the "all-or-nothing" algorithm is the most widely used. Traffic between any O-D pair is all assigned to the cheapest route and none to any other route. This algorithm also happens to yield a system-optimized trip allocation.

As stated previously, user-optimization is a rather poor assumption, and there are computer packages available that allow a "diversion assignment" (Brokke, 1967). The two cheapest routes between an O-D pair are also assigned a portion of the total traffic. There is also the possibility of multiple-route assignments (Burrell [1968]).

The system-optimized pattern is represented by minimum-network cost algorithms. The solution to the single O-D uncapacitated, directed network can be formulated as a LP problem, and solved efficiently using the dual LP.

3. DETERMINATION OF PROBLEM PARAMETERS AND FORMULATION OF ALTERNATIVE SOLUTIONS

Based on the findings of the previous step; i. e., Traffic Facilities Analysis and Allocation, it now becomes apparent whether or not a problem does indeed exist and, if so, the extent of the problem. If there is a problem, its parameters must be identified and the decision variables defined.

Although it is difficult to generalize in this case, typical decision variables from the public and private sectors are as illustrated in Table 2. Exactly which variables are decision variables is dependent upon the scope of the study and the constraints of the situation. In urban planning, for example, a totally new elevated rapid transit system may not be a possibility, due to limited public funds for such a purpose.

4. EVALUATION OF ALTERNATIVE SOLUTIONS AND RECOMMENDATIONS

Once a set of solutions have been generated, each element of the alternative must be evaluated. In the private sector, techniques used in the allocation step

TABLE 2. TYPICAL DECISION VARIABLES PUBLIC AND PRIVATE SECTORS

Private	Public
Direct	*Direct*
Source: Location of distribution centers, warehouses, factories, and other fixed-facilities.	Traffic regulations; vehicle restrictions
Mode: selection of mode: private vs. common vs. lease, truck vs. train vs. air, etc.	*Indirect* Design of public transit:
Link/schedule: routing/scheduling decisions.	1. capacity
	2. routes
Indirect	3. schedules
Marketing Efforts:	4. station location
1. Advertising campaigns	Legislative measures:
2. Pricing	1. zoning laws
	2. traffic regulations

are also used for the evaluation process. These include vehicle scheduling for the routing elements, modal selection for determining the mode, and locational algorithms for determining optimal location of warehouses, distribution centers, and other fixed facilities. The trip assignment and trip distribution models of the public sector will come into play in forecasting how the public would react to any proposed alternative transportation system.

Measures of Performance

It is important to note, however, that many elements combine to make up a single solution. All the elements, likewise, are interactive and therefore, must be evaluated simultaneously for each alternative. Thus, more extensive models must be used. These include cost/benefit and cost/effectiveness analyses, and computer simulation analysis.

The trade-off generally made in the evaluation of a transportation alternative is cost versus level of service. In the private sector, levels of service are represented by variability of delivery times, physical condition of delivered goods, and response time to special orders. In the public sector, service levels are congestion levels, such as percent of designed capacity for a corridor, transit times within the city both by private and public vehicles, accessibility for minority groups (related specifically to travel times and geographical comprehensiveness of the public transit system), accident rates, and noise levels among others.

For any large scale transportation problem, evaluation of alternatives is rarely a totally quantitative process. Due to the extent of the problem, unprogrammable qualitative factors are usually always present. Thus, the techniques used in evaluation can only clarify certain aspects of the whole problem.

Method of Analysis

Computer simulation is one of the most important tools at this stage of the generic process. The most useful characteristic of simulation is that it can integrate a great many of the quantitative aspects of the transportation system. Thus, given that some assumptions are made concerning the qualitative variables, previously discussed, alternative solutions can be tested, yielding a number of service level parameters associated with each cost level.

One of the best of these simulation models is the LREPS (Long Range Environmental Planning Simulator) model developed by Bowersox (1972) of Michigan State University. The LREPS model is capable of dynamically simulating the physical distribution of packaged goods. The principal objective of the model is to assist management in the design and evaluation of present and alternative physical distribution configurations.

The primary comparative measure used in evaluating different physical distribution configurations involves customer service capability (speed and reliability of servicing orders) and the associated total cost. In general, as the customer service capability increases, the associated total cost also increases, and management must decide the appropriate trade-offs. A few additional characteristics of the LREPS model need to be highlighted in order to appreciate the effectiveness of this model.

1. It is dynamic in that it provides planning over time with adequate feedback provisions, to ensure that the future impact of any decision can be appropriately treated.

2. It is stochastic by providing for demands and order cycle times, communications, order processing, and transportation times in a probabilistic manner. A deterministic mode is also available.

3. It is able to integrate inventory allocation and facility location, thereby treating temporal and spatial attributes simultaneously.

4. It is multi-echelon. The first echelon can handle from one to one hundred manufacturing plants with adjacent warehouses. The second echelon can handle from one to one hundred distribution centers, which may stock a wide variety of products. The final echelon can provide up to 20,000 demand units, which may represent individual customers and/or groups of customers. Linkages between and within the different echelons are provided for in terms of product flows and information flows.

The LREPS model has been successfully used in the planning and evaluation of distribution systems for firms in the leather goods, agri-chemical, frozen foods, plumbing and heating, and packaged chemical industry.

LREPS does, however, have its limitations, These include:

1. A large amount of data is necessary for the model, and not all firms possess the required data. Acquiring the data may be very costly and time-consuming.

2. There is some degree of unsuitability for "minor studies." The LREPS model is best suited for large scale distribution systems.

There exist other simulation models for planning and evaluating physical distribution systems. The most useful of these appears to be Distribution System Simulator (Connors, et al. [1972]). A prominent characteristic of DSS is a feature known as "programming by questionnaire." The characteristics of the simulation model are automatically determined from answers to over 450 yes/no questions. Information determined from the questionnaire includes characteristics of customer demand, buying patterns of customers, order filling policies, replenishment policies, factory locations, production capability, and other significant elements. All of these are functional elements that should be readily available in most cases. The answers to these questions determine which of the possible 10^{12} functionally different simulation models will be built from the Program Library.

Once the form of the simulation program is established, an Editor Program generates a specific listing of the data necessary to complete the analysis. Because of this, the cost of information associated with simulating different alternatives can more easily be weighed against the possible benefits to be derived from such an evaluation. In this way, a firm can avoid possible excessive data acquisition costs by obtaining exactly the data that is needed for exactly the type of analysis desired.

DSS can be easily scaled down through proper use of the questionnaire, making it very valuable to the middle or small sized firm. Another advantage to the smaller firm is that a great deal of programming expertise is not necessary. Perhaps the greatest advantage of questionnaire programming is the increased interdepartmental communication. DSS allows the executive to be more of a participant in the modelling process (through the questionnaire), thereby instilling in him more confidence and understanding in the model.

Although a "canned program" such as this may seem too automatic to be useful, a surprisingly high degree of sophistication and complexity can be obtained. DSS can incorporate three structural entities: demand points, stocking points, and production resources. The interrelationships are arbitrary. The channels of distribution can be bidirectional, the stocking points can all be connected to each other, demand can take place at any point in the system, and any stocking point can have access to any production resource. Measures of performance normally center around the stocking points, which are usually defined as regionally distributed warehouses. Unfortunately, the integration of time and space dimensions, and the dynamic behavior of LREPS are features not available in DSS. However, DSS seems to fill in very nicely the gaps left by LREPS, in that it can provide a less costly and more comprehensive analysis designed more for the smaller firm, in which the problem of acquiring and structuring data is partially solved with questionnaire programming and explicit data specification.

Many firms have come to realize that a very significant cost savings in their distribution system is possible with proper aggregate planning, and these simulation models provide a means for this planning. These models are able to provide management with the required information enabling a well designed (or redesigned) system to be established to handle present and future demands. Many firms, however, do not have as an alternative a completely new physical distribution system. However, whatever constraints do indeed exist may be built into the simulation models.

Although not as frequently as in the private sector, computer simulation models have also been used in the public sector. One such model was used in evaluating alternative transportation systems for Boston, Houston, New Haven, and Tucson (General Research Corporation [1968]).

As useful as they are, computer simulation models cannot incorporate nonquantifiable variables. The techniques which attempt to organize the entire set of quantitative and nonquantitative variables are the cost/benefit and cost/effectiveness models. Cost/benefit models attempt to list the various quantitative and qualitative levels of service associated with each level of total cost. Often, the two sides are equated using some sort of cost per unit factor. When considering that some of the factors involved include pollution, congestion, service to minorities, and safety hazards, it becomes quite clear that attempting to equate some of these factors with dollars is practically impossible.

This realization has led to the development of the cost/effectiveness model. The main purpose of this model is to present as clearly as possible the measurers of service associated with each level of total cost, while retaining the original units of each variable. Some examples would be travel times, accident rates, pollution levels, and comfort factors. Once presented in a clear manner, the alternatives may then be "graded" by a group of "experts," just as a teacher may grade school papers.

In a study by Dodson [1969], the alternatives were grouped together into four categories:

1. No change.

2. Conventional Improvement: general modifications of the current fixed system.

3. Gradualism: some component changes are accelerated, but no large scale modifications.

4. Technological Revolution: major system changes such as the construction of overhead rapid transit.

Experts were asked to grade each of these four from A to E in a great many categories. Some involved factors such as comfort, convenience, reliability, and safety. Other categories determine how the experts thought different segments of the public would react to the four different alternatives. These grades were then used to help establish the overall feelings of the experts.

Cost/benefit and cost/effectiveness analyses are the most comprehensive models available. They act, essentially, to combine the results of the more specific models, especially the computer simulation models, with the relevant nonquantifiable variables. The total set of alternatives is clearly organized, so as to illustrate the associated trade-offs. However, the final decision still requires a great deal of judgement and insight on the part of the decision-makers.

5. DEVELOPMENT OF PROTOTYPES AND FINAL TESTING

It is rather common practice to develop operative prototype models for evaluating new plants and processes in industry. Public highway departments employ the same sorts of testing, through prototype simulation for pavements, striping, guideways, and signalization.

There is more and more attention being paid to prototypes and simulation as a final testing technique. Spectacular successes within the aerospace industry have spunoff noteworthy prototype simulations in engineering and management, in both the public and private sectors.

One example in the public sector would be the construction of a single express-bus lane in a situation where the chosen plan of action was to construct express-bus lanes on 25 arteries of a city. In the private sector, a plan for managing inventories of one-way truck rentals for a national truck leasing company may be implemented in a single city rather than over the entire nation.

An advantage to the use of prototypes, aside from the obvious cost reduction and accident prevention, is the capability for gathering feedback. This applies in a technical sense, as well as the increasingly important public reaction sense.

6. IMPLEMENTATION

This section provides a summary of the problems and impediments towards implementation of the chosen transportation alternative. The problems and impediments should be identified in order to aid the analyst to have a direct effect on decision-making.

Decision-Making Factors

Related problems and impediments for generic models of transportation analysis have to do with their probability of implementation through the decision-making process. There is much experience and knowledge to justify the similarity of decision-making as a process in both the public and private sectors—at least with regards to transportation. It has been shown, in many cases, that difficulties arising within the decision-making process tend to impede the following of recommendations from generic models.

One kind of problem within the decision-making process has to do with special interests. This tends to be related to subjective bias and fears within influential factors in the decision-making process. This might occur, for example, when an optimal solution suggests a solution which is new or previously untried within an organization. Fear, or the so-called "comfort-factor," may lead to outright rejection. Similar examples are known to exist, with special interests favoring specific solutions as well as biases against a set of solutions.

Closely related to the above is the problem of interest groups within the decision-making process, be it public or private. These groups tend to support and advocate certain types of solutions. Within the context of group dynamics, these solutions may be relatively predictable. The transportation analytical model does not usually contain the assumptions and biases of a number of groups; thus, it would be rare that such a model would predict a solution that would be satisfactory to all groups. Hence, it can be assumed that within any complex decision-making organization concerning transportation, an optimal solution will necessarily lead to some groups opposing, some groups supporting, and some groups taking no stand. This means that the solution that is accepted will have to be settled within a public or private political process.

Environmental and Community Impact

Another area of impediments of implementation of generic models in the transportation process has to do with the importance of environmental and community impact. Most transportation affects communities and their environment, whether it is within the private or public sector. Within recent years, there has been significant national, state, and local legislation dealing with the need to analyze transportation proposals, in order to insure that they will not have negative effects on communities or the environment. It is common knowledge that the modeling of transportation systems will have to undergo an additional stage of refinement in order to minimize environmental and community negative-impact. While there has been some effect to include environmental and community impact variables in generic models of transportation analysis, the results have so far been unconvincing and costly (Southeast Wisconsin Planning Commission [1966]). Thus, it must be realized that environmental and community impact requires some change in optimal solutions generated through modeling, and future efforts should include such parameters, variables, and constraints in both quantitative and qualitative terms.

7. A CLASSIC EXAMPLE

Leslie C. Edie's [1954] classic work involving The Port of New York Authority (Port Authority) and the problems of traffic delays at toll booths will be used as an illustrative example to demonstrate the application of the generic process as shown on page 480.

Edie's work was the first application of OR to a Port Authority problem. Many other applications have been made since 1952, when the toll booth study was initiated; however, the toll booth study is the best known, and is very well thought of (it received the First Lanchester Prize in 1955).

The basic problem involved the collection of vehicular tolls at the various Port Authority tunnels and bridges. Staffing requirements for the tunnels and bridges resulted in a substantial payroll, and the Port Authority was very interested in minimizing the number of toll collectors, while at the same time providing uniformly good service to the public and properly spaced relief periods for the toll collectors. The basic trade off involved determining the best compromise between the level of customer service and the corresponding costs involved.

Prior to the study, a "rule of thumb" work standard unrelated to service was used to determine the number of toll collectors necessary for operating a toll plaza. "Rule of thumb" judgement was also used to allocate manpower and control the number of toll booths opened at any time. This method resulted in traffic delays ranging from 2 to 50 seconds. It was felt a more analytical approach involving the basic principle of probability theory could be used to better understand the relations between traffic volumes, number of toll booths, and overall service.

The basic objectives of the study were:

1. To evaluate the grade of service given to patrons and determine how it varied with the volume of traffic handled by toll lanes.
2. To establish the optimum standards of service.
3. To develop a more precise method of controlling expenses and services, while at the same time providing adequate reliefs to the toll collector.

In essence, these three objectives required the solution of a queueing problem, an optimizing problem, and a scheduling problem.

With the problem defined and the objectives of the study clearly stated, an illustration of the generic process, as shown on page 480, will be made.

Traffic Demand Forecasting

The first step in the process involves traffic demand forecasting (this is precisely the first step taken by Edie). Observations were made every 30 seconds to measure the number of traffic arrivals at a particular plaza and the number of vehicles in line at each open toll lane. Observations were grouped into twenty minute periods, and occupancy values and delay ratio values (the average waiting time in the queue expressed as a multiple of service time) were computed for each period. These values were plotted, and the resulting empirical curves were compared to the classical queueing theory curves for single server and multiple servers in parallel. These curves have since proven to be very effective in terms of predicting traffic arrivals and delays.

Traffic Facilities Analysis and Allocation

A very important by-product finding of Edie's study involved the adverse effect of right-hand toll booths on service. A right-hand booth is one on the right side of a vehicle, opposite the driver. It was determined that right-hand booths caused substantial delays to traffic and, as a result of this finding, the Port Authority reconstructed all major toll plazas to provide only left-hand booths.

It was also concluded from the observations that the serving time per vehicle was reduced when the traffic handled per lane increased.

Determination of Problem Parameters and Formulation of Alternative Solutions

It was obvious that a problem did indeed exist and something needed to be done to improve service at a reasonable cost, while providing adequate relief periods for the collectors. A number of curves were developed by Edie in order to clearly and definitively characterize the queueing problem. The curves included:

1. Occupancy delay curves for differing numbers of toll booths and differing occupancy percents.
2. Average booth holding time (service time) for differing volumes of traffic per hour per lane and differing number of total lanes.

Once these two sets of curves were developed, the queueing problem and its parameters were clearly defined.

The optimizing problem involved establishing criteria for opening and closing toll lanes to fit traffic demands. After evaluating various alternatives, the original decision was made to maintain service as close to an average delay of 11 seconds as possible, and to limit maximum queue length to no more than three vehicles above the point at which the Poisson distribution broke down.

The scheduling problem, primarily concerned with the assignment of men to toll booths, proved to be the most difficult of the three problems. At first, a trial and error Gantt chart method was used for manpower scheduling, and its results were not satisfactory. A second attempt was made using LP, but it also produced unsatisfactory results for several reasons, including that answers involving fractional parts of a man were meaningless.

The methodology which proved satisfactory was an iterative process, with decision rules for assigning regular and relief collectors. With this procedure, various schedules could be determined.

Evaluation of Alternative Solutions and Recommendations

Once the queueing problem, the optimizing problem, and the scheduling problem had been clearly defined and various alternatives tested, it was necessary to select the set of alternatives that would be implemented.

Edie did not employ a large model encompassing the three individual problems, but rather each problem was looked at individually, and then results were compared. For example, by using the two types of curves developed for the queueing problem (the occupancy delay curves and the booth holding time curves), Edie was able to compute delay curves for varying levels of traffic volume and number of lanes, and thus arrive at one solution to the queueing problem after empirically testing various alternatives. This solution was then used as input in solving the optimizing problem.

Development of Prototypes and Final Testing

Field tests were made to evaluate the original solutions to the queueing and optimizing problems. In addition, a rigid trial schedule was followed in the opening and closing of lanes and in relieving the collectors for rest and meal periods.

Implementation

The solutions recommended were implemented by the Port Authority.

Feedback and Further Improvements

It is indeed interesting to look at the feedback that evolved over the initial Edie study. This feedback is briefly summarized below.

1. A better control of service and cost, and a sound understanding of the interrelationships existing between them.
2. The reconstruction of toll plazas to provide only left hand lanes.
3. The development of automatic printing and punching traffic counters to help provide for an improved method of traffic analysis.
4. The development of a special camera for monitoring traffic to help provide for a quicker response to changing traffic conditions.
5. Input for the planning of automating toll collection.
6. The stimulus for other early OR studies of various aspects of toll booth and tunnel policy, such as foot patrol and motorized patrol.

In general, it is difficult to directly measure the overall impact of this study, but suffice it to say that the impact was indeed very substantial.

8. TYPICAL PROBLEMS ENCOUNTERED IN THE GENERIC TRANSPORTATION PLANNING PROCESS

The Data-Information Dilemma

The data available to the transportation analyst is generally not sufficient. Transportation tends to be treated as any other expense item, yet, the data collected tends to be meager. While it is true that such data is difficult to collect, it is insufficient to use this reason as a justification. The information that is generated from this dubious data tends to be less than satisfactory. As a result, it becomes an expensive process to obtain the necessary information for both the process and modeling of transportation analysis. A number of cases from the public sector have shown great amounts of money being expended in order to obtain information to allow for transportation analysis (Mouchahoir [1972]). Similar cases can be drawn from the private sector, in which efforts have been very costly.

A related source of problems to data and information is the treatment and measurement of many variables which tend to be nonquantitative or intangible. A paradox exists as to the measurement of the tangible and quantifiable variables, in that what often is done is to guess at the values for such variables with little or no benefit of data. This tends to lend an air of artificiality to the models used in transportation analysis. While it may be appropriate, in many instances, to assign subjective values to these variables, it may also be appropriate to highlight such variables for treatment at later stages.

When the data and information dilemma is compounded with the problems of measurement of tangible but qualitative variables within the context of complex models, a new impediment to success arises. This is related to the problem of error propagation. There have been a number of analyses which have indicated that in some transportation models, error propagation, due to complexity of mathematical and arithmetical operations combined with the above problems of data and information as well as intangible and nonquantifiable variables, can rise to above 50% (Alonso [1968]).

Conservatism in Optimal Solutions

A source of criticism in the transportation field concerning modeling activities has been that optimal solutions to transportation problems tend to be relatively conservative. This arises because the transportation problem, as such, requires a relatively specific set of constraints which tend to be stated in fixed terms. When this is coupled with subjective estimates of the values of certain kinds of variables, as well as the exclusion of many variables which are very difficult to measure, it becomes apparent that the types of solutions generated can be relatively mundane—indeed in some cases trivial. For example, in urban transportation planning, the major benefits are often expressed in terms of minutes saved by commuters and minimization of system construction and operating costs. It has become quite apparent that true user benefits are far more complex than time saved, and it is quite well known that there are many cases in which the minimum system cost solution is by no means what is really needed. In general, there is also the argument that transportation today requires major changes. These solutions do not always come from optimal solutions generated through quantitative models.

An approach that may allow for greater applicability of the modeling process for transportation analysis is to define other types of solutions than the optimal. These other types of solutions can be refinements, extensions, modifications, extrapolations, or revisions of an optimal solution. One method, somewhat similar to Dodson's [1969] approach, might be to define four sets of solutions (Catanese and Steiss [1970]). The first set, as a logical starting point, would be the determination of the optimal solution for the problem as defined. A second set would be the minimal set for which solutions related to the optimal are recommended on the basis of doing the least and spending the least in time, effort, and resources. This might be called the "extrapolation of present trends" alternative. A maximal set could be considered as that set of solutions which requires as much effort and resources as possible, and as much improvement in the transportation system and process as possible. This might be considered the "doing as much as possible" alternative. In many cases, resource constraints dictate that the optimal solution be also the maximal solution. The reference here is to a situation in which all available resources are not necessarily used in the recommended solution, such as the construction of a single highway with State Highway Department funds.

It has been our experience to find that optimal solutions in transportation lie within a range defined within the maximal-minimal solution sets. An additional set of solutions which might be considered appropriate is the normative set. This group of recommendations may or may not be related to the optimal solution, and tend to be more concerned with what "ought to be" rather than what seems appropriate in terms of analytical processes.

Thus, it has been suggested that this sort of analytical framework and the use of alternative sets, as well as mixes within these sets, might be a way to use optimal solutions as generating sources for a range of proposed solutions. This range of proposed solutions can then be tested against the range of problems discussed above, as well as acceptibility for implementation. This approach might better enable use of the modeling process in transportation.

9. CONCLUSIONS

At this point, it might be worthwhile to review some of the insights gained from this exposition of both public and private transportation OR models.

It was determined that a much heavier forecasting burden is placed on the analyst in the public sector. This is reflected in the many trip distribution and trip assignment models designed specifically to predict the movement desires of the public. This is related to two other realities.

First, it is obvious that control of many more components of traffic demand is centralized with the enterprise in the private sector, as opposed to the public sector, where control is essentially distributed over millions of people.

Secondly, the objectives of planning in the two sectors are quite different.

The objectives in the private sector are generally related to profit. In the public sector, however, the objective is to satisfy the desires of millions of different people. Thus, it is often quite difficult to define criteria for decisions in urban transportation planning, and it may become necessary to establish policies as to what are the legitimate goals and which are important.

A case in point, illustrating the differences and similarities between public and private models, is a comparison between modal split models of the public sector and modal selection models of the private sector. Both are concerned with alternative transportation modes. Both attempt to define the costs and benefits associated with each available mode. In the public sector, however, control of the modal selection process is maintained by the public; thus, the modal split models attempt to *predict* the proportion of the public choosing each available mode as a function of the costs and benefits of each mode. In the private sector, control of the modal selection process is generally held by the planning organization; thus, the private modal selection models determine which mode or modes *are the best* in terms of the characteristics of the different modes. The proposition that models in the private sector are generally *optimization-oriented*, while models used in the public sector are generally *forecasting-oriented*, holds true for most of the steps in the generic transportation planning process.

For the immediate future, we can expect a larger degree of models being used in transportation analyses in both the public and private sectors. It has been argued that new models will be simpler, less complex, and deal with specific problems rather than the global problems previously treated (Lee [1973]). The day of the large-scale, complex, and costly modeling process attempting to include all of the variables, as well as many of the nonquantitative factors, in one explicit analytical model is probably over. The future will undoubtedly see more use of simulation and operational gaming to deal with such matters.

REFERENCES

Alonso, W., "Predicting Best With Imperfect Data," *J. Am. Inst. Planners* 34 (4) pp. 248–255 (July 1968).

Appa, G. M., "The Transportation Problem and its Variants," *Operational Res. Quart.*, 24, (1) pp. 79–99 (March 1973).

Bluestone, David W., "U.S. Airline Passenger Traffic Will Soar in the Seventies," *Airline Management and Marketing Including American Aviation*, 2, (1) pp. 24–32 (January 1970).

Bowersox, D. J., "Coping: Dynamic Simulation of PD," *Distribution World Wide*, pp. 24–31 (December 1972). Also, "Planning Distribution Operations with Dynamic Simulation," *J. Marketing*, pp. 17–25 (January 1972).

Brokke, G. E., "Urban Transportation Planning Computer System," American Association State Highway Officials Conference, Minnesota (1967).

Burrell, J. E., "Multiple Route Assignment and its Application to Capacity Restraint," Fourth International Symposium on Theory of Traffic Flow, Karlsruhe (1968).

Catanese, A. J. and A. W. Steiss, *Systemic Planning: Theory and Application*, D.C. Heath, Boston (1970).

Chicago Area Transportation Study, Illinois Department of Public Works and Buildings in cooperation with the Bureau of Public Roads, U.S. Department of Commerce, Vols. I-III (1959, 1960, 1962).

Clark, C. and G. H. Peters, "The Intervening Opportunities' Method of Traffic Analysis," *Traffic Quart.*, **19**, (1) pp. 101–119 (January 1965).

Connors, M. M., C. Coray, C. J. Cuccaro, W. K. Green, D. W. Low, and H. M. Markowitz, "The Distribution System Simulator," *Management Sci.*, **18**, (8) pp. 425–453 (April 1972).

Creighton, R. L., *Urban Transportation Planning*, University of Illinois Press, Chicago, 1970.

Dodson, E. N., "Cost-Effectiveness in Urban Transportation," *Operations Res.*, **17**, (3) pp. 373–394 (May-June 1969).

Dreyfus, S. E., "An Appraisal of Some Shortest-Path Algorithms," *Operations Res.*, **17**, (3) pp. 395–312 (May–June 1969).

Eatherly, B. J., "Summary of a Simple Model of Mode Choice," *Management Sci.*, **19**, (2) pp. 201–204 (October 1972).

Edie, L. C., "Traffic Delays at toll Booths," *Operations Res.*, **11**, (1) pp. 107–138 (May–June 1954).

Fratar, T. J., "Forecasting Distribution of Interzonal Vehicular Trips by Successive Approximations," Highway Research Board Proceedings, 33rd Annual Meeting, pp. 376–384 (1954).

Garrison, W. L. and D. F. Marble, *A Prolegomenon to the Forecasting of Transportation Development*, Transportation Center Report, Northwestern University (August 1965).

General Research Corporation, *Systems Analysis of Urban Transportation, Vols. 1–4* (January 1968).

Heanue, K. E. and C. E. Pyers, "A Comparative Evaluation of Trip Distribution Procedures," *Public Roads*, pp. 43–51 (June 1966).

Heggie, I. G., "Are Gravity and Interactance Models a Valid Technique for Planning Regional Transport Facilities?," *Operational Res. Quart.*, **20**, (1) pp. 93–110 (March 1969).

Kirby, R. F., "A Preferencing Model for Trip Distribution," *Transport. Sci.*, **4**, (1) p. 1–35 (February 1970).

Kriebel, F. E., "Transportation in the 70's," *Distribution World Wide*, pp. 39–42 (July 1970).

Lee, Douglas B., "Requiem for Large Scale Models," *J. Am. Inst. Planners* **39**, (3) pp. 163–178 (May 1973).

McQuie, R., "Cargo Vehicle Productivity," *Management Sci.*, **18**, (2) pp. B36–B51 (October 1971).

Mouchahoir, G. E., "Economy in Data Collection for Planning Studies," *Traffic Quart.*, **26**, (2) pp. 289–298 (April 1972).

Parrish, R. L., "Lockheed's 'Paper Airline'," *Airline Management and Marketing Including American Aviation*, pp. 64–65 (January 1970).

Potts, R. B. and R. M. Oliver, *Flows in Transportation Networks*, Academic Press, Inc., New York (1972).

Southeast Wisconsin Regional Planning Commission, *Recommended Transportation and Land Use Plan: 1990*, Milwaukee (1966).

Stouffer, S. A., "Intervening Opportunities: A Theory Relating Mobility and Distance," *Amer. Soc. Rev.*, **5**, pp. 845–867 (1940).

Tomazinis, A. R., "A New Method of Trip Distribution in an Urban Area," *Highway Research Board Bulletin 347*, pp. 77–99 (1962).

Tomlin, J. A., "A Mathematical Programming Model for the Combined Distribution-Assignment of Traffic," *Transport. Sci.*, **5**, (2) pp. 122–140 (1971).

Verleger, Philip K., Jr., "Models for the Demand for Air Transportation," *The Bell Journal of Economics and Management Science*, **3**, (2), pp. 437–457, (Autumn 1972).

Voorhees, A. M., "A General Theory of Traffic Movement," *Proc. Inst. Traffic Engineers*, pp. 46–56 (1955).

Wachs, M., "Relationships Between Drivers' Attitudes Toward Alternate Routes and Driver and Route Characteristics," *Highway Res. Board Record* **197**, pp. 70–87 (1967).

Wardrop, J. G., "Some Theoretical Aspects of Road Traffic Research," *Proc. Inst. Civil Engineers*, **1**, Part II, pp. 325–378 (1952).

II-5

MILITARY SYSTEMS

Edward S. Quade

1. INTRODUCTION

1.1 The Beginnings

The application of analysis of the type we would now call operations research (OR) to military decisions has its roots deep in antiquity. Although the provision of military advice was originally conceived as a task of God, by the third century B.C. we find Hieron, King of Syracuse, asking Archimedes, a scientist, to devise schemes for breaking the Roman naval siege of his city. It was not, however, until the late 19th century and early 20th, when the field of management emerged, that analysis resembling today's OR received any sort of specialized attention or began to develop distinguishing techniques.

These techniques, when applied to military operations, sometimes turned out to be little more than old approaches—not very well documented even within the military—to which had been added some mathematical sophistication. For example, except for a greater emphasis on quantitative analysis, the steps laid down for carrying out what we now term a systems analysis differ little from the outline used by a military staff to prepare the traditional "estimate of the situation."

While the term "operational research" (which became operations research when Americanized) was not coined until 1938 at Bawdsey, England (to describe the activities of a small section of the Air Ministry Research Station there), the type of thinking it has come to represent is not new to the military.

An example appears in the Report of the Board on Fortifications and Other Defenses, U. S. War Department [1886]. Two types of 12-inch breech loading rifles were under consideration by the War Department for use by the Coast Artillery for coast defense. One was a steel, Krupp-type rifle of then standard design, and the other was a new U. S. development of cast iron. To help in the choice, an analysis based on actual performance tests and manufacturing costs had been carried out. This showed the ratio of effectiveness to cost for the steel gun to be only 0.8 of that for the new cast-iron gun. The measure of effectiveness was the "power" of the gun, the energy at the muzzle expressed in foot-tons. This first analysis did not fully satisfy the Board and further analysis was ordered.

The following statement from the Report described that analysis:

> By virtue of certain well-established principles in gunnery, relative to the similitude of guns, with similiarity of loading, it is easy to deduce the caliber and weight of a piece, of either of the above types, which shall possess a given power, or which shall have the *same* power, for instance, as a piece of the other type. In this way we may reduce our data to the same absolute standard, and thus give the analysis a strictly *quantitative* character.

When the analysis was carried out, the cast-iron gun that would produce the same muzzle energy as the steel gun turned out to cost only 0.8 as much as the steel gun. Furthermore, when a Krupp-type gun with the same muzzle energy as the cast-iron was designed and costed, it turned out to cost about 20% more than the cast-iron gun.

The Board then made an emphatic decision—they recommended steel. Let me quote a few of the arguments as given in the Report—somehow they sound like those we hear today:

> ". . . we have no evidence touching the endurance of cast-iron guns . . ."

> ". . . the difference in cost is not great, particularly when it is remembered that *cheapness* is the chief merit claimed for cast-iron . . ."

> ". . . their production in quantity . . . will unquestionably delay the development of the steel industry of this country . . ."

> "It would be singular if, after waiting for so many years with the alleged intention of profiting by the experience of nations foremost in the manufacture of heavy ordnance, we should begin the long-neglected defense of the country with accepting a material for guns which, after having been tried by leading European nations, has been deliberately rejected in favor of steel."

Some OR was done during World War I, both for the U. S. Navy and for the Army. Let me cite two examples.

The first, Thomas A. Edison's work on antisubmarine warfare, was described in Lloyd N. Scott's *Naval Consulting Board of the United States*, Government Printing Office, Washington, D. C., 1920. In bringing Edison on the Board, it was mutually agreed that his inventive and analytic abilities were desired, not his executive talents. He started his work with experiments on underwater listening devices but, following good OR precepts, he soon concluded that his objective was to save ships, and that improving listening devices for finding submarines was only a means to that end. Whitmore [1953] quotes Scott:

His first step was to go to Washington in the summer of 1917 with three assistants, *intending to make a thorough study of the statistics of submarine activities and their results, and to develop therefrom strategic plans according to some ideas that he had in mind. He expected to find on the Government records understandable and full details, charted, of the sinkings that had already taken place. Not finding this, he and his assistants, worked day and night to prepare the charts and data.* (Scott, p. 166.)

Copies of these charts are included in Scott's history.

From a study of these, it was quite apparent that the steamship companies had been sailing their vessels on the same routes as before the war. From the statistics of the numerous sinkings it appeared that only 6% of the ships had been sunk at nightime . . . . It was also apparent from the statistics of sinkings that the steamship companies had not learned the lesson of night sailing in the danger zone. From an examination of Lloyd's Register, it appeared that only about 4% of the first-class British merchant ships had modern sounding apparatus aboard, and at that time wireless apparatus was almost unknown on board the British merchant ship.

With all these facts and this data before him, Mr. Edison commenced to work out his plan, which, broadly stated, was for the ships to sail in and out of the danger zone at night; to forsake as much as possible the old standard lines of travel; to anchor through the day in comparatively shallow waters and harbors where submarines could not approach them, steaming only at night to other ports of anchorage on the way to their ultimate destination. (Scott, p. 166.)

Unfortunately, very little came from Edison's work. The reports seem to have been buried in files somewhere. At the start of World War II the U. S. Navy had to rediscover his statistical procedures.

The army had somewhat more success in actually using the OR work done for them, possibly because the man in charge, Colonel Leonard Ayres, had the opportunity to draw up the Army regulation setting up the office where the work was done, the Statistical Branch of the General Staff. He made arrangements to report to the Chief of Staff directly—not through channels. The unit collected statistics but also did some OR as the following anecdote from Ayres' [1940] collection shows.

"When I came into the War Department I did not know much about being in the headquarters of the War Department. I was taken almost the first day into an office where they computed the turnarounds of the troop and cargo ships, and projected ahead the amounts of cargo and numbers of troops which would be landed on the other side month by month—joint Army and Navy affairs. All the computations were working out badly: practically nothing came out right. Week after week they had been making these computations and the actual turnarounds were always a little off. I told them they always would be wrong and that their computations should be changed. Statistics of rates and speeds are never the same as those of quantities and amounts . . . . "For illustration, suppose your cargo fleet consists of three vessels; one slow vessel which takes 50 days to make a turnaround and two fast vessels which take 25 days each. The average of these three would be 33 and one-third days; that would mean on the average three turnarounds per vessel in a hundred days, and for three vessels nine turnarounds in a hundred days. But actually the two fast vessels make four turnarounds each in 100 days and the slow one makes two, and that makes ten turnarounds in all. That means that one answer is nine turnarounds and the other is ten, and both answers are based on perfectly good arithmetic.

"The next day an orderly came around and said the Chief of Staff presents his compliments and would like to see the colonel at his convenience. You all know what that meant, and, dropping everthing, I hurried to his office and was told he had gone to this secret room of the General Staff. I went there and to my consternation I found that not only the Chief of Staff and his associates, but the Chief of Naval Operations and his associates were seated at the long council table. General March said, 'It has been reported that you looked over the data of our turnarounds in the Transportation Section yesterday and said that the present methods of computation should be abandoned and that something you called the "effective average" should be substituted. What is the "effective average"?' I said, 'Sir, in mathematical terms the effective average is the harmonic mean.'

"The general asked what it was used for, and I answered, "In this connection it should be used where rates and speeds are concerned.' Then I found out one of the reasons why he was Chief of Staff. He said, 'Define the harmonic mean.' I said, 'Sir, the harmonic mean is the riciprocal of the mean of the reciprocals of the several variates,' The Chief of Staff said, 'Precisely so, and it will be computed that way from now on.' "

1.2 The Development

After organized OR appeared in the British Army, it was rapidly taken up by the Military elsewhere. Operations analysis units in the U. S. and Canadian armies were soon established. A major factor in this rapid spread was the introduction of new weapons, based on technical know-how foreign to past military experience. These weapons and weapons systems (radar is the outstanding example) were so novel in concept and design that their exploitation could not be planned purely on the basis of traditional military experience. Scientific knowledge, and thus scientists, were required. A great deal of the initial value of operations analysis came from the fresh approach these scientists brought. A classic example is the success of the airdropped depth charge, once P. M. S. Blackett and his successors solved its problems. They brought this about by a scientific examination of the records of its use and the employment of probability and statistics.

During World War II, the applications were largely tactical: how first to use "window" or "chaff" as a radar countermeasure; how to determine more effective bombing patterns; how to find better antisubmarine search procedures; or how to deploy destroyers to best protect a convoy. The work pertained essentially to studies of the most efficient use of existing resources with known technical characteristics. Thus, for these applications, contrasted with those undertaken later, the inputs were known, the objectives clear, and the uncertainties limited.

After the war, the emphasis changed immediately from "tactical" problems to "planning" problems. Analysts were called upon to apply their techniques to problems of a more complex type—the design and selection of weapons for future wars. OR was then later extended to deal not only with weapon selection and routine peacetime housekeeping operations, but also with questions of national strategy and the choice of major military policy alternatives.

For example, an important application for the earlier analysis was to discover an optimum search pattern with which our destroyers might locate enemy submarines threatening our convoys. In a corresponding post-war application, the analyst must not only consider the threat by enemy submarines to shipping but their threat to cities and bases as well. To discover ways to meet either threat, he must apply his techniques to evaluation of entirely new combinations of detection and interception devices, some not yet in production or even developed. He must also search for the appropriate tactics for using these devices. In short, the application of analysis to weapons and strategies for future wars presents a new kind of problem, essentially different from any treated by OR in World War II.

OR applied to the problem of putting together the defense program is usually termed systems analysis. It differs little, except in scope, from OR in the conventional sense, but is not performed exclusively or even primarily by people who might be identified as operations researchers. A common analysis in this category has to do with considerations of deterrence and the design of the forces that can bring it about.

The term systems analysis came into use for the new type of study because the first post-war applications of OR for the military were concerned with the selection and evaluation of weapons systems, particularly aircraft bombing systems, that had not yet been developed. Since development of a modern weapon system requires several years, such applications no longer dealt exclusively with operations for which the inputs were known and the objectives were clear. Economics became more important; with no war to test effectiveness, attention centered on costs, and a special form, cost-effectiveness analysis, developed. A typical application might deal with such a question as the least costly program to achieve a given goal—say, of five proposals in an all-weather fighter competition, which, for a fixed budget, would be the most effective. The more difficult question of whether a new fighter should be developed at all was not an application that came up very often until later when the days of expanding military budgets had ended.

Although a distinction between systems analysis and OR may be useful (Schlesinger [1963]), the OR profession makes no such distinction and, in fact, tends to treat all forms of advisory analysis as OR.

1.3 Types of Applications

OR and its derivatives—systems analysis, management science, and cost-effectiveness , for instance—can be applied to every aspect of military endeavor, and have been applied to many, ranging from the routine, day-by-day, housekeeping operations of the services, to "hot war" and crucial one-time decisions of national security.

The spectrum of military applications may be divided for the purpose of discussion into categories, according to the type of problem faced:

How shall men, weapons, and equipment be managed in peacetime, keeping in mind the need for economy and readiness? Examples:

(a) What control procedures shall be used for a general supply center: (Stedry and Groswold [1962])

(b) How should the requirements for enlisted personnel in various military occupational specialties be forecast? (Wilson [1969])

What is the best method of using men, weapons, and equipment on hand in order to achieve a given military aim? Examples:

(a) How many defensive weapons should be carried per bomber to insure penetration of air-to-air defense? (Fawcett and Jones [1970])

(b) Given an existing missile force and a set of targets, what is the optimal allocation of weapons to targets? (Matlin [1970])

Given, in broad terms, the defense policy, what weapons, equipment, men, materiel should be designed, developed, purchased, and deployed? Examples:

(a) How much and what type strategic airlift is needed? (Mihram [1970])
(b) What is the best plan for the development of military equipment such as aircraft and missiles? (Klein and Meckling [1958])

What defense policy should the United States adopt?

(a) Given current intelligence estimates and forecasts, what sort of strategy should the United States strive for? (Brodie [1959])
(b) How should the United States handle an international crisis? (Averich and Lavin [1964])

1.4 Characteristics

These categories are arrayed, roughly, in an order which increases with respect to the policy level at which decisions about questions occurring within them are made, and which decreases with respect to the capability of the analysis to produce firm and actionable recommendations. The divisions are not clear-cut. Ordinarily, problems associated with a given category require that solutions be available for problems found in all lower categories.

Applications of the types associated with Force Posture and Defense Policy involve not only engineering, economic, scientific, and behavioral considerations, but also political and ethical ones. In fact, for this reason, no "solutions" to problems associated with the latter two categories exist in any strict sense— merely a resolution of some sort. As one might expect, the less data that is available for analysis, the less exact it is, and the less it is based on experience, the more imprecise are the conclusions, no matter how sophisticated the OR techniques with which the analysis is carried out.

In the first category, the applications take their most mathematical form and, in a sense, their most fruitful role. Except for the context, much of the analysis is essentially no different from applications of OR to decisionmaking and resource allocation in commerce and industry—stock control, personnel assignment, reliability checkout, transportation routing, and so forth. It is the application of OR or management science in the narrow sense—an attempt to increase the efficiency of a man-machine system in a context where it is fairly clear that "more efficient" means something like the military equivalent of maximizing profits. A frequent characteristic of problems in this category is that OR can be helpful simply by applying systematic computational routines to a generic "model," which can be made relevant to a wide variety of operations merely by modifying the parameters.

Notwithstanding the economic importance of the applications of OR to the management of the peacetime operations of the Military—management tools developed by operations researchers for handling the spare parts inventory for the Air Force alone are producing savings of something like $250 million a year—we will not emphasize applications of this type, since they are not essentially different, except for the parameters and the great emphasis on readiness for conflict, from applications in nonmilitary contexts.

The strictly military application, however, in the remaining three categories, always involves the element of conflict, and frequently requires that it not only be explicitly considered in the choice of parameters, but that the presence of the enemy be taken into account in the model. It is the interaction, or potential interaction, with the enemy, and not the interaction of one's own alternatives and costs, that is likely to be the main problem with the strictly military application. The normal business or industrial analysis is, thus, likely to be conceptually simpler; conflict plays only a minor role. As Albert Wohlstetter [1963] pointed out,

> Somebody in the Bell Telephone System has to worry about slugs or plugged nickels in their coin boxes, but in general Bell does not have to worry about anybody jamming their microwave relay as an interruption of their normal peacetime business.

There are, nevertheless, no methods or techniques of OR that are completely unique to the military. Even the classical 3-room war game has found application in the civilian sector, although mostly for training and education.

The paradox of military OR is that, of the combat operations studied, very few are ongoing and many of the remainder, if we are lucky, will never actually exist. The weapon system or combat operation investigated frequently becomes obsolete without being tested in actual combat, and we are fortunate to never really know how correct our analysis was. Even the weapons that are deterrents against war itself and which operate in peacetime depend for their effect on calculations of how they would behave in war.

A major difficulty with military OR thus lies in obtaining fundamental quantitative information that can be used for prediction. Even when hostilities are ongoing, there is little opportunity for experimentation during actual combat. Sources of data are training exercises, field experiments (often OR is not used to design them in such a way that useful results can be obtained), map exercises, and military experience (which is unlikely to be very relevant for future wars with radically different weapons).

To get a basis for planning the acquisition of future weapon systems, the effectiveness of those systems in different combat situations has to be estimated by theoretical calculations. These are, of course, based on data available for different parts of the system. This means that, during peacetime, the military

OR analyst works less with statistical analysis of operational data and more with theoretical calculations based on very uncertain data. This has led to the development of new analysis techniques—operational gaming and simulation, for instance—and stress on methods for planning under uncertainty, such as sensitivity testing.

1.5 Organization

After World War II, many countries continued, or set up, organizations to carry out military operations research (MOR). Except for the United States, these were almost all within the services and were largely manned by military officers. Here, in addition to those "in house," each of the services and the Department of Defense has associated with it more or less independent organizations, staffed mainly by civilians who carry out analytic studies. The best known is the Rand Corporation (Smith [1966]); others prominent in MOR are the Center for Naval Analysis, the Institute of Defense Analysis, the Stanford Research Institute, and the Research Analysis Corporation (now part of General Analysis Corporation). In addition, much of aerospace industry and many other profit making firms carry out MOR.

In fact, OR developed in the United States largely with the financial support from the military until the late 1960s, when Congressional action forced the defense establishment to reduce their support of basic research. Much of the methodology of OR—game theory, linear programming, dynamic programming, network flow theory, simulation, and other tools—was developed with the support of such sources as the Office of Naval Research, The Army Operations Research Office, the Air Force Office of Scientific Research, and the Air Force Project Rand. The total effort that has gone into the military applications of OR is very large. The U. S. General Accounting Office [1971] estimated the total investment in all *active* models, simulations, and games in the Department of Defense inventory as $170.5 million. This, of course, represents only part of the MOR effort.

1.6 An Example

To illustrate some of the considerations in MOR consider the following realistic but hypothetical example—one that tackles a simplification of a question that recently faced the U. S. Congress: should the strategic missile force be defended by an ABM (anti-ballistic missile) force?

An important component in U. S. security is the land based strategic missile force—a force that stands ready to retaliate if an enemy should attack. To fulfill this role, it must be capable of surviving an enemy attack in sufficient force. There are many actions that might keep it survivable. One can hide the missiles, make them mobile, shelter them, make the force so large that no enemy can hope to destroy it all, or one can actively protect it. Suppose that an anti-missile system for providing active protection is feasible and has been partially developed. The discussion that follows is designed to illustrate the sort of analysis that might help someone who had to make a decision in this situation.

First, a few general observations. Without analysis, it is obvious that, if a defense is cheap and efficient and if there is an appreciable danger of attack, we should buy a defense. But just how expensive? How efficient? How appre-ciable the danger? And what sort of a defense? These considerations are relative. They depend on many factors and parameters, some of which are known, some of which can be discovered, some that must be assumed; but they are interde-pendent, and to make a rational decision a decisionmaker needs a scheme that will tie together the relationships between the various aspects of the problem. OR can provide such a scheme.

One might tackle this problem somewhat as follows:

(1) Identify the objectives or goals that one hopes to attain with the defense system being considered. There are clearly many systems involved. One is the defensive system for the strategic missiles; that is the one being proposed for further development and procurement. But the analysis must be concerned with a larger system, the one that includes not only the defense, but the defended missiles themselves and everything significant to their operation—the enemy's capabilities, the warning radars, the political environment, etc. It is possible to evaluate a defense only in terms of how it helps or hinders (by consuming resources) that which is defended. Thus, when we talk about the goals of the system, it is the overall goal of both the strategic system and the defense for that system that the analyst has to consider. Whether or not we should plan to defend our offensive missiles depends on what we plan to do with those missiles. If we intend to use them to initiate a surprise war there would be little point in defending them. Assuming this is not the case, suppose we take deterrence of an enemy attack as an approximation to what we would like to achieve with our strategic missiles and their defense. I say approximation because there are other capabilities beside deterrence that we would like our strategic missiles to have.

(2) Assuming deterrence is the goal, since different systems presumably lead to different degrees of deterrence, we need some way to measure these differ-ences. That is we need a way to measure the worth or value to deterrence of adding a defense.

A reasonable choice might be to measure deterrence in terms of the number of operationally ready strategic missiles surviving an enemy surprise attack; this measure doesn't include all the aspects of deterrence, but it is at least in the right direction. This step is really the crucial one in many analyses. If we can find a satisfactory measure of effectiveness, we are likely to be able to do a good analy-sis; if not, the outcome is always going to be in doubt. Do we have a satisfactory scheme here? Not completely. Deterrence is an aspect of the mind, and of the enemy's mind at that. If we have two systems, one of which will have 500 strategic missiles surviving an enemy first attack and another only 250 , it is not possible to say how much more deterrence the system with twice as many surviving missiles will supply.

(3) As the next step, we forecast, or make assumptions, about the political and military environment in which our defensive system is to operate. Here, questions such as the following are relevant: Do we need to consider scenarios (that is, hypothetical sequences of plausible events) in which the war starts as a result of the degeneration of a crisis situation, or deliberate escalation, or, as is often assumed, solely by an attack from "out of the blue"? Because the different alternatives may have different states of alertness or readiness or different costs to maintain them in a state of alertness or readiness, the assumptions about how a war is likely to start may drastically affect the comparison.

(4) Now we must define the alternative systems. (They must be examined for feasibility, and cut down to a reasonable number that differ only in significant aspects.) There are at least two. The most obvious alternative of all is to provide no defense whatsoever, and to use the available funds to buy additional missiles.

(5) Choose the approach. Shall we compare the alternatives for a fixed budget, or shall we first fix the mission requirements? Since we very likely have no idea how many surviving missiles will be needed to attain deterrence, but may have a good idea of how much money will be available to buy defense, it looks reasonable to take the approach of fixing the budget and seeking to maximize effectiveness. In fact, we can formulate our criterion or rule of choice on this basis and suggest adopting the alternative which, for the fixed cost, leads to the greatest number of surviving missiles.

(6) Formulate a scheme or model for working out the costs. This, to be useful, must be capable of taking account of changes in operating philosophy during development. As a first approximation, this cost can be the dollars or their equivalent required to maintain the current force, plus the cost of augmenting it either with a defense of one kind or another or with more missiles. To carry the analysis further, we need to find out what forces are obtainable with a given budget. This is not necessarily an easy or a simple job. We should explore the significant resource restraints and also the nonmonetary costs. There may be undesirable side effects that may interfere with implementing the program—say, that arise from the location selected for the launching sites—that require looking into.

(7) Develop a model to evaluate the alternatives. What we are looking for is a scheme or process—a set of mathematical equations or a computer program, for instance—that will project, for each choice of alternative, the number of surviving missiles under various assumptions. These assumptions must specify, among other things, the given budget, the properties of the enemy attacking

missiles (accuracy, reliability, destructive power, numbers, etc.), the properties of the alternatives (reliability, probability of shooting down an attacking missile, etc.), and the properties of the missiles being attacked (hardness, location, number, etc.).

Let us not derive a cost model but simply assume that: M = the number of undefended missiles we can buy with the given budget; s_M = the cost of one undefended missile; and s_D = the cost of defense for that one missile. Then Ms_M = the given budget and $s_M + s_D$ = the cost to defend the missile plus the missile itself.

The effectiveness model described here is based on one used by Burke [1963] for examining hard point defense of missile sites; the idea for the example was suggested by Specht [1968].

Factors that are relevant to any effectiveness model are: A = number of shots "fired" at our missiles by an attacker; p = probability that one such shot kills an undefended missile; and p_D = probability that one shot kills a defended missile.

Consider first the case of an attack upon an undefended missile force. If there are A attacking shots against M targets, then there are A/M shots per target. In order to simplify the arithmetic in this presentation, we assume that the number A/M is an integer. The probability that the missile survives all A/M shots is $(1 - p)^{A/M}$, and the expected number of missiles that survive the attack is then $M(1 - p)^{A/M}$.

The numerical value obtained from this model depends on still other models. For example, consider the probability, p, that a "shot" kills an undefended target. In this case, its value must be calculated by making assumptions about the character of the target, about accuracy, and about the attacking weapon.

Now for the defended force. Since we know the total budget, Ms_M, and the cost of a missile plus its defense, $s_M + s_D$, the number of defended missiles we can purchase for the given budget is $Ms_M/(s_M + s_D)$.

In a defended case, we assume the same number of attackers, A, but with a reduced kill probability, p_D, due to the defense. The number of attackers or shots per defended missile is then

$$A \div \frac{Ms_M}{s_M + s_D} = \frac{A(s_M + s_D)}{Ms_M}.$$

Again we made the simplifying assumption (for this example, but not for the original analysis) that the number of attackers per missile is an integer. Then, as before, given the p_D is the probability that a defended missile is destroyed by one attacker, the probability that the missile survives all attackers is

$$(1 - p_D)^{A(s_M + s_D)/Ms_M}.$$

Hence, the expected number of defended missiles to survive the full attack is the above probability multiplied by the number of such missiles.

Now, recall the criterion: We decided to recommend buying defense for the missile force if this leads to a greater number of missiles surviving. Comparing expected values, we would buy a defense system provided:

$$\frac{Ms_M}{s_M + s_D}(1 - p_D)^{A(s_M+s_D)/Ms_M} > M(1 - p)^{A/M}.$$

Given several choices, we would buy that defense for which the left hand side turned out to be the greatest. For certain reasons it may also be necessary to examine the entire probability distribution of the number of surviving missiles; however, this will not be considered in this example.

It must be obvious to you that we have omitted a number of important factors from the analysis. We have not considered the possibility of buying defense for only part of the force. We have not considered ways to decrease the cost of defense—say, by grouping together or hiding our missiles. Of course, we wouldn't want to hide too well (for if the enemy didn't know we had our offensive missiles, we would not have deterrence), or to group them too closely so that one attacker could destroy more than one missile. We have not considered other policies for the attacker—using reconnaissance between shots to avoid hitting already destroyed missiles, or saturation, or attacking the defenses themselves first, for example.

These factors could all be taken into account by more complex models and more costly analysis. You could think of others. Warnings, decoys, electronic countermeasures.

(8) See that the major uncertainties are thoroughly explored. We want to know whether or not the important differences stem from unresolvable uncertainties about the future state of the world or from matters of engineering. For example, we have not said anything about the risk and possible time delays in development. We also want to perform sensitivity analyses, in order to find out how our lack of certainty about the values of various parameters affect the results. For example, we might want to study the dependence of the kill probability on the attacker's accuracy and on the hardness of the sites. This would require investigating another, more specialized model. In general, we want to vary key parameters both one by one and in sets, say, using some Monte Carlo technique across a range of values.

(9) Consider the factors thus far not taken into account. There are considerations in the problem, that is, idealizations, or omissions from the model, that cannot be treated easily in any mathematical way. For example, such intangibles as the values, military and political, that may come just from owning a larger missile force apart from survival in the attacks considered, or from having a defense even though inefficient, for it may boost civilian morale, or how the possession of a defensive system may affect arms limitations talk.

(10) Decide what, if anything, we can recommend on the basis of the analysis.

In recommending an action on the basis of his analysis, an analyst is likely to be on shaky ground, for invariably the decisionmaker's choice hinges on far more factors than can be included in the comparisons. He must consider, for example, the distribution of benefits and costs among the interest groups affected by the action, as well as their net totals. Setting up a new defensive system would or might require taking land from a particular group; others in the neighborhood might be concerned for fear of becoming a target; these people may have to be compensated not only for their out-of-pocket expenses but also for their intangible losses due to disruption of their lives. Since this may not be easy, the political viability of the action made may be endangered.

2. NONCOMBAT OPERATIONS

The military are faced with many problems of operation and management almost identical to similar problems found in business and industry. Examples are the use of maintenance and replacement theory in the provisioning of spares, queuing and stock theories in the determination of the optimum size of repair pools, linear programming in the study of vehicle and aircraft loading, and critical path analysis in the development and production of new weapons and equipment. The military, in fact, took the leadership in applying OR to many of the common functional processes found in both military and nonmilitary affairs.

One aspect that is different in considering noncombatant housekeeping operations of the military is the need for taking into account the possibility that the situation may change suddenly into one of conflict, varying from the need to participate in a "show-of-force" to major war. There is no parallel for a similar expansion of activities in nonmilitary affairs. The extent to which this possibility affects the analysis depends, of course, on the activity being analyzed. It is likely to be of overriding importance in determining the characteristics and number of planes for the Military Airlift Command, but of minor concern in working out efficient scheduling for the transportation of the dependents and household effects of servicemen stationed abroad.

2.1 Logistics

In the military services, logistics means planning and carrying out the design, acquisition, storage, movement, and maintenance of materiel; the construction and operation of facilities, and the provision of services. It has thus been a fertile area for the development and application of OR techniques, and has facilitated the design of integrated logistics systems. The latter coordinate several aspects of logistics, such as supply, transportation, spares, maintenance, and data control, so that equipment readiness is high and support costs low (Axtell [1969] and Blanchard [1967]). Other approaches to weapon support planning have been considered by Field [1961] and Browne [1959].

Military applications of forecasting and inventory control have been very cost effective. Of special note are studies on decision rules to determine whether to retain or dispose of stock in excess of normal stock quantities by Kaplan [1969]. Policies for stocking *insurance items*—items which rarely if ever need replacement but require a few spares because of their critical nature and long leadtime for reorder—are treated in Deemer [1969]. A statistical treatment of inventory analysis is given in Campbell [1967]. Inventory control models used in the U.S. Navy are discussed in Schrady [1971]. Kamins and McCall [1961] have mathematically arrived at rules for replacement of aircraft and missile parts.

The decision whether to repair an item of equipment is ordinarily based on economic criteria, that is, on such factors as repair, replacement, and support costs, salvage value, life expectancy, obsolescence, time to repair, and so on. A complete decision logic repair network for repair/discard decisions has been developed, using repair expenditure limits based on economic rationality (Logistic Management Institute [1968]). See also Bell and Kamins [1963] and Feeney, et al. [1963].

Simulations, both manual and computer, have been widely used to study military logistics problems. An outstanding example is SAMSOM, an acronym for Support-Availability Multi-System Operations Model. It is a computer simulation model designed to study the influence of resource and policy changes on aircraft capabilities—that is, the interactions between logistics and operations. It considers aircraft characteristics of reliability and maintainability by subsystem, operational and logistics policies and schedules, and the manpower and aerospace ground equipment needs for the support of such policies and schedules. See Bell [1968], Bell and Smith [1962], and Smith, [1964]. Simulation was also used to develop and evaluate alternative policies for logistic support of the intercontinental ballistic missile system, based on new operational policies.

Applications have also been made to manpower problems. An early example concerns the utilization of blacks in the U.S. Army (Hausrath [1954]; a later example is Canby [1972]).

2.2 Airlift and Sealift

An early application of transportation theory was the scheduling of a military tanker fleet (Flood [1954]). In examining the design requirements for counterinsurgency and tactical aircraft, the availability of airfields is important. The influence of airfield availability on airplane requirements was studied by Kamrass and Navarro [1967].

Analytic work on the Berlin airlift involved linear programming. Manne [1956] provides an example where an initially simple analysis became more complex and realistic as the problem began to be understood. The analysis evolved from the first linear program to a dynamic model, and ended as a combination dynamic model and simulation. Summerfield [1961] describes a Monte Carlo model used to investigate military airlift, including the transition from peace to war. The characteristics of items preferred for air cargo are considered in Glazer, et al. [1961].

3. COMBAT OPERATIONS

The initial purpose of OR was to investigate the operational performance of new equipment or weapons, with a view to suggesting improvements either in the instrument or in the way it was to be used. Good descriptions of World War II methods are found in Blackett [1948], in the Summary Technical Report of the National Defense Research Committee [1946], and in Morse and Kimball [1951].

OR, carried out by military staff units, still has chiefly the above functions. In tactical areas, OR work on weapon or equipment performance can often be tested against field data from experiments and planned field exercises, such as mock air battles, and sometimes against actual combat operations. Proven techniques have sometimes emerged. In fact, no other area of application has been a more fertile place for the invention and development of OR techniques. Almost every aspect of combat operations has been the subject of analyses; too many for us to do more than briefly mention a few of the more active.

Problems in this section are often complicated and may require sophisticated and complex techniques. Following Shubik and Brewer [1972], four approaches to their solution can be distinguished: analytic (mathematical) models, machine simulations, man-machine games, and manual games. Since the applications are varied and difficult to classify, the discussion is divided into sections according to the principal technique used.

3.1 Analytic Models

An analytic model tends to be abstract, to treat very few variables, and to force quite drastic simplifications on the problem. Hence, they are usually too restricted to solve an actual operational problem directly. But they often provide valuable insight, as many game theory models do.

Applications of mathematical modeling to bombing, anti-aircraft, artillery, and missile firing problems abound. Various studies take into account two or more factors that influence a choice of tactics, such as the geometry of the target, aim point, number of bombs or rounds, firing pattern, aiming errors, damage function, vulnerability of the target, and so on. Much World War II OR dealt with this sort of problem; see Germond and Hastings [1944], Brothers [1954], Kolmogorov [1948], and Langner [1944].

With the advent of nuclear weapons, rockets, and ballistic missiles, the parameters of interest for today's problems changed. Calculations for the same types of application are still being carried out. In some cases they duplicate earlier work. Soviet work is discussed in a translation of Kirillov [1960]; Echler and Burr [1972] provide a summary of this topic, plus that of missile allocation.

Many military problems are concerned with the allocation of forces in space and/or in time to combat. Others are concerned with duels (for example, between tank and tank or aircraft and aircraft or tank and aircraft—see Dresher [1961]), or with pursuit and search (aircraft looking for a submarine, for instance—see Isaacs [1965]). The theory of games has been applied to many such problems, leading, at a minimum, to an increase in understanding and sometimes, to rules for practical use.

Certain aspects of warfare have been represented by game-theoretic mathematical models in which two-sided (even sometimes more than two-sided) combat is considered explicitly, using zero-sum theory. However, combat situations more complex than simple tactical encounters are frequently not well represented by "zero-sum games" because they may, as in nuclear warfare, not be situations of pure opposition. Furthermore, elements omitted from the analysis in the interests of tractability—"human factors," for example—may be crucial to understanding what is going on. Useful applications have been made, nevertheless, to military doctrine (Haywood [1954]), to tactical air war (Fulkerson and Johnson [1957] and Berkovitz and Dresher [1959]), and to fighter versus bomber combat (Caywood and Thomas [1955]), for instance.

On the whole, the military applications of game theory have been of more benefit to the way one thinks about conflict situations than they have to practical use. Clayton Thomas [1964] of Operations Analysis Office USAF, put it this way:

> Applications of game theory have been neither nonexistent on the one hand, nor yet very dangerous to sound defense planning on the other hand. The theory has been most useful at a 'tactical' level, well below that of "grand strategy."

Certain principles—for example, that of "no soft-spot" (Dresher [1961]), which holds that each defended target should restrict the attacker to the same payoff—has had considerable application in the allocation of defenses.

3.2 Machine Simulation

Machine simulation of military problems, in contrast to mathematical modeling, tends to involve many more variables and to make almost a fetish of "realism." Large-scale computer simulations have been rather easy to "sell," and hence, there are literally hundreds of such simulations in the Department of Defense's current inventory. The large-scale simulations are very costly. In their survey of models, simulations, and games (MSGs), Shubik and Brewer [1972] conclude:

> There is every indication that the larger MSGs have been of little utility. The size, length of time under development, and generality of an MSG all appear to be directly related to the difficulty of controlling, validating, and using it. Undesirable outcomes resulting from changes in personnel, bad documentation, poor conceptualization, and poor professional communication and review are only exaggerated with large MSGs.

Large-scale digital simulations of strategic bombing operations are common. An early example was the Strategic Operations Model, developed at Rand as a strategic planning aid (Dalkey and Wegner [1958]). It was an attempt to simulate, using a high-speed computer, most of the major elements in a strategic air war. It followed through, in time, the detailed areas of base operations, dispatching planes and flying them along their routes, refueling, attacks by fighters and local defenses, bomb damage to the offensive installations, and restriction of the operations by fallout—all within the concrete limitations of geography, forces in being, aircraft characteristics, defense effectiveness, base capacities, and weapon effects.

This model, and similar simulations, deal with war in a straightforward fashion —about the way anyone might think through the course of a two-sided conflict if he could keep track of all the details. They start with a list of initial conditions for each side, namely, aircraft (bombers, tankers, transports), bomber bases, defense installations (radar sites, local defense sites, and fighter bases), including the status of all these. In addition, there must be a set of plans for each side. These plans are much more than mere control schedules of takeoffs and check points. They must take into account contingencies that arise during the course of the war, and allow for alternative actions.

The Forward Air Strike Evaluation Model (FAST-VAL) (Lind [1965]) measures the influence of close air support, mortars, and small arms on the outcome of a fire fight involving infantry engagements of regimental size or smaller. The model has been developed in considerable detail, and follows the situation being modeled in a reasonably straightforward manner (Spring and Miller [1970]).

A somewhat different type of study considers complex interactions among military, technical, geopolitical, and socioeconomic factors, which constitute major problems for counterinfiltration programs intended to inhibit the movement of hostile forces across defined boundaries. A report by Schilling and Turner [1971] describes two versions of an on-line computer program that incorporates the methodology of a model of border control developed in (Schilling [1970]). It enables the user to analyze insurgency situations without mathematical manipulations. The computerized versions of the model permit the ready investigation of specific situations and the rapid testing of new concepts with regard to their probable utility under different contingencies. It also permits testing of quantitative sensitivity analyses of candidate border security systems and programs. Outputs include a detailed account and projected time sequence of the number of guerrillas in the area of interest as a result of infiltration, interdiction, recruitment, and attrition. For any future date, these numerical data are given in terms of actual numbers, area densities, and rates of change.

3.3 War Gaming

War Gaming, or operational gaming, as it is usually called outside of the military, is highly intertwined with both game theory and simulation, and is often applied to the use of any analytic model or simulation to investigate conflict, a use tending to encompass all military OR. (Gaming is discussed in the chapter III-5 on Game Theory and Gaming, in the companion volume, Handbook of Operations Research: Foundations and Fundamentals.)

In this type of game, computers may be used to assist the players, but often only in a simple bookkeeping role. OR has converted the classical military three-room war game (Young [1959]), originally used largely for tactical training and the exploration of projected campaigns (Hoffman, et al. [1952]), into a modern research tool. A good description of the development of war gaming is given in Thomas [1961], and of the methods in McHugh [1966] and Weiner [1959].

A good example of free-form games are those in the SIERRA series of war games, described by Paxson [1963] and Weiner [1959]. The research objectives were to uncover possible deficiencies in military capabilities, in doctrine, and in weapons systems for the prosecution of limited wars and to suggest feasible improvements. These were "free" games, replete with planning factors. However, the events were generally adjudicated by umpires rather than by completely prescribed rules. Games of this type have been used to compare different weapons, to examine force requirements, and to compare programs for military assistance (Wolf [1962]). Such games may be simple and informal; for example, Morse's [1953] solution of an antisubmarine air search problem; or highly aggregated with extensive computer support, for example, Bruner and Flournoy's [1970] technique for evaluating the structure of U.S. Army forces.

Games may also take the form of extensive exercises involving troops and equipment, for example, Sagebrush. Such games provide valuable lessons; the summary for Sagebrush contained no fewer than 78 recommendations, a number of which were implemented at Department of Defense and Department of Air Force Levels (Deems [1956]). The Combat Development Center at Fort Ord, California, has conducted what are, in essence, Monte Carlo war games played with actual troops and equipment.

Man-machine games involve both a digital or an analogue computer and people playing roles in the situation being modeled. The people are there because human factors—judgment and intuition—are important and difficult to model, but sometimes because they are simply cheaper than software.

Early examples of man-machine simulation were the air-defense experiments carried out at Rand's Systems Research Laboratory between 1952 and 1954 (Chapman, et al. [1959], Kennedy and Chapman [1955]). As a consequence of these experiments, the Systems Development Corporation has founded and undertaken much of the training of personnel for U.S. air defense.

The Tactical Air Ground Study (TAGS) is an early example of a man-machine game played on a general analogue computer (Siska et al. [1954] and Brom [1955]). This game emphasized the allocation problems of tactical air commanders in a major theater who must assign daily, in some proportion, their residual stocks of combat-ready fighters, fighter bombers, and bombers to counter-air (against airfields), interdiction, and close support of ground forces. Subsequently, Berkowitz and Dresher [1959] were able to formulate analytically, and solve by game theory, a very slightly simplified version of TAGS.

Man-machine gaming exercises are currently little used in the military, except for teaching or training in staff colleges (Shubik and Brewer [1972] pp. 60–66).

3.4 Judgmental Methods

The first use of Delphi in a military context (Dalkey and Helmer [1963]) involved a 1951 use of experts to estimate bombing requirements against industrial targets. Recently, Delphi methods have been widely used by the military, largely for technological forecasting (Martino [1972]).

The ever-present, hard-to-quantify, political aspects of a complex decision sequence are addressed explicitly by the contextual study approach (Ellis and Greene [1960]). The method, used in conjunction with war gaming, is designed as a means for accounting for the dynamic interaction of political variables with physical variables.

4. FORCE POSTURE

"All military problems are, in one of their aspects economic problems in the efficient allocation of resources" (Hitch and McKean [1960]).

Unless the time available is too short, there is, typically, an infinity of ways to carry out a military mission—different strategies, tactics, forces, and weapons and, in addition, different ways to develop, procure, and maintain forces and weapons. OR can be and is used to help in the choices that must be made. For resource allocation at an early stage, however, the traditional formulation of problems in terms of ends and means must be expanded—ends and means interact.

By that interaction is meant that what are objectives from one point of view are means from another; that what is worth trying to do depends on what is possible to do, or on how effective the means for doing it are; and that any given objective is likely to be one of a number of alternative ways of achieving a still broader objective (Enthoven [1962]).

OR applied to the determination of force posture—that is, to the selection of future weapons systems and to the management of the process for developing and acquiring these weapons—is usually called systems analysis. The problems are varied and complex; for examples and their difficulties, see Quade [1964], Tucker [1966], Enke [1967], Quade and Boucher [1968], and Enthoven and Smith [1971].

The use of OR at the national policy level has been much criticized, particularly with respect to two important tools of defense management—cost-effectiveness and the Planning-Programming-Budgeting System (PPBS).

4.1 Cost-Effectiveness

The term "cost-effectiveness" refers to military-economic studies, which compare alternative ways of accomplishing national security objectives by trying to determine the way that contributes the most for a given cost or achieves a given objective for the least cost.

High costs have spawned many applications of OR to the tradeoffs between quantity and performance of military hardware. These are sometimes simple expositions. For example, Bergey [1972] points out that since the F-14 costs five times as much as the F-4, eight times as much as the F-8, and ten times as much as the A-4M, according to the Lanchester Square Law, it would have to be 25, 64, and 100 times as effective, respectively, as these other aircraft, in order to justify the smaller procurement quantities available with a fixed budget.

To illustrate cost-effectiveness analysis, assume there is a requirement for an expanded world-wide secure and reliable military communications system. While other alternatives are possible, suppose the following are under consideration:

A. An improved wideband and HF system, using conventional media such as cables, land lines, commercial satellites, etc.
B. A synchronous satellite system, dedicated to military uses, consisting of a number of satellites in an equatorial orbit with their associated ground terminals, adequate for world-wide coverage.

The analysis might proceed by determining the extent of these alternatives, so that they had almost equivalent effectiveness as measured by traffic capacity, or by traffic capacity and some combination of other factors such as relative invulnerability under hypothesized combat conditions, redundancy, and availability. The "total" systems costs (Fisher [1971]) for these alternatives could then be determined. (Since the costs for various aspects of the alternative systems would occur at different times, the costs would have to be discounted to the same date.)

Unfortunately, certain of the cost elements or parameters are likely to cause great uncertainty in the total costs; for example, the discount rate, because the systems might have investment and operating costs in widely differing proportions; or the overall mean-time-to-failure (MTBF) of the satellite system, or the probability, P, of successful launch of the boosters, including initial and replenishment launchers.

Suppose MTBF and P are the significant uncertainties. A range of values would then be considered. For example, a comparison might be constructed as in Figure 1 below.

For a given probability of a successful launch, P, if the MTBF exceeds the value determined by the intersection of the curve and the cost line for A, then B is superior. This data can be cross-plotted with P vs. MTBF, to determine the regions in which either A or B is preferred.

Since these graphs are based on specific values of many parameters other than MTBF and P, further analysis would be needed to assess the sensitivity of the results to uncertainties in these other parameters; for example, to costing (Fisher [1971]), especially if the analysis were done at an early stage before the systems were fully developed.

Sensitivity testing is often done by considering variations in one variable at a time. If there are many uncertainties, Monte Carlo sampling is likely to be a more efficient method.

The determination of the dollar and other costs of future systems is an important aspect of cost-effectiveness analysis. Although military cost and resource analysis has been developed to a greater extent than elsewhere in the government, cost overruns have been a major source of dissatisfaction with military programs. The most thorough discussion of methods is found in Fisher [1971].

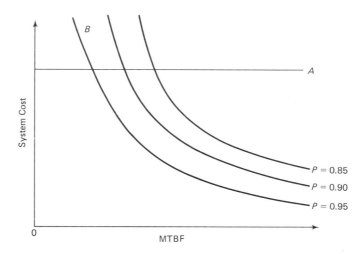

Fig. 1. Comparison of systems A and B for fixed effectiveness.

4.2 Management

Managerial decisions affecting a weapon system must be made throughout all phases of its life cycle, from conception and definition through acquisition, including development and production, to operation and final disposal. OR techniques have found many applications here. For the acquisition of individual weapons systems, these include the use of Gantt and milestone charts and the line of balance technique (LOB) to improve scheduling and status reporting and, for complex one-of-a-kind operations, the critical path method (CPM) or the program evaluation and review technique (PERT) (Holtz [1969]).

To realize the most effective allocation of resources available to the Department of Defense, PPBS was adopted as the key instrument for managing its manifold and far-flung activities (Tucker [1966], Novick [1965]).

The PPBS was designed to provide:

(1) A set of program options, presented in a form that emphasized the program goals; indicating for each alternative, over an extended time period, what the money spent would accomplish—say, strategic retaliation, continental defense, airlift and sealift—as opposed to how it would be spent—for manpower, construction, procurement.

(2) An analytic process to discover and design alternative programs, estimate their costs and effectiveness, rank them, and supply arguments pro and con.

(3) A data and management information system to tell the policymakers how their programs were getting along and to provide a means of control.

The characteristics of PPB thus forced a dependence on analysis and did much to increase its use in the Defense Department and in the Services proper. Although the system has changed considerably and is still changing, largely due to criticism by Congress and the Services, the dependence on analysis remains.

4.3 Criticism of OR

The report of the Subcommittee on National Security [1970] (p. 11) offers an example:

"The PPB approach was used to justify the purchase of a $277 million oil-fueled aircraft carrier that was obsolete before it was launched. Also, a perversion of cost-effectiveness was used, after the fact, in the largest single military aircraft contract in history, to rationalize the choice of an airplane whose costs are soaring, if not its performance. . . ."

Consider the attempt by the Navy to have the CVA-67 constructed as a nuclear carrier. In reply to the Navy's request, Secretary McNamara spelled out in detail the kinds of analysis he regarded as necessary. Studies were done, but the Secretary did not find them convincing, and he made a further request for additional information. The second set of studies again did not convince Secretary McNamara (nor did the others that followed) that the increased performance resulting from nuclear propulsion was worth the cost (Whitehead [1967]).

5. DEFENSE POLICY

OR is applied to politico-military decisions at the highest policy levels—as witness the 1969 hearings of the Senate Subcommittee on National Security [1970] (pp. 659–683) on ballistic missile defense and the later involvement of the Operations Research Society of America [1971]. Decisions to base the deterrent force at sea rather than on land, to increase or decrease the defense budget, or to enter some specific arms control arrangement are all problems where OR has assisted. These are not simply optimization problems but choice-of-objectives problems with opponents who may sometimes be intelligent, sometime obtuse. They are also full of political, economic, behavioral, and technical uncertainties. The calculations most helpful with the related decisions are generally—not always, of course—of a sort that require no sophisticated mathematics and can be understood by those without training in OR. Disagreement with the analysis comes mainly at the level of the assumptions as to what aspects are important and how conservative or optimistic the calculations ought to be. As a consequence, very broad systems studies and war-gaming (computer-assisted but *not* left to an overall computer problem) are likely to be the useful techniques, for they can explore the sensitivity of the possible decisions to the full range of uncertainties, including the political and behavioral.

5.1 Systems Analysis

A study that had significant impact on U.S. strategy policy is the analysis of the selection and use of strategic air bases by Wohlstetter, et al. [1954]. The summary report, originally Top Secret, has been declassified.

The study examined the critical factors in strategic-base selection, and then analyzed the basing of the 1956–1961 bombing force. It took into account the effect of a base decision on the total cost of the entire strategic force—how, for example, it affected the costs of extending the range of bombers that cannot reach the target unrefueled, the routes they must fly through enemy territory, the consequent losses they may suffer from the defenses en route, and the difficulties the bases may have in recuperation from attack. Political considerations affecting overseas bases and domestic constraints were also considered.

Although the final calculations involved no sophisticated mathematical models, many of the supporting papers did. The calculations to determine bomber attrition, bomb damage, the selection of routes and refueling points, mission profiles, penetration paths, vulnerability of ground installations, electronic countermeasures and decoys, and so forth, ranged from simple map exercises to elaborate optimizations.

The Air Force estimated (*Life* [1959]) that this analysis saved the U.S. over a billion dollars in base construction costs alone; but more importantly, it changed defense policy. This was the first study to raise as a major issue the vulnerability of SAC, then the world's most powerful force, indicating that it might be rendered completely ineffective by an enemy attack. As a result, the necessary fixes were adopted to protect SAC against the joint threat of aircraft and ballistic missiles, and the role of active air defense was reevaluated. Originally commissioned as a logistics exercise to locate overseas bases, it became a study of U.S. strategic deterrent policy. Further discussion is found in Smith [1966].

5.2 Political-Military Exercises

Simulation and gaming have been applied to defense policy problems. A good description of the history and methods of political gaming in the national security context is found in Goldhamer and Speier [1959]. SAFE (Strategy and Force Evaluation), a manual game, examined alternatives in procurement strategies, research and development planning, strategic intelligence, force composition, and operational strategies (to test the preceding planning) for a possible strategic air war (Helmer and Beckner [1961]). In an instruction version, it has been used as part of the curriculum for the first class of the U.S. Air Force Academy.

Politico-military exercises at the JCS level, based essentially on manual or free gaming (although with some computer assistance), were mentioned earlier. Immensely more sophisticated forms are available, however, making extensive use of on-line time-shared (OLTS) computing. An example is XRAY (Paxson [1972] pp. 78–81). Each exercise uses four teams: Blue, Red, Yellow, and Green. The first three simulate the core position at the highest decision-making level in their respective governments. Green serves as staff for the other three, preparing special studies on request; plays the bureaucratic and public surrounds of the decision cores; and represents all nations allied to Red, Blue, and Yellow, as well as the uncommitted and neutral nations.

An exercise has two major phases. The teams first plan a total strategic posture for the next twelve years, staying under a year-by-year budget ceiling which rises in proportion to gross national product, and choosing weapon systems from a rich menu of existing and proposed systems. After intelligence information and an initial scenario, the teams are allowed to update their postures. The next phase then starts, with the teams exchanging political and military blows of any intensity, constrained only by Green in its roles of staff, domestic sector, and international actor. Coercive bargaining, offers to negotiate, delivery of ultimata can share the play with military events.

The employment of OLTS computing is vital to the exercise. The philosophy is to have previously constructed and stored independent modules (programs) for posture-planning, missile-defense managements, aircraft deployments, bomber stream penetrations, fallout from surface bursts, and the like. The modules are called up when required, the desired parameter values inserted, and the results obtained almost instantaneously.

The posture planning model (Fisher [1971] p. 286ff) is important and possibly the most dramatic of these modules. The program has, in memory, cost descriptions of programmed and feasible future weapon systems. These include the time schedules for research and development costs, the overlapping production lead time monies, production and annual operating costs. The posture planner can select dates to phase-in new systems or phase-out old ones. Phase-in rates and final force levels can be prescribed. The program allows for production learning—lower average cost per unit the more purchased—and readjusts prices if a major component like an airplane is common to two or more systems. A total posture may involve 30 or more weapon systems.

6. LITERATURE

Since most military applications of OR are originally classified, examples of actual work found in the open literature tend to be out of date or to deal with peacetime operations, such as logistics or systems management. For the latter, the *Naval Research Logistics Quarterly* is a rich source. Another is *Operations Research*. Articles on other topics that have been rewritten to reduce their classification also appear there, and, with much less frequency, in the OR publications of foreign countries.

Other sources are the publications of contractors in the defense industry and of research centers such as the Institute for Defense Analysis. Of the latter, the publications of the Rand Corporation of Santa Monica, California (indexed in the quarterly Selected Rand Abstracts and deposited in many libraries) are the most extensive and easily available. The Research Institute of National Defense, 10450 Stockholm 80, Sweden, also issues a series, FOA Reports.

For classified material, the Defense Documentation Center serves government agencies and nongovernment organizations that have contracts with the U.S. Department of Defense. For those with proper clearances, instructions and forms necessary for establishing service may be obtained from the Defense Documentation Center, Cameron Station, Alexandria, Virginia 22314. Classified papers also are presented twice a year at symposia sponsored by the Military Operations Research Society, 101 South Whiting Street, Alexandria, Virginia 22304, and later published in its *Proceedings*.

While classified material eventually reaches the open literature, the delay contributes to a tendency for analysts to redo analysis that has been done before.

Whitmore [1961] offers an example:

> An illustration may be drawn from the history of air interdiction of transportation. It is generally conceded that the tactical air bombing of the rail transportation net in Normandy made a signal contribution to the success of the invasion of Europe. A detailed account is to be found in (Craven and Cate [1951]). It covers in particular the much-debated question of which method of attack was more lucrative—the attrition campaign by heavy bombers against rail centers and marshalling yards, or the precision attack by fighter/bombers against open rail lines and bridges. As Craven and Cate notice, this remained an open question at the end of the campaign. Finally, an AAF evaluation board report based largely on French railway records concluded after a laborious examination of evidence and balancing of factors: "The pre–D-day attacks against French rail centers were not necessary, and the 70,000 tons involved could have been devoted to alternative targets," (Craven and Cate [1951] p. 161). As a contributor to the report referenced, I am pleased that the interdiction attacks were inferentially preferred by the rejection of the rail-center attacks.
> Whatever the internal debates about targeting modes, it should have been clear that transportation attacks were effective in isolating a battlefield; that tactical aircraft were excellent instruments for bombing rail and road nets; and that unified planning of such attacks was essential to ensure complete isolation. Nevertheless, a study with which I was involved in the spring of 1951 found that the interdiction effort in Korea was splintered among several commands, that the transportation center argument was still raging, and that the rail-link analysis developed in Normandy was not being applied. A more unified attack was planned a year later, but failed of enemy strangulation for a number of reasons, though the officer in charge was able to point to a significant drop in the number of enemy rounds of artillery delivered. By 1955, I was still engaged in debating the value of interdiction attacks with members of a team studying limited war, most of whom were ignorant of the statistical evidence from the Normandy campaign.

Texts devoted to military OR are Zehna [1971] and Army [1968]. There is a corresponding Russian text by Chuev [1970]. Five excellent, but hypothetical, case studies of military systems analysis are to be found in Snyder [1967]. Bibliographical material on the military applications of OR is to be found in Malik [1969] and Shubik, et al. [1972].

OR has had extensive applications to military affairs and the applications can but increase in number. Military operations are likely to become even more expensive and prone to catastrophe than they are today. As a consequence, OR calculations, imperfect as they are, will more and more appear as desirable precursors to such operations.

REFERENCES

Averch, H. and M. M. Lavin, *Simulation of Decisionmaking in Crisis: Three Manual Gaming Experiments*, The Rand Corporation, Santa Monica, California, RM-4202 PR (August 1964).

Axtell, George C., "Designing an Integrated Logistics System," *Defense Ind. Bull.* 5, No. 7: 30–33, 44 (July 1969).

Ayres, Col. Leonard P., "The Uses of Statistics in War," AIC 196 (3/15/40), The Army Industrial College, Washington, D.C. (March 4, 1940).

Bell, C. F., "SAMSON: A Logistics Simulation," in E. S. Quade and W. I. Boucher (eds.), *Systems Analysis and Policy Planning: Applications on Defense*, American Elsevier, New York (1968).

Bell, Chauncey F. and Milton Kamins, *Determining Economic Quantities of Maintenance Resources: A Minuteman Application*, The Rand Corporation, RM-3308-PR (AD 407200), (January 1963).

—— and T. C. Smith, *The Oxnard Base Maintenance Management Improvement Program*, The Rand Corporation, RM-3370-PR (AD 292909), (November 1962).

Bergey, Karl H., letter, *Aviation Week*, p. 122 (April 24, 1972).

Berkovitz, L. D. and M. Dresher, "A Game Theory Analysis of Tactical Air War," *Operations Res.* 7, pp. 499–620 (September–October 1959).

Blackett, P. M. S., "Operations Research," *Adv. Sci.* 5, No. 17 (1948).

Blanchard, Ben S., "Cost Effectiveness, Systems Effectiveness, Integrated Logistic Support, and Maintainability," *IEEE Trans. Aerospace and Electronic Syst.* AES-3, pp. 186–194 (March 1967).

Brodie, Bernard, *Strategy in the Missile Age*, Princeton University Press, Princeton, New Jersey (1959).

Brom, J. R., *Narrative Description of an Analytic Theater Air Ground Warfare System*, The Rand Corporation, RM-1428-PR, (February 1955).

Brothers, Leroy A., "Operations Analysis in the United States Air Force," *J. of ORSA* 2, No. 1 (February 1954).

Browne, S. H., *Missile and Spacecraft Support Systems*, Lockheed Aircraft Company, LMSD-285107, Sunnyvale, California (December 1959).

Bruner, J. A. and W. N. Flournoy, *A Technique for Evaluating the Structure of U.S. Army Forces in an Area Domination Role*, RAC-TP-412, Research Analysis Corporation, McLean, Virginia (December 1970).

Burke, T. F., *Cost-Effectiveness of AICBM for the Defense of ICBM Sites*, RM-3515-ARPA, Parts I-V, The Rand Corporation (1963–1964). Official Use Only.

Campbell, Harrison S., "Procurement and Management of Spares," in Enke (1967).

Canby, Steven L., *Military Manpower Procurement: A Policy Analysis*, Heath & Company, Lexington, Massachusetts: Washington D.C. (1972).

Caywood, T. E. and C. J. Thomas, "Applications of Game Theory in Fighter Versus Bomber Combat," *J. of ORSA* 3, pp. 402–411 (1955).

Chapman, R. L., J. L. Kennedy, A. Newell, and W. C. Biel, "The Systems Research Laboratory's Air-Defense Experiments," Management Sci. (April 1959).

Chuev, Yu. V., "Issledovanie operatsij v voennom dele," (Operations Research in the Military), *Voenizdat*, Moscow (1970).

Craven, W. F. and J. L. Cate (ed.), "The Army Air Forces in World War II," Vol. 3, "Europe –Argument to V. E. Day (Jan. 44 to May 45), " University of Chicago Press (1951).

Dalkey, N. C. and O. Helmer, "An Experimental Application of the Delphi Method to the Use of Experts," *Management Sci.* 9, No. 3: 458–467 (April 1963).

—— and L. H. Wegner, *The Strategic Operations Model: A Summary Report (U)*, The Rand Corporation, RM-2221, (DDC No. AD 304988), July 28, 1958 (Confidential).

Deemer, Robert L., *Insurance Items Stockage Policies*, U.S. Army Logistics Center, Fort Lee, Virginia, [AD-691732], (1969).

Deems, Co. Paul S., "War Gaming and Exercises," *Air Univ. Quart. Rev.* **9**, No. 1: 98-126 (Winter 1956-57).

Dresher, Melvin, *Games of Strategy: Theory and Applications*, Prentice-Hall, Englewood Cliffs, New Jersey (1961).

Echler, Ross A. and Stefan A. Burr, "Mathematical Modes of Target Coverage and Missile Allocation," *MORS*, Alexandria, Virginia (1972).

Ellis, J. W., Jr. and T. E. Greene, "The Contextual Study: A Structure to the Study of Political and Military Aspects of Limited War," *Operations Res.* **8**, pp. 639–651 (September–October 1960).

Enke, S., *Defense Management*, Prentice-Hall, New Jersey (1967).

Enthoven, A. C., "Operations Research at the National Policy Level," Address before Operations Evaluation Group, Vicennial Conference, Washington, D.C. (May 16, 1962). Also in Tucker [1966].

—— and K. W. Smith, *How Much is Enough: Shaping the Defense Program, 1961-1969*, Harper & Row, New York (1971).

Feeney, G. J., J. W. Petersen, and C. C. Sherbrooke, *An Aggregate Base Stockage Policy for Recoverable Space Parts*, RM-3644-PR, The Rand Corporation, [AD 408943], (May 1963).

Fawcett, C. D. and C. D. Jones, "Effectiveness Determination of Bombers Penetrating Through an Air-to-Air Defense," *Operations Res.* **18**, pp. 516-525 (May–June 1970).

Field, R. G., Jr., "A Basic Approach to Weapon Support Planning," MINUTEMAN Prog. Office, Space Technology Laboratories, Los Angeles, California (1961).

Fisher, G. H., *Cost Considerations in Systems Analysis*, American Elsevier, New York (1971).

Flood, Merrill M., "Applications of Transportation Theory to Scheduling a Military Tanker Fleet," *J. of ORSA* **2**, No. 2: 150-162 (May 1954).

Fulkerson, D. R. and S. M. Johnson, "A Tactical Air Game," *Operations Res.* **5**, No. 5: 705–712 (October 1957).

Gajalo, S., "NICP Forecasting Techniques," U.S. Army Logistics Management Center, Fort Lee, Virginia, [AD-822934], (1967).

Germond, H. H. and C. Hastings, Jr., "Scatter Bombing of a Circular Target," Applied Mathematics Panel Report, 10.2R (May 1944).

Glazer, H., J. H. Engel, and J. Steinhardt, "The Selection of Cargo Air Transport" in *Proceedings of the Second International Conference on Operations Research*, English Universities Press Ltd., London (1961).

Goldhamer, H. and H. Speier, "Some Observations on Political Gaming," *World Politics* **12**, pp. 71-83 (1959).

Hausrath, Alfred, H., "Utilization of Negro Manpower in the Army," *J. of ORSA* **2**, No. 1 (February 1954).

Haywood, O. G., Jr., "Military Decision and Game Theory," *J. of ORSA* **2**, No. 4 (November 1954).

Helmer, O. and R. E. Bickner, *How to Play SAFE: Book of Rules of the Strategy and Force Evaluation Game*, The Rand Corporation, RM-2865-PR (ASTIA No. AD 266900) (November 1961).

Hitch, C. J. and McKean, R. N., *The Economics of Defense in the Nuclear Age*, Harvard University Press, Cambridge (1960).

Hoffmann, Rudolf, List, Wilhelm, et al., *War Games* (trans. by P. Luetzkendorf), F. B. Robinson (ed.), MS. No. P-094, Department of the Army, Office of Military History, Washington, D.C. (1952).

Holtz, J. N., "An Analysis of Major Scheduling Techniques in the Defense Systems Environment" in D. I. Cleland and W. R. King (eds.), *Systems, Organizations, Analysis, Management*, McGraw-Hill, New York (1969).

Isaacs, Rufus, *Differential Games; A Mathematical Theory with Applications to Warfare and Pursuit, Control and Optimization*, John Wiley, New York (1965).

Kamins, M. and J. J. McCall, Jr., *Rules for the Replacement of Aircraft and Missile Parts*, The Rand Corporation, RM-3810-PR (1961).

Kamrass, Murray and Joseph A. Navarro, "An Analysis of Tactical Air Systems" in Cost-Effectiveness Analysis, T. A. Goldman (ed.), Frederick A. Praeger, New York, pp. 116–130 (1967).

Kaplan, Alan J., *Economic Retention Limits*, U.S. Army Logistics Center, Fort Lee, Virginia, [AD-691731], (1969).

Kennedy, L. J., and R. L. Chapman, "The Background and Implications of the Systems Research Laboratory Studies," The Rand Corporation, p. 740 (September, 1955).

Kirillov, V. I., *Bombometanie*, Moscow Translation, AD-287-703 and 63-13182 (1960).

Klein, Burton and William Meckling, "Application of Operations Research to Development Decisions," *Operations Res.* **6**, No. 3: 352–363 (May–June 1958) (also The Rand Corporation).

Kolmogorov, A. N. (ed.), *Collection of Articles on the Theory of Firing I*, Translation T-14, The Rand Corporation (October 1948).

Langner, Herbert, "Number of Rounds Required and Destruction Probability in the Form of Tables and Graphs," Institut fur Theoretische Ballistik in der Luftfahrtforschungsanstalt Herman Goring, (1944), Translation T-11, The Rand Corporation (April, 1948).

Life Magazine, p. 101 (May 11, 1959).

Lind, J. R., *FAST-VAL: A Model for Forward Air Strike Evaluation*, P-3076, The Rand Corporation (March 1965).

Logistics Management Institute, *Guidelines for Making Repair Expenditure Decisions*, (Task 68-6 Report), Washington, D.C. (1968).

Malik, H. J., *Bibliography on Military Applications of Operations Research*, Computation and Analysis Section, Defense Research Board, Ottawa, Canada (March, 1969).

Manne, A. S., *Allocating MATS Equipment with the Aid of Linear Programming*, RM-1612, The Rand Corporation (January 1956).

Martino, J. R., *Technological Forecasting for Decisionmaking*, American Elsevier, New York (1972).

Matlin, Samuel, "A Review of the Literature on the Missile Allocation Problem," *Operations Res.* **18**, No. 2: 334–373 (March–April 1970).

McHugh, F. J., *Fundamentals of War Gaming*, 3rd ed., U.S. Naval War College, Newport, R.I. (1966).

Mihram, G., "A Cost Effectiveness Study for Strategic Airlift," *Transport. Sci.* **4**, No. 1: 79–96 (February 1970).

Morse, P. M., "Trends in Operations Research," *J. of ORSA* **1**, No. 4: 159–165 (August 1953).

—— and Kimball, G. E., *Methods of Operations Research*, Massachusetts Institute of Technology, The Technology Press and John Wiley & Sons, New York (1951).

National Defense Research Committee, "Methods of Operations Research," Summary Technical Report of Division 6, Vol. 2A (1946).

Novick, David (ed.), *Program Budgeting: Program Analysis and the Federal Budget*, Harvard

University Press, Cambridge, Massachusetts (1965) Paperback, Holt, Rinehart and Winston (1969).

Operations Research Society of America, "Guidelines for the Practice of Operations Research," *Operations Res.* **19,** No. 5: 1149–1237 (September 1971).

Paxson, E. W., *War Gaming,* The Rand Corporation, RM-3489-PR (February 1963).

Paxson, E. W., "Computers and National Security," in *Computers and the Problems of Society,* American Federation of Information Processing Societies, New York, pp. 65–92 (1972).

Quade, E. S. (ed.), *Analysis for Military Decisions,*" North-Holland Publishing Co., Amsterdam (1964).

Quade, E. S. and W. I. Boucher (eds.), *Systems Analysis and Policy Planning: Applications in Defense,* American Elsevier Publishing Co., New York (1968).

Schilling, G. F., *Analytic Model for Border Control,* The Rand Corporation, RM-6250-ARPA (December 1970).

—— and M. Turner, "On-Line Computer Programs for the Analysis of Border Control Problems," The Rand Corporation, R-687-ARPA (Febuary 1971).

Schlesinger, James R., "Quantitative Analysis and National Security," *World Politics* **15,** No. 2 (January 1963).

Schrady, D. A., "Inventory Models" in Zehna (1971).

Shubik, Martin and Garry D. Brewer, *Models, Simulations, and Games—A Survey,* The Rand Corporation, R-1060-ARPA/RC (May 1972).

—— and E. Savage, *The Literature of Gaming, Simulation, and Model Building: Index and Critical Abstract,* The Rand Corporation, R-620-ARPA (June 1972).

Siska, C. P., L. A. Gramboni, and J. R. Lind, "Analytic Formulation of a Theater Air Ground Warfare System," The Rand Corporation, RM-1338 (September 1954).

Smith, Bruce L. R., *The Rand Corporation,* Harvard University Press, Cambridge, Massachusetts (1966).

Smith, T. C., *SAMSOM: Support-Availability Multi-System Operations Model,* The Rand Corporation, RM-4077-PR (AD 601813) (June 1964).

Snyder, William P., (Lt. Col., USA), *Case Studies in Military Systems Analysis,* Industrial College of the Armed Forces, Washington, D.C. (1967).

Specht, R. D., "The Nature of Models," in Quade and Boucher (1968).

Spring, S. G. and S. H. Miller, *FAST-VAL: Relationships Among Casualties, Suppression, and the Performance of Company-Size Units,* The Rand Corporation, RM-6268-PR (March 1970).

Stedry, A. C. and John Griswold, "The Development of Supply Control Procedures for the Defense General Supply Center," Proceedings, U.S. Army Operations Research Symposium, Part 1, Army Research Office, Durham (March 1962).

Strauch, R., *A Preliminary Treatment of Mobile SLBM Defense: Game Theoretic Analysis,* The Rand Corporation, RM-4439-ARPA (June 1965).

Subcommittee on National Security, U.S. Senate, *Planning, Programming, Budgeting,* Government Printing Office, Washington (1970).

Summerfield, John R., "A Model for Evaluating Fleets of Transport Aircraft" in Proceedings of the Second International Conference on Operations Research, English Universities Press Ltd., London (1961).

Thomas, Clayton J., "Military Gaming," in *Progress in Operations Research, Vol. 1,* Russell L. Ackoff (ed.), John Wiley, New York (1961).

——, "Some Past Applications of Game Theory in the United States Air Force," Paper presented at the NATO Conference on the Theory of Games and Its Military Applications, Toulon, France (June 29-July 3, 1964).

Tucker, S. A., *A Modern Design for Defense Decision: A McNamara-Hitch-Enthoven Anthology*, Industrial College of the Armed Forces, Washington, D.C. (1966).

U.S. Department of Army, "Mathematics of Military Action, Operations and Systems," DA PAM 70-5, Headquarters, Washington, D.C. (January 1968).

U.S. General Accounting Office, "Computer Simulations, War Gaming and Contract Studies," A Report to the Committee on Appropriations, House of Representatives, Washington, D.C., p. 8 (February 23, 1971).

War Department, *Report of the Board on Fortifications and Other Defenses* (H.E. 49-1, Vol. 28, Pt. 1), pp. 11–12 (January 23, 1886).

Weiner, M. G., *War Gaming Methdology*, The Rand Corporation, RM-2413 (July 1959).

Whitehead, Clay T., *The Uses and Limitations of Systems Analysis*, The Rand Corporation, P-3683 (September 1967).

Whitmore, William F., "Edison and Operations Research," *J. of ORSA* **1**, No. 2: 83–84 (February 1953).

———, "Symposium on Military Operations Research," *Operations Res.* **9**, No. 2: 258 (March–April 1961).

Wilson, N. A. B., *Manpower Research in a Defense Context*, American Elsevier, New York (1969).

Wohlstetter, A. J., "Strategy and the Natural Scientists," in Robert Gilpin and Christopher Wright (eds.), *Scientists and National Policymaking*, Columbia University Press, New York (1963).

Wohlstetter, A. J., F. S. Hoffman, R. J. Lutz, and H. S. Rowen, *Selection and Use of Strategic Air Bases*, The Rand Corporation, R-266 (April 1954).

Wolf, Charles, Jr., "Defense and Development in the Less Developed Countries," *Operations Res.* **10**, No. 6: 828–838 (November–December 1962).

Young, J. P., *A Survey of Historical Developments in War Games*, ORO-SP-98, Operations Research Office, The Johns Hopkins University, Bethesda, Maryland (March 1959).

Zehna, Peter W., (ed.), *Selected Methods and Models in Military Operations Research*, Office of Naval Research, Washington, D.C. (1971).

II-6

THE ELECTRIC UTILITIES

Leonard L. Garver
General Electric Co.

1. INTRODUCTION

Electricity is a means of moving energy from sources such as burning coal, oil or gas, falling water, or nuclear reactions, to demands for heat, light, or motion. Electrical energy cannot be stored, but must be generated and delivered as the demand arises. Its inventory is in the form of the generation and delivery capacity, which the electric utility industry is charged with owning and operating.

A comprehensive introduction to the electric utility industry is contained in the four-volume 1970 National Power Survey published by the Federal Power Commission between 1970 and 1972 (FPC [1970]). Industry profiles, growth, fuels, generation, transmission, polution, esthetics, reliability, coordination, financing, and R&D are all covered with many examples from individual utilities. Therefore, the following paragraphs will proceed directly to discussions of OR applications.

Two types of operations research (OR) activities have occurred in the utility industry. First came the team approach with operating personnel, engineers, mathematicians, and other disciplines tackling a problem and implementing the solution. Dispatching—recognizing losses—is one example (Section 3.2), and generation reserve planning using probability methods is another (Section 4.1). The second type of activity includes techniques specifically identified with OR. Short term forecasting, using exponential smoothing (Section 2.1), multi-system dispatching, using diakoptics and decomposition (Section 3.6), and transmission network planning, using linear programming (LP) (Section 5), are examples.

The following sections cover OR-related activities in forecasting, operating, and investment planning. Forecasting includes both peak rate of supply (power demand) and volume (energy demand) for both long-term investment decisions and short-term operating decisions. Operating applications include allocation of output (dispatching), unit startup selection (unit commitment), hydrothermal coordination, and maintenance scheduling. The investment planning applications cover the generation and transmission systems. Operations research activities in the electric utility industry are expanding at such a rapid rate that not all applications and proposals could be mentioned. The following material is offered as a base from which the reader can launch into his own study of the industry.

2. LOAD FORECASTING

Load forecasting in electric utilities involve three distinct features; the forecasted quantity, the time period and the method used.

A. Quantity forecasted:
  1. Megawatts[1] of peak power demand in a day, season, or year.
  2. Shape of the demands curve in a day, week, or year.
  3. Megawatt-hours of energy in a day, month, or year.
B. Time period:
  1. Short term—one hour to several weeks ahead.
  2. Long term—one season to many years into the future.
C. Forecasting methods used:
  1. Same as a similar day or sequence of days.
  2. Extrapolate a time series.
  3. Separate total into components.
  4. Correlate to other quantities such as weather, number of customers, or business indicators.
  5. Moving average.
  6. Exponential smoothing.

Both energy and demand forecasting go on continually in a utility. The financial departments forecast energy to estimate revenue, fuel expenses, etc., while the operating and planning departments forecast peak demand to schedule capacity changes. In the same utility separate departments often make separate forecasts with occasional rivalry, each attempting to better the forecast accuracy

---

[1] Electric energy is measured in watt-hours and the rate of use is measured in watts. Because one watt is such a small quantity the industry often refers to demands in millions of watts, a megawatt. For example the peak load of the Baltimore Gas and Electric Co. in 1973 was 3,334,000,000 watts or 3,334 MW and the energy delivered during the year was 15,395,121 MWhr.

of the others. This competitive atmosphere keeps each forecaster constantly looking for improved methods.

The goal of a forecast is to be within an acceptable margin such as 3%, and preferably to errors less than 2%. The measurement error for demand metered at the generators is in the order of 1% and thus, is a bound on the accuracy possible (Sandiford et al. [1956]).

2.1 Short Term Forecasting

What is the demand for electricity going to be at noon tomorrow? The experienced system operator will look at today's demand at noon, look at the demand a week ago and its relation to the day before, and look at a time when the same sequence of weather was forecast. By trending and weighting the data, taking into account special business activity, he forecasts the demand. See for example, the TVA discussion of short term forecasting in the 1970 National Power Survey (FPC Committee [1970]).

This forecasting system is hard to improve. Continual learning takes place as each forecast is checked a day later. A good data retrieval system is built up as an operator soon learns what to remember and what to ignore. And a natural weighting of data occurs as older or less important data are forgotten.

In one case, which illustrates the difficulty in computerizing short term forecasts, a computer program to forecast one day ahead was sold to a midwestern utility. To improve its accuracy and the chances for its acceptance, the system designer visited the dispatcher to learn the current forecasting method, planning to incorporate some of the procedure into his program. The dispatcher, who had years of experience in forecasting but none with computers, could not understand why he should describe the present system, when the computer was going to tell him what the demand was going to be. Later, when the completed system was installed, it was used for a few weeks and then run less and less as the dispatcher went back to his own methods. He was tired of keeping the program data bank up-to-date when the forecasts weren't any better than his own.

A more successful case is reported by Chen and Winters [1966], who review the manual methods used by a utility and then use a four component model to predict peak load one day in advance. Their model includes:

Peak Demand = Base + (Day of week effect)

+ (Temperature effect) + (Cloud cover effect)

The base and day-of-week effect values are updated by exponential smoothing, while the temperature and cloud effects are determined by regression analysis. Their results indicated that about 65% of the time the errors will be less than 3%. During this same time the company, using the current procedure, made forecasts with twice that variation.

The base-plus-components method illustrated by Chen and Winters has been independently developed and applied by many utilities, and represents a successful application of both regression analysis to determine load versus weather effects, and of exponential smoothing to adapt the base and day-of-week effect values for each new daily data point.

Christiaanse [1971] describes an application of general exponential smoothing using a Fourier series of nine frequencies to forecast the next 24 hours of loads on the American Electric Power System. It is not being used because it did not improve forecast accuracy.

Others to approach the short range 24-hour forecasting problem with impressive mathematical models and less than impressive acceptance have been Lijesen and Rosing [1971] and Gupta and Yamada [1972]. They both analyze base, weekly effect, and weather effect data, and determine the base by a seven-day moving average. Lijesen and Rosing then used the expected value or long term average over the season to determine the weekly effect and the two largest eigenvalues in the covariance matrix in modeling the weather. Gupta and Yamada use exponential smoothing to determine their weekly effect, and determine the weather effect by regression of load versus average temperature. The discussors' comments on both of these papers indicate the criteria for application; the models are judged to be too cumbersome (were 1344 numbers really necessary or could 60 have done just as well), too linear (5° of temperature change has a different affect at 70° than at 90°), and generally too hard to explain to potential users.

Thompson's discussion (Gupta and Yamada [1972]) is particularly enlightening, for he points out that data and model requirements do not always line up. The Pacific Gas and Electric territory encompasses four distinct weather areas and yet, load is monitored only as a single quantity, the total generation. The four components of load are not available, and to gather them at the major delivery points (substations) would require extensive telemetering. Utilities with compact service areas, such as the Baltimore Gas and Electric Co., are able to monitor their distribution system (Hubbard [1969]), and their service area includes only one weather area. Spread-out systems, which need more detailed data, find that data collection is very expensive.

2.2 Long Term Forecasting

Given the load history to date, what will be next summer's peak load and the peak loads for the next 20 summers? How much energy will be demanded next July or for the whole year? Only once a year can the models used for these long term forecasts be checked and updated, as contrasted with the almost daily updating of short term models. Their applications are also long term in nature, the budgeting of revenue and expenses and the planning of capacity additions. The forecasting procedures are those associated with nonstationary economic time-series analysis.

Long-term forecasting procedures for four utilities, Tennessee Valley Authority,

Pennsylvania Power & Light Co., Southern California Edison Co., and Commonwealth Edison Co. (Chicago) are summarized in the Federal Power Commission's 1970 National Power Survey (FPC [1970]). All but Commonwealth begin by extrapolating energy use by classes of service such as commercial, domestic, agriculture, industrial, and others. Then, the energies are added, to arrive at a total system energy for the season or year. The peak demand is computed by first deriving a ratio of peak to total energy from historical records, and then multiplying by the energy forecast. No mention is made of forecasting more than an expected value.

Commonwealth Edison forecasts the peak demand directly, using a two component model, a base and a weather sensitive adder. The base load is determined after removing the weather sensitive demand from the historical loads, along with a load component correlated to the Federal Reserve Board Index of Industrial Production and special items such as voltage reductions or industrial layoffs. The weather sensitive component includes the effects of eight quantities; cooling degree days for three days, three dry bulb readings, and the relative humidity two hours before the peak and the year and day number. The final forecast is an expected value, with possible variations stated with probabilities.

Lev [1970] studied Commonwealth's monthly peak demand forecasting experience for the years 1959 through 1966 and concluded that the distribution of the errors was affected more by the month to be predicted than by the time interval from prediction to realization. For example, the December demand can be predicted ten months ahead with the same accuracy as predicting the September peak one month ahead. Lev concludes that the frequent forecast updating, which occurs every 3 to 6 months in actual practice, is of questionable value.

Public Service Electric & Gas (New Jersey) also remove a weather sensitive component of peak demand before "trending" the growth of the base (Heinemann et al. [1966]). The weather variable used in the linear regression of demand versus weather includes such items as wet and dry bulb temperatures, relative humidity, and a heat build-up factor. A third component of unexplained variability was also included. More work on the model was needed because a variation of 5.8% from the forecast resulted when nine years of history were checked and the average error was 2.4%. Several additional factors, such as business levels, were suggested by the discussors of this paper. Discussions by utilities in Cleveland, the Northwest, Rochester, N.Y., Philadelphia, and Long Island indicate the widespread modeling of the weather effects for removal before forecasting system growth.

The study of the weather-sensitive component of load was accelerated in 1966, when several midwest utilities experienced peak demands 8% higher than expected. Two relatively cool summers followed by a very hot summer in 1966 set them up for this forecasting error. Union Electric (St. Louis), one of the utilities affected, now separates the weather sensitive demand into residential and commercial components (Kind [1969]). The base component, modeled using an exponentially weighted regression function, grows at 6% per year, while the weather sensitive demand is growing at 14 to 16% a year, and in 1969 was $\frac{3}{8}$ths of the total summer peak demand. Kind indicates that, while the quantitative results have not differed significantly from those achieved in the past, the forecast is on a firmer basis and provides a measure of uncertainty.

The Purdue Energy Research & Education Center, after plotting demand versus temperature, fit a "U" shaped curve to the resulting scatter plot (FPC, [1970], Stanton & Gupta, [1970]). Three line segments are fitted to the plot by assuming two temperatures between which the load is insensitive to temperature. The magnitude of this temperature-insensitive load and the rates of change of load with winter and summer temperatures are solved for by linear regression.

The Stanton and Gupta method was tried by several utilities but has not been widely adopted. The results were found to be very dependent on the temperature range selected for the insensitive load portion of the "U" curve. The forecasts were not considered enough of an improvement over existing methods to warrant the additional effort. Broussard of Gulf States Utilities (Stanton and Gupta discussor [1970]) indicates that, over a period of six years, forecasts of peak demand made with the least sum minimization method have been 1.4% low to 2.6% high and sees no need to go to more complicated methods.

The Louisiana Power & Light Co. (Davey et al. [1973]) used multiple regression to fit the daily peak loads for a summer season, resulting in the following expression for a summer season daily peak:

Load = - 1464
+ 11.9 (°F at 3 p.m. on the current day)
+ 7.3 (°F at noon on the current day)
+ 4.1 (°F average of three days)
+ 1.9 (relative humidity at 3 p.m., current day)
+ 1.5 (°F average of 3 previous days)
- 2.9 (wind velocity at noon, current day).

These are not independent variables, and so the model might be judged inferior by a statistician. However, it works well, and is being used for forecasting summer peaks 5 to 10 years in the future. By providing a weather-sensitive model for each past year and playing 12 years of weather history (the amount available) againts each year's model a distribution is built up, plotted on semi-log paper, and projected (Figure 1). The mean annual peak loads are extrapolated graphically, and any trend in the variance is also extrapolated.

A 1972 survey of load forecasting methods (EEI [1973b]) reported that 30 of 57 companies include some type of weather factor in their forecasts. But weather is only one factor that influences load. Additional components are needed to explain load growth. Latham, et al. [1968] describes how the

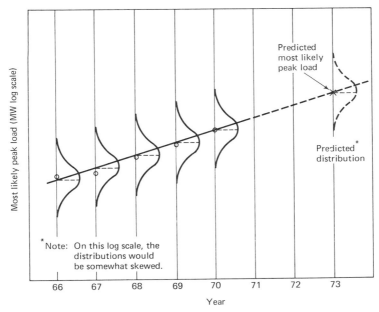

Fig. 1. Peak demand forecasting using weather history.

Public Service Electric and Gas Co. forecasts the energy for a month, using four components:

1. Number of Residential Customers
2. Basic KWH Use Per Customer
3. Residential Cooling Energy-Factor
4. Weather Variable

They use a combination of historical data and experience judgement to form normal distributions of all four components. The experienced judgement is quantified as subjective distributions by asking knowledgeable personnel to complete statements such as "There is one chance in ____ that the number of residential customers next year will exceed ____." After the distributions are merged, taking into account correlation, the results are reported in the same understandable manner; e.g., "There is one chance in 2 of the energy in June next year exceeding X MWHr, one chance in 4 of exceeding Y MWHr, etc."

News of TVA (Latham, et al. discussor [1968]) describes the use of Monte Carlo gaming to merge their distributions which are not required to be normal. Latham, in the closure, indicates a major savings in computer time by avoiding Monte Carlo calculations.

Utility forecasters, demonstrating their natural conservatism in long range forecasts, reported that 57 utility 1971/72 peak forecasts made ten years earlier were an average of 6% below the peaks actually experienced (EEI [1973b]). Forecasts made five years before the data were 1.5% below the actual peak, while one year before were 2% above the actual value. The natural tendency in long term forecasts is to judge that a 7% to 8% growth rate cannot continue and so a tapering off is predicted about five years in the future. Then, as the distant future comes closer and the growth rate has been sustained or even accelerated, the forecasts are increased. A one year forecast suffers from another form of conservatism, the penalties for being too high are less severe than those for being too low, encouraging a forecast that overshoots the actual peak.

One hour to 30 year forecasting models have been proposed, using simple trends, exponential smoothing, and multiple regression. The successful applications cluster around simple-to-explain models, usually developed by the user and requiring easily obtainable input data. No matter how sophisticated the method, the forecasts are reviewed and modified by experienced judgement (EEI [1973b]).

3. OPERATIONS PLANNING

Operations planning selects the generating units to synchronize to the system and the load sharing between operating units. The costs of operating these units, whether powered by falling water, burning fuel, or nuclear reaction, is to be minimized, subject to serving the ever changing load from a secure system state.

Seven operations subjects, including security, will be discussed in this section. Table 1 is offered as guide to the reader wishing to locate particular operations research topics.

3.1 Dispatching Ignoring Losses

Dispatching is the allocation of demand (load) among operating electric power generators. When the electrical energy losses are small, as in compact city networks, then the dispatching problem appears in its simplest form. For example, if the two units in Figure 2 are to serve a 60-MW load, how should they share the load to minimize fuel costs? The dispatch problem is to minimize fuel costs while serving the total load, and with all units operating between their minimum and maximum output limits.

$$\text{Minimize:} \quad \sum_{\substack{\text{all} \\ \text{units}}} \text{FUELCOST} \tag{1}$$

$$\text{Subject to:} \quad \sum_{\substack{\text{all} \\ \text{units}}} \text{POWER} = \text{LOAD} \tag{2}$$

TABLE 1. OPERATIONS RESEARCH TOPICS RELATED TO POWER SYSTEM OPERATION

Subject	OR Topic Keys
1. Dispatching Ignoring Losses†	LP, NLP, DP
2. Dispatching Including Losses	LP, NLP
3. Hydro-Thermal Coordination	LP, NLP, DP
4. Unit Commitment	IP, DP, SP
5. Security	LP, NLP, NF
6. Dispatching Large Systems	D&D, NF
7. Maintenance Scheduling	IP

Key: LP Linear Programming
     NLP Non-Linear Programming
     IP Integer Programming
     DP Dynamic Programming
     SP Stochastic Processes
     NF Network Flows
     D&D Decomposition & Diakoptics

†The word "dispatching" in the context of electric utilities means "scheduling of production".

$$PMIN \leqslant POWER \leqslant PMAX \text{ for all operating units} \qquad (3)$$

$$POWER = 0 \qquad \text{for all non-operating units} \qquad (4)$$

The FUELCOST for each unit is a function of the POWER output (Figure 3), and FUELCOST = 0 if POWER = 0.

As early as 1933 it was recognized that the units should be operated at equal incremental costs (Steinberg and Smith [1943]). The industry refers to this incremental cost as the system "lambda," acknowledging its origin in the proof using Langrange multipliers. A digital computer determines the dispatch by interating on lambda, using the incremental cost curves of Figure 4. Once the outputs of the two machines add to the total the interations stop.

Equal incremental dispatching is discussed in detail in Kirchmayer [1958] and

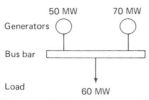

Fig. 2. Symbolic diagram of electric power dispatch problem.

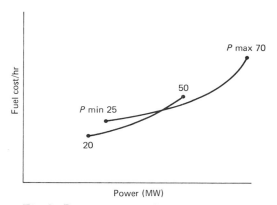

Fig. 3. Power generator input-output curves.

is also presented in Stevenson [1962], Knight [1972], and Sasson & Merrill [1974].

Equal incremental dispatching is universally accepted and implemented in modern dispatch computers, but not without some complications. Secure operating states must be used, losses are significant in a dispersed system, and the input-output curves of the individual units are not linear or quadratic functions. We will consider this last problem of input-output in more detail.

Most generating units in the U.S. have more than one steam valve to control the output of the unit. These valves cause "valve loops" in the input-output curve (Figure 5 (IEEE Committee [1971]). Operating with a valve just cracked open causes very high throttling losses, and so this operating point is to be avoided. In 1959, a team of experts in thermodynamics, mathematics, and

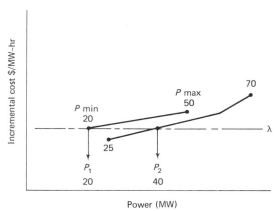

Fig. 4. Power generator incremental cost curves and system.

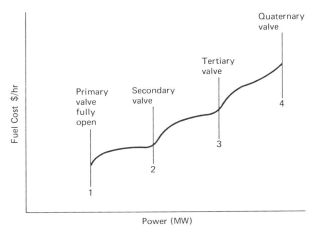

Fig. 5. Generator input-output curve with valve loops.

optimization began developing an accurate method for calculating an input-output curve and optimizing a dispatch recognizing the exact nonlinear function [Ringlee and Williams, 1963].   Using dynamic programming (DP), optimum dispatches were determined exactly and then compared with various approximate methods.   The results showed that an input-output model, using stepped-incrementals, gave consistently lower costs than the sloped incrementals shown in Figure 4, which was almost universally used in the industry.

Ten years later, sloped-incremental cost curves are still widely used in the industry, even though stepped incrementals have been shown to give lower cost. The reason is the difficulty of accurately knowing where the valve loops are located.   If the model indicates that 50 MW may be the output before opening the next value, and due to aging or other causes the valve now opens at 49 MW, then stepped-incremental dispatching, which places most outputs at the start of the next step, 50 MW, will cause the unit to operate with a valve cracked open, precisely its worst point.   There is no easy way to learn when a valve is about to open.   A few utilities have installed special equipment to monitor throttle pressures and temperatures to detect valve openings and send these signals or some composite back to the central dispatch office.   Therefore, dispatching recognizing valve loops must wait until accurate data becomes available at the central dispatch office.

3.2 Dispatching, Including Losses

Transmitting electric power is accompanied by energy losses. The largest loss component is heating computed by the current-squared times the resistance, (Chapter 2 of Stevenson [1962]). The greater the distance the higher the resistance, and the greater the power the higher the current at a given voltage. Therefore, when the generating units and loads are dispersed in a network such as Figure 6, it is more economical to generate power at slightly higher incremental cost closer to the loads and incur lower losses, than to generate at the same incremental cost but at a distant location.

The losses enter into the constraint Eq. (2) as follows:

$$\sum_{\text{all units}} \text{POWER} = \text{LOAD} + \text{LOSSES}, \tag{5}$$

where the LOSSES are a nonlinear function of the POWER variables. The practical method for handling this nonlinear constraint has been to fit a quadradic function of the POWER variables to the LOSSES function and derive penalty factors to modify each unit's incremental cost before equating it to the system lambda. It was first proposed in 1943 but became practical only after Gabriel Kron developed a series of loss invarient transformations, making it possible to compute the loss formula coefficients, termed "B" constants (Kirchmayer [1958]).

The loss formula method was developed by a team approach: utility operators, who would implement the methods, working with a mathematician and an electrical engineer. Their results showed that loss formula dispatches save about $150,000 on a system with loads varying from 800 to 1900 MW and served by eight steam plants (Kirchmayer [1958]). The loss formula approach has gained wide industry application (Lamont and Tudor [1970]) but does require some important judgements and approximations (Dandeno [1960]; Brownlee [1970]).

Overcoming the loss formula approximations requires solving the network equations while minimizing the fuel costs. The single equation (5) is replaced by two equations for every node in the network. The first equation states

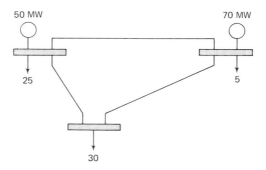

Fig. 6. Network representation of dispatch problem.

that the real power summation around a node must equal zero.

$$POWER - LOAD = \sum_{\substack{All\ lines \\ at\ the\ node}} LINEFLOWS, \qquad (6)$$

where LINEFLOWS are the power flows away from the node.

The second equation states that the reactive power summation around each node must equal zero.

$$VARS - LOADVARS = \sum_{\substack{All\ lines \\ at\ the\ node}} LINEVARS, \qquad (7)$$

where VARS are the reactive power generated at the node, LOADVARS are the reactive power demanded at the node, and LINEVARS are the reactive power flows away from the node. Reactive power is required to supply electric fields, called excitation, to electrical motors, transformers, and around any electrical conductor. Applying the Kuhn-Tucker conditions to this much expanded problem, and extending Newton's method to include a steepest descent technique produced a minimum cost dispatch (Peschon, et al. [1968]).

The publication of the Peschon et al. paper in 1968 began a search for the best combination of mathematical programming methods and sparcity programming (Tinney and Hart [1967]) for solving the optimal load flow problem. The methods of LP (Jolissaint, et al. [1972]), QP (Nicholson & Sterling [1973]), constrained gradient (Sasson [1969]) and gradient methods with penalty functions (Peschon, et al. [1972]; Sullivan [1972]; Billinton & Sachdeva [1973]), have been applied. The reduced gradient approach with penalty factors (Dommel & Tinney [1968]) was evaluated to be one of the best methods available (Sasson, et al. [1971]).

The papers presented at the Fourth Systems Computation Conference (Laughton [1972] Vol. 2) by authors from England, France, Russia, Sweden, and Australia indicate that the optimization of generation dispatching with network effects is receiving world wide attention, but only Carpentier of Electricité de France indicates that the methods are being applied to daily dispatch situations.

Frequent recalculation of a new dispatch (2 minutes to 2 seconds) and limited computer size require that the applied method be simple in structure and fast in calculation (DyLiacco et al [1972]). The loss formula method has provided a simple and fast procedure that produces dispatches with no significant cost differences from the rigorous optimal load flow approach (Happ [1974]). It does have the disadvantage of tracking network changes only by recomputing a new B-matrix and this, coupled with the need to have network load flow solutions available for contingency checking, will probably bring the mathematical programming approach into wider use.

3.3 HydroThermal Coordination

Up to this point, only thermal powered generating units, whose total energy available is unlimited, have been considered; i.e., fuel burning steam plants. Falling water is a prime source of energy, but when it is limited in quantity its use must be coordinated with thermal plant operation to minimize costs. Figure 7 illustrates a system with two hydro plants in series so that the water from one plant becomes the input to the second plant. The coordination of these two hydro plants with the thermal plants requires the study of several days to weeks of operation in order to use the water to minimize costs. The dispatch problem formulation now becomes time dependent, and includes the limits on the hydro plant energy output.

$$\text{Minimize} \quad \sum_{\substack{\text{Time}}} \sum_{\substack{\text{All} \\ \text{thermal} \\ \text{units}}} \text{FUELCOST,} \tag{8}$$

$$\text{Subject to} \quad \sum_{\substack{\text{All} \\ \text{units}}} \text{POWER} = \text{LOAD for each time period:} \tag{9}$$

$$\sum_{\substack{\text{Time}}} \sum_{\substack{\text{All} \\ \text{hydro} \\ \text{units}}} \text{ENERGY} \leqslant \text{ENERGYMAX for each set of hydro units,} \tag{10}$$

where ENERGY is the integral of POWER over time. Equations (8) and (9) replaces (1) and (2), which do not involve time. The total energy generated by the hydro system is limited to the maximum energy for the period (10).

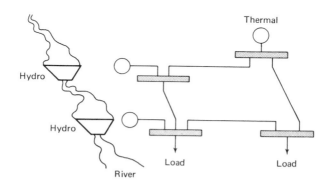

Fig. 7. Hydrothermal generation coordination problems.

Watchorn [1967] describes the typical utility approach of assigning a water conversion coefficient, thus allowing the hydro units to participate in the incremental dispatch. The discussions of this paper introduce many of the practical aspects, such as startup of steam units, load pickup rate-of-response factors, advance notification time, and inclusion of losses. Experience in the U.S., Canada, Japan, and Sweden is presented.

Linear programming was applied in Japan (Fukao & Yamazaki [1960]), and Ontario Hydro studied a gradient method applied to a 16 hydro plant, 4 thermal plant system (Bainbridge, et al. [1966]). The optimal load flow problem of the previous section has been coupled with hydro coordination, using the Fletcher-Reeves method on a small example (Billinton & Sachseva [1972] Bonaert, et al. [1972a]). The methods are yet to be widely applied.

Dynamic programming was successfully applied to dispatching of two hydro plants in series on the Susquehanna River (Anstine and Ringlee [1963]), but variational methods were considered to be more appropriate for larger hydro systems (Kirchmayer and Ringlee [1963]).

Successive approximations of dynamic programming are applied in three various methods and compared in a two hydro-unit system by Bonaert, et al. [1972b]. Rees and Larson [1971] describe a dynamic programming application to the scheduling of a pumped storage hydro unit, two hydro plants, sixteen steam plants, and three interchange contracts over time spans from two days to one year. Hicks, *et al.* [1974] use the conjugate gradient method of Fletcher and Reeves to solve a model of the Bonneville Power Administration system with 38 reservoir and 45 run-of-river plants. A study of 49 time periods, using only 10% of the former engineering man-hours, produced a dispatch with nearly 1% more energy output than a previous cut-and-try solution.

3.4 Unit Commitment

Because the demand peaks during the day and falls at night, cost savings are possible by shutting down less efficient generating units during the low load hours. In Figure 8, showing the load fluctuation from the peak of one day to the peak of the next, six units must operate to serve the peak with a reserve for contingencies, but as the load falls unit 6 and then unit 5 may be shutdown. This reduction in the number of operating units reduces production costs. However, there are significant costs, both fuel and increased wear, associated with shutting down and starting a unit. These costs, increasing with the number of hours shutdown, to saturate at the cold start cost, make it uneconomical to shut down for just a few hours. Operating rules require six to eighteen hour shutdowns, depending on the design of the plant.

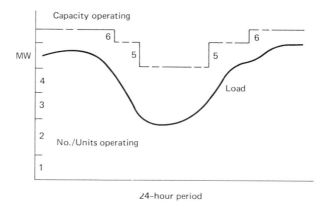

Fig. 8. Daily load fluctuation and unit commitment.

The selection of the units to commit for operation has been formulated as and ILP problem (Garver [1963], Muckstadt and Wilson [1968]), an integer DP problem (Lowery [1966]; Ayoub and Patton [1971]; Guy [1971]), and using B&B procedures (Carpentier [1973b]). But all attempts to use mathematical programming methods have been frustrated by the practical requirements listed in Table 2. A fast, simple procedure is needed because the problem is so large, and is usually solved on small process computers. The industry is using priority lists, based on full load average costs with some heuristic logic for shifting the order of the units, and performing a limited search for improved commitment schedules (Kerr et al. [1966]; Davidson, et al. [1967]; Happ et al., [1971].

3.5 Security

Security refers to operating a system so that creditable disturbances, such as the sudden loss of the most heavily loaded generating unit or transmission circuit, will not cause the outage of any other facility. Sudden generator outages are handled by operating more capacity than needed to serve the load and dispatching, so that they all may rapidly increase power output in case of an emergency. Sudden transmission outages are more difficult to handle because each outage has a unique system effect, requiring a network flow calculation to identify.

Wells [1968] used a dc (real power) network model and a stepped incremental cost generation model in a LP to minimize cost while observing security constraints. For several years the New York Power Pool has been using the method of Wells, (Aldrich, et al. [1971]) to allocate the pool generation to serve the load

TABLE 2. EXAMPLE REQUIREMENTS FOR METHODS OF SCHEDULING ELECTRIC POWER GENERATORS

1. Any unit may be made unavailable for a part of or for the whole scheduling period.
2. Any unit may change its maximum or minimum limits during the scheduling period.
3. Area security checks for a minimum number of units running and for transmission line loadings near limitations must be made at least each hour.
4. Unit minimum downtime and uptime constraints must be observed.
5. A limited number of units at the same location can start at the same time.
6. Change a unit's loading at a rate within specified limits.
7. Load pickup margin must be scheduled on all units so that the system may follow the continually changing demand; e.g., one, three, and five minute pickup requirements.
8. Scheduling for 24 hours should be possible, along with more detailed studies of 4 hours and general studies of one week.
9. Hydro-driven generators with water storage capacity (pondage), recognizing storage limitations, should be scheduled.
10. Weekly pumped-storage hydro schedules must be developed.
11. Minimize total costs.
12. Use only a limited amount of fast-access computer memory.
13. Complete a 24-hour optimization in less than an hour while sharing the computer with higher priority functions.
14. Consider systems in the order of 150 generating units.
15. Always provide a feasible solution if one exists, even if time has not allowed an optimum solution to be found.

and satisfy the transmission security constraints while minimizing the fuel costs. Shen and Laughton [1970] extended the method of Wells, allowing the problem size to vary as the number of critical line outages change. The solution of a 23 bus example is presented in detail.

An alternate approach, also using LP, has been suggested by Kaltenbach and Hajdu [1971], and by Thanikachalam & Tudor [1971]. Their procedure brings a vulnerable system into a secure state by minimizing the departure of each generator from the current economic schedule. Small examples are worked out but no further application is indicated.

Stadlin's discussion of Daniels and Chen [1972] indicates three problem areas when modeling security: (1) the choice of the objective function: minimizing the shift in generation or minimizing the cost of generation; (2) the choice of the power system model, i.e., the operating point of linearization; and (3) the choice of constraints to treat as "hard" and "soft" limits. Knowing the operating state of the system is a major problem in security assessment. State estimation from partial or conflicting information on line flows and equipment status is being developed in utilities such as American Electric Power Corp (Dopazo, et al. [1973]) and Ontario Hydro (Porretta and Dhillon [1973]).

3.6 Large System Dispatching

Dispatching large systems or systems made up of several individual utilities have been accomplished using the closely related methods of diakoptics and decomposition (Benthall [1968]; Haman & Brameller, [1972]; Revington [1972]; Carpentier [1973a]).

Kron's diakoptics played a major role in the development of the dispatching procedure for the New York Power Pool, allowing them to economically interchange power while the local companies maintain control over their generation sources (Aldrich, et al. [1971]). The interconnection models are being built and upgraded, using the Transportation Method to form the necessary topological matricies (Nour and Happ [1974]).

3.7 Maintenance Scheduling

Scheduling generating unit maintenance, including boiler, turbine and generator, involves selecting the weeks during a year when each unit will be taken out of service and given a minor or major overhaul. Attempts have been made to optimize these schedules using ILP, B & B, and DP. The problem will be illustrated and then the optimization models discussed.

In its simplest form, the scheduling of a system's yearly generating unit maintenance involves fitting the units into a graph of reserve capacity, such as in Figure 9. The generating units are modelled by their rating and the number of weeks of maintenance required. An example system of units is displayed in Table 3, indicating that unit A, rated 300 megawatts, requires 1 week of maintenance during the year. Maintenance requirements usually vary from 1 week to 8 weeks,

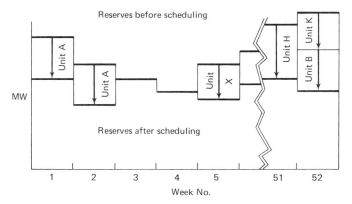

Fig. 9. Weekly generation reserves and units scheduled for maintenance.

TABLE 3. GENERATING UNITS REQUIRING MAINTENANCE

Unit (1)	Rating (2)	Required Weeks of Maintenance (3)	Starting Week For Maintenance (4)
A	300 MW	1	
B	300	1	
C	100	6	To Be Determined
H	400	5	
K	250	1	
X	250	1	
–	–	–	
–	–	–	

with the majority above 2 weeks. The year in which maintenance is to be scheduled is modelled by the reserve before maintenance, as in Table 4, which indicates that Week 1 has 1000 MW of reserve, Week 2 has 800 MW, etc.

Starting dates for maintenance and the amount of capacity on maintenance each week are to be determined in a manner that produces nearly equal reserves, after maintenance, for those weeks with maintenance. Essentially, there are blocks of maintenance requirements, megawatts high by weeks long, to be placed into a graph of reserve for each week, as shown in Figure 9.

Several real world problems complicate the scheduling process. The number of crews available will limit the number of units that can be worked on at one time. If certain units are out others in the same plant cannot be out, because of working space or because one unit must be available to help in system operation. Pro-

TABLE 4. TIME AND RESERVE AVAILABLE FOR MAINTENANCE

Week (1)	Installed Generation (2)	Peak Load (3)	Reserves Before Scheduling (4)	Capacity on Maintenance (5)	Reserves After Scheduling (6)
1	4600 MW	3600 MW	1000 MW	To be	To be made nearly equal.
2	4600	3800	800	determined	
3	4600	3900	700		
4	4600	4000	600		
5	4600	3750	850		
–	–	–	–		
–	–	–	–		
51	4800	3700	1100		
52	4800	3600	1200		

duction costs should be minimized. Reliability, rather than reserve, should be maximized. The worst real-world complication is the constant change in the problem: loads differ from forecasts, and generating units experience prolonged forced outages at unexpected times.

Currently, the maintenance problem is being solved by hand or computerized heuristic methods (Buchmeier [1973]). Linear, integer, and dynamic programming methods were considered (Christiaanse and Palmer [1972]) and found to be too unwieldy in the number of variables, the number of linear and nonlinear constraints, and the computer time used to solve the problem. By recognizing that an optimum solution will have nearly equal weekly reserves, a heuristic procedure was created to sequentially build up a schedule that always meets the manpower and other constraints, while tending to equalize the reserves. When applying this heuristic search procedure to a major utility, many types of constraints were encountered, including crew and equipment allocation, keeping units available at a location, transmission limitations, lapsed time since last maintenance, and regulations on boiler inspections (Christiaanse [1973]). Studying the optimization of unit maintenance resulted in a computer program used by maintenance engineers to update schedules as new situations arise and to explore the use of overtime, more crews, and other constraint variations.

Several real-world problems have been included in a model solved by B & B methods (Dopazo and Merrill [1974]). The cost function they use causes each unit to be scheduled as close to a preferred time of year as possible, while keeping reserves above a given minimum. For example, a unit maintained in December the previous year should be maintained near December in the next schedule. A second problem solved involves changing a schedule once a unit forced outage has occurred. A schedule with a minimum of changes is sought, while keeping all units close to their original dates to begin maintenance. For example, in Figure 9, the failure of unit "K" during Week 4 will require doing its maintenance in Week 5 instead of 52. Unit "X" cannot simply take the place of "K" because the 47 week change in its schedule is too great. The minimum amount of rearranging is required to keep the starting date for "X" close to Week 5.

During informal discussions, several utility representatives told of scheduling programs written by focusing on the flexibility to include constraints and a simple search procedure to equalize reserves. Most of the programs in use were engineered by the person using them, and though they would like to have used some sophisticated mathematics, they found the flexibility to introduce constraints more important then the solution procedure.

Future improvements appear headed in the direction of minimizing the production costs while meeting all of the constraints. The risk can be minimized by using an equivalent load change instead of a unit's rating in the calculation of the weekly reserve quantity (Garver [1972]). No easy production cost surrogate has yet been found. The most important quality for a schedule is its adaptability to changing conditions such as load level or unit forced outages. This quality remains the most difficult one to model.

3.8 Additional Operating Problems

Several other operating studies shall be mentioned, but their results are not yet widely applied. The amount of capacity above an expected load, "spinning reserve," has been studied by probability and Markov process formulations (Anstine, et al. [1963] ; Billinton and Jain [1972] ; Bubenko and Anderson [1973]). Scheduling the operation of pumped-hydro storage plants has been formulated as LP and DP (Akiyama and Sekine [1961] ; Cobian [1971]). Optimal control theory has been applied to small example problems, but the difficulty in measuring all of the necessary state variables limits its usefullness (Fosha & Elgerd [1970] ; Bechert & Kwatny [1972] ; Yu and Moussa [1972]). The rearranging of network connections to better distribute the load is a form of dispatching studied by B & B methods (Couch and Morrison [1972] Sekine and Kawakawiz [1972]).

3.9 Further Introductory Reading

The following references provide broad overviews of system operation problems. Computer system requirements for an operations control center are introduced in a non-technical manner by Friedlander [1965b]. Lamont and Tudor [1970] overview the operating problems by listing present and future computer functions resulting from their survey of 118 operating companies in the USA. The description of the control system designed for the Cleveland Electric Illuminating Co. catalogues the problems encountered in an application (DyLiacco, et al. [1972]). The planning and operating of interconnected systems is illustrated by specific instances in a report edited by Brown [1968] , and based on the experiences of the East Central Area Reliability Council, the Western Systems Coordinating Council, and the Ontario Hydro System.

4. GENERATION EXPANSION PLANNING

Electric utility investments include the power generating plants, the power transmission network to the major voltage step-down stations, and the distribution network to the users. Operations research activities have concentrated on the expansion of the generation and transmission plant because these facilities represent major capital expenditures. One generating unit, which may represent a company's total generating investment for one or several years, commands careful planning of when, what size and fuel type, and where it will be located.

Probability mathematics has played a significant role in generation expansion planning, and guiding the selection of reserve capacity levels during the transition from isolated utility systems with small, e.g. 100-MW, units to interconnected power pools with units now over 1000 MW in size. More recently, probability techniques have also been used to include random forced outages of generating units in production simulations, without the expensive Monte Carlo procedure.

Optimization mathematics have been more difficult to apply in generation planning, but several attempts will be mentioned. In transmission network planning, to be discussed in Section 5, just the reverse is true. Probability mathematics has not played a large role because of the enumeration problems encountered, but optimization methods such as min-cut max-flow and LP have been used effectively.

4.1 Generation Reserve Studies

What happens when too many people try to use electricity in too large an amount? The lights go off. Not just for the last man to turn on a switch, but for everyone within the control of a fuse or circuit breaker. This is in sharp contrast to receiving a busy signal on a telephone, where prior users of the network are unaffected by a call that overloads the system.

Because an overload or capacity shortage interrupts service to all users in an area, the utility industry is particularly sensitive to maintaining reserves above demand. Investment decisions cannot wait until the present facilities are fully loaded because of the disaster proportions of a power shortage and the two to ten year lead times for generating plants. Major amounts of capital, approaching $1000/kW in 1975 for a 1,000,000 kW power plant, are to be committed before the demand materializes. These three factors of large capital requirements, many years before the in-service date and the disaster proportions of a power shortage, focus major attention on generation reserve planning.

The need for new generating capacity is signaled by the load forecast exceeding the level of installed capacity less required reserves. Most electric utilities determine their required reserves using probability-based procedures such as the Loss-Of-Load Probability (LOLP) Method. Through its application a system planner may determine, for example, that a 4600-MW system, made up of 32 individual generating units, requires 600 MW of installed reserve to reliably serve an annual demand curve and thus, when the load forecast exceeds 4000 MW another generating unit is needed.

The computation procedure for the LOLP method which grew out of work beginning about 1946 (AIEE [1960]), will be illustrated and then applications to reserve planning discussed. The basic calculation is the probability of the available generating capacities being less than a specific load. For example, if two 50-MW units and a 100-MW unit are installed, what is the probability of not meeting a 130-MW demand? By assuming that each unit has two states, available or not, and that the 50-MW units have 0.02 probability of outage and the 100-MW unit has 0.03 probability of outage, a table of different outage capacity states with their exact and cumulative probabilities can be computed as in Table 5. For example, 100 MW on outage can occur with both 50-MW units out, (.02) $\times$ (.02) $\times$ (.97), or the 100-MW unit out, (.98) $\times$ (.98) $\times$ (.03), resulting in the exact probability of 0.029200. The cumulative table in Table 5 can be computed recursively adding one unit to the system at a time (Page 102 of Billinton [1970]), and bypassing the enumeration of system states and the exact probability calculation.

How much capacity must be unavailable before the 130-MW demand cannot be met? No demand is unserved until the capacity on outage exceeds the reserve, which is 200 – 130 = 70 MW. What is the probability of the capacity on outage exceeding the 70 MW reserve? It is the probability of more than 70 MW on outage, equal to 0.030388, in Table 5. If 100 MW or greater are on outage, there is a loss of load; hence the loss-of-load probability for a day with a 130 MW peak is 0.030388.

The LOLP method examines a series of loads to represent a year. Some LOLP variations use 8760 loads (one per hour), some use 365 loads (one per day), some use 260 loads (one per weekday). Whatever the number of loads to represent a year the probabilities of not serving them are summed together, resulting in the expected number of days with capacity shortages. For example: if three loads, 110, 130, 90 MW, were studied by the LOLP method, the results would be as shown in Table 6.

To review, the LOLP method first enumerates the outage states of the generating system with their associated cumulative probabilities of the outage or greater, and, second, sums the probabilities of outage exceeding reserves for a given list of loads. The resulting quantity, 0.061964 days in the example, is given several names, such as "loss-of-load probability" (a misnomer because it is an expected value not a probability), risk, or the expected need for capacity. There is no standard term.

TABLE 5. CAPACITY OUTAGE TABLE FOR A THREE UNIT SYSTEM
The system is composed of two 50-MW units with 0.02 probability of outage and one 100-MW unit with 0.03 probability of outage.

State	Capacity On Outage	Exact Probability	Cumulative Probability of Outage or Greater
1	0 MW	0.931588	1.000000
2	50	0.038024	0.068412
3	100	0.029200	0.030388
4	150	0.001166	0.001188
5	200	0.000012	0.000012

Monte Carlo gaming, popular in the late 1950's, was tried in generating reserve planning, but too much computer time was required and the recursive procedure is now widely used (Latham, et al [1968] p. 504).

An appreciation of the widespread application of probability-based generation reserve planning may be gained by referring to the 1970 National Power Survey (FPC [1970], see especially the Northeast report pages II-1-52 to 58, and the general overview, pages I-18-8 to 10). Also, Cash and Scott [1969] report 11 European countries using probability methods for generation capacity planning. However, it took nearly 20 years for probability-based reserve planning methods to be accepted. Decision makers did not know how to interpret a quantity such as 0.06 days/year. Is 0.06 good or bad? By relating the result for a future system to the result for a past-known system, understanding and acceptance were built up for the new probability measure. For example, 0.06 days/year might be the same risk as computed for the 1968 system, and lower than the risks in 1967 and 1970, indicating that the future system should be as reliable as 1968 and better than 1967 and 1970.

A sensitivity analysis of the days/year quantity also aided in understanding and accepting the new probability measure. By computing and plotting the annual risk for various load levels, as in Figure 10, planners came to understand how unit additions affect system capability. For example, with the first 600-MW unit added to the 4600-MW system, the load may increase only 362 MW before the risk returns to its value before the addition. However, when the fifth 600-MW unit is added, the load may increase by 508 MW. Determining this nonlinear relationship between unit size, unit forced outage probability, system size, and load change is one of the most important uses of probability mathematics in generation planning. A method of estimating this relationship has been developed by noting that the plots of risk versus load in Figure 10 are nearly straight lines (Garver [1966]).

An early successful application of the LOLP method was its role in predicting that generating unit sizes would continue increasing (Kirchmayer, et al. [1955]),

TABLE 6. LOSS-OF-LOAD PROBABILITY CALCULATION USING THE 200-MW SYSTEM SHOWN IN TABLE 5

Day Number	Load	Reserve	Probability of Capacity Shortage
1	110 MW	90 MW	.030388
2	130	70	.030388
3	90	110	.001188
	Expected number of capacity shortage days = .061964 days		

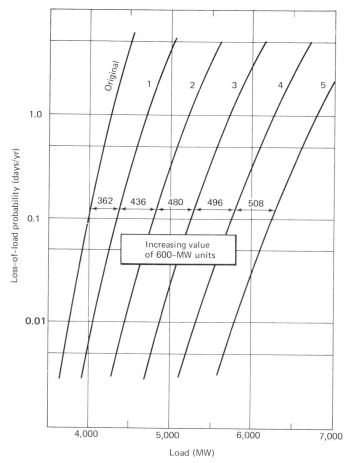

Fig. 10. Loss-of-load probability versus annual peak load for generating systems differing by the number of 600-MW units.

especially as utilities interconnected with one another (Kirchmayer, et al. [1957]). One discussor in 1958 states the prevailing industry opinion that there was no incentive to build 500-MW units, when two 250-MW units (very large by 1958 standards) would be more reliable and cost nearly the same amount (Funk discussion of Pitcher, et al. [1958]). The probability studies showed that as system sizes increased, unit sizes could also be increased with no significant reserve penalty and also, when two systems interconnected, they could rapidly increase unit size with no reserve penalty. Unit sizes did increase rapidly in the 1960's as sys-

tems interconnected, approaching 1300 MW, which is much larger than anticipated by the 1955 study.

The effects of interconnections on the reserve requirements in two areas may
be examined by a two-area LOLP method developed by Cook, et al. [1963], and
used in several studies of the trade-offs between transmission capacity and generating reserve (Kirchmayer, et al. [1957]; Paris and Valtota [1968]; Davies
[1970]). All of the studies show substantial reserve reductions are possible
when two nearly equal size systems interconnect. Attempts to model the interconnection of more than two areas and include transmission limitations has met
with only limited success, measured in terms of computer codes with reasonable
running times. Spears, et al. [1970] report the application of a Y-connected
three area program to the New England, New York State, and Ontario interconnection. The complexities increase rapidly with the number of systems, as noted
by Vassell and Tiberts [1972] when they developed methods for use with the
utilities in Ohio and neighboring states. Their paper is enhanced by the illustrations used to make the results visible and understandable to management.

There are data complications in using probability methods for reserve planning. For example, all methods require a listing of the generating unit capacities
and forced outage probabilities (termed forced outage rates by the industry) and
scheduled maintenance time. But the capacity may vary much like that shown
in Figure 11, raising several difficult questions. Should the capacity in the "available" state be the maximum ever attained during the year? What terminates the
"available" state, the capacity dropping below 100%, 80%, or 50%? How should

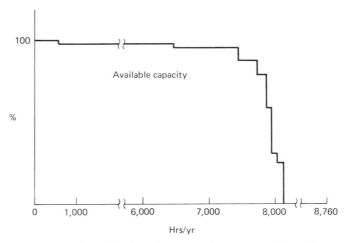

Fig. 11. Capacity duration curve for a generating unit.

the "outage" state be split into its two components, "planned outages" representing scheduled maintenance, and "forced outages"? Lynskey and Sloane [1964] discuss data gathering and fitting capacity, forced outage hours, and planned outage hours to the data gathered from utilities.

The available capacity model can be extended to allow more than just three states (i.e., available planned outage, and forced outage). Partial availability can be modeled (Cook, et al. [1969]), but this solution comes at the price of increased data and slower computation times, which explains why it is not widely used.

A unit's available capacity model should be time dependent, since experience has shown that the number of forced outage hours experienced during the first few years of service are 2 to 3 times greater than those of a mature unit (EEI [1973a]).

Besides the probable number of days with capacity shortages, the utility planners would like to know how frequently these shortages occur and their duration. For example, one utility operator, when told that his system was designed to 0.1 days/year, did a mental calculation and replied that a 12-minute capacity shortage each month was unacceptable. The flaw in the operator's reasoning was his attempt to derive outage duration and frequency information from a calculation based on only average values.

Frequency and duration measures can be computed using a Markov process model of the generation capacity and a two-state daily load model (Billinton, et al. [1973]). Introducing a second recursive procedure into LOLP computer programs provides both the days/year reliability measure and also the years between shortages and the hours of shortage. The 0.1 days/year is usually associated with 7 to 8 years between occurrences and 4 to 6 hours of shortage. This added information does not alter the reserve requirements significantly and therefore, the new computations are not yet widely used.

Generation reserve planning by probability methods is being extended to recognize the uncertainty of unit installation dates and fuel availability (Billinton, et al. [1973]), to allocate capacity responsibility among power pool members (Firestone, et al. [1969]), and to model hydro units that are energy rather than capacity limited (Graham, et al. [1971]).

Probability methods determine how much reserve a system needs and thus, when more capacity will be needed as the demand grows. The size or sizes of units and their fuel types are determined by the interplay of investment and production costs, the subjects of the next section.

4.2 Economic Comparisons

Once a reserve study has established the need for additional generating capacity, various unit sizes and fuel types are examined for their impact on investment and production costs. Cost comparison studies have traditionally been accomplished by engineering economic procedures, including the present worth of annual revenue requirements (Jeynes [1968]; IEEE Committee [1972]). More recently corporate models, which detail the impact on earnings and cash flow of major investment decisions, are coming into use.

One of the first corporate modeling activities was initiated by the Boston Edison Co. to evaluate alternate expansion and financing plans (Carlin, et al. [1969]). By simulating the financial and accounting system, the computer model indicates revenues and expected regulatory control required to produce acceptable earnings. If revenues are constant then the model indicates return for a specific plan. The 26 references on corporate models in the Bibliography on Engineering Economics (IEEE Committee [1972]) include four references to utility models—Public Service Electric and Gas (New Jersey), Long Island Lighting Co., Boston Edison, and Victoria, Australia.

The utilities are not the only ones to benefit from corporate models. During a paper presentation, three employees told of the promotions they had received as a result of the modeling activity. Building the model had given them a structured way of learning about the company's operation, and the knowledge gained opened up new career opportunities.

Production costs, which are a major cost component in the decision on unit size and fuel type, have been computed by both deterministic and probabilistic models. Deterministic models, with the hourly loads for a year given and no random forced outages of units, duplicate the operating procedures of the utility such as incremental cost loading, unit committment by priority lists, pondage and run-of-river hydro scheduling, and pumped-hydro optimization (Bailey, et al. [1963]; Galloway, et al. [1969]).

Linear programming is being used to forecast production costs (Day [1971]) in a comprehensive expansion planning program (Day, et al. [1973]). The LP formulation includes costs for starting, running, maintenance, and interchange of energy, and the constraints include spinning reserve, load requirements, unit availability restrictions, hydro capacity, and energy and intertie limits. Computer running time was reasonable, but the costs computed were found to be consistantly 7% below those obtained using an older dispatching program (see page 818 of Day [1971]). However, when relative cost differences between alternate plans are desired rather than absolute costs, the method is considered to be adequate.

Though total costs are the major result of a simulation calculation, identifying the operation of individual units is almost as important. Deterministic simulations attribute too little production and operating time to the smaller, lightly used "peaking" units when compared with actual operating records because the model cannot include the random forced outages of the larger units.

In the late 1950's, Monte Carlo simulation was used in an attempt to include forced outages and obtain improved individual production estimates, but it proved too expensive, and deterministic simulations became the industry norm (Anderson, et al. [1970]).

A new method for including unit forced outages in production cost estimates which is gaining industry acceptance, is based on convoluting the load duration curve for a period, with the generating capacity outage table permitting the expected energy and operation hours of each generating unit to be calculated.

The original idea was presented by Baleriaux, et al. [1967], and expanded upon by Booth [1972] and by Sager, et al. [1972]. This development brought the art of production costing full circle. The industry began by using load duration curves for hand calculation of costs, then went to more detailed hour-by-hour dispatch simulation as larger and larger computers became available. Now the load duration curve is again in use, but as part of a probability calculation. The time periods for each curve are shorter—not a year but half a day—and the recursive equation of the LOLP method is used to convolute the remaining loads as each unit is studied.

The probability calculations of reserve planning have been brought into the production costing areas with the added benefit that both the expected costs and a reliability measure, the expected energy shortage, are computed at the same time. The expected operation of individual units computed by the probability model come within 5% to 15% of observed values (Goodrich and Rees discussion of Sager et al. [1972]).

Once the year-by-year production costs are computed, they are combined with the annual revenue requirements for generation investment in either a corporate model or a present worth calculation. These total costs then guide the selection of the size, fuel, and type for the next generating unit.

4.3 Generation Planning Models

Several generation planning models have been developed to encompass the three major components of reserve, production costs, and investment costs. An early DP formulation ran into high computer costs, even though simplified reserve and production cost models were used (Dale [1966]). The program could search out the best expansion from several thousand but was too expensive to use in exploring the entire range of unit states. No actual generation expansion studies were reported using this procedure. Booth [1972] discusses an open loop feedback approach to reduce the dimensionality of DP in expansion planning but does not mention any real study results.

Electricité de France applied LP and NLP techniques to expansion planning, beginning in 1954. Bessiere [1970] summarizes the methods and results of a 1965 to 1985 study to select investments in nuclear, hydro, conventional fossil, and gas turbines, and to select siting regions from among 6 possibilities. The nonlinear formulation allowed a failure cost to be included, an item often discussed but little used (see, for example, the 8 discussions of Shipley et al. [1972]), and having little influence on the optimal decisions. Bessiere also brought out the need to develop plans for the central assumptions about the future and then to test the consequences of optimistic and pessimistic assumptions on these plans. He concludes with a comment typical of many other studies, that the input assumptions were changed shortly after the study was completed. In EDF's case the load forecast was increased 8 percent. The complicated model could have been solved again but the time and effort did not appear to be justified. Here is an additional challenge to the OR function, to provide an operating system for the planning models that encourages the study of further alternatives and assumptions.

A planner's wishbook of programs resulted from an ambitious industry study of nuclear capacity planning (Gilleland, et al. [1970]). The mathematical model needs included a 30-year system expansion model, a 3 to 5 year operating strategy model, an annual planning model, and a short term dispatching model. To solve this multi-staged decision model they hoped to use both DP and LP. By 1973 the results of this work had yet to be published.

Anderson [1970] used simplified planning models ammenable to LP in the context of non-USA utility planning problems. Nuclear, fossil and hydro generating plants are considered, along with interconnections and plant location. To simplify production cost calculations, an annual load duration curve is used. The use of a load duration curve implies that only the magnitude of the load affects the cost. This is correct only if unit commitments are unchanged. Since unit commitments change between weekday and weekend, and even from daytime to nighttime, more accurate cost models use four or more load duration curves per week, instead of one per year. The installed reserve requirement was modeled as a percent of load, a practical assumption for optimization methods but unacceptable to many system planners.

A more detailed LP formulation for optimized generation planning has been introduced (Day, et al. [1973]). A standard LP code is used to minimize the present worth of investment and production costs subject to load and reserve requirements. Its most important feature is the reduced time and effort required in its use, as compared with using larger simulation programs.

One major barrier to the use of LP or DP methods has been the sensitivity of the solution to the sophistication of the model. The global optimum to a simplified model is not optimum when entered into the convention as probability models of reserve and production costs. Yet the probability models are too large and expensive to use with DP procedures and are nonlinear, precluding LP.

An alternative to optimizing simplified models has been to use detailed models and heuristic rules to seek out near-optimum solutions. Adamson, et al. [1973] describe one of over 20 electric utility studies performed with the model illustrated in Figure 12. The variable inputs include the system load growth, the generator characteristics such as mature and immature forced outage rates, heat rate, fuel costs, plant costs, operating and maintenance costs, and hydro data. The study factors include the various types of generating units among which to optimize, the spinning reserve rule, the days/year risk index for installed reserve planning, the fixed charge rate for investment costing, a present

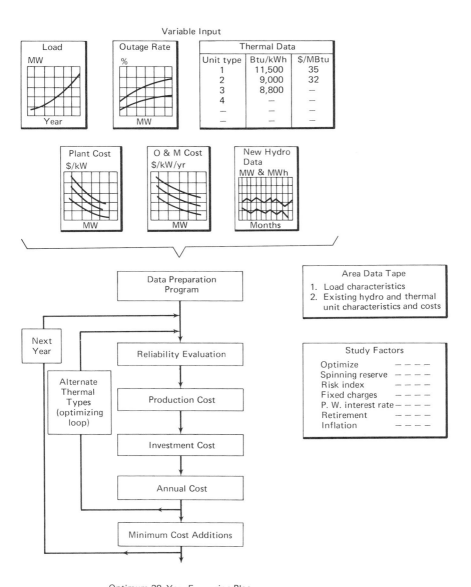

Fig. 12. Generation expansion planning model.

worth interest rate, a retirement policy of X years after installation, and inflation factors for plant cost and fuel costs.

The lowest cost expansion plan in many practical situations consists of the annual additions, which are lowest cost in the year of addition. This has occurred often enough that expensive optimizing logic has been replaced with a simple lowest-cost-each-year heuristic, modified by a look ahead feature to anticipate changes in fuel costs (Marsh, et al. [1974]).

Any "optimum" expansion plan may be found to be sub-optimum or optimal-infeasible when analyzed by more exacting models, such as corporate models (indicating financing difficulties), transmission models (indicating excessive costs), or environmental models (indicating unacceptable uses of resources or excessive pollution). The challenge is to bring more of these important details into a manageable planning model.

5. TRANSMISSION EXPANSION PLANNING

Transmission expansion planning determines the connections to be added to a network, so that power deliveries may continue as demands grow and new generating plants are added. The expansion problem has been modelled, using LP, DP, and heuristics. One model, combining LP and heuristics, has been used by seven different U.S. power pools for developing 10 to 25 year network expansion concepts. The planning problem and the many different approaches will be introduced, followed by a discussion of the LP model.

5.1   The Expansion Problem

Transmission planning follows the forecasting of demands at distribution points in the network and the planning of new generating capacities at the supply points. The desired results are lists of yearly circuit additions showing terminals and voltage level; i.e., in 1986 add a 345-kV circuit between PLANT A and SUBSTATION H. These expansions illustrate planning concepts, such as the dependence of the network development on the selection of generating plant sites or the savings possible if both 765 and 345 kV are used instead of just 345 kV. The future network plans also provide a starting point for more detailed investigations, using load flow and stability computations (Stagg and El-Abiad [1968]).[2]

---

[2]Three types of network flow models will be mentioned, a.c. load flow, d.c. load flow and capacitated network. An a.c. (alternating current) load flow solves a set of complex equations for the circuit (branch) real and reactive power flows and bus (node) voltages and phase angles. A d.c. (direct current) load flow solves a set of real equations for the circuit real power flows and the bus phase angles. Both a.c. and d.c. load flows minimize a quadratic loss function by making the sum of the voltages (phase angles) around any loop equal to zero. A capacitated network model solves for approximate power flow by minimizing a linear cost function and the phase angles are not required to sum to zero around loops.

The fundamental transmission planning problem is illustrated in Figure 13. A portion of a large existing 345/138 kV network is shown along with a new sub-station (demand), a new voltage step-down station, and a new generating plant. All of the demands are raised to a future level perhaps doubled or triple today's values. What combination of 345-kV and 138-kV additions will provide a sufficient network and minimize cost? The additions should not only meet the particular requirements of the one load level, but fit into a growth pattern for continued low cost expansion.

5.2 Proposed Solution Methods

The first approach to the problem concentrated on computerizing the engineering process. A.c. load flow and stability studies are used by utility planners to design networks, and therefore it seems natural to just include some circuit selection procedure to automate the planning. This approach was followed, and culminated in a very detailed computer program able to dispatch generation, compute an a.c. load flow, and take corrective action when overloads appeared (DeSalvo and Smith [1965]). It has not been as successful as hoped because of four major difficulties. First, the large data requirements deterred starting a study with the new program. Second, the very accurate load flow analysis was costly. Third, the future year studied had to have only a small increase in demand, so that the nonlinear equations in the a.c. load flow would converge to a usable result. Thus, to study 10 or 20 years in the future required that every second or third year be planned. At the time this seemed acceptable, since through-time expansions were desired. However, studying only small demand increases produces only small overloads which in turn are economically corrected

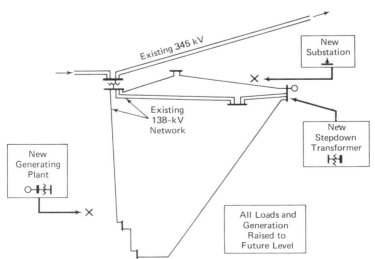

Fig. 13. The transmission expansion problem: an existing network and future generating plants and loads.

by small network changes. A series of small network changes produced network designs unacceptable to the planners, the fourth and fatal difficulty.

The circuit selections could be improved using DP procedures to search many possible expansion sequences. A DP method using predefined network states for each future period was outlined (Henault, et al. [1970]) but never extended past a small example. A simplified load flow, DP, discrete optimization, and random sampling were all packaged into an investigation of the many directions transmission planning could take (Dusonchet and El-Abiad [1973]), but no readily applicable results have yet emerged. Dynamic programming coupled with an even simpler load flow approximation (the min-cut max-flow concept) is being used in Belgium and the U.S. (Baleriaux, et al. [1970]). Instead of solving the network at certain periods, the problem is turned around and the nearest period requiring network reinforcement is solved for using a linear load growth assumption. Several alternate network additions are identified. A truncated DP procedure uses this information in forming sequential decision trees and searching out the minimum and several near minimum expansion patterns.

Kaltenbach, et al. [1970] used a d.c. load flow to find the shortages in several test cases, located the set of capacity changes to correct these shortages using LP, and then considered DP as a method to round off these capacities to whole numbers of circuits. They discuss the tremendous number of decision alternatives and the difficulty in expressing the reliability constraints in any easily usable manner.

The amount of calculation time in an expansion problem can be reduced with the simultaneous application of sorting, optimal ordering, Gaussian elimination, revised-simplex LP, and sparcity programming (Ogbuobiri [1971]); for example, from 20 minutes to 20 seconds for a 100 branch system. But a practical design model is yet to be completed.

Boardman and Hogg [1972] use the computer in an interactive mode, with the planner suggesting feasible starting designs and the computer testing and altering these using heuristic logic. They note that several designs will have nearly the same cost, indicating a flat optimum. A 17-node example is solved, and they believe that the method can be extended to realistic system sizes.

A unique method of computing sensitivity factors for new circuit possibilities is based on work in the electronic circuit design field (Puntel, et al. [1974]). The "adjoint network" method is included in an automated planning procedure, using the d.c. load flow and a heuristic search for integer circuit additions. The adjoint method appears especially promising because of its fast calculation speed and reasonable storage requirements.

Discussion of security criteria for networks, the uncertainty of substation sites, and various LP and DP models proposed in Europe are contained in Knight, Chapter 7 [1972].

5.3 Application of a LP Model

The method used by several U.S. power pools to initiate conceptual planning studies combines the capacitated network model of LP with heuristic rules for selecting additions (Garver [1970]). By minimizing the megawatt-miles of overload, where miles may be economic-miles, the LP solution determines if a network is short of capacity and if so, how much is short and where new capacity should be considered. The major advantages are simpler input data requirements, fast computing times, and the ability to always solve any future condition, even if no network exists. The actual circuit selections are determined by first studying the horizon year, ten to twenty years in the future, to identify the major needs and therefore justify large high-voltage circuit additions. Then, a through time sequence is studied using the horizon network as a guide to planning.

The results surprise utility engineers for they don't believe a nonelectrical model can solve electrical network expansion problems. When the plans are subjected to a.c. load flow studies, the results confirm that the network will work. But the networks can also be improved.

Early in the model development, attempts were made to use optimization logic to find the network that could not be improved on by the planner. In the course of that effort it was necessary to clearly define what a planner considered optimum. A test was set up. A midwestern state was designed for a 20-year horizon using four alternate sets of logic and producing four plans greatly different in the location of the high-voltage lines but of nearly the same cost. Four system planners were invited to view these maps and select the optimum. Each planner found a favorite idea embodied in one of the plans, but no aggreement could be reached on which plan was best. Not one of the four plans could be unanimously accepted or rejected. Because of that meeting, the goal of the expansion planning model was reoriented towards rapidly providing a low cost plan which met all of the requirements and would serve as a good starting point for the planner's own creativity. To aid in creating alternate plans, all new circuit possibilities are evaluated, using the dual variables, for their value in correcting capacity shortages.

After learning that optimum was impossible to define, work began on a useable transmission planning procedure. Useable in this case meant that the program developer would also be its principle user in consulting studies. The original concept was to put together a medium size computer program that could be used to study the expansion of very highest voltage levels in a power pool on a conceptual rather than a final design basis. Instead of striving for complete detail, the model would be broadened to include the complete scope of the problem, but with only the most fundamental details.

The problem is made very large by the great number of test conditions that a network must pass. For example, the test requirements for just one year might include 6 to 8 dispatches such as a summer peak load dispatch, a summer low-load dispatch (with the older units located near the load shutdown and also any pumped-hydro units receiving rather than generating power), and several different generation outage combinations such as the two largest units out in the eastern part of the system, then central, then southern, etc. Other seasons might also require description by a few dispatches, but this has usually not been necessary.

In addition to many dispatches, the test cases also include reliability requirements. Any single circuit outage should not cause an overload during the normal peak load dispatch. Moreover, many utilities now require that any pair of circuit outages should not cause an overload. Thus, the test cases for one year may include over 100 network problems. A power pool study of 20 years required 93 dispatches to describe the peak-load, low-load, and generation outage cases. Then, an additional 3600 circuit outages were tested. A total of 4500 network solutions were required at 15 765-kV circuits, 39 345-kV underground, and 79 345-kV overhead circuits were planned between 90 locations.

The capacitated network procedure of LP (Charnes and Cooper [1961- Chapter 17]) has provided the fast and flexible model needed for capacity shortage testing. By modelling two types of links, "circuits" which have limited capacity and low cost, and "overload paths" which have unlimited capacity but very high cost, the network solution displays the amount of the shortage on the route best suited for a circuit addition. Electrical models display overloads on circuits and then require a search to locate new routes that parallel the overload. By eliminating the search for the best new route and using the simplified LP model, a planning study is completed at one hundredth of the computer cost associated with load flow studies. The reduced cost and a convenient input/output package have made possible the study of many more future possibilities such as unit sites, new voltage levels, d.c. transmission, and underground circuits.

The results of a tran_mission expansion study often solve an unexpected problem. Instead of being the desired result, the list of additions frequently points out overlooked constraints and unstated design preferences. Several trial plans are made with the planner shaping the input data to improve the model of his system. Thus, the time and effort spent on any one plan must be kept small to make it practical to repeat the study with input modified for model improvements, or when the model is acceptable, with input modified for unit-siting, voltage level, and route preference variations.

The development of the LP network model and its associated data handling system, which began in 1963, has moved conceptual transmission planning from a time consuming trial and error procedure to the rapid evaluation of 10 to 25 years of growth. The original goal of providing plans that could not be improved on, when discovered to be impossible, was replaced by the goal of providing the best plan for starting the creative process. The result is a procedure used and reused by utilities and power pools to explore the possibilities for future network development.

REFERENCES

Adamson, A. M., J. F. Kenney, and R. W. Moisan, "Parametric Sensitivity Method for Establishing Optimum Long Range Generation Mix," *Proc. Am. Power Conf.* **35**: 467–472 (1973).

AIEE Committee Report, "Application of Probability Methods to Generating Capacity Problems," *AIEE Trans.* **79**, Pt. III: 1165–1177 (1960). 6 discussions.

Akiyama, T. and Y. Sekine, "Economic Operation of Power-Generating Systems Comprising Hydroelectric, Thermal and Pump-Up Plants: An Application of Network Flow Theory and the Decomposition Principle of Linear Programming," *Electrical Eng. Japan* **86**: 74–85 (1966).

Aldrich, J. F., H. H. Happ, and J. F. Leuer, "Multi-Area Dispatch," *IEEE Trans.* **PAS-90**: 2661–2670 (1971). 3 discussions.

Anderson, D., "Models for Determining Least-Cost Investments in Electricity Supply," *Bell J. Economics Management Sci.* **3**: 267–299 (1972).

Anderson, S. W., R. T. Jenkins, D. Joy, E. T. Merrill, and T. D. Wolsko, "Methods of Planning Generating Unit Operation," *Proc. Am. Power Conf.* **32**: 123–130 (1970).

Anstine, L. T. and R. J. Ringlee, "Susquehanna River Short Range Hydrothermal Coordination," *IEEE Trans.* **PAS-82**: 1885–191 (1963). 1 discussion.

——, R. E. Burke, J. E. Casey, R. Holgate, R. S. John, and H. G. Stewart, "Application of Probability Methods to the Determination of Spinning Reserve Requirements for the Pennsylvania–New Jersey–Maryland Interconnection," *IEEE Trans.* **PAS-82**: 726–735. 5 discussions.

Ayoub, A. K. and A. D. Patton, "Optimal Thermal Generating Unit Committment," *IEEE Trans.* **PAS-90**: 1752–1756 (1971).

Bailey, E. S., E. S. Hawkins, C. D. Galloway, and A. J. Wood, "Generation Planning for Interconnected Systems," *IEEE Trans.* Special Publication T-151, pp. 761–788 (1963). 1 discussion.

Bainbridge, E. S., J. M. McNamee, D. J. Robinson, and R. D. Nevison, "Hydrothermal Dispatch with Pumped Storage," *IEEE Trans.* **PAS-85**: 472–485 (1966).

Baleriaux, H., E. Jamoulle, and F. Linard, "Simulation de l'exploitation d'un parc de Machines Thermiques de Production d'électricité couplé à des Stations de Pomage," *Review E* (edition SRBE) **V**: 3–24 (1967).

——, P. Douliez, and J. VanKelecom, "Optimal Investment Policy for a Growing Electrical Network by a Sequential Decision Method," CIGRE International Conference on Large High Tension Electric Systems, 1970 Session Paper 32-08.

Bechert, T. E. and H. G. Kwatny, "On The Optimal Dynamic Dispatch of Real Power," *IEEE Trans.* **PAS-91**: 889–898 (1972). 1 discussion.

Benthall, T. P., "Automatic Load Scheduling in a Multiarea Power System," *Proc. IEEE* **115**: 592–596 (1968).

Bessiere, F., "The 'Investment '85' Model of Electricite de France" *Management Sci.* **17**: B-192–211 (1970).

Biggerstaff, B. E. and T. M. Jackson, "The Markov Process as a Means of Determining Generating-Unit State Probabilities for Use in Spinning Reserve Applications," *IEEE Trans.* **PAS-88**: 423–430 (1969). 3 discussions.

Billinton, R., *Power System Reliability Evaluation*, Gordon and Breach, New York, 1970.

—— and A. V. Jain, "Unit Derating Levels in Spinning Reserve Studies," *IEEE Trans.* **PAS-90**: 1677–1688 (1971). 2 discussions.

——, "The Effect of Rapid Start and Hot Reserve Units in Spinning Reserve Studies," *IEEE Trans.* **PAS-91**: 511–516 (1972).

——and S. S. Sachdeva, "Optimal Real and Reactive Power Operation in a Hydrothermal System," *IEEE Trans.* **PAS-91**: 1405–1411 (1972). 1 discussion.

——, "Bibliography on the Application of Probability Methods in Power System Reliability Evaluation," *IEEE Trans.* **PAS-91**: 649–660 (1972). 1 discussion.

——, R. J. Ringlee, and A. J. Wood, *Power-System Reliability Calculations*, The MIT Press, Cambridge, Massachusetts 1973.

—— and S. S. Sachdeva, "Real and Reactive Power Optimization By Suboptimum Techniques," *IEEE Trans.* **PAS-92**: 950–956 (1973). 2 discussions.

Boardman, J. T. and B. W. Hogg, "Computer Method for Design of Electricity-Supply Networks," *Proc. IEE* **19**: 851–856 (1972).

Bonaert, A. P., A. H. El-Abiad, and A. J. Koivo, "Optimal Scheduling of Hydro-Thermal Power Systems," *IEEE Trans.* **PAS-91**: 263–270 (1972a).

——, "Effects of HydroDynamics on Optimum Scheduling of Thermo-Hydro Power Systems," *IEEE Trans.* **PAS-91**: 1412–1420 (1972b). 1 discussion.

Booth, R. R., "Optimal Generation Planning Considering Uncertainty," *IEEE Trans.* **PAS-91**: 70–77 (1972). 1 discussion.

Brewer, C. and A. M. Revington, "Linear Programming For Optimizing Generation and Immediate Spare: Development and Application (LP5)," IEE Conference on Computers in Power System Operation and Control, Bournemouth College of Technology, England, pp. 115–134 (1972).

Brown, W. D., "Three C's of System Reliability," *Electrical World* **160**: 61–76. (August 26, 1968).

Brownlee, W. R., "Discussion of Improved Loss Formula Computation by Optimally Ordered Elimination Techniques by Meyer and Albertson," *IEEE Trans.* **PAS-90**: 67 (1970).

Bubenko, J. A. and M. Anderson, "Probabilistic Evaluation of the Operation Reserve in a Power System," *IEEE PICA Conf. Proc.*, pp. 240–250 (1973).

Buchmeir, F. A., Jr., "Replacement Energy Costs Set Outages," *Electrical World* **180**: 116–117 (September 15, 1973).

Carlin, J. F., R. H. Lyons, J. R. Mitiguy, E. F. Murphy, C. D. Galloway, M. A. Sager, A. J. Wood, "Corporate Model of an Electric Utility," *IEEE Spectrum* **6**: 75–84 (1969).

Carpentier, J. L., "Differential Injections Method a General Method for Secure and Optimal Load Flows," *IEEE PICA Conf. Proc.*, pp. 255–262 (1973a).

——, "Total Injections Method, A Method for the Solution of the Unit Commitment Problem Including Secure and Optimal Load Flow," *IEEE PICA Conf. Proc.*, pp. 263–267 (1973b).

Cash, P. W. and E. C. Scott, "Security of Supply in the Planning and Operation of European Power Systems," *IEEE Trans.* **PAS-88**: 6–21 (1969).

Charnes, A. and W. W. Cooper, *Management Models and Industrial Applications of Linear Programming*, Wiley & Sons, New York (1961).

Chen, Gorden, K. C., and P. R. Winters, "Forecasting Peak Demand for an Electric Utility With a Hybrid Exponential Model," *Management Sci.* **12**: B-531–B-538 (1966).

Christiaanse, W. R., "Short-Term Load Forecasting Using General/Exponential Smoothing," *IEEE Trans.* **PAS-90**: 900–910 (1971). 3 discussions.

——, A. H. Palmer, "A Technique For The Automated Scheduling of the Maintenance of Generating Facilities," *IEEE Trans.* **PAS-91**: 137–144 (1972).

———, "A Program For Calculating Optimal Maintenance Schedules Recognizing Constraints," *IEEE PICA Conf. Proc.*, pp. 230–239 (1973).

Cobian, M. J., "Optimal Pumped Storage Operation With Interconnected Power Systems," *IEEE Trans.* **PAS-90:** 1391–1399 (1971). 1 discussion.

Cook, V. M., C. D. Galloway, M. J. Steinberg, and A. J. Wood, "Determination of Reserve Requirements of Two Interconnected Systems," *AIEE Trans.* **PAS-82:** 18–33 (1963). 8 discussions.

———, R. J. Ringlee, and A. J. Wood, "Frequency and Duration Methods for Power System Reliability Calculation, Part IV: Models for Multiple Boiler-Turbines and for Partial Outage States," *IEEE Trans.* **PAS-88:** 124–1232 (1969). 1 discussion.

Corpening, S. L., N. D. Reppen, and R. J. Ringlee, "Experience With Weather Sensitive Load Models for Short and Long-Term Forecasting," *IEEE Trans.* **PAS-92:** 1966–1972 (1973). 3 discussions.

Couch, G. H. and I. F. Morrison, "Substation Switching–An Approach to the Determination of Optimal Sequences," 4th PICA Proceedings, Grenoble, September 11–16, 1972, paper 2.1/1 18 pages.

Dahlin, E. B. and D. W. C. Shen, "Optimal Solution to the Hydro-Steam Dispatch Problem for Certain Practical Systems," *IEEE Trans.* **PAS-85:** 437–458 (1966). 1 discussion.

Dale, K. M., "Dynamic Programming Approach to the Selection and Timing of Generation Plant Additions," *Proc. IEE* **113:** 803–811 (1966).

Dandeno, P. L., Discussion of "Direct Calculation of Transmission Loss Formula-I," L. K. Kirchmayer, H. H. Happ, C. W. Stagg, and J. F. Hohenstein, *AIEE Trans.* **79,** Pt. III: 968 (1960).

Daniels, H., and Mo-Shing Chen, "An Optimization Technique and Security Calculations for Dispatching Computers," *IEEE Trans.* **PAS-91:** 883–888 (1972). 3 discussions.

Davey, J., J. J. Sacks, G. W. Cunningham and K. W. Priest, "Practical Application of Weather Sensitive Load Forecasting to System Planning," *IEEE Trans.* **PAS-92:** 971–977 (1973). 2 discussions.

Davies, M., "Probability Studies of Interconnection Capacity," *Proc. IEE*, **117:** 1382–1389 (1970).

Davidson, P. M., T. B. Payne, F. L. Kohlerman, G. L. Masters, J. R. Evans, K. M. Lovewell, and G. R. Shaefer, "Unit Commitment Start–Stop Scheduling in the Pennsylvania–New Jersey–Maryland Interconnection," *IEEE Conf. Record*, 1967 Power Industry Computer Applications Conference, 31C69, pp. 127–131 (1967).

Day, J. T., "Forecasting Minimum Production Costs with Linear Programming," *IEEE Trans.* **PAS-90:** 814–823 (1971). 1 discussion.

———, A. J. Federowicz and E. E. Menge, "Optimizing Generation Planning," *Power Eng.* **117:** 32–35 (July, 1973).

DeSalvo, C. A. and H. L. Smith, "Automatic Transmission Planning with A-C Load Flow and Incremental Transmission Loss Evaluation," *IEEE Trans.* **PAS-84:** 156–163 (1965). Disc. pp. 249–253, 8 discussions.

Dommel, H. W. and W. F. Tinney, "Optimal Power Flow Solutions," *IEEE Trans.* **PAS-87:** 1866–1876 (1968). 2 discussions.

Dopazo, J. F., O. A. Klitin, G. W. Stagg, and M. Watson, "An Optimization Technique for Real and Reactive Power Allocation," *IEEE Trans.* **55:** 1877–1885 (1967).

———, S. T. Ehrmann, O. A. Klitin, and A. M. Sasson, "Justification of the AEP Real Time Load Flow Project," *IEEE Trans.* **PAS-92:** 1501–1509 (1973). 4 discussions.

——— and H. M. Merrill, "Optimal Generator Maintenance Scheduling Using Integer Programming," IEEE Conference Paper C74 162-4 (1974). 8 pages 12 references. To be Published in the IEEE Transactions on Power Apparatus and Systems.

Dusonchet, Y. P. and A. El-Abiad, "Transmission Planning Using Discrete Dynamic Optimizing," *IEEE Trans.* **PAS-92:** 1358–1371 (1973). 13 discussions.

DyLiacco, T. E., "The Adaptive Reliability Control System," *IEEE Trans.* **PAS-86:** 517–532 (1967). 6 discussions.

——, B. F. Wirtz, D. A. Wheeler, "Automation of the CEI System for Security," *IEEE Trans.* **PAS-91:** 831–844 (1972). 10 Discussions.

EEI, *Report of Equipment Availability for the Thirteen-Year Period 1960-1972*, EEI Publication No. 73–46, Edison Electric Institute, New York, N.Y. (1973a).

EEI System Planning Committee, *System Planning Committee Surveys Load Forecasting Methods*, Edison Elec. Inst. Bulletin, March/April, p. 89 (1973b).

El-Hawary, M. E. and G. S. Christensen, "Functional Optimization of Common-Flow Hydro-Thermal Systems," *IEEE Trans.* **PAS-91:** 1833–1840 (1972). 2 discussions.

Elgerd, O. I., *Electric Energy Systems*, McGraw-Hill, New York (1971).

Enns, M. and W. F. Tinney, Eds: *Computers In the Power Industry, Proc. IEEE* **62:** 868–1024 (1974).

Fanshel, S., E. S. Lynes, "Economic Power Generation Using Linear Programming," *IEEE Trans.* **PAS-83:** 347–356 (1964).

Firestone, L., W. D. Masters, and A. H. Monteith, "The CAPCO Group Probability Technique for Timing Capacity Additions and Allocation of Capacity Responsibility," *IEEE Trans.* **PAS-88:** 1174–1182 (1969). 2 discussions.

Fosha, C. E., Jr. and O. I. Elgerd, "The Megawatt-Frequency Control Problem: A New Approach Via Optimal Control Theory," *IEEE Trans.* **PAS-89:** 563–477 (1970).

FPC, *1970 National Power Survey*, 4 Volumes, U.S. Government Printing Office, Issued between 1970 and 1972.

FPC Committee, "Descriptions of Forecasting Practices," Appendix A, of the 1970 National Power Survey, Part IV, Federal Power Commission, 1970.

Friedlander, G. D., "Computer-Controlled Power Systems, Part I–Boiler-Turbine Unit Controls," *IEEE Spectrum*, **2:** 60–82 (1965a).

——, "Computer-Controlled Power Systems, Part II–Area Controls and Load Dispatch," *IEEE Spectrum*, **2:** 72–92 (1965b).

Fukao, T. and T. Yamazaki, "A Computational Method of Economic Operation of Hydro-Thermal Power Systems Including Flow-Interconnected Hydro-Power Plants," *Electrotechnical J. of Japan* **6:** 22–26 (1960).

Galloway, C. D. and R. J. Ringlee, "An Investigation of Pumped Storage Scheduling," *IEEE Trans.* **PAS-85:** 459–465 (1966). 1 discussion.

Galloway, C. D., L. L. Garver, L. K. Kirchmayer, and K. A. J. Wood, "Generation-Transmission Planning and Economic Evaluation," 3rd International Power Systems Computation Conference, Rome, Italy, June 23–27, 1969, Paper P. 3. 12 references.

Garver, L. L., "Power Generation Scheduling by Integer Programming-Development," *AIEE Trans. (Power Apparatus and Syst.)* **81:** 730–735 (1963). 2 discussions.

——, "Effective Load Carrying Capability of Generating Units," *IEEE Trans.* **PAS-85:** 910–919 (1966). 2 discussions.

——, "Transmission Network Estimation Using Linear Programming," *IEEE Trans.* **PAS-89:** 1688–1697 (1970). 4 discussions.

——, "Adjusting Maintenance Schedules to Levelize Risk," *IEEE Trans.* **PAS-91:** 2057–2063 (1972). 4 discussions.

Gent, M. R. and J. W. Lamont, "Minimum-Emission Dispatch," *IEEE Trans.* **PAS-90:** 2650–2660 (1971). 2 discussions.

Gilleland, J. E., R. E. Hoskins, W. M. Kiefer, and E. F. Koncel, "Fitting Nuclear Capacity into Utility Planning," *Proc. Am. Power Conf.* **32:** 116–122 (1970).

Graham, E. G., G. E. Gunter, D. C. Muttart, N. D. Reppen, R. J. Ringlee, and A. J. Wood,

"Generation System Planning Models for Hydro-Thermal Systems," *Am. Power Conf. Proc.* **33**: 1160–1168 (1971).

Gungor, R. B., N. F. Tsang, and B. Webb, "A Technique For Optimizing Real and Reactive Power Schedules," *IEEE Trans.* **PAS-90**: 1781–1790 (1971). 3 discussions.

Gupta, P. C. and K. Yamada, "Adaptive Short-Term Forecasting of Hourly Loads Using Weather Information," *IEEE Trans.* **PAS-91**: 2085–2094 (1972). 4 discussions.

Guy, J. D., "Security Constrained Unit Commitment," *IEEE Trans.* **PAS-90**: 1385–1390 (1971). 3 discussions.

Hajdu, L. P., L. Peschon, W. F. Tinney, and D. S. Piercy, "Optimum Load-Shedding Policy for Power Systems," **PAS-87**: 784–795 (1968). 1 discussion.

Hamam, Y. M. and A. Brameller, "Diakoptical Optimization of Electrical Power Systems," IEE Conference on Computers in Power System Operation and Control, Bournemouth College of Tech., England, 158–167 (1972).

Hano, I., Y. Tamura, and S. Narita, "An Application of the Maximum Principle to the Most Economical Operation of Power Systems," *IEEE Trans.* **PAS-85**: 486–494 (1966).

Happ, H. H., "Large Scale Hydro-Thermal Unit Commitment-Method and Results," *IEEE Trans.* **PAS-90**: 1373–1384 (1971). 4 discussions.

——, "Power Pools and Superpools," *IEEE Spectrum* **10**: 54–62 (March 1973).

——, "Optimal Power Dispatch," *IEEE Trans.* **PAS-93**: 820–830 (1974). 4 discussions.

Hara, K., M. Kimura, and N. Honda, "A Method for Planning Economic Unit Commitment and Maintenance of Thermal Power Systems," *IEEE Trans.* **PAS-85**: 427–436 (1966).

Heinemann, G. T., D. A. Nordman, and E. C. Plant, "The Relationship Between Summer Weather and Summer Loads–A Regression Analysis," *IEEE Trans.* **PAS-85**: 1144–1154 (1966). 5 discussions.

Henault, P. H., R. B. Eastvedt, J. Peschon, and L. P. Hajdu, "Power System Long-Term Planning in the Presence of Uncertainty," *IEEE Trans.* **PAS-89**: 156–164 (1970). 2 discussions.

Hicks, R. H., C. R. Gagnon, S. L. S. Jacoby, and J. S. Kowalik, "Large Scale Nonlinear Optimization of Energy Capability for the Pacific Northwest Hydroelectric System," *IEEE Trans.* **PAS-93**: 1604–1612 (1974).

Hubbard, J. C., "Monitoring Electric-Load Forecasts," *IEEE Trans.* **PAS-88**: 797–801 (1969).

IEEE Committee Report, "Present Practices in the Economic Operation of Power Systems," *IEEE Trans.* **PAS-90**: 1768–1775 (1971). 3 discussions.

IEEE Committee, "Bibliography on Engineering Economics," *IEEE Trans.* **PAS-91**: 1976–1984 (1972).

Jeynes, P. H., *Profitability and Economic Choice*, The Iowa State University Press, Ames, Iowa (1968).

Jolissaint, C. H., N. V. Arvanitidis, D. G. Luenberger, "Decomposition of Real and Reactive Power Flows: A Method Suited for On-Line Applications," *IEEE Trans.* **PAS-91**: 661–670 (1972). 2 discussions.

Kaltenbach, J., J. Peschon, and E. H. Gehrig, "A Mathematical Optimization Technique for the Expansion of Electric Power Transmission Systems," *IEEE Trans.* **PAS-89**: 113–119 (1970). 1 discussion.

Kaltenback, J. C. and L. P. Hajdu, "Optimal Corrective Rescheduling for Power System Security," *IEEE Trans.* **PAS-90**: 843–851 (1971). 8 references.

Kerr, R. H., J. L. Scheidt, A. J. Fontana, Jr., and J. K. Wiley, "Unit Commitment," *IEEE Trans.* **PAS-85**: 417–421 (1966).

Kind, C. G., "Probability Technique Adds New Meaning To Demand Forecasting," *Electric Light & Power*, pp. 78–82 (January 1969).

Kirchmayer, L. K., A. G. Mellor, J. F. O'Mara, and J. R. Stevenson, "An Investigation of the

Economic Size of Steam-Electric Generating Units," *AIEE Trans.* **74**, Pt. III: 600–614 (1955). 7 discussions.

——, A. G. Mellor, and H. O. Simmins, Jr., "The Effect of Interconnections on Economic Generation Expansion Patterns," *AIEE Trans.* **76**, Pt. III: 203–214 (1957). 7 discussions.

——, *Economic Operation of Power Systems*, John Wiley & Sons, New York, (1958).

——, *Economic Control of Interconnected Systems*, John Wiley & Sons, New York, (1959).

—— and R. J. Ringlee, "Optimal Control of Thermal System Operation," IFAC Congress, Basel, Switzerland (September 1963).

Knight, U. G., *Power Systems Engineering and Mathematics*, Pergamon Press, Oxford, England (1972).

Lamont, J. W. and J. R. Tudor, "Survey of Operating Computer Applications, *Proc. Am. Power Conf.* **32**: 1142–1148 (1970).

—— and M. R. Gent, "Environmentally-Oriented Dispatching Techniques," *PICA Conf. Proc.*, pp. 421–427 (1973).

Latham, J. H., D. A. Nordman, and J. S. Voorhis, "Probability Approach to Electric Utility Load Forecasting," *IEEE Trans.* **PAS-87**: 496–504 (1968). 5 discussions.

Laughton, M. A. (editor), *3rd Power Systems Computation Conference Proceedings*, Rome (June 23–27, 1969). 2 volumes.

—— (editor), *Fourth Power Systems Computation Conference*, University of Grenoble (September 11–16, 1972). 3 volumes PSCC Proceedings.

Lev, Baruch, "A Note on the Analysis of Peak-Demand Forecasts of an Electrical Utility," *Operations Res.* **18**: 174–179 (1970).

Lijesen, D., P. J. Rosing, "Adaptive Forecasting of Hourly Loads Based on Load Measurements and Weather Information," *IEEE Trans.* **PAS-90**: 1757–1767 (1971). 1 discussion.

Lowery, P. G., "Generating Unit Commitment by Dynamic Programming," *IEEE Trans.* **PAS-85**: 422–426 (1966).

Lynskey, J. P. and R. J. Sloane, "Computer Analysis of Outage Data," *IEEE Trans.* **PAS-83**: 386–396 (1964).

Marsh, W. D., R. W. Moisan, and T. C. Murrell, "Perspectives on the Design and Application of Generation Planning Programs," Proceedings of the Nuclear Utilities Methods Symposium, Chattanooga, Tennessee (January 16–18, 1974). Sponsored by the American Nuclear Society, ORNL-TM-4443 (1974).

McDaniel, G. H. and A. F. Gabrielle, "Dispatching Pumped Storage Hydro," *IEEE Trans.* **PAS-85**: 465–471 (1966). 3 discussions.

Merrill, H. M. and F. C. Schweppe, "Bad Data Suppression in Power System Static State Estimation," *IEEE Trans.* **PAS-90**: 2718–2726 (1971).

Muckstadt, J. A. and R. C. Wilson, "An Application of Mixed-Integer Programming Duality to Scheduling Thermal Generating Systems," *IEEE Trans.* **PAS-87**: 1968–1978 (1968). 3 discussions.

Nabona, N. and L. L. Freris, "Optimisation of Economic Dispatch Through Quadratic and Linear Programming," *Proc. IEEE* **120**: 574–580 (1973).

Nicholson, H. and M. J. H. Sterling, "Optimum Dispatch of Active and Reactive Generation By Quadratic Programming," *IEEE Trans.* **PAS-92**: 644–645 (1973). 2 discussions.

Noakes, F. and A. Arismunandar, "Bibliography on Optimum Operation of Power Systems: 1919–1959," *AIEE Trans.* **81**, Pt. III: pp. 864–878 (1963). 2 discussions.

Nour, N. E. and H. H. Happ, "The Application of Transportation Techniques in Modelling Power Pools," *J. Computers and Operations Res.* **1**: 15–29 (1974).

Ogbuobiri, E. C., "Sparcity Techniques in Power-System Grid-Expansion Planning," pp.

219–230 of *Large Sparce Sets of Linear Equations*, J. K. Reid, (Ed.) Academic Press, New York (1971).

Paris, L. and M. Valtota, "Planning the Installation of Large Units in Interconnected Systems," CIGRL 22nd International Conference on Large Electric Systems at High Tension, Vol. II (1968). Paper 32-12.

Patton, A. D., "Short-Term Reliability Calculation," *IEEE Trans.* **PAS-89:** 509–513 (April 1970). 1 discussion.

Peschon, J., D. S. Piercy, W. F. Tinney, O. J. Tveit, and M. Cuenod, "Optimum Control of Reactive Power Flow," *IEEE Trans.* **PAS-87:** 40–48 (1968). 2 discussions.

——, H. W. Dommel, W. Powell, and D. W. Bree, Jr., "Optimum Power Flow for Systems with Area Interchange Controls," *IEEE Trans.* **PAS-91:** 898–905 (1972). 3 discussions.

PICA, 8th Power Industry Computer Application Conference, Minneapolis, Minnesota (June 4–6, 1973).

Pitcher, W. J., L. K. Kirchmayer, A. G. Mellor, and H. O. Simmons, Jr., "Generator Unit Size Study for the Dayton Power and Light Company," *AIEE Trans.* 77, Pt. III: 558–563 (1958). 2 discussions.

Porretta, B. and R. S. Dhillon, "Performance Evaluation of State Estimation form Line Flow Measurements on Ontario Hydro Power System," *IEEE Trans.* **PAS-92:** 1702–1712 (1973). 2 discussions.

Prewett, J. N., "Applied Algorithms to Load Dispatching," IEEE Conference on Computers in Power System Operation and Control, Bouremouth College of Technology, England, pp. 309–317 (1972).

PSCC, Power Systems Computation Conference (see Laughton, editor).

Puntel, W. R., N. D. Reppen, R. J. Ringlee, J. E. Platts, W. A. Ryan, and P. J. Sullivan, "An Automated Method for Long-Range Planning of Transmission Networks," *IEEE Trans.* **PAS-93** Abstract p. 3. discussion p. 12. (1974).

Rees, F. J. and R. E. Larson, "Computer-Aided Dispatching and Operations Planning for an Electric Utility with Multiple Types of Generation," *IEEE Trans.* **PAS-90:** 891–899 (March/April 1971). 1 discussion.

Reid, G. F. and L. Hasdorff, "Economic Dispatch Using Quadratic Programming," *IEEE Trans.* **PAS-92:** 2015–2023 (1973). 4 discussions.

Revington, A. M., "Application of Dual Decomposition Methods to Power System Loading," IEEE Conference on "Computers in Power System Operation and Control," Bournemouth College of Technology, England (May 1972).

Ringlee, R. J. and D. D. Williams, "Economic System Operation Considering Valve Throttling Losses, II – Distribution of System Loads by the Method of Dynamic Programming," *AIEE Trans.* **PAS-81:** 615–622 (1963). 5 discussions.

Sager, M. A. and A. J. Wood, "Corporate Model Programs for System Planning Evaluations," *IEEE Trans.* **PAS-91:** 1079–1084 (1972). 1 discussion.

Sager, M. A., R. J. Ringlee, and A. J. Wood, "A new generation production cost program to recognize forced outages," *IEEE Trans.* **PAS-91:** 2114–2124 (1972).

Sandiford, P. J., B. Bernhotz, and W. Shelson, "Three Applications of Operations Research in a Large Electric Utility," *Operations Res.* 4: 663–673 (1956).

Sasson, A. M., "Nonlinear Programming Solutions for Load-Flow, Minimum-Loss, and Economic Dispatching Problems," *IEEE Trans.* **PAS-88:** 399–409 (1969). 3 discussions.

——, F. Aboytes, R. Cardenas, F. Gomez, and F. Viloria, "A Comparison of Power System Static Optimization Techniques," *IEEE PICA Conf. Proc.*, pp. 329–337 (1971).

——, S. T. Ehrmann, P. Lynch, and L. S. Van Slyck, "Automatic Power System Network Topology Determination," *IEEE Trans.* **PAS-92:** 610–618 (1973). 4 discussions.

——, A. M. and H. M. Merrill, "Some applications of optimization techniques to power systems problems," *Proc. IEEE* 62: 959–972 (1974).

Sekin, Y. and J. Kawakawi, "Optimal Line Dispatching of Transmission Lines and Transformers," 4th International Power Systems Computation Conference, Grenoble, France (September 11–16, 1972). Paper 2.1/3, 15 pages.

Shen, C. M. and M. A. Laughton, "Power-System Load Scheduling with Security Constraints Using Dual Linear Programming," *IEEE Proc.* **117**: 2117–2127 (1970).

Shipley, R. B., A. D. Patton, and J. S. Denison, "Power Reliability Cost vs Worth," *IEEE Trans.* **PAS-91**: 2204–2212 (1972). 8 discussions.

Spears, H. T., K. L. Hicks, and S. T. Y. Lee, "Probability of Loss of Load for Three Areas," *IEEE Trans.* **PAS-89**: 521–526 (1970). 1 discussion.

Stadlin, W. O. "Economic Allocation of Regulating Margin," *IEEE Trans.* **PAS-70**: 1776–1781 (1971).

Stagg, G. W. and A. H. El-Abiad, *Computer Methods in Power System Analysis*, McGraw-Hill, New York (1968).

Stagg, G. W., J. F. Dopazo, O. A. Klitin, and L. S. VanSlyck, "Techniques for the Real-Time Monitoring of Power System Operations," *IEEE Trans.* **PAS-89**: 545–555 (1970). 5 discussions.

Stanton, K. N. and P. C. Gupta, "Forecasting Annual or Seasonal Peak Demand in Electric Utility Systems," *IEEE Trans.* **PAS-89**: 951–959 (1970). 1 discussion.

Steinberg, M. J. and T. H. Smith, *Economy Loading of Power Plants and Electric Systems*, John Wiley & Sons (1943).

Stevenson, W. D., *Elements of Power System Analysis*, McGraw-Hill, N.Y., 2nd Edition, (1962).

Sullivan, R. L., "Controlling Generator MVAR Loadings Using a Static Optimization Technique," *IEEE Trans.* **PAS-91**: 906–910 (1972). 2 discussions.

Thanikachalam, A. and J. R. Tudor, "Optimal Rescheduling of Power For System Reliability," *IEEE Trans.* **PAS-90**: 2186–2192 (1971). 1 discussion.

Theilsiefje, K. and H. Wagner, "Digital Method of Calculation for Optimum Instantaneous Reserve in Interconnected Operation," *Electrotechnische Zeitschrift (A)* **89**: 397–402 (1968).

Tinney, W. F., and C. E. Hart, "Power Flow Solution by Newton's Method," *IEEE Trans.* **PAS-86**: 1449–1460 (1967). 6 discussions.

Vassell, G. S. and N. Tibberts, "Analysis of Generating-Capacity Reserve Requirements for Interconnected Power Systems," *IEEE Trans.* **PAS-91**: 638–649 (1972). 5 discussions.

Watchorn, C. W., "Inside Hydrothermal Coordination," *IEEE Trans.* **PAS-86**: 106–117 (1967). 7 discussions.

Weedy, B. M., *Electric Power System*, 2nd Edition, John Wiley & Sons, New York (1972).

Wells, D. W., "Method for Economic Secure Loading of a Power System," *IEEE Proc.* **115**: 1190–1194 (1968).

Yu, Yao-nan and H. A. M. Moussa, "Optimal Stabilization of a Multi-Machine System," *IEEE Trans.* **PAS-91**: 1174–1182 (1972). 1 discussion.

II-7

THE PROCESS INDUSTRIES

Gary E. Blau
Richard R. Klimpel

The Dow Chemical Company (USA)

1. INTRODUCTION

In this chapter, the use of operations research (OR) in the process related industries will be demonstrated. Before presenting typical problem formulations, the nature of the industrial sector involved with processing will be discussed. An understanding of the "processing" concept is necessary for meaningful OR efforts.

The common dictionary definition of a process is: "a series of actions that lead to the achievement of a defined final state or characteristic." This general definition indicates the nature of the processing problem: control of a series of engineering operations to achieve a desired final product(s) with total overall minimum cost, time, manpower, etc. Knowledge of engineering operations is essential in OR applications. Each such operation usually involves the chemical or physical change of a substance(s) into some other desired and/or undesired substance(s). Because these engineering operations are based on fundamental concepts or "laws" in chemistry, physics, biology, etc., it is possible in theory, to mathematically describe any given processing problem in a completely fundamental or "microscopic" fashion, after which nothing more could be said mathematically to describe the process situation at hand. OR methodology could then be applied using these ideal or microscopic models. Usually these complete models consist of many variables and are highly nonlinear in nature, often involving differential equation representations and elements which are random variables.

Figure 1 illustrates conceptually the description of any one of these engineering operations (the nth operation from N distinct operations in the total process). Basically, each operation has an associated transition function (model), $\mathcal{T}_n$, capable of describing the change in the condition of any process state variables, x_n to y_n, (percent conversion, composition of product, degree of polymerization, etc.) as a function of the control variables (temperature, residence time, pressure, etc.). Also associated with each operation is an economic return function, R_n, (rate of return, net present value, etc.). It is the manner in which the N operations are placed relative to each other, plus the form of the transition and return functions, which give rise to various problem formulation classes. These problem structure classifications will be discussed later in some detail.

In actual practice, a complete microscopic transition model is usually not available, nor can one be developed within reasonable constraints of time, cost, or available knowledge. Thus, the problem is deciding what is a suitable mathematical approximation for the process? Formulating a suitable model depends on a variety of factors, and is indeed the crucial problem in OR applied to process environments. These factors are worthy of enumeration. They include: the state of the art of scientific or engineering know-how on the individual operations of concern; the data gathering capability of existing operations from both instrumentation and personnel points-of-view; the purpose of the effort such as design or feasibility analysis versus existing process improvement; limitations on availability of resources such as time, capital, manpower, etc.; the ability of existing and available mathematical solution methods to handle, in a practical

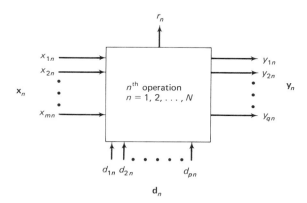

Transition function $y_n = T_n (d_n, x_n)$

Return function $r_n = R_n (d_n, x_n)$

Fig. 1. General engineering operation model.

manner, certain classes of models (and model sizes); and the degree of know-how and cooperation that exists among operating personnel.

The flow of this chapter will be directly related to demonstrating how the above factors interact in an OR study. Emphasis will be placed on important and commonly used problem formulations rather than on details of problem solution. Initial examples will begin with simple engineering operation models that are linear (or approximately linear) in form, deterministic in nature, and the goal of the analysis oriented towards planning and/or feasibility studies. This will be followed by formulations which are increasingly nonlinear in nature and oriented towards actual process description, control, and/or design. The final portion of the chapter will be devoted to some areas of current research, with emphasis on describing how to build general nonlinear models having elements that are random variables.

The problem formulations presented in this chapter are heavily oriented towards mathematical programming methodology. While other types of OR methodology are also prevalent in the processing environment, they generally take on a form similar to those of most other industries, and hence will not be specifically pointed out in this chapter. A large number of references are available describing OR applications in the various process industries. Some of these are Klimpel [1973], A Decade of Digital Computing [1969], Klimpel [1969], IBM KWIC Index [1967], and OR Literature Digest Service [1961-present]. The examples presented in this chapter are meant to be typical in nature (although somewhat simplified), and no attempt is made to be exhaustive by either class of application or by the various industries making up the processing sector of the economy.

The use of OR techniques in any particular industrial firm may vary greatly, even within those having a common class of processes. In addition to the factors mentioned previously, the beliefs and backgrounds of high-level management personnel play the vital roles in the extent and support of OR studies. Management holds the key in overcoming organizational difficulties. In many processing firms, the current attitudes towards OR studies were partially set by the capabilities and success of the initial personnel involved in such work during the late 1950's and early 1960's. Most of these personnel were not directly trained in OR. Quite frankly, the value of OR was over-sold in many firms and the efforts were subsequently discarded. Second generation efforts are beginning anew with better success. It can safely be said that, presently, almost all processing related industrial firms do use at least a part of the methodology discussed in this Chapter; for example, linear programming (LP). With regard to the benefits, it is difficult to sometimes measure such value directly. It has been the authors' experience that the use of optimization techniques can and has resulted in significant operational and design improvements that can be measured in financial terms. At the very least, one should gain from an OR study a better understanding of the underlying phenomena, sensitivity, and alternatives involved in the problem at hand.

2. DISTRIBUTION RELATED PROBLEMS

In most processing environments, the problem of distributing resources in a reasonably optimal fashion is almost a daily problem. This includes the classical "customer demand-product source" shipping allocation problem, which can occur in many contexts. Usually, such a minimum cost shipment problem is analyzed in conjunction with some other important, directly related problem, such as process operation scheduling, material blending, warehouse inventory analysis, etc. The nature of the material and cost representations involved in distribution problems are often suitably approximated by linear functions so that LP may be used. In some cases, the cost functions are nonlinear so that quadratic or separable programming may be required.

2.1 Coal Distribution Analysis

A typical distribution formulation is that of coal distribution in the open-pit region of Central Pennsylvania (Manula and Kim [1966]). The major coal market in this area is in the thermal generation of electricity, which requires large guaranteed deliveries of coal, consisting of relatively uniform grades. The problem arises in that the majority of coal mining operations in the region are of insufficient size to take advantage of the economics of large tonnage shipping. Even more important is the rather heterogeneous nature of coal production in the area. So, quality control by individual mines is limited. In order to meet utility requirements and to equalize outside competition, it is possible to pool individual resources and make adjustments to existing types of operations, rather than change current handling methods or layouts at the mine sites.

Thus, the problem objective is to indicate mine operating levels to the coal producers such that their net delivered price of the make-up coal on a BTU basis is maximized. In addition, the mixed coal product must satisfy the utility requirements. Let the decision variables be denoted by d_{in} where d_{in} is the amount of coal shipped from mine i (total of p mines) to collection point n (total of N central collection points). The constraint set consists of the following: total production leaving ith mine must be less than or equal to the daily capacity of that mine:

$$\sum_{n=1}^{N} d_{in} \leqslant q_i, \quad i = 1, 2, \ldots, p \tag{1}$$

The amount received from the mines must equal the projected daily demand by the utility (known in advance):

$$\sum_{i=1}^{p} \sum_{n=1}^{N} d_{in} = y \tag{2}$$

If a_i is the percentage of ash in the coal from the ith mine, and if a is the permissible ash percentage of the mix, the total permitted level at the generating station is:

$$\sum_{i=1}^{p} \sum_{n=1}^{N} a_i d_{in} \leqslant ay \tag{3}$$

Similar constraints can be set up for sulfur, moisture, volatile matter, ash fusion, and fixed carbon:

$$\begin{aligned}
\sum\sum s_i d_{in} &\leqslant sy \quad \text{sulfur} \\
\sum\sum w_i d_{in} &\leqslant wy \quad \text{moisture} \\
\sum\sum v_i d_{in} &\geqslant vy \quad \text{volatile matter} \\
\sum\sum f_i d_{in} &\geqslant fy \quad \text{ash fusion} \\
c_l y \leqslant \sum\sum c_i d_{in} &\geqslant c_u y \quad \text{fixed carbon limits}
\end{aligned} \tag{4}$$

Nonnegativity is required so that

$$d_{in} \geqslant 0, \quad i = 1, 2, \ldots, p, \quad n = 1, 2, \ldots, N \tag{5}$$

Finally, the return function may be stated as:

$$\text{maximize} \sum_{i=1}^{p} \sum_{n=1}^{N} (\lambda_i - \gamma_{in}) d_{in}, \tag{6}$$

where λ_i is the delivered price of coal at the collection points, and γ_{in} is the transportation (truck) charges from mine i to site n. A number of distribution plans were evaluated using this model.

3. BLENDING PROBLEMS

Many operations utilize material blending, somewhere in the process, for the purposes of promoting chemical reactions or meeting product specifications. In many cases, blending models are taken to be linear and deterministic in nature. Rather extreme care should be exercised when using such models because the physical nature of the blending process is inherently nonlinear. Often, these nonlinearities are convex in nature and may be linearized quite easily. Two examples will be given to illustrate typical blending problems. In some cases, quadratic or separable programming is required to suitably describe the situation at hand. This area will be illustrated in more detail in later sections.

3.1 Particulate Blending of Chemicals

The first example is concerned with the blending of batches of a homogeneous chemical substance in particle form so as to meet a desired final product quality mix (Klimpel [1973]). This problem represents a blending formulation which allows for statistical variation in the data. Let z_k be the quantity of material available in the kth batch of differing size distribution, and p be the number of such batches available for blending into V, the quantity (weight) of final mixed product. If m size intervals are to be considered, then the fractional size-weight distribution for the kth batch is $a_{1k}, a_{2k}, \ldots, a_{mk} \left(\sum_{i=1}^{m} a_{ik} = 1.0 \right)$, and for the blended product is $b_1, b_2, \ldots, b_m \left(\sum_{i=1}^{m} b_i = 1.0 \right)$. Using the notation of Figure 1, let the output state be the constant y_i representing the actual weight of size interval i desired in the final product, so that $y_i = Vb_i$. The decision variables d_i represent the amount of material of the ith batch used in producing the blended product mix. Using the least absolute sum of errors criterion for quantifying the goodness of match between various blends, the return function takes the form:

$$\text{minimize} \quad \sum_{i=1}^{m} (u_i + v_i). \tag{7}$$

The u_i's and v_i's are slack variables representing positive and negative error in the m balance constraint equations:

$$a_{i1}d_1 + a_{i2}d_2 + \cdots + a_{ip}d_p + u_i - v_i = y_i, \quad i = 1, 2, \ldots, m \tag{8}$$

Also needed are a conservation of material equation

$$\sum_{j=1}^{p} d_j = V, \tag{9}$$

and p batch quantity limitation equations:

$$d_j \leqslant z_j, \quad j = 1, 2, \ldots, p. \tag{10}$$

A centering of errors equation (when desired) can be imposed

$$\sum_{i=1}^{m} u_i - \sum_{i=1}^{m} v_i = 0, \tag{11}$$

and, of course, the standard $(p + 2m)$ nonnegativity constraints:

$$d_j \geqslant 0, \qquad\qquad j = 1, 2, \ldots, p$$
$$u_i \geqslant 0, \quad v_i \geqslant 0, \qquad i = 1, 2, \ldots, m. \tag{12}$$

Solution of this formulation represents a mix that best satisfies the desired final product blend according to the least absolute sum criterion (with its corresponding statistical interpretation for a double exponentially distributed error). A similar formulation was also established, using a minimax criterion. In this case, the return function takes the form:

$$\text{minimize } \gamma \tag{13}$$

There are $2m$ balance equations required of the form:

$$a_{i1}d_1 + a_{i2}d_2 + \cdots + a_{ip}d_p + \gamma \geqslant y_i$$
$$a_{i1}d_1 + a_{i2}d_2 + \cdots + a_{ip}d_p - \gamma \leqslant y_i, \qquad i = 1, 2, \ldots, m. \tag{14}$$

In addition, the conservation (9) and quantity constraints (10) given before are necessary, plus $(p + 1)$ nonnegativity constraints:

$$\gamma \geqslant 0; d_j \geqslant 0; j = 1, 2, \ldots, p \tag{15}$$

A related multiple equipment scheduling problem is often present when analyzing blending operations. An integer programming formulation of grinding circuit scheduling related to the chemical blending problem just discussed, for example, has been reported (Klimpel and Austin [1971]).

3.2 Metal Alloy Blending

The second example is a classic in the blending area, consisting of a linear model for metal alloy blending in a single furnace operation. The goal here is to determine how to make the most economical use of raw materials of known cost, availability, and composition, in computing a furnace charge that will make a specified aluminum alloy blend.

The decision variables in this problem represent the amount, in pounds, of each of the raw material sources available for use in the final blend. The return function, to be minimized, is then represented by a linear function giving the total cost of the raw materials. The selection of the latter are, in turn, subject to three sets of constraints. The first set of constraints represent the limits of each ingredient element which may be present in the final alloy. The second set state the raw material availability limitations, and the final constraint insures that the minimum weight of furnace charge is satisfied. An example of this type of problem, applied to the manufacture of aluminum alloys, is given in the reference (IBM-Aluminum).

4. LINEAR MODELS OF SINGLE ENGINEERING OPERATIONS

In previous sections of this chapter, a variety of processing situations have been described which involved linear model representations. The formulations presented were aimed at analyzing specific problems yet did not directly involve the description of specific engineering operations (e.g., a particular piece of equipment or chemical reaction, etc.). A complete "microscopic" model of a given engineering operation usually involves nonlinear equation representations. However, in practice, approximate models are often necessary and sufficient. In this section, a typical example will be presented, in which a linear model is used to represent a single engineering operation. Usually, any single engineering operation so modeled is part of a larger overall process. Thus, analysis of such a model alone, represents a sub-optimal outlook which should, if at all possible, be placed in a total process context. This total outlook should at least be one of applying experience if not done quantitatively.

4.1 Blast Furnace Production Scheduling

A good example of a single engineering operation linear model is the problem of production planning of a steel producing blast furnace operation that maintains material balances and chemical equilibrium while minimizing material cost (Fabian [1967]). The model allows for the allocation of some input materials among four outputs (metal, slag, top gas, top dust) and determines the coke, limestone, and air requirements. The p decision variables are represented by d_j, where each d_j represents the amount of the jth material used in the operation, and where each material is composed of constituent elements or compounds.

The constraint set consists of equations obtained from a variety of sources, including chemical mass balance considerations, empirical relationships, etc. Because of the complexity and length of description necessary to the understanding of this example, only selected types of constraints will be given. Readers interested in the complete model should consult the original source (Fabian [1967]). A large number of chemical element balances are required. For example, if q_j is the fraction of the jth input in the hot molten section (as contrasted to the escaping gases), and z_j is the fractional phosphorus analysis of the jth material, then the weight of phosphorous availability may be expressed as:

$$\sum_{j=1}^{p} q_j z_j d_j = y_{\text{Phosphorus}}. \tag{16}$$

There are a number of possible constraints related to material availability, etc.

Various other constraints describing coking coal requirements must be deduced from heat requirements, and require knowledge of the heat involved with chemical reactions, heat loss to cooling systems, etc. Thus, for example, the heat content, z, in the molten section, would be given by:

$$\sum_{j=1}^{s} y_j h_j = z, \qquad (17)$$

where h_j is the heat holding capability per unit of weight of material j, and s represents the number of materials present $(s < p)$ in the molten material. Oxygen is a necessary material for reaction and must be carefully controlled. If t_j is the fractional usable oxygen content of the jth material, then the weight of oxygen, O, may be given by:

$$\sum_{j=1}^{p} t_j d_j + 0.23\, d_{\text{wind}} = y_O. \qquad (18)$$

There are also restrictions on the amount of wind that can be added, because of limitations on heating and blowing equipment as well as requirements that the composition of the exit gases (including oxygen) must meet.

The return function is the minimization of costs involved in using the various available materials, and takes the form

$$\text{minimize} \sum_{k=1}^{v} \lambda_k d_k, \qquad (19)$$

where v is the number of raw materials to be purchased $(v < p)$, and λ_k the associated costs. The return function is subject to the type of constraints presented previously plus variable nonnegativity constraints:

$$d_i \geqslant 0, \quad i = 1, 2, \ldots, p. \qquad (20)$$

Thus, the final solution gives a mode of operation (production schedule) that yields a product of specified quality and quantity in the cheapest manner possible from the raw material point of view. This return function could be modified to include maintenance and operating costs, as well as certain product credits that can be derived.

5. LINEAR MODELS OF SIMULTANEOUS MULTIPLE ENGINEERING OPERATIONS

In this section, several problem formulations will be given, illustrating how an entire processing environment can be analyzed. It is with such problems (the simultaneous analysis of multiple engineering operations) that OR begins to achieve its full potential as a key input in the decision making function. By nature, this type of analysis tends to be rather difficult to formulate and bring to successful use. This is because of the magnitude of the technical problems involved (the many models and variables required) and the organizational/ personnel problems usually present (cutting organizational lines, philosophies, etc.).

As to model development in a study of this type, linear models have been most prevalently used, due to the general availability and ease of use of LP; however, care must be exercised when using linear approximations for such a potentially complicated problem. Each operation should be analyzed separately as to model suitability (and the goal of the overall analysis) before the overall analysis is actually carried out. It is very easy to end up with physically meaningless results if such care is not exercised. In the processing environment, the major problem is usually one of suitably representing, by linear models, known physical and/or economic nonlinearities.

Several comments on the use of the post-optimality capabilities of LP are appropriate, before the presentation of the example problem formulations of this section. The sensitivity analyses offered by the use of shadow prices and/ or coefficients ranging are inherent and efficient by-products of many LP computational algorithms. It is this ease of "testing" the numerical sensitivity of a final optimal solution that adds to the usefulness of LP problem formulations. Unfortunately, such sensitivity testing is much more difficult to achieve when nonlinear or integer variables are introduced into a formulation.

It has been the authors' experience that the practice of using shadow prices and coefficient ranging is very important, but too often neglected by many industrial analysts. In industrial practice, it is rarely possible to use or implement the results of a calculated optimal solution exactly as given. The reasons for this are many, and include equipment requirements, conflict with management policies, uncertainty in the model coefficients, etc. It is very important, for example, to know how dependent the optimal solution is on the numerical values of coefficients in the problem formulation (especially right hand side values and objective function coefficients). In most processing problems, it is essential for an analyst to develop knowledge of a "region" of practical (operational) optimality. If this is not done, the probability of an OR approach being successfully implemented is considerably diminished. For this reason, many industrial analysts rely very heavily on concepts of random-element simulation (Klimpel [1973]), rather than on optimization models, even when the later are more appropriate.

This is somewhat unfortunate, as the proper use of the available post-optimality characteristics of LP can help greatly with this aspect. Such information is useful in a wide variety of applications, including setting raw material and product prices, sizing of plant and warehouse facilities, determining manpower pools, and setting quality control standards.

5.1   Investment Analysis of a Mining and Processing Complex

The first formulation example to be given is an investment analysis problem (Klimpel and Klein [1966]). The problem is one of determining future capital investment requirements and optimal sizing of production plants in a chemical-mineral processing complex under consideration.   An attempt to analyze this problem immediately encounters two specific problems common to almost every multiple operation process: integer variables and a mixture of convex and nonconvex relationships.   The integer variable representations arise in such areas as scheduling chemical reaction vessels which are either running or idle, investment set-up costs, etc.   Nonlinear functional relationships arise in areas such as chemical kinetics, blending, the maintenance of variable fluid flow ratios, the increasing returns of scale in capital cost of plants, etc.

In sizing production plants, for example, a plant of double capacity requires less fixed capital than two plants of single capacity, so that a relationship of the following form holds:

$$\text{Capital cost} = aV^b, \tag{21}$$

where V is capacity, a is a cost coefficient, and b (for chemical plants) is between 0.5 and 0.8.   Figure 2 illustrates the situation that would be necessary for simple logical linearization techniques to be applied.   Figure 3 demonstrates the situation where either multiple case studies of a linear program should be run (at points B, C, etc.), or where separable LP or appropriate nonlinear programming techniques could be used.

Consider the evaluation of a new investment plant, shown in Figure 4, for the treatment of an abundant but hard-to-process natural resource x_{11}, and its

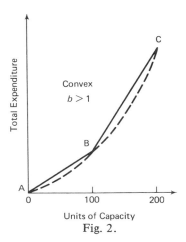

Fig. 2.

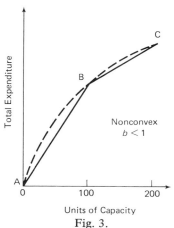

Fig. 3.

conversion to a variety of products. Because of the goal of this analysis, investment feasibility of plants not yet built, the model relationships are kept as simple as possible. The basic process at plant 1 yields three streams—y_{11}, y_{21}, and y_{31} —which are related to x_{11} by steady-state chemical mass balance transition functions:

$$y_{11} = 41.62x_{11}$$
$$y_{21} = 5.59x_{11} \tag{22}$$
$$y_{31} = 0.555x_{11}.$$

The product y_{31} is readily marketable, whereas a portion of y_{11}, where

$$y_{11} = (d_{11} + d_{21} + d_{31} + x_{12}), \tag{23}$$

has several limited markets such that

$$d_{11} \leqslant 1200$$
$$d_{21} \leqslant 3000. \tag{24}$$

The stream y_{11} may also be converted (either totally or in part) by another proposed plant 2, which produces a product y_{12}. The third stream y_{21} where

$$y_{21} = x_{13} + x_{14}, \tag{25}$$

is convertible to two alternate products, y_{13} from plant 3, and y_{24} from plant 4. The material balance transition relationships are

$$y_{13} = 0.855\, x_{13}$$
$$y_{24} = 2.62\, x_{14}. \tag{26}$$

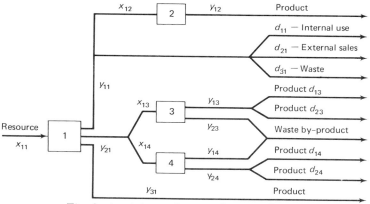

Fig. 4. A mining and processing complex.

The products y_{24} and y_{13} are visualized to enter two markets: foreign (d_{14} and d_{13}) and domestic (d_{24} and d_{23}), with quite different revenues per unit:

$$y_{24} = d_{14} + d_{24} \text{ and } y_{13} = d_{13} + d_{23}. \tag{27}$$

The products have the following market saturation limits imposed:

$$d_{13} \leqslant 300$$
$$d_{14} \leqslant 250 \tag{28}$$
$$d_{24} \leqslant 300,$$

with the product d_{24} exhibiting strong elasticity in its demand curve. One waste product ($y_{23} + y_{14}$) requires costly waste disposal facilities, with costs increasing strongly with increasing amount. The generation of waste is given by:

$$y_{23} = 4010 \, x_{13}$$
$$y_{14} = 1340 \, x_{14}. \tag{29}$$

As demand growth and price changes over time are visualized to be moderate because of the bulk character of the materials, it is assumed that plants will be built once, originally, for their full capacity, and would operate at their capacity levels. It is also assumed that the processes become obsolete within a decade, so that evaluation is made for a ten year life period. The required fixed plus working capital for plant n of capacity V_n follows the function:

$$\text{total capital of } n = (a_n) + b_n V_n + c_n V_n^{qn}. \tag{30}$$

The annual operating cost is approximated as:

$$\text{annual cost of } n = (e_n) + f_n V_n + g_n V_n^2 + h_n V_n^{qn}. \tag{31}$$

The constants a_n and e_n are vanishing fixed expenditures (integer set-up costs), incurred only when a plant is built and operated. Revenues are taken to be linear functions, except in the case of product d_{24}, as mentioned previously. The annual cash flows are calculated algebraically, discounted to the present, and summed over the selected ten-year horizon to get the algebraic net present value return function.

The return function exibiting the various product and plant characteristics mentioned is then:

$$\text{maximize} \quad R = -16{,}000\, x_{11}^{0.9} - 1{,}950\, x_{11} + 0.17\, x_{11}^{2}$$

$$+ 840\, d_{11} + 672\, d_{21} + 100\, y_{31}$$

$$- 24{,}000\, y_{12}^{0.8} + 7{,}000\, y_{12} - 3{,}000{,}000\, y_{12}^{*}$$

$$- 38{,}000\, y_{13}^{0.85} - 12{,}000\, y_{13} + 1.5\, y_{13}^{2}$$

$$+ 51{,}000\, d_{13} + 26{,}000\, d_{23} - 1{,}000{,}000\, y_{13}^{*}$$

$$- 12{,}000\, y_{24}^{0.87} - 26{,}000\, y_{24} + 54{,}000\, d_{14}$$

$$+ 47{,}500\, d_{24} - 63.3\, d_{24}^{2} - 2{,}000{,}000\, y_{24}^{*}$$

$$- 0.75\, (y_{23} + y_{14})^{1.05} - 0.33\, (y_{23} + y_{14}),$$

subject to the engineering and market constraints plus nonnegativity of the variables. The variables y_{12}^{*}, y_{13}^{*}, and y_{24}^{*} relate to the set-up costs and should assume the value either zero or one ($y_{12}^{*} = 0$, if $y_{12} = 0$ and $y_{12}^{*} = 1$, if $y_{12} > 0$, etc). The problem was solved using a linear constrained nonlinear programming algorithm (Klimpel and Klein [1966]) and more recently with a mixed integer LP approach (Klimpel and Burroughs [1974]).

With this type of formulation, the following questions were answered: should the project be undertaken? if undertaken, what should the rate of resource x_{11} processing be? and which supplementary conversion plants should be built and to what capacities?

5.2 Oil Refinery Scheduling

The second multiple operation formulation to be given is that of oil refinery production scheduling (IBM-Introduction to LP [1964]). This application area represents a "classic" use of OR in the processing industry. A refinery consists of a number of operations for separating, changing, or combining different crude oil components (fractions). In the formulation to be presented here, only two operations, a pipe still and a catalytic cracking unit, will be analyzed. The pipe still is essentially a distillation column which separates a given crude into three general fractions: light naphtha, medium distillate, and heavy residium (fuel). A catalytic cracking unit (cat cracking) operates on the medium distillate fraction and by chemical means (breaking of heavy molecules into lighter and smaller molecules) changes it into three outputs: catalytic naphtha, light cycle stock, and heavy cycle stock. The later two outputs may be recycled back into the cat cracker. The terms virgin naphtha and virgin distillate refer to fractions not processed further but only used for blending.

From these two processes, seven components are obtained which may be combined to produce four products. The seven components and products are listed in Table 1. Mnemonic variable names will be used in this example to assist in problem understanding. The profitability of the refinery operation depends, of course, on costs of raw materials and costs of operation, the characteristics of the various operations involved, and the prices of the final products. Like any processing plant, considerable flexibility is available in running the refinery, including the choice of crudes, operating characteristics of the pipe still and cat cracker, the component proportions used in blending final products, and the mix of final products. Table 2 lists the refinery operations, illustrated schematically in Figure 5, that will be discussed in the following paragraphs. In Figure 5, rectangular boxes indicate engineering operations while boxes with peaked roofs indicate material flow balancing points. The constraint set and return function data are tabulated in Table 3.

The return function is one of maximizing profit and represents a straight-forward summation of costs and incomes of the various components and products. The material balance equations are statements indicating that material

TABLE 1. REFINERY VARIABLES

CR1F	Crude 1 run to fuel, MB/D
CR1D	Crude 1 run to distillate, MB/D
CR2F	Crude 2 run to fuel, MB/D
CR2D	Crude 2 run to distillate, MB/D
CATVD	Cat feed virgin distillate, MB/D
CATLC	Cat feed light cycle, MB/D
CATHC	Cat feed heavy cycle, MB/D
RSFUL	Residuum to fuel, MB/D
HCFUL	Heavy cycle to fuel, MB/D
LCFUL	Light cycle to fuel, MB/D
VDFUL	Virgin distillate to fuel, MB/D
VNAPD	Virgin naphtha to distillate (heating oil), MB/D
VDISD	Virgin distillate to distillate (heating oil), MB/D
LCCYD	Light cycle to distillate (heating oil), MB/D
VN1R	Virgin naphtha (crude 1) to regular gasoline, MB/D
VN2R	Virgin naphtha (crude 2) to regular gasoline, MB/D
CNPR	Catalytic naphtha (crude 1) to regular gasoline, MB/D
VN1P	Virgin naphtha (crude 1) to premium gasoline, MB/D
VN2P	Virgin naphtha (crude 2) to premium gasoline, MB/D
CNPP	Catalytic naphtha to premium gasoline, MB/D

TABLE 2. REFINERY RELATIONSHIPS

VNAP1	Virgin naptha 1, material balance, MB/D
VNAP2	Virgin naphtha 2, material balance, MB/D
VDIS	Virgin distillate, material balance, MB/D
RESID	Residuum, material balance, MB/D
CATN	Catalytic naphtha, material balance, MB/D
LCCY	Light cat cycle oil, material balance, MB/D
HCCY	Heavy cat cycle oil, material balance, MB/D
CRBAL	Crude balance (crude 1 = $\frac{1}{3}$ total), MB/D of crude 1
PSCAP	Pipe-still capacity, MB/D
CR2AV	Crude 2 availability, MB/D
TFCAT	Total feed cat capacity, MB/D
FREQ	Fuel oil volume requirement, MB/D
DREQ	Distillate (heating oil) volume requirement, MB/D
DSPEC	Distillate (heating oil) specification, M CON. B/D better than spec.
RREQ	Regular gasoline volume requirement, MB/D
RSPEC	Regular gasoline specification, M OCT. B/D better than spec.
PREQ	Premium gasoline volume requirement, MB/D
PSPEC	Premium gasoline specification, M OCT. B/D better than spec.
where	MB/D = thousands of barrels per day
	$M/D = thousands of dollars per day
	M CON. B = thousand contamination number of bbls.
	M OCT. B = thousand octane number bbls.

flow must balance (the sum of input flow must equal the sum of output flow). Thus, for example, the constraint VNAP1 refers to virgin naphtha from crude 1. At the point indicated on Figure 5, the material flowing in must equal the material flowing out to the two types of gasoline:

$$0.1 \text{ CR1F} + 0.15 \text{ CR1D} = \text{VN1R} + \text{VN1P}. \qquad (32)$$

The coefficients of the first four material balance constraints are summarized in Table 4. The next three material balance constraints relate to the catalytic cracking unit operating characteristics summarized in Table 5. Thus, for example, a balance on the gasoline outputs from the unit would be:

$$0.7 \text{ CATVD} + 0.6 \text{ CATLC} + 0.3 \text{ CATHC} = \text{CNPR} + \text{CNPP}. \qquad (33)$$

The constraint CR2AV is a statement of the maximum availability of crude 2 per day which is 75,000 barrels.

The pipe still constraints are related to the requirement that crude 1 can make up no more than one-third of the total crude input:

$$\text{CR1F} + \text{CR1D} \leqslant 0.5 \text{ CR2F} + 0.5 \text{ CR2D}, \qquad (34)$$

and that the pipe still has a total limiting capacity of 100,000 barrels per day:

$$\text{CR1F} + \text{CR1D} + \text{CR2F} + \text{CR2D} \leqslant 100. \qquad (35)$$

TABLE 3. REFINERY RETURN FUNCTION AND CONSTRAINTS

Column groups:
- **Pipe-still activities:** CRIF, CRID, CR2F, CR2D
- **Cat-cracker activities:** CATVD, CATLC, CATHC
- **Fuel-blending activities:** RSFUL, HCFUL, LCFUL, VDFUL
- **Heating oil-blending activities:** VNAPD, VDISD, LCCYD
- **Regular gasoline-blending activities:** VN1R, VN2R, CNPR
- **Premium gasoline-blending activities:** VN1P, VN2P, CNPP

Row Name	CRIF	CRID	CR2F	CR2D	CATVD	CATLC	CATHC	RSFUL	HCFUL	LCFUL	VDFUL	VNAPD	VDISD	LCCYD	VN1R	VN2R	CNPR	VN1P	VN2P	CNPP	RHS
PROFT (Return function)	-3.0	-3.0	-3.1	-3.1	-.1	-.15	-.16	+2.5	+2.5	+2.5	+2.5	+4	+4	+4	+4.5	+4.5	+4.5	+5	+5	+5	
VNAP1	-.1	-.15										1			1			1			= 0
VNAP2			-.2	-.25												1			1		= 0
VDIS	-.25	-.4	-.2	-.35	.1						1		1								= 11
RESID	-.6	-.4	-.5	-.3	.1			.9													= 0
CATN					-.7	-.6	-.3										1			1	= 0
LCCY					-.3	1	-.7			1				1							=-11
HCCY					-.5	-.5	1	.1	1												= 0
CR2AV			1	1																	≤ 75
CRBAL	1	1	-.5	-.5																	≤ 0
PSCAP	1	1	1	1																	≤ 100
TFCAT					1.6	1.2	1.1														≤ 46
FREQ								1	1	1	1										≤ 50
DREQ												1	1	1							≥ 30
DSPEC												-5	-1	10							≤ 0
RREQ															1	1	1				≤ 10
RSPEC															0	1	-7				≤ 0
PREQ																		1	1	1	≥ 25
PSPEC																		4	5	-3	≤ 0

Row groupings:
- Material-balance constraints: VNAP1, VNAP2, VDIS, RESID, CATN, LCCY, HCCY, CR2AV
- Pipe-still constraints: CRBAL, PSCAP
- Cat-cracker constraint: TFCAT
- Fuel-blending constraint: FREQ
- Heating oil-blending constraints: DREQ, DSPEC
- Regular gasoline-blending constraints: RREQ, RSPEC
- Premium gasoline-blending constraints: PREQ, PSPEC

The cat cracker constraint is again a maximum capacity constraint which takes into consideration recycle streams:

$$1.6\,\text{CATVD} + 1.2\,\text{CATLC} + 1.1\,\text{CATHC} \leqslant 46. \tag{36}$$

A constraint on the maximum production of fuel oil is desired so that:

$$\text{RSFUL} + \text{HCFUL} + \text{LCFUL} + \text{VDFUL} \leqslant 50. \tag{37}$$

The distillate (heating oil) blending characteristics are described in Table 6, and lead to the two constraints listed in Table 3. The first is the minimum requirement on heating oil production:

$$\text{VNAPD} + \text{VDISD} + \text{LCCYD} \geqslant 30; \tag{38}$$

and the second, stating that the contamination number of the heating oil must be no greater than 55:

$$50\,\text{VNAPD} + 54\,\text{VDISD} + 65\,\text{LCCYD} \leqslant 55\,\text{VNAPD} + 55\,\text{VDISD} + 55\,\text{LCCYD}. \tag{39}$$

The gasoline capacity and octane requirements are established in exactly the

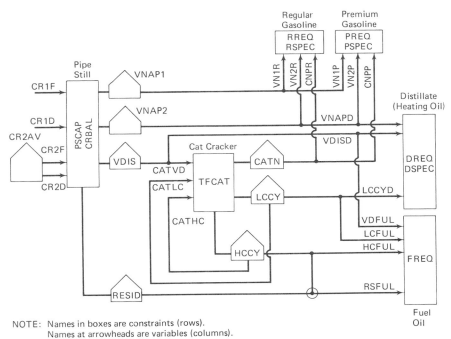

NOTE: Names in boxes are constraints (rows).
Names at arrowheads are variables (columns).

Fig. 5. Flow diagram of refinery process.

TABLE 4. FRACTIONAL YIELDS WHEN OPERATING PIPE STILL FOR MAXIMUM FUEL OR MAXIMUM DISTILLATE

| | Crude 1 | | Crude 2 | |
	Fuel	Distillate	Fuel	Distillate
Virgin naphtha	.10	.15	.20	.25
Virgin distillate	.25	.40	.20	.35
Residuum	.60	.40	.50	.30

same fashion as that of heating oil, with the necessary operating characteristics given in Table 7.

Complete process analyses, such as that of the refinery model, often play a major role in the scheduling of short-term operations, because of changes in costs, demand, raw material availability, etc. The complexity of these processes simply does not allow for such changes to be profitably incorporated into operating schedules without mathematical analysis. Such an approach is standard operating procedure for large processing complexes.

6. OPTIMIZATION OF MULTIOPERATION SERIAL SYSTEMS

Frequently, the N engineering operations, described in Figure 1, are structured or connected in such a way that the output from the first operation or stage is an input to the second stage, the output from which goes into the third stage, and so on. A process with this head-to-tail information flow structure is said to be a serial process. In such systems, a decision made at some stage will only influence the information flow in subsequent or downstream stages. For a serial process, Bellman's Principle of Optimality may be stated in the following form: "A serial process is optimized when the decisions for the downstream stages constitute an optimal policy with respect to the input they receive from

TABLE 5. CATALYTIC CRACKER OPERATING CHARACTERISTICS

	Virgin Distillate	Light Cycle	Heavy Cycle
Direct feed	1.1	1.0	1.0
Internal recycle, bbl.	0.6	0.2	0.1
Cat Naphtha, bbl.	0.7	0.6	0.3
Light cycle, bbl.	0.3	–	0.7
Heavy cycle, bbl.	0.5	0.5	–

TABLE 6. DISTILLATE BLENDING CHARACTERISTICS

	Contamination Number	Volume
Virgin distillate	54	As produced plus 11 MB/D from storage
Virgin naphtha 2	50	As produced
Light-cycle stock	65	As produced less 11 MB/D to storage
Specification	55	At least 30 MB/D

upstream." By applying this principle it is possible to tear down or decompose the original $N \otimes p$ variable optimization problem into a sequence of N optimization problems, each having p variables. This decomposition is particularly important in the process industries, where N is frequently large; i.e., $N > 10$. The example chosen to illustrate this technique is the staging of chemical reactors. Not only is this an important industrial application, but it has the advantage of introducing basic concepts which will be used later.

6.1 Chemical Reaction in a Stirred Vessel

Chemical reactions designed to turn raw materials into more valuable products are often conducted in large stirred vessels called reactors. Raw materials flow into the reactor and a product stream is withdrawn, as shown in Figure 6. The composition and temperature of the contents of the reactor are kept uniform throughout by sufficient agitation. Suppose m different components, $A_1, A_2,$ $\ldots, A_m$ are taking part; i.e., being consumed or being produced, in the chemical reactions in the vessel. Let $\mathbf{r} \equiv (r_1, r_2, \ldots, r_m)$ be an m-dimensional column vector, representing the rate at which the different species are reacting (i.e., the change in the amount of the components present per unit volume). From elementary reactor theory $\mathbf{r} = \mathbf{r}(\mathbf{x}, T)$, where $\mathbf{x} \equiv (x_1, x_2, \ldots, x_m)$, is an m-

TABLE 7. OCTANE NUMBERS OF GASOLINE BLENDS

	Octane Number	Volume
Virgin naphtha crude 1	85	
Virgin naphtha crude 2	84	
Catalytic naphtha	92	
Premium specification	89	At least 25 MB/D
Regular specification	85	At most 10 MB/D

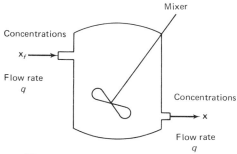

Fig. 6. Chemical flow reactor.

dimensional column vector representing the amounts or concentrations of the components in the reactor and T is the temperature. The microscopic model form of $r(x, T)$, describing a simple reaction, is complex and difficult to obtain. Therefore, in practice an empirical model is used of the form:

$$r_i(\mathbf{x}, T) = k_i \prod_{j=1}^{m} x_j^{a_{ij}} - k_i' \prod_{j=1}^{m} x_j^{b_{ij}}, \qquad i = 1, 2, \ldots, m, \tag{40}$$

where a_{ij} and b_{ij} are positive real numbers, usually integers, including zero, and k_i and k_i' are constants (which change with temperature). The first group of terms on the right hand side of Equation (40) represents the forward reaction rate in the production (consumption) of A_i, whereas the second group represents the reverse reaction rate. As A_i is being produced (consumed) initially, the forward rate is greater than the reverse rate. Then, as the amount of A_i increases (decreases), the rate slows down until the two rates are equal. At this equilibrium condition:

$$\mathbf{r}(\mathbf{x}_e, T) = \mathbf{0}, \tag{41}$$

or alternatively:

$$k_i \prod_{j=1}^{m} (x_j)_e^{a_{ij}} = k_i' \prod_{j=1}^{m} (x_j)_e^{b_{ij}}, \qquad i = 1, 2, \ldots, m, \tag{42}$$

where the subscript e denotes that these are concentrations at equilibrium; i.e., the maximum or minimum concentration of a component, depending on whether it is being produced or consumed by the reaction.

If the volume, V, of the reactor is kept constant, the flow rate out of the vessel must be equal to the flow rate, q, into the vessel. Since the contents of the vessel are fully mixed, the concentrations $\mathbf{x}$ in the vessel are the same as those in the product. Hence, the rate at which any component A_i is produced, (consumed) is the difference between the rate at which it flows out of the reactor and the rate at which it flows in. The rate of reaction r_i is defined as the rate at which the amount of A_i is increased per unit volume. For an input stream of composition x_f, a mass balance on each component gives the reactor design equation:

$$q(\mathbf{x} - \mathbf{x}_f) = V\mathbf{r}(\mathbf{x}, T), \tag{43}$$

or equivalently:

$$\mathbf{x} = \mathbf{x}_f + \theta\mathbf{r}(\mathbf{x}, T), \tag{44}$$

where $\theta \equiv V/q$ is the average holding time of the reactor; i.e., the time required to "turn over" the contents of the reactor.

Now suppose the problem is to maximize the amount of component A_i produced in the reactor at a constant temperature T, starting with an input stream with given concentration x_{f_i}. According to Equation (44), this can be accomplished by increasing θ, r_i, or both. Now θ is increased either by using a larger vessel V or reducing the throughput q; both are economically unattractive. The rate r_i decreases as the amount of A_i produced increases and, in fact, goes to 0 as the maximum concentration x_{ie} is approached. This suggests that the reaction be carried out in two or more vessels, the product of the first being fed to the second and so on; then, since the exit concentration of the first would be at a lower concentration than in the second and succeeding reactors, the reaction rate in the first would be greater than in succeeding reactors. Therefore, by allowing the reaction to occur in several vessels, it is possible either, 1) to obtain a greater output concentration for the same volume V, or 2) to obtain the same output concentration as with a single vessel but with a smaller total volume. The optimization problem is to choose the sizes of the vessels to meet some economic criterion.

6.2 Chemical Reaction in a Series of Stirred Vessels

Consider a general process of N reactors, shown schematically in Figure 7. For convenience, the vessels are numbered from the end to the beginning, so that the input stream enters vessel N and the final product leaves from vessel 1. This is a serial process, where the N engineering operations of Figure 1 correspond to the N reaction vessels. Here, the state variables are the concentrations of the components and the outputs for the general model are the inputs to the next stage. The decision variable $d_n = \theta_n$, is the holding time for the nth reactor. The reactor design Equation (44) serves as a transition function, since the output x_n can be obtained from the input x_{n+1} and decision θ_n, although a numerical iteration method may be necessary. Therefore, one may write

$$\mathbf{x}_n = \mathfrak{T}_n(\mathbf{x}_{n+1}, \theta_n). \tag{45}$$

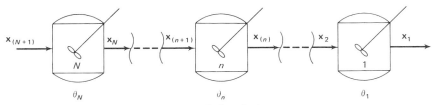

Fig. 7. Series of chemical reactors.

The return function for this process can be formulated in many different ways. A form which frequently occurs is one in which the objective is the sum of profits from each vessel. These profits can be expected to be functions of x_{n+1}, x_n, and θ_n. However, x_n can be expressed in terms of x_{n+1}, and θ by Equation (45) so that

$$P = \sum_{n=1}^{N} R_n(x_{n+1}, \theta_n), \qquad (46)$$

where R_n is the profit or return from the nth stage. One important problem in design is to maximize the exit concentration of a single component x_{i1} for an input stream of known composition, x_{N+1}, and flowing at a rate q. If α represents the cost of the vessel relative to the composition, then the return function is

$$\text{maximize } x_{i1} - \alpha \left(\sum_{n=1}^{N} \theta_n \right) \text{ so that } R_n = x_{in} - x_{i,n+1} - \alpha\theta_n. \qquad (47)$$

Since the sum contains the additional constant term $-x_{i,N+1}$, the maximum value must be modified, but the optimal policy $\{\theta_n^*: n = 1, 2, \ldots, N\}$ will be the same.

Summarizing in mathematical programming terms, the optimization problem is to:

$$\underset{\{\theta_n \, n=1,2,\ldots,N\}}{\text{maximize}} \, P = \sum_{n=1}^{N} R_n(x_{n+1}, \theta_n), \qquad (48)$$

subject to the $N \otimes m$ equality constraints

$$x_n - \mathfrak{I}_n(x_{n+1}, \theta_n) = 0 \qquad (49)$$

In all practical problems the state and decision variables are nonnegative, and in most cases bounded above and below so that the univariate constraints:

$$\theta_n^l \leqslant \theta_n \leqslant \theta_n^u \quad \text{and} \quad x_n^l \leqslant x_n \leqslant x_n^u \qquad (50)$$

also are imposed.

6.3 Decomposition and Suboptimization by Dynamic Programming

Rather than solve this N variable equality-inequality constrained problem directly, the principle of optimality can be applied to decompose the problem into a sequence of N one variable univariate constrained problems. The selection of θ_n only effects subsequent states $x_n, x_{n-1}, \ldots, x_1$, and has no effect on the preceding ones $x_N, x_{N-1}, \ldots, x_{n+1}$. Hence, this is a serial system. From the principle of optimality, all n stage serial systems; i.e., systems consisting of stages $1, 2, \ldots, n(n \leqslant N)$, are optimal with respect to their input states. Let:

$$f_1(x_2) = \underset{\theta_1}{\text{Max}} \ [R_1(x_2, \theta_1)] \tag{51}$$

be the maximum profit from the last reactor. The optimal policy for this reactor is dependent on the input state x_2, and may be written $\theta_1^*(x_2)$. Now, this policy has no effect on any of the $N - 1$ preceding stages. It is obtained by a one variable optimization for different values of x_2. Next, consider the last two reactors. The return function is:

$$\underset{\theta_2, \theta_1}{\text{Max}} \ [R_2(x_3, \theta_2) + R_1(x_2, \theta_1)]. \tag{52}$$

For any value of θ_2, R_2 can be evaluated and the value of x_2 calculated by the transition Equation (45). However, the optimal choice of θ_1 for any x_2 is $\theta_1^*(x_2)$, so that values of the sum $R_1 + R_2$ are obtained simply by specifying θ_2. Thus, Equation (52) can be written:

$$f_2(x_3) = \underset{\theta_2}{\text{Max}} \ [R_2(x_3, \theta_2) + f_1(x_2)], \tag{53}$$

which is another one variable optimization problem that yields an optimal decision policy for θ_2, $\theta_2^*(x_3)$.

Continuing in an analogous fashion, stage by stage, the optimum decision at the nth stage is that value $\theta_n^*(x_{n+1})$ which satisfies the equation

$$f_n(x_{n+1}) = \underset{\theta_n}{\text{Max}} \ [R_n(x_{n+1}, \theta_n) + f_{n-1}(x_n)], \tag{54}$$

where

$$x_n = \mathcal{T}_n(x_{n+1}, \theta_n), \qquad n = 1, 2, \ldots, N, \tag{55}$$

provided $f_o(x_1) \equiv 0$. Thus, the optimal decision policy for the whole series $\{\theta_n^*(x_{N+1}) \ n = 1, 2, \ldots, N\}$ is generated by sequentially solving this equation for $n = 1, 2, \ldots, N$ starting with $f_o = 0$. This decision policy may be presented in tabular or graphical form for simple systems. The actual mechanics of using dynamic programming (DP) are discussed in Bellman [1957], Bellman and Dreyfus [1962], Aris [1964], and Nemhauser [1966].

6.4 Sequential Chemical Reaction with Temperature Regulation

In the above example, it has been tacitly assumed that the regulation of temperature did not involve a cost. If the reaction generates heat it will be removed at a certain rate. Let $\hat{Q}_n$ be the rate of heat removal by the cooling system, C_p be the heat capacity of the reacting mixture, and $(-\Delta H_i)$ the heat of reaction involving the ith component. Then a heat balance on the reactor; i.e., the heat brought into the reactor plus the heat generated by the reaction equals the heat going out in the exit stream plus the heat that is removed by the cooling system, gives

$$\hat{Q}_n = q C_p (T_{n+1} - T_n) + V_n (-\Delta H')\mathbf{r}(\mathbf{x}_n, T_n), \tag{56}$$

or equivalently

$$Q_n = T_{n+1} - T_n + \theta_n \left(\frac{-\Delta H'}{q C_p}\right)\mathbf{r}(\mathbf{x}_n, T_n), \tag{57}$$

where $Q_n = \hat{Q}_n/(q C_p)$. This equation is a transformation equation for temperature. That is, given values for the state variable T_{n+1}, $\mathbf{x}_{n+1}$ and the decisions, θ_n and Q_n, the simultaneous solution of this equation with the mass balance Equations (45) gives T_n and $\mathbf{x}_n$. Temperature has been included as a state variable since it affects the required heat removal. The cost of heat removal is proportional to Q_n. Hence, the return function of Equation (47) becomes:

$$R_n = x_{in} - x_{i,n+1} - \alpha \theta_n - \mu Q_n. \tag{58}$$

Notice that Q_n is now a decision variable, $\mathbf{d}_n = (\theta_n, Q_n)$, so that a two variable suboptimization problem must be solved for each stage in the system.

6.5 Application of Dynamic Programming to Non-Serial Systems

In many industrial processes, some of the material leaving one or more of the stages is diverted forward or back to other stages in the process. A typical configuration is shown in Figure 8. A number of procedures have been developed for applying DP to these systems (Aris, et al. [1964], and Beightler et al. [1965]). Basically, these procedures consist of introducing additional state variables corresponding to the various loops in the process and then using DP to decompose this larger problem. The interested reader is referred to the excellent treatment of this subject by Wilde and Beightler [1967].

6.6 Concluding Remarks

In this section it has been shown how DP can be used to decompose a large system optimization problem into a sequence of smaller problems by exploiting the serial structure of the system. Although DP, as embodied in the principle of

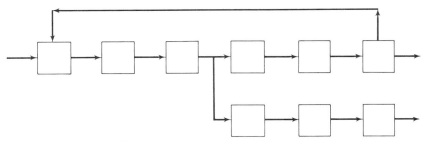

Fig. 8. A complex nonserial system.

optimality, is a relatively simple concept, difficulty arises in the formulation of a particular problem, because DP is a strategy of optimization rather than having a clearly defined method to follow (such as LP). Each case requires an individual analysis and a proper formulation which can mean the difference between success and failure.

The question of when to use DP to decompose a serial system has been discussed by several authors (Aris [1964], Nemhauser [1966]). The price one pays for decomposing the system into smaller parts is the need to solve a large number of suboptimization problems which do not eventually become part of the optimal plan. This process of imbedding into a larger class of problems must be balanced by the computational advantage of working with fewer variables. The best indicator of when to use DP is the number of state variables, m. A limit of three or possibly four is within the range of computational feasibility. An exhaustive search of more than this is impossible, even with the capabilities of large digital computers. Two alternatives are available. A new approach has been developed, called state increment DP, which significantly reduces the computational requirements by solving the iterative functional Equation (54) in a different way (Larson [1968]). The second approach is to use a different method of decomposition called the maximum principle, which again leads to a sequence of suboptimization problems but loses the desirable unique optimum feature of DP except for special cases (Pontryagin, et al. [1962]). This latter approach does not have large digital computer memory requirements, so the number of state variables is not of primary concern.

7. OPTIMAL ENGINEERING DESIGN BY GEOMETRIC PROGRAMMING

In the previous sections it has been demonstrated how the economical design and operation of process systems can be formulated as optimization problems, in which some economic criterion is optimized while certain technological or design relations are satisfied. Until recently, however, optimization methods were not used for detailed engineering design because suitable mathematical methods were not available for treating the nonlinear functions which typically arise.

Engineering design as contrasted to the design, say, of Section 6, involves the actual sizing of pumps, motors, heat exchanger internals, etc., rather than simply determining the overall size of a vessel or the residence time. These engineering design relations are not only nonlinear but also nonconvex. For example, in Section 5 the capital cost estimating relation for new plants and plant equipment was shown to be (Capital cost) $= aV^b$, where V is the capacity, a is a cost coefficient, and b is a positive exponent usually between 0.5 and 0.8. The economic criterion, or return function in terms of the general model of Figure 1, used in engineering design consists almost exclusively of sums and differences of cost estimating relations of this type. The coefficients are obtained from literature cost data, while the exponents usually reflect an experience factor gained by equipment manufacturers in building similar plants.

In engineering design problems, the transition functions are obtained by performing material and energy balances both on the individual operations and on the entire process. These balances usually consist of design relations which are obtained by dimensional analysis or by fitting power functions to experimental data. The most general form of such a function h, with P dimensionless groups is:

$$h(\mathbf{x}) = k \prod_{i=1}^{P} \left(\prod_{j=1}^{m} x_j^{\alpha_{ij}} \right)^{a_i}, \tag{59}$$

where $\mathbf{x} \equiv (x_1, x_2, \ldots, x_m)$ is an m dimensional vector of design and/or physical variables, α_{ij} is an unsigned integer, and k and a_i's are real number constants determined by experimentation on the physical system involved.

Since both the cost estimating relations and design relations are posynomial functions, one might expect that the resultant optimal design problem would be a geometric program. Because problem formulation is nontrivial, however, the generation of a true geometric program depends on the skill of the designer. Each problem must be considered on its own merits so that no general purpose formulation procedure is available. One neglected area in the development of geometric programming has been providing some methodology for helping the designer select appropriate design variables—approximate nonposynomial design relations by posynomials—and manipulate complex material balance constraints to obtain posynomial equality and inequality constraints. These remarks are best illustrated by an example.

7.1 Design of a Liquid-Liquid Heat Exchanger

The design of heat transfer equipment to regulate the temperature of a process or to insure efficient utilization of heat is an important engineering design problem. In Section 6.4 for example, the optimal design of the reactor sequence involved an optimal policy for the rate of heat removal from each reactor. Having determined this rate Q, the engineering design problem is to size the heat transfer equipment to achieve this rate for the minimum cost.

Consider a liquid-liquid heat exchanger in which a process fluid having a flow rate W_p must be cooled from a temperature T_{pI} to T_{pO} by a stream of cooling water, W_s, available at a given temperature T_{sI} (Blau [1971]). Figure 9 depicts such a system. The rate of heat transfer from the process stream to the cooling water is

$$Q = W_p C_p (T_{pI} - T_{pO}), \qquad (60)$$

where C_p is the heat capacity of the process stream. The optimal design problem is to size the exchanger; i.e., determine its heat transfer area, number and size of tubes, baffle spacing etc., and determine the flow rate W_c of cooling water to meet the heat transfer rate Q, while minimizing the annual cost of the exchanger.

The return function for the exchanger consists of four items: 1) fixed charges on the exchanger, c_F; 2) cost of cooling water, c_w; 3) cost of pumping water through the exchanger, c_s; and 4) cost of pumping the process fluid through the exchanger, c_p.

(1) *Fixed Charges:* Assuming that the exchanger is of the conventional shell and tube variety, a cost estimating relation for fixed charges is:

$$c_F = c_1 A^{0.55}, \qquad (61)$$

where c_1 is the unit cost of the exchanger, including yearly depreciation, and A is the heat transfer surface area.

(2) *Cost of Water:* The cost of water is usually a function of flow rate so that

$$c_w = c_2 H W_s, \qquad (62)$$

where c_2 is the unit cost of cooling water and H is the yearly operating time.

(3) *Pumping Costs:* The pumping costs are the following linear functions of

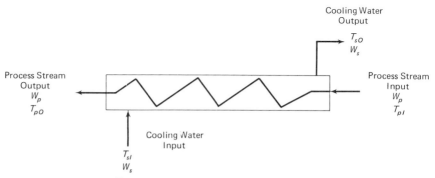

Fig. 9. Liquid-liquid heat exchanger.

the power requirements:

$$c_s = c_3 H(HP_s) \qquad (63)$$

$$c_p = c_3 H(HP_p), \qquad (64)$$

where c_3 is the unit power cost, and HP_s and HP_p represent the horsepower losses for the cooling water and process streams, respectively.

Summing these four terms, the optimal design problem is to find the values of A, W_s, HP_s and HP_p which minimize

$$R = c_F + c_w + c_s + c_p. \qquad (65)$$

In order to keep this example at a manageable level, the following exchanger data will be specified: 1) standard 1 in., 16BWG, 16 ft exchanger tubes; 2) number of tube passes = number of shell passes = 1; 3) square $1\frac{1}{4}''$ in. pitch with baffle spacing = $\frac{2}{5}$ of shell diameter. Power use, HP_s and HP_p, can be expressed in terms of the design variables A, W_s, and W_p in the following manner. Assuming that cooling water passes through the tube side of the exchanger, the power loss through the tube side is given by:

$$HP_s = K_s A h_s^{3.5}, \qquad (66)$$

and through the shell side by:

$$HP_p = K_p A h_p^{4.75}, \qquad (67)$$

where K_s and K_p are functions of the thermophysical properties of the two fluids, and h_s and h_p are individual heat transfer coefficients for the tube and shell side respectively. A dimensional analysis for heat flow gives the design relations:

$$h_s = 0.023 \left(\frac{k_s}{D_s}\right) (\text{Re}_s)^{0.8} (\text{Pr}_s)^{1.3} \left(\frac{\mu_s}{\mu_w}\right)^{0.14} \qquad (68)$$

and

$$h_p = 0.23 \left(\frac{k_p}{D_p}\right) (\text{Re}_p)^{0.6} (\text{Pr}_p)^{0.33}, \qquad (69)$$

where Re and Pr are the dimensionless Reynolds and Prandtl numbers, while the thermal conductivity and viscosity of the fluids are given by k and μ respectively, and D is the tube diameter. These two design relations are precisely of the form of Equation (59).

Collecting terms describing the thermophysical characteristics of the fluids and expressing Equations (68) and (69) in terms of mass flow rates and surface area, one obtains:

$$h_s = e_1 \phi_s \left(\frac{W_s}{A}\right)^{0.8} \qquad (70)$$

with

$$\phi_s \equiv k_s \left(\frac{1}{\mu_s}\right)(\text{Pr}_s)^{1.3}\left(\frac{\mu_s}{\mu_w}\right)^{1.04} \tag{71}$$

and

$$h_p = e_2\,\phi_p\,\frac{W_p^{0.6}}{A^{0.57}} \tag{72}$$

where

$$\phi_p \equiv \frac{k_p}{\mu_p}\,\text{Pr}_s. \tag{73}$$

The coefficients e_1 and e_2 are fixed by the units employed. Substituting the design relations (70) and (71) into Equations (66) and (67) respectively, the return function (64) becomes

$$R = [c_1]A^{0.55} + [c_2H]\,W_s + [c_3\,HK_s(e_1\phi_3)^{3.5}]\,\frac{W_s^{2.8}}{A^{1.8}}$$

$$+ [c_4\,HK_p(e_2\phi_p)^{4.75}]\,\frac{W_p^{2.85}}{A^{1.71}}, \tag{74}$$

where the terms in braces are constants for a given system.

Two constraints must be imposed. First, the heat transfer surface required to transfer the heat load Q is given by the design relation

$$Q = UA\,\Delta T_{LM}, \tag{75}$$

where U is the overall heat transfer coefficient and ΔT_{LM} is the log-mean temperature difference. U is related to the individual coefficients h_s and h_p and a fouling factor R_D by the posynomial function:

$$\frac{1}{U} = \frac{1.15}{h_s} + \frac{1}{h_p} + R_D. \tag{76}$$

Log mean temperature difference is not a posynomial. However, for liquid-liquid systems with similar approaches at both ends of the exchanger; i.e., $(T_{pO} - T_{sI}) \sim (T_{pI} - T_{sO})$, ΔT_{LM} can be approximated by ΔT_{AM}, the arithmetic mean temperature difference. That is:

$$\Delta T_{LM} \simeq \frac{(T_{pO} - T_{sI}) + (T_{pI} - T_{sO})}{2}. \tag{77}$$

Substituting for h_s and h_p from Equations (70) and (72), Equation (74) becomes

$$Q\left(\frac{1.15}{e_1\phi_sA^{0.2}W_s^{0.8}} + \frac{1}{e_2\phi_pA^{0.45}W_p^{0.6}} + \frac{R_D}{A}\right) = \frac{T_{pO}}{2} - \frac{T_{sI}}{2} + \frac{T_{pI}}{2} - \frac{T_{sO}}{2}. \tag{78}$$

The second constraint is imposed by performing an energy balance to insure that the heat lost by the process stream is taken up by the cooling water. That is:

$$Q = W_p C_{p_p}(T_{P_I} - T_{P_O}) = W_s C_{p_s}(T_{s_O} - T_{s_I}). \tag{79}$$

The optimal design problem has now been formulated as a nonlinear equality constrained mathematical program in the three design variables A, W_s, and T_{s_O}. The return function (74) is already a posynomial. The constraints can be transformed into the following posynomial equality constraints:

$$\left[\frac{C_{p_p} W_p (T_{P_O} - T_{P_I})}{C_{p_s}} \right] \frac{W_p}{T_{s_O}} + [T_{s_I}] \frac{1}{T_{s_O}} = 1 \tag{80}$$

and

$$\left[\frac{1.15Q}{e_1 \phi_s E_T} \right] \frac{1}{A^{0.2} W_s^{0.8}} + \left[\frac{Q}{e_2 \phi_p E_T W_p^{0.45}} \right] \frac{1}{A^{0.45}} + \left[\frac{R_D}{E_T} \right] \frac{1}{A} + \left[\frac{1}{2E_T} \right] T_{s_O} = 1, \tag{81}$$

where $E_T \equiv (T_{P_O} - T_{s_I} + T_{P_I})/2$. Heuristic rules have been developed for transforming these equality constraints into inequalities so that convexity is preserved (Blau and Wilde [1969]). Alternatively, an algorithm developed specifically for equality constrained problems may be used, although the unique optimum guaranteed by convexity is lost (Blau and Wilde [1971]).

8. BUILDING MATHEMATICAL MODELS OF ENGINEERING OPERATIONS

In the previous sections of this chapter the emphasis has been on formulating the optimization problems associated with various processes. In all the examples considered it was assumed that the transition functions were known either as physically meaningful models (Sections 6 and 7), or as linear approximations to these models (Sections 2-5). However, in modelling engineering operations, the only realistic way of determining the suitability of a model is to verify the model either from existing experimental measurements taken on the operations or by performing additional experiments on the operations. Once this experimental data is available, nonlinear least squares techniques must be used to estimate key parameters in the model. The uncertainty in the resultant parameter estimates should be reflected in any subsequent analysis using the model.

Frequently, several realistic models can be postulated to describe an engineering operation. This is particularly true in modelling operations involving chemical reactions because they are inherently complex, and experimental data is sparse and/or expensive to obtain. Since the models are nonlinear, standard statistical tests based on linear models cannot be applied to identify the most suitable model. Consequently, nonlinear statistical techniques have been developed for discriminating among rival models from the data available (Reilly [1970], Blau, et al. [1970, 1972a, 1972b]). Another group of workers have been developing a methodology for designing key experiments such that the data from these experiments will discriminate the models (Box and Hill [1967]). This methodology, based on maximizing the expected information from the data, can be formulated as a mathematical program.

Once a suitable model has been identified, the uncertainty in the parameter estimates may be so great that the model cannot be incorporated in the formulation of any mathematical programming problem. Here again, statistical techniques have been developed for locating experiments which will maximize the expected improvement in the parameter estimates (Box and Hunter [1963], Atkinson and Hunter [1968]). This maximization problem can be formulated as another mathematical program.

The three mathematical programs mentioned above will be formulated in this section. The treatment will be completely general, with no attempt being made to identify the functional form of the specific models. It will become apparent that efficient algorithms for solving the programs are absolutely essential, because a large number of parameters and potential models are frequently involved and the mathematical program must be solved repeatedly as new data becomes available.

8.1 Nonlinear Parameter Estimation

Suppose that s measurements $(\mathbf{y}_n)_k\, k = 1, 2, \ldots, s$ have been made on the output states of an engineering operation for different values of the input states $(\mathbf{x}_n)_k$ and decisions $(\mathbf{d}_n)_k$. (For convenience the subscript n, denoting the process stage, will be deleted where the meaning is clear.) These measured values are related to the true values, $\mathbf{w}_k$, by the relation:

$$\mathbf{y}_k = \mathbf{w}_k + \boldsymbol{\epsilon}_k, \quad k = 1, 2, \ldots, s, \tag{82}$$

where $\boldsymbol{\epsilon}_k \equiv (\epsilon_{1k}, \epsilon_{2k}, \ldots, \epsilon_{qk})$ is a q-dimensional vector representing the experimental error in measuring $\mathbf{y}_k$. Consider a transition function model $\mathbf{f}(\boldsymbol{\theta}, \mathbf{d}, \mathbf{x})$, where $\boldsymbol{\theta} \equiv (\theta_1, \theta_2, \ldots, \theta_t)$ is a t-dimensional vector of unknown parameters. If $\mathbf{f}$ adequately describes the data, then there exist a set of parameters $\boldsymbol{\theta}^*$ such the vector of residuals:

$$\mathbf{e}_k = \mathbf{y}_k - \mathbf{f}(\boldsymbol{\theta}^*, \mathbf{d}_k, \mathbf{x}_k), \quad k = 1, 2, \ldots, s \tag{83}$$

are estimates of the experimental error, $\boldsymbol{\epsilon}_k$. If the joint probability density function for the experimental errors is known, then substituting the residuals $\mathbf{e}_k$ into this function gives the familiar likelihood function $L(\boldsymbol{\theta})$. The set of parameters which best, in a statistical sense, describes the data, are those values $\boldsymbol{\theta}^*$ which:

$$\underset{\boldsymbol{\theta}}{\text{maximize}}\; L\,(\boldsymbol{\theta}). \tag{84}$$

In many cases $\boldsymbol{\theta}$ is nonnegative and bounded above. However, for convenience it is sufficient to assume that $\boldsymbol{\theta}$ satisfies the univariate constraints

$$\boldsymbol{\theta}_l \leqslant \boldsymbol{\theta} \leqslant \boldsymbol{\theta}_u \qquad (85)$$

where the subscripts u and l denote upper and lower bounds respectively. Therefore, the determination of $\boldsymbol{\theta}^*$ is a univariate constrained nonlinear optimization problem.

The form of $L(\boldsymbol{\theta})$ depends on the experimental error structure. For example, if $\epsilon \sim N(\mathbf{0}, I\sigma^2)$, then the maximum likelihood problem becomes the familiar weighted least squares minimization problem:

$$\underset{\boldsymbol{\theta}}{\text{minimize}}\; L(\boldsymbol{\theta}) = \sum_{k=1}^{s} \sum_{j=1}^{q} \frac{e_{jk}^2}{\sigma_k^2}, \qquad (86)$$

subject to the univariate constraint Equations (85). The form of the likelihood function for different distributions are described by Hogg and Craig [1967]. It still remains to perform a statistical goodness of fit test to see if the model $f(\boldsymbol{\theta}^*, \mathbf{d}, \mathbf{x})$ adequately describes the data. If not, a different model or models must be postulated and maximum likelihood estimates determined for these models. In cases involving chemical reacting systems, it is frequencly possible to eliminate models in this fashion until one or more candidate models are found (Blau, et al. [1970, 1972a, 1972b]). Further experimentation is usually required to discriminate among these candidate models.

8.2 Experimental Design for Model Discrimination

Several criteria have been developed for locating additional experiments, $\mathbf{x}_k$, $\mathbf{d}_k$ $k = s + 1$, $s + 2, \ldots$ to show up differences between rival models (Reilly [1970]). The most frequently used criterion locates experiments sequentially to maximize the expected decrease in entropy (Box and Hill [1967]). Entropy, as used here, is the concept used in information theory. Suppose that P rival models $f_1, f_2, \cdots, f_p$ are postulated and s experimental points $\mathbf{S} \equiv \{(\mathbf{x}_k, \mathbf{d}_k, \mathbf{y}_k)$ $k = 1, 2, \ldots, s\}$ are available. Then Bayes theorem can be applied to calculate the normalized posterior probability of each model, $\Pr(f_l|\mathbf{S})$, after the experimental points S have been collected, by the relation:

$$\Pr(f_l|\mathbf{S}) = \frac{\Pr(f_l) \cdot L_l(\boldsymbol{\theta}_l^*)}{\displaystyle\sum_{l=1}^{P} \Pr(f_l) \cdot L_l(\boldsymbol{\theta}_l^*)}, \qquad (87)$$

where $\Pr(f_l)$ is the prior probability and $L_l(\boldsymbol{\theta}_l^*)$ is the likelihood function, both for the lth model. The entropy of the system at this point is

$$E = -\sum_{l=1}^{P} \Pr(f_l|\mathbf{S}) \cdot \ln\left(\Pr(f_l|\mathbf{S})\right), \qquad (88)$$

where E is zero when one model is the correct one, and a maximum when all P models have equal probability. The greatest expected change in entropy resulting from the $(s + 1)$st data point is obtained by finding the values x^*_{s+1}, d^*_{s+1} which:

$$\text{maximize } D, \qquad\qquad (89)$$
$$x_{s+1}, d_{s+1}$$

where D is given in Table 8. The reader interested in multi-response models is referred to the literature (Box and Hill [1967]).

Note that this is a $m + p$ variable optimization problem which searches all feasible values of the state and decision variables once the likelihood estimates θ^* have been found for the first s points. Further, the optimal parameter estimates must be updated, the posterior probabilities recalculated, and the entire problem carried out as each additional experimental point becomes avaliable. Although this represents an enormous amount of computation, experience has shown that only four or five data points are required to achieve adequate discrimination. Balancing the calculational cost with the cost of experimental work makes this approach well worthwhile—at least in an industrial environment.

8.3 Experimental Design for Parameter Estimation

Once a suitable model has been found, it may be necessary to perform additional experimentation to improve the precision of the parameter estimates. It has been suggested that each successive experiment be located to provide the most

TABLE 8. CRITERIA FOR MODEL DISCRIMINATION

$q = 1$ Output State, $P = 2$ Rival Models

$$D = \max_{x_{s+1}, d_{s+1}} \left(\frac{1}{2} \Pr(f_1 | S) \cdot \Pr(f_2 | S) \right.$$
$$\left. \cdot \left\{ \frac{(\sigma_2^2 - \sigma_1^2)^2}{(\sigma^2 + \sigma_1^2)(\sigma^2 + \sigma_2^2)} + (f_1 - f_2)^2 \left[\frac{1}{\sigma^2 + \sigma_1^2} + \frac{1}{\sigma^2 + \sigma_2^2} \right] \right\} \right)$$

$q = 1$ Output State, P Rival Models

$$D = \max_{x_{s+1}, d_{s+1}} \left(\frac{1}{2} \sum_{j=1}^{P} \sum_{i=1}^{P} \Pr(f_i | S) \cdot \Pr(f_j | S) \right.$$
$$\left. \cdot \left\{ \frac{(\sigma_j^2 - \sigma_i^2)^2}{(\sigma^2 + \sigma_j^2)(\sigma^2 + \sigma_i^2)} + (f_j - f_i)^2 \left[\frac{1}{\sigma^2 + \sigma_j^2} + \frac{1}{\sigma^2 + \sigma_i} \right] \right\} \right)$$

where (i) σ^2 is the population error variance applied to a single measurement
(ii) $\sigma_i^2 = (d_{s+1}, x_{s+1})(X_i' X_i)^{-1}(d_{s+1}, x_{s+1})' \sigma^2$
(iii) X_i is the Jacobian matrix of first derivatives of f_i evaluated at (x_{s+1}, d_{s+1}).

desirable expected posterior parameter distribution (Box and Hunter [1963], Atkinson and Hunter [1968]). This would be, for example, a distribution which reduces as much as possible, the joint confidence region for all t parameters in the model $f(\boldsymbol{\theta}, \mathbf{d}, \mathbf{x})$. If the model is linearized, minimization of this joint confidence region is equivalent to finding the values $\mathbf{d}^*, \mathbf{x}^*$ which:

$$\max_{\mathbf{d}, \mathbf{x}} \Delta = \left| \sum_{i=1}^{q} \sum_{j=1}^{q} \sigma_{ij} \mathbf{X}_i \mathbf{X}_j \right|, \tag{90}$$

where $\mathbf{X}_i$ is the Jacobian matrix for f_i, evaluated for some estimate of θ^*. Actually, the matrix $\mathbf{X}_i$ is the moment matrix of residuals, assuming that the experimental errors are approximately normally distributed and the model is approximately linear near the maximum likelihood estimates obtained after s experiments. Finding successive values of $\mathbf{d}^*, \mathbf{x}^*$ by maximizing the determinant Δ is the third mathematical programming problem. Once again, this requires an efficient algorithm because of the iterative nature of the experimentation-analysis scheme.

8.4 Concluding Remarks

Three mathematical programming problems have been formulated in this section. Solution of the first one, a univariate constrained nonlinear parameter estimation problem, has been well documented. However, at the time of writing this book, existing methods are adequate for solving the other two programs—Equations (89) and (90)—when the number of state and decision variables is small; i.e., $\leqslant 3$, and the number of models is small, i.e.; $\leqslant 4$, and then only when a large digital computer is available. New algorithms are necessary before the use of mathematical programming to help build models of engineering operations will become accepted practice in a processing environment.

REFERENCES

A Decade of Digital Computing in the Mineral Industry, Post City Press, Baltimore (1969).

Aris, R., *Discrete Dynamic Programming*, Blaisdell Publishing Co., New York (1964).

———, *The Optimal Design of Chemical Reactors*, Academic Press, New York (1961).

———, G. L. Nemhauser, and D. J. Wilde, *AIChE J.*, **10**, No. 6: 913–919 (1964).

Atkinson, A. C. and W. G. Hunter, "The Design of Experiments for Parameter Estimation," *Technometrics* **10**, No. 2: 271–289 (1968).

Beightler, C. S., D. B. Johnson, and D. J. Wilde, *J. Math. Anal. and Appl.* **12**, 1: 96–104 (1965).

Bellman, R., *Dynamic Programming*, Princeton University Press (1957).

——— and S. E. Dreyfus, Applied Dynamic Programming, Princeton University Press (1962).

Blau, G. E., "Optimization of Models Derived by Dimensional Analysis Using Generalized Polynomial Programming," *J. Franklin Institute* **292**, No. 6: 519–526 (1971).

——— and D. J. Wilde, "A Lagrangian Algorithm for Equality Constrained Generalized Polynomial Programming," *Am. Inst. Chem. Eng. J.* **17**, 235–242 (1971).

——, "Generalized Polynomial Programming," *Canadian J. Chem. Eng.* **47**, 317–326 (1969).

Blau, G. E., R. R. Klimpel, and E. C. Steiner, "Equilibrium Constant Determination by Nonlinear Optimization," *Ind. Eng. Chem. Funda.* **9**, 334–341 (1970).

——, "Nonlinear Parameter Estimation and Model Distinguishability of Physicochemical Models at Chemical Equilibrium," *Canadian J. Chem. Eng.* **50**, 399–409 (1972).

——, "Equilibrium Constant Estimation and Model Distinguishability," *Ind. Eng. Chem. Funda.* **11**, 324–332 (1972).

Box, G. E. P. and W. J. Hill, "Discrimination Among Mechanistic Models," *Technometrics* **9**, No. 1: 57–71 (1967).

—— and W. G. Hunter, "Sequential Design of Experiments for Nonlinear Models," Proceedings of the IBM Scientific Computing Symposium on Statistics, p. 113 (1963).

Fabian, T., "Balst Furnace Production Planning," *Management Sci.* **14**, No. 2: 1–26 (1967).

Hogg, R. V. and A. T. Craig, *Introduction to Mathematical Statistics*, 2nd Ed., MacMillan, New York, New York (1967).

IBM Data Processing Application: An Introduction to Linear Programming, International Business Machines Corporation, White Plains, New York (1964).

IBM Data Processing Application: Linear Programming-Aluminum Alloy Blending, International Business Machines Corporation, White Plains, New York, no date listed.

IBM KWIC Index in Operations Research, International Business Machines Corporation, White Plains, New York (1967).

Klimpel, R. R., "Operations Research in the Chemical Industry, Parts I and II," *Chem. Eng.* **80**, No. 9 and 10: 103–108, 87–94 (1973).

——, "Recent Advances in the Use of Mathematical Optimization in the Mineral Industries," *Minerals Sci. and Eng.* **1**, No. 1: 15–23 (1969).

——, "The Use of Mathematical Modeling to Evaluate Grinding and Blending Alternatives in an Industrial Comminution Facility," Proceedings of the International Conference in Particle Technology, Illinois Institute of Tech. (1973).

—— and L. G. Austin, "The Optimization of an Industrial Rotary-Cutter Milling Facility," Proceedings of the Third European Symposium on Grinding, Cannes, France (1971).

—— and W. J. Burroughs, "Some Industrial Experiences in Plant Site Selection," paper presented at 1974 ORSA Meeting in Boston.

—— and M. Klein, "An Application of Nonlinear Optimization Using the Gradient Projection Method," Proceedings of the Symposium on O.R. in the Mineral Industries, University Park, Pennsylvania (1966).

Larson, R. E., *State Increment Dynamic Programming*, Elsevier, New York (1968).

Manula, G. and Y. Kim, "A Linear Programming Simulator for Coal Distribution Problems," Proceedings of the Symposium on O.R. in the Mineral Industries, University Park, Pennsylvania (1966).

Nemhauser, G., *Introduction to Dynamic Programming*, John Wiley & Son, New York (1966).

"Operations Research/Management Science Literature Digest," Executive Sciences Institute, Whippany, New Jersey, yearly beginning 1961.

Pontrayagin, L. S., V. G. Boltyanskii, R. V. Gamkrelidze, and E. F. Mischenko, *The Mathematical Theory of Optimal Processes*, Interscience, New York (1962).

Reilly, P. M., "Statistical Methods of Model Discrimination," *Canadian J. Chem. Eng.* **48**, pp. 168–173 (1970).

Shannon, C. K., *Bell Syst. Tech. J.* **27** (1948).

Wilde, D. J. and C. S. Beightler, "Foundations of Optimization," Prentice-Hall, Englewood Cliffs, New Jersey (1967).

II-8

THE LEISURE INDUSTRIES

William W. Swart
California State University, Northridge

Charles E. Gearing
The State University of New York at Binghamton

Turgut Var
Simon Fraser University

I. INTRODUCTION

A number of forces are at work leading to an increase in leisure time available to persons in the industrialized nations of the free world. The reduced work week, the increasing number of time-saving appliances and convenience products, and improved means of communications and travel have all contributed to making more time available for leisure. Holman [1961] estimates that, whereas 27% of a person's total active time was spent in leisure activity (on the average) in 1900, that portion had increased to 34% in 1950, and is projected to be 38% in the year 2000. Accompanying this increase is a redistribution of leisure time activity, as shown in Table 1.

Income also has increased, although at a much greater rate than has leisure time. According to Clawson and Knetch [1966], this shift of the leisure income balance (toward income) will continue to create an increase in the means available for people to make the most of their leisure time. The economic consequences have been manifest in the development of what might be called "the leisure industries."

For our purposes, "the leisure industries" will refer to the economic activities providing facilities or services that accommodate persons engaged outside the home in the enjoyment of time that is not committed to work, or to tasks of a

TABLE 1. TIME DIVISION OF LEISURE 1950, 2000

| | Percent of Leisure Time | |
	1950	2000
Daily Leisure Hours	42	34
Weekend Leisure Hours	39	44
Vacation	8	16
Retired	5	5
Other	6	1

personal and social nature. Components of the leisure industries are governmental agencies (e.g., U.S. National Park Service), public institutions (e.g., municipal, cultural, or spectator facilities), or private organizations (e.g., hotels, amusement parks).

In general, operations research (OR) techniques have not been broadly applied in support of the managerial functions in institutions in the leisure industries, though scientific and analytical procedures have been applied in some specific areas in recent years. Ten years ago, Clawson [1966] cited the increasing research efforts that had been directed toward outdoor recreation and predicted an accelerating growth in professional and scientific competence in the economics of outdoor recreation. Today this same prediction could be made relative to OR competence in the broad leisure industries.

Up to now, two general areas have received the most attention from operations researchers: (1) recreation, travel, and tourism and (2) sports. The second volume of *The Journal of Operations Research* contains a technical note by Mottley [1954], which had, as its apparent intention, the encouragement of the use of OR by athletic coaches—an attempt which fell short of its goal, as evidenced by the lack of any other publications relating OR and sports for several years thereafter. On the other hand, the first formal identification of OR with the area of recreation, travel, and tourism did not occur until 1969, when the first issue of the Journal of Leisure Research contained a paper by Cesario [1969] entitled "Operations Research in Outdoor Recreation."

The commonality between the early quantitative work in sports and in recreation, travel, and tourism is that there is little if any evidence of the use of decision models. The focus was, instead, on developing statistical descriptions of certain phenomena (such as the relative frequency of ways of gaining and losing possession of a basketball), on developing predictive models for forecasting, and on developing measures to estimate the benefits that would result from certain forms of leisure activity. Of course, it should be recognized that a decision model does require, in many instances, data that is the product of a forecast, as well as requiring a quantitative measure of effectiveness (benefit) that can be associated with each alternative decision. Hence, the early work can be considered as a necessary prerequisite to the development of decision models.

Although there still is not a universally accepted approach to measuring benefits associated with certain leisure time activities, decision models are appearing in the current literature with ever increasing frequency. In addition, what appear to be the first books (Ladany [1975], Gearing, Swart, and Var [1976]) dealing with OR approaches to segments of the leisure industry are currently in press. This, coupled with the regular appearance of sessions dealing with OR in travel and tourism and with sports at the recent joint meetings of ORSA and TIMS, make it apparent that OR is indeed coming of age in the leisure industries.

This chapter will review some of the specific achievements of OR in the leisure industries. It will be subdivided into three separate sections, each followed by a conclusion. The next section will discuss the nature of OR studies in the field of recreation, travel, and tourism, and present some of the later and more significant approaches to forecasting, benefit measuring, and decision modelling. The third section will discuss OR in sports, with particular attention paid to the approaches developed for performance evaluation, selection of strategies, determination of team composition, and the optimization of training plans. The last section will then provide a conclusion to the chapter.

2. OR IN RECREATION, TRAVEL, AND TOURISM

Before progressing much further into the applications of OR in recreation, travel, and tourism, it would be appropriate to define these three interrelated terms. Recreation, according to Burton and Noad [1968], is not an easily defined homogeneous entity. It includes all pursuits—other than those associated with work and necessary tasks of a personal and social nature—which are undertaken in leisure, or uncommitted time. The essence of recreation is free choice; it includes only those activities which are chosen freely.

Given the above definition, tourism could be considered as a form of recreation which involves mobility. According to Webster [1966], a tourist is "one who makes a tour; one who travels for pleasure." Tourists, according to the International Union of Official Travel Organizations (IUOTO), are temporary visitors staying at least 24 hours in a country visited, when the purpose of the journey can be classified as either leisure or business, family, mission, or meetings.

As opposed to "tourism," the term "travel" refers to passing through or making a journey from place to place in any conveyance. In this chapter, the main concern is travel for the purposes of pleasure, which, according to some sources, in 1970 accounted for 75% of international travel and nearly half of domestic travel in the United States. On the other hand, according to the IUOTO estimates, approximately 75% of all tourist spendings are made within the traveler's own country. These figures vary from 44% for Switzerland to 74% for the United States (Lundberg [1972]).

Even though the definitions given above do distinguish between the three terms, it must be realized that a strong interrelationship exists between all three areas, particularly when questions relating to the development of the tourism sector or of the development of recreational facilities are examined. The importance of identifying these "synergistic relations" is discussed in detail by Egan [1975], in light of his experience over the past 30 years in tourism development at several international locations.

Cesario [1969], in his pioneering paper, described the uses of OR in outdoor recreation as being primarily confined to (a) predicting recreation travel flow from population centers to recreation sites, and (b) estimating the primary economic benefits of outdoor recreation. Since then, work has continued to appear dealing with those two areas, but, in addition, the state of the art advanced to the point where decision models have been developed and used, primarily in the tourism planning sector.

2.1 Forecasting and Tourism Flow Models

In a recent article by Wilkinson [1973], a review of models used to predict the consumption of outdoor recreation is given. The types of models reviewed are: time series projection, economic, gravity, systems theory, and inertia. In this section, forecasting models will be classified, as suggested by Chamber, Mullick, and Smith [1971], into qualitative, causal, and time series, and a typical application of a model in each class will be briefly discussed.

Time Series Analysis. An excellent discussion of the nature, impact, and importance of seasonality in tourism has been provided by Baron [1972, 1973]. In his two publications, Baron describes the use of the time series analysis program "X-11," developed by Shiskin at the U.S. Bureau of the Census, to quantify the trend, seasonal, and cyclical components of several time series associated with the tourism industry in Israel. Specifically, the following time series are analyzed in Baron [1972]:

a) Tourists arriving and departing by air.
b) Tourists arriving.
c) Foreign currency—income from tourism in Israel.
d) Residents departing.
e) Bed nights in tourist recommended hotels broken down into visitors from abroad, Israelis and totals.

In Baron [1973], these series were compared to those of several other countries. Furthermore, it is shown how the Israel Ministry of Tourism uses the results of the forecasts to determine the Maximal Annual Utilization Factor constrained by seasonality (MUS.) which represent the percentage of peak season facilities that can be utilized over the entire year. This information then provides a guideline for planning studies designed to alter or spread the seasonality of tourism through providing off-season activities, introducing a second (and possibly third) season, etc. Amongst the benefits of the spread of tourism seasonality are:

a. More enjoyable holidays for larger numbers of people without the overcrowding so common in peak seasons
b. Better utilization of tourism facilities, including a less intense load on the economy and ecology of the area
c. More even employment of hotel and other tourist staff, aiding their caterers and improving service offered.

Causal Models. The Battelle Research Centre in Geneva Switzerland (Armstrong [1972]) has developed one of the more complete causal forecasting models for international tourist flow reported in the literature. The model is stepped since it begins by hypothesizing a simple relationship between the number of tourists annually generated to country j by country i and the latter's population; then a number of other independent variables such as per capita income, language similarity, attractiveness, and similarity are progressively introduced in order to obtain the most satisfactory outcome. The model hypothesizing the relationship between these variables is

$$N_{ij} = \frac{A_j P_i^{\alpha j} G_i^{\beta j} L_{ij}^{\gamma j} T_n^{\epsilon j}}{D_{ij}^{\sigma j}},$$

where

N_{ij} number of tourist arrivals recorded in country j coming from country i.

P_i Population of country i.

G_i Per capita income of country i (GNP per capita).

D_{ij} The distance between generating country i and recipient country j.

L_{ij} A value given to the adjacency of frontiers and/or common language, if any, between countries i and j.

A_j A value given to the tourist appeal of country j.

T_n Value of time (considered for values of n = 1963, 1967, 1975, and 1980).

$\alpha_j, \beta_j, \gamma_j, \epsilon_j, \sigma_j$ elasticities of the corresponding variable with respect to country j.

The variable T_n, representing value of time, is one that serves to explain progressive changes over the period up to 1980, in such factors as population distribution, education level, and leisure time available.

The variables actually used in the model are those for which sufficient data exists. Improvements in tourism information gathering systems would permit the inclusion of other variables in the model, although the forecasts generated with this model do correlate very closely to those generated by IUOTO.

In Crampon and Tan [1973] and Crampon [1974], a set of factors are defined which influence the flow of tourists in the Pacific. Specifically, it is shown how it is possible to define several elements as, 1) the "destination element," which represents the attributes that make it possible for a destination to attract and serve visitors during a particular time period, and 2) the "tie element," which represents the various ties that exist between the origin and destination during a particular time period. Included among the tie elements are transportation and information, two ties which are necessary if any travel is to exist between the two points. These two sets of elements, together with more traditional elements such as total travel volume emanating from a particular origin, and the geographical distance between an origin-destination pair, become the independent variables in a flow model which predicts the travel volume from an origin to a destination during a particular period. The model has been developed and implemented for selected areas in the Pacific.

Cline [1974], in conjunction with the Midwest Research Institute, has used a traditional multiple regression model for predicting future travel growth to Pacific destinations. His model is more traditional in the sense that the causal variables are hypothesized to be various economic time series. The results obtained have been used routinely by the Midwest Research Institute and others to support various planning activities.

Qualitative Models. Although both the Battelle model and the Crampon model contain subjective factors, as do most other traditional flow models surveyed in Var, Gearing, and Swart [1975], their basic nature is that of a causal model in which the subjective factor is expressed as an index. (Some recent approaches to obtaining this index are discussed later).

A primarily qualitative procedure, suggested by Gaumnitz, Swinth, and Tollefson [1974], illustrates how consensus seeking and group decision making methods can be of use. The approach is based on methodology similar to that presented in the OR literature (Bowman [1963]), and involves the concept that an action, such as the visit to some lake by a person or family, is assumed to be the result of a decision. Such a decision is a mental cognitive process; that is, it is a conscious mental consideration and evaluation of the characteristics of various possible courses of action, in the light of one's needs, goals, and limitations (e.g. funds, time, skills, etc.). Accordingly, it should be possible to characterize the decision processes of a person in the form of a program. One ought to be able to specify a series of statements, questions, or commands which, if followed, will produce choices that match those of the individual. This program, or discrimination net, can then be helpful to a planner/manager in predicting actual choices of potential visitors, and hence, usage rates or forecasts. Of course, this forecast is contingent on an analysis of the structure of the discriminant nets of a sample of individuals in the general client population.

3.2 Measuring Benefits

In the process of developing tourism planning methodology, several approaches to the measurement of "benefit" have been developed. For a developing country to increase its buying power in the community of nations, the establishment of a tourism industry is an important tactic for the generation of foreign exchange, and the additional foreign exchange so generated is the most direct measurement of benefit that can be adopted. Bargur and Arbel [1974] have developed a mixed integer programming model for comprehensive planning of Israel's tourism industry (to be further discussed in section 3 of this chapter). The objective function of this model reflects contribution to total net income in foreign currency resulting from tourism activities. Powers [1974] identifies as additional benefits the domestic resource savings due to reduced marginal costs, and the value of additional tourist services made available to domestic visitors. He then prescribes the net present value as the criterion to use in making decisions regarding the development of the tourism sector.

In addition to the direct benefits of development in the tourism sector, the indirect benefits should also be taken into account. Archer and Owen [1971] discuss how to calculate the multiplier effects of tourist expenditures, while Archer [1972] examines the composition of the indirect and induced flows, to see which sectors of the economy benefit from the multiplier effect, and presents (Archer [1973]) the contributions multiplier analysis can make toward policy making and planning.

When evaluating benefits associated with investments which do not result in direct economic benefits (e.g. national parks, state recreation areas, etc.), the measurement methodology becomes much more subjective and a source of controversy. On one side of this controversy are various approaches developed and/or espoused by Clawson and Knetch [1966], and Cesario [1969]. These approaches have as their central theme the idea that the worth of a recreational facility is related to the amount of income a user is willing to give up (cost of driving to the site, admission fee, etc.) in order to use the facility. On the other side of the controversy is an approach developed by Mack and Myers [1965], who contend that it is not possible to assign a price to recreational benefits that is comprehensive and reliable. They suggest that investments by governments in recreation should be made so as to maximize the resulting social welfare. As a measure of social welfare they suggest the merit weighted user days of recreation that can be gotten in return for investing in recreation. The merit weights are assigned on the basis of the policy, conservation, and priority considerations supported by the government.

The current research thrusts in this area are provided by the Parks Canada section within the Canadian Outdoor Recreation Division Studies (CORDS). CORDS technical notes of particular relevance are given in the references (Beaman [1974], Cesario [1973]).

Another approach toward measuring the benefit associated with the development of tourist accommodations and attractions is the development of a utility measure which reflects the touristic attractiveness of a given area. Gearing, Swart, and Var [1974] developed an approach for the quantification of the notion of touristic attractiveness by constructing a multi-attribute utility function. This function incorporates weights derived by a procedure similar to that suggested by Churchman and Ackoff [1954]. The approach required that the following be determined:

(1) The criteria by which touristic attractiveness is judged; and
(2) The relative importance of those criteria one to another, as indicated by a series of numerical weights.

Then, with these two requirements satisfied, it was possible to

(3) employ the judgments of experts in making evaluations against these criteria and; using these inputs, to
(4) compute a numerical measure (utility value) of the "relative attractiveness" of the touristic area.

The results of the procedure were used to support the planning acitivities of the Turkish Ministry of Tourism. In particular, a ranking was obtained for the 65 geographical areas in Turkey which have been defined as touristic areas. The numerical utilities constituted, as it were, an "inventory," or assessment of the state of things in Turkey vis-à-vis the tourist. In an application to be discussed below, this methodology was adapted to form a surrogate measure for the net foreign exchange earnings that would result from constructing in each of these areas. This surrogate measure was then used as the objective function in an integer optimization model.

2.3 Decision Models

Decision models are the essence of OR, and constitute one of the characteristics that distinguishes OR from other quantitatively oriented disciplines (Wagner [1969]). It was not until 1972 that a decision modelling approach to a tourism problem appeared in the Literature (Gearing, Swart, and Var [1972]); this was an integrated OR study dealing with planning of the tourism sector of a developing country. Specifically, the model was developed and the results used to provide guidance to Turkey for planning its investment policy in the tourism sector during the Third Five-Year Plan. It may be stated as:

$$\text{Maximize} \quad \sum_{i=1}^{N} \sum_{j=1}^{K_i} d_{ij} X_{ij},$$

$$\text{Subject to} \quad \sum_{i=1}^{N} \sum_{j=1}^{K_i} C_{ij} X_{ij} \leqslant b$$

$$X_{iL} - X_{iM} \geqslant 0, \quad \text{for} \quad i = 1, N \quad \text{and} \quad (L, M) \epsilon P_i$$

$$X_{ij} = 0 \quad \text{or} \quad 1, \quad \text{for} \quad i = 1, N; j = 1, K_i$$

where

N the number of touristic areas into which the country is subdivided (=65 for the Turkish application).

K_i The number of projects proposed for implementation in touristic area i during the planning period. (The Third Five-Year Plan for the Turkish Application).

X_{ij} 1, if project j at touristic area i is selected for implementation, and is zero otherwise.

d_{ij} Measure of benefit accrued if project j is undertaken at touristic area i (discussed below).

C_{ij} The estimated cost (at completion) of project j proposed for touristic area i.

P_i Index set of precedence relations between proposed projects at touristic area i.

b Budget devoted to the development of the tourism sector during the planning period.

The measure of benefit, d_{ij}, defined above must reflect the relative merits of alternate project proposals, and it must have the property of being summable across all the projects in a particular allocation plan, so as to define a measure of benefit for the entire plan. Although the initial choice for such a measure of benefit might appear to be the net present value of the stream of monetary returns that the project will generate over its useful life, this measure rapidly proves to be inadequate. The inadequacy of the measure is due, in part, to the large variety of projects that are under consideration when planning regional or national development. Some projects, such as hotels and vacation villages, will indeed generate a stream of monetary returns, but projects such as road construction, excavation of ruins, and museums do not, in general, provide a stream of monetary returns. Nevertheless, these non-revenue-generating projects do require expenditures, and must compete for the scarce capital funds allocated to a program of tourism development.

The measure of benefit that was selected provided a common denominator by which to measure the benefit from the diverse projects under consideration while, at the same time, providing a surrogate measure for foreign currency generated when considering the aggregate impact of tourism development on the entire nation. Specifically, the measure is a marginal utility which reflects the project's contribution toward enhancing the "touristic attractiveness" of the region. This marginal utility was developed from concepts of benefit measurement, as discussed briefly in the preceding section and as presented in detail by Gearing, Swart, and Var [1973]. Let $A_i^{(M)}$ be a vector which reflects the touristic attractiveness (on each of seventeen criteria for the Turkish example) of touristic area i, when project M has been completed (including all its immediate predecessors). The marginal impact of completing the project, on each of the criteria, is then given by the "impact" vector $T_i^{(M)}$, given by

$$T_i^{(M)} = A_i^{(M)} - A_i^{(L)},$$

where L denotes the set of projects which are immediate predecessors to project M. For example, the construction of a hotel in the area can only be undertaken if there is approval to build a road to the hotel site. Hence, the road project immediately precedes the hotel project. Similarly, it is possible for a specific project to have more than one immediate predecessor. It should be pointed out that each touristic area has a planning project and an infrastructure project associated with it, and that these are predecessors to any and all other projects in the area. The purpose is to ensure proper development planning before any actual development is started, and to ensure that each touristic area has at least adequate infrastructure to satisfy minimal touristic quality standards.

Letting W denote the vector of weights representing the relative importance of the attractiveness criteria, then the benefit associated with project j at touristic area i as measured by the multiattribute utility function, is given by:

$$d_{ij} = W\,T_i^{(j)}, \qquad i = 1, N; \;\; j = 1, K_i.$$

The computational aspects of this model have been developed, from a LP standpoint, in Swart, Gearing, Var, and Cann [1974] and more generally in Gearing, Swart, and Var [1976].

The following limiting characteristics of the model are the subjects of current research (initial results of the research have been reported by Gearing, Swart, and Var [1975]):

—It was formulated as a static, single period decision structure.
—It was based on the perspective of developing the entire "tourism package"

of the country and did not differentiate among the different geographic regions as to current tourist densities.

—It did not recognize the limited capacity of geographic areas for tourism development.

Another OR study of tourism planning is the the comprehensive planning model of the tourist industry for Israel developed by Bargur and Arbel [1974], and presented by Gearing, Swart, and Var [1976]. The model is a mixed integer program and may be described as follows:

The objective function, to be maximized, represents the total net income in foreign currency from tourist activities, subject to the following constraints:

(a) The economic efficiency criterion—the cost of a unit of net value added of foreign exchange.
(b) Supply constraints of local projection factors (accommodation facilities, manpower, and recreational sites).
(c) Demand constraints for the planning horizon, based on demand forecasts which were developed exogenously under varying assumptions.

The analysis resulting from the application of the model is designed to provide satisfactory answers to the following facets of planning:

(a) Determination of feasible and optimal level of output, and its mix from the viewpoint of the national economy.
(b) Balancing optimal supply and demand and the identification of surplus or deficit within the above categories.
(c) Determination of required inputs necessary to satisfy the optimal levels of output, in terms of major projection factors.
(d) Determination of the regional distribution of the various activities, subject to the touristic potential of each specific region.
(e) Determination of the feasible and preferred seasonal distribution of the various activities.
(f) Realization of the shadow prices; i.e., the marginal values of changes in basic assumptions, input data, and optimal results.

Within the context of tourism planning, McMahon [1974] presents a dynamic programming model for the selection of tourism development projects in Puerto Rico, subject to limitations in funds and the quantity of skilled manpower available.

In a different context and of different scope, Saitta and Schnedeman [1972] present a LP model to aid managers of individual state parks in planning the expansion of their facilities, so as to satisfy the ever-increasing user demands. The solution to the model provides information which indicates the number of additional recreational facilities which could be built under varying amounts of capital investment, maintenance costs, land requirements, and overall state recreation requirements.

2.4 Conclusion to Section 2

In the preceding parts of this section, some of the uses of OR in recreation, travel, and tourism have been presented. The large body of literature that exists in the area of forecasting is due largely to its being one of the first areas attacked by economists. As such, the nature of the existing methods differs from those often encountered in other fields where OR is routinely applied. A classification of the econometric methods of forecasting prevalent in the recreation field has been provided by Ciccetti, Fisher, and Smith [1973] in their taxonomic summary of economic models utilized to analyze Recreational Decisions, and it will not be duplicated here.

Based on the results obtained with time series methods by Baron [1972, 1973], it seems that an increase in the use of this type of model for forecasting in the travel and tourism sector will prove to be of value. In particular, the advantages of time series models, in terms of costs and data storage requirements, make it surprising that they have not had more prevalent use in situations requiring short to medium term forecasts of tourism or recreation data. The weaknesses of time series models for long term forecasting are well documented and would account for their absence in the literature dealing with this problem.

A recent approach to the modelling of tourist flows has been presented by Demers [1974]. The main contribution of the approach is that it views a region as being composed of tourist attractions (nodes), connected by arcs. The flow in these arcs are tourists. This representation then allows for the analysis of the resulting network by methodologies which are well-developed in the OR literature, but heretofore not applied to this area. This approach seems to be one that will be exploited more fully in the future by OR practitioners involved with problems dealing with forecasting tourist flows.

To support the forecasting activities, and other management and planning needs, the effective design of information gathering systems at recreational sites has been an emerging topic of discussion. It can be expected that management information systems for the recreation, travel, and tourism sector will be an area which will see signficant development in the future, a development which appears to be spearheaded by the Canadian Government (Taylor [1973]).

In the area of benefit measurement for the recreation, travel, and tourism sector, many of the same issues and problems are encountered as those that have faced OR practitioners and theoreticians alike in deriving measures of effectiveness for applications in Urban Systems and Health Services; the crux of the problem being that subjective factors must be meaningfully quantified for incorporation into the measure of benefit. It can be expected that as new methodologies are developed to quantify subjective factors, these will be adapted for use in this sector.

The one area that can be expected to receive the most attention from OR practitioners in the recreation, travel and tourism sector is that of decision modelling. The pioneering work described in the previous sections has unequivocally demonstrated that there is room for the application of formal OR models in this area, and that the state of the art in forecasting and benefit measurement is advanced enough to where the results can be meaningfully incorporated into mathematical or/and simulation models.

The contemporary research thrusts in outdoor recreation have been identified by Smith [1971] (a summary of these is given in Table 2). In examining this table, it becomes apparent that OR can lend an important and new dimension to many of the thrusts, and that OR practitioners and theoreticians alike should be made aware of this area as one in which major significant contributions can be made.

3. OPERATIONS RESEARCH IN SPORTS

In 1954, Charles Mottley [1954] stated that, "the possibility of applying scientific methods to athletic games does not appear to have received much attention by the OR community, . . . A preliminary study of football and

TABLE 2. RESEARCH THRUST IN OUTDOOR RECREATION

A. *Geographic (micro and regional patterns) and macro (national and international patterns):*
  1. Fieldwork (traverse, interview, landscape surveys)
    a. Aesthetics of landscape—perception of beauty in terms of physical environment, wilderness, development,
    b. Site attraction in terms of natural environment and man-made environment,
    c. Intensity of participations.
  2. Gathering and analysis of statistical data
    a. Recreational travel,
    b. Tourist industry,
    c. Projection of recreational needs for particular region,
    d. Propagation of innovation waves in facility designs.
B. *Economic, Political, Sociological:*
    a. Supply and demand studies of recreation,
    b. Resource allocation and cost-benefit analysis and related policy considerations,
    c. Economic impacts of recreation,
    d. Sociological and psychological impacts of travel,
    e. Other economic, political and sociological studies.
C. *Miscellaneous:*
    a. Biological studies (ecology),
    b. Engineering feasibility studies for various projects, design studies of site characteristics to optimize,
    c. Capacity of outdoor areas,
    d. Nature of aesthetic appreciation of a setting.

basketball from an OR point of view reveals that the essential phenomena characteristic of operating situations are displayed by such sports. It is quite possible that, if coaches were to use the scientific method to help them make decisions regarding the future course of the "operations" under their control, they might be able to make significant improvements in team performance." Twenty years later, Lilien [1974] echoed that statement when he wrote. "A seemingly fruitful area for management science applications is that of competitive athletics. Competitive sports suffer from fewer of the typical complexities which plague management science applications in other areas: data bases are relatively well maintained and updated (people seem to have an extraordinary interest in these data); the actions are repetitive so that often many observations of a process under essentially the same conditions are available; the rules are "well-defined" (perhaps the essence of sports) so that no one "changes the game" while in mid-progress. And, "management" in this area is possibly more receptive to technological innovation than in most other areas: coaches actively seek the so-called competitive edge."

As Mottley's and Lilien's statements are similar, so is the apparent state of the art of OR in sports in 1954 and 1974, as evidenced by the published literature. Of course, one must wonder if the alleged pursuit of the competitive edge by coaches does not assure that many, and especially the successful, applications of OR in sports remain a jealously guarded secret. This conjecture appears to have received some substance from a recent article in Reader's Digest (Clarke and Trengove [1975]).

Be that as it may, the remainder of this section will be devoted to presenting various applications that have been reported in the literature. The section has been subdivided into studies dealing with team competition, team sport strategy evaluation, individual sport strategy evaluation, and issues dealing with athletic training and management.

3.1 Team Composition

Robert Machol [1970] was one of the first individuals to suggest the use of the assignment algorithm to select individuals to fill team positions. He suggested the selection of a medley relay team by a swimming coach amongst a number of swimmers, several of whom are good in more than one stroke. A more complex application of the same idea was applied to select a starting team from the 38 football players on a squad (Patterson and Wolfe [1972]). Perhaps one of the more interesting aspects of this application was the manner in which the objective function coefficients are obtained. Specifically, they are obtained by the following:

(a) Each coach lists the attributes (both mental and physical) athletes should possess to play the position he coaches. From these, an attempt is made to form a set of n mutually exclusive and totally exhaustive attributes (in other words, an attempt is made to define independent attributes).

(b) Each coach rates the relative importance of each attribute listed in step (a) for the position he coaches, using the Churchman-Ackoff [1954] procedure. Denote the composite matrix of weights by $\mathbf{B}$ (b_{ij}—weight of the ith attribute for position j).

(c) The head coach rates the relative importance of each of the M positions on a team in contributing to team strength, using the Churchman-Ackoff procedure (w_j—weight of position j).

(d) The coaching staff rates each of the L players on all attributes listed in step (a). The results are placed in matrix $\mathbf{A}$ (a_{ij}—rating of player i with regard to attribute j).

With the results of the above sequence of steps, a rating c_{ij} is obtained which reflects the "ability" of player i at position j, where c_{ij} is given by

$$c_{ij} = \sum_{k=1}^{n} a_{ik} b_{kj},$$

and, if desired, the contribution d_{ij} of player i at position j can be obtained by

$$d_{ij} = c_{ij} w_j.$$

Consequently, the problem is to determine the solution to the standard LP assignment problem; that is, the 0, 1 indicator variables, X_{ij}, are to be determined which maximize the $d_{ij} X_{ij}$ products over all positions and players, subject to the constraints that all positions be manned and each player be assigned to at most one position. This procedure was applied to an actual situation. The reported feedback that was received from the coaches was positive and there was consensus regarding the fact that the approach does provide useful input into the positioning problem.

3.2 Team Sport Strategy Evaluation

Baseball is the sport that has perhaps been subject to the greatest amount of formal analysis, but, even so, by 1968 there were only 4 articles which had appeared in "reputable literature" that could be considered as serious analysis (Lindsey [1968]). One of the more popular books on baseball (Cook [1967]), which was reviewed in *Operations Research*, was pronounced to be of interest to baseball fans, but should be kept carefully out of the sight of students of the theory of probability (Lindsey [1968]). This statement is not only suggestive about the book, but also about the nature of OR studies on baseball to that time; i.e., that they are, in essence, applications of statistics and data analysis. For example, in (Lindsey [1968]), the expectation for a team under particular circumstances in three areas are calculated: 1) the dependence of the batting average on the batter's and pitcher's handedness; 2) the binomial distribution of hits; 3) expectations with the bases full for the defense. Lindsey [1963], in a later article, examined specific strategies available to maximize the probability of winning the game. In another study by Freeze [1974], a Monte Carlo simulation model was constructed, based on the *Sports Illustrated* Baseball Game, a commercially available game (*Sports Illustrated* Games, Time and Life Building, New York, N.Y., 10020). This simulation was used to test several hypotheses based on suggestions made by Cook [1967].

Motivated by the studies on baseball, Carter and Machol [1971] analyzed 8,373 plays from the first 56 games of the 1969 schedule of the National Football League. In particular, they calculated the expected point value of possession of the football with first down and ten yards to go. During their analysis, two significant discoveries regarding offensive strategy evolved. First, they pointed out that on fourth down and goal, the ball should be rushed as opposed to routinely kicked for a field goal try (barring special circumstances such as needing a field goal to win when there are but a few seconds left on the clock, etc.). Also, they suggest that when a team is behind by seven points or less, it should never call a time-out, for the purpose of stopping the clock, when there are more than thirty seconds to play if it has the ball, or more than a minute to play if the opponents have the ball.

In a different vein, Bierman [1968] analyzed the decision process faced by the Cornell University football coach when he decided to go for two points after their first score late in the 1967 game with Harvard (Harvard was winning 14–6 at the time). A decision tree analysis demonstrated that under three reasonable assumptions, the coach made the correct decision—unfortunately, the actual game outcome contradicted the analysis, since the two point attempt failed and Cornell lost the game 14–12. This analysis was extended by Means [1968] who concurs with Bierman's analysis and further shows that a decision by Cornell to tie the game might have been illogical.

In terms of winning the championship in National Football League play, Silverman and Schwartz [1973] show that the optimal strategy for winning the championship can include losing certain games. In specific, they cite the 1971 season, when the Washington Redskins were assured of a spot in the playoff series. Going into the weekend of their last game with Cleveland, they still had a chance for the championship of the Central Division. If they beat Cleveland, then they would have been assured of a game against a strong team in the first round of playoffs, while if they lost (which they did) they would play a relatively weak team in the first round of playoffs. In other words, by winning the Central Division title, Washington would have expected to face two hard games instead of one. From here, the analysis is carried on, using Markov Chains, to develop decision rules that a team should follow to determine whether to play for a win or a loss under various circumstances.

3.3 Individual Sport Strategy Evaluation

Ladany [1975], who is an Olympic athlete as well as an OR practitioner and teacher, presents a model to optimize the expected height that a jumper (pole vault or high jump) will achieve as a function of his initial jumping height. In these jumping events, the competition starts with one of the competitors attempting to clear the bar placed at a relatively low height. The bar is usually raised from this height in constant steps. Each competitor is allowed three tries to clear each height. Only after clearing a given height is the competitor allowed to jump the next height to which the bar is raised. The score achieved by a competitor is the last height cleared regardless of failures on prior trials.

A competitor is entitled to start at any height higher than the initial height. Although failure to clear this selected height will result in a score of zero, the advantage is that the athlete is fresh, hence the risk of a zero score is balanced by the better chances for clearing all successive heights.

The model developed expresses the expected height of the jump the jumper will clear as a function of the initial jump height that the athlete attempts to clear. Based on the model, the optimal starting height can then be determined. In addition, the acquisition of data for the model is discussed in some detail.

Lilien [1974] attacks the problem faced by an individual weight lifter in competition. The decision problem in weight lifting arises in that a competitor has a maximum of three lift attempts; his "score" is the weight he lifts on his best lift. He cannot, however, go down in his selected weight once a weight is selected for a lift, the weight he chooses on his next lift must be at least as high. A lifter who attempts to lift too little may have almost no chance of winning the competition; the lifter who attempts too much has a significant chance of scoring zero. The problem is viewed as a sequential decision process, and diagrammed as a decision tree. Based on this representation, a NLP model is formulated whose objective function is to maximize expected "utility" subject to the competitive restrictions. The model is made specific for several methods of defining utility.

Pollock [1974] presents a probabilistic model of the game of golf. The model is developed under the following assumptions.

(a) A player is completely characterized by a probability distribution over the number of strokes he will take on each of 18 holes of a golf course.
(b) This distribution is stationary.
(c) Hole-to-hole scores are independent.
(d) A player's individual hole scores are independent of the other player's score.

The model developed can then answer questions such as:

(a) What are the odds of player A beating player B at medal play, or match play?

(b) What are the odds of A and B tying at medal or match play?
(c) What are the odds of A and B tying at match play?

These questions can be answered for any A with handicap H_A playing against B with handicap H_B. Conversely, knowing the player's probability distribution of game scores, the expected handicap can be calculated.

Scheid [1972] presents an approach to determine golf handicaps, based on simulating more than a million matches from data obtained from actual score cards turned in at a country club. The data were fitted by regression, using a series of cubic curves that express the percent of games won by the strongest player as a function of the handicap difference and the number of strokes actually given to the weaker player by the stronger player. The results suggest that the current United States Golf Association handicapping system leaves the stronger player with an extortionate advantage over the weaker in two-man competition.

Hsi and Burych [1971] developed a model to determine the probability of winning games involving two opposing players. The focus of the model is to evaluate the effect of serving rules on the probability of winning the match for a given player. Examples are given for badminton and tennis, which do give strategic insights and which suggest various rule changes to "better" the game. In a later paper, George [1973] developed probability models to evaluate the probability of winning in tennis as a function of serving strategies. In particular, he shows how it is not always optimal to use a different first and second serve in tennis. The analysis is illustrated with data obtained from a professional tournament.

3.4   Athletic Training and Management

Huska [1974] presents certain approaches relevant to the management of a major league soccer team. One of the specific concerns addressed is the composition of the total team. This is a critical problem in that a soccer team in international competition can have at most 20 players on its home roster and can play no more than 14 members in any one game. Consequently, the issue of "optimal redundancy" is examined in some detail. In addition, issues of concern analyzed are the optimal age structure of the team, its hierarchic pyramid in terms of lower division (or farm) teams, and its regeneration halftime; i.e., the turnover cycle in player personnel.

One model which seems to have rather wide potential for application in developing athletic training programs was developed by Ladany [1975]. The particular application discussed was the development of an optimal weekly training program for a pentathlon athlete. The variables of the model (x_i) represented the number of hours per week the athlete should devote to training activity i. The training activities belonged to two categories: category one included those activities contributing to general conditioning ($i = 1, 5$), and category two included the technical training activities ($i = 6, 10$). The first step in formulating the model was to explicitly define the causal relationships between performance in an event (the pentathlon consists of five events) and the time devoted to each of the training activities. The form of the relationships was hypothesized to be

$$Y_j = a_{oj} + \sum_{i=1}^{10} a_{ij} x_i,$$

where Y_j represented the outcome of event j in appropriate units (e.g. seconds for running events, meters for field events). The coefficients were estimated using stepwise linear regression on accumulated data and, for all five events, the lowest coefficient of correlation reportedly found was 0.98. The next step in the model development was to express the pentathlon score as a linear function of the event performance. This was accomplished only after the contribution to the total score from the long jump was approximated by a piece-wise linear function. This linear expression was then maximized, subject to the following constraints:

a) The total time per week that an athlete has available to devote to training.
b) The total time per week devoted to strength training should not exceed a specified maximum.
c) The amount of weekly speed training should be at least as much as the amount of endurance training.
d) The amount of conditioning training should be more than the amount of technical training.
e) The minimal and maximal weekly hours of technical training should be between 50% and 200% of the average time devoted to these presently.
f) The upper and lower limits to the time devoted to muscular strength building, aerobic development of the body, and anaerobic development of the body for increasing endurance should be those required to prevent over-stress and ill effects of overtraining.

The above constraints were expressed as linear functions, and the x_i in the model were obtained using LP. The computations yielded acceptable solutions, which had to be applied with care and full understanding of the assumption used in building the model.

3.4 Conclusion to Section 3

It is indeed surprising that sports have not received more attention from OR practitioners and theoreticians than is evident in the published literature. In providing the implied taxonomy of OR applications in sports evident in the previous parts of this section, one can agree with Mottley [1954] and Lilien [1974] that sports are a natural applications area for OR.

The particular methodology whose absence is most conspicuous from the area of sports is Game Theory. Any sporting event, by its very nature, is a competitive game that should be amenable to analysis by the substantial body of knowledge which has been accumulated under this heading. Furthermore, experimental data in the area of sports is normally plentiful, and a real life laboratory can usually be found under the control of a sympathetic and interested high school or college athletic coach.

The ice has been cracked, so to speak, in relation to the use of optimization models for many applications. The team composition papers discussed appear to be promising models for evaluating team structure and the manning of playing positions. The use of optimization models for individual event strategy analysis in pole vaulting and weight lifting should open up applications in other sports, while the training program optimization model provides a new dimension to the scientific development of athletic potential. As a matter of fact, this model is simply an adaptation of the classical LP blending model—an adaptation which clearly illustrates the wide diversity of problems that are amenable to analysis by OR methodologies, and the potential benefits awaiting those willing to consider a departure from the conventional approaches in which the management of athletic activities is viewed strictly as an artistic exercise by athletes and coaches.

4. CLOSING

In this chapter no attempt has been made to provide a description of every OR application in every aspect of the leisure industry. Instead, two principal areas within the leisure industry were identified as having received some definite thrusts from OR, and within these areas some of the applications of particular interest have been mentioned. Within the periphery of the areas addressed in this chapter applications dealing with the design of spectator facilities can be found (Kottas [1975]), as well as those dealing with various aspects of the hospitality industry (Ladany [1974], Croft [1974]). In addition, studies have been made for analyzing the wage structure of baseball (Scully [1974]), and other issues of economic significance to sport leagues (El Hodiri and Quirk [1971]). A list of references has been provided which should serve as a partial guide to the literature for those individuals wishing to seek additional or more detailed information.

REFERENCES

Archer, B. H., "The Primary and Secondary Beneficiaries of Tourist Spending," *Tourist Rev.* 27, No. 2: 42–45 (1972).
———, "The Uses and Abuses of Multipliers," A paper presented to the Fourth Annual Travel Research Conference held in Sun Valley, Idaho (August 12–15, 1973).

——, and Owen, C. B., "Towards a Tourist Regional Multiplier," *Regional Stud.* **5**, 224–294 (1971).

Armstrong, C. W. G., "International Tourism: Coming or Going," *Futures*, pp. 115–125 (June 1972).

Artus, R., "An Econometric Analysis of International Travel," *Staff Papers—International Monetary Fund*, **XIX**, No. 3: 579–614 (November 1972).

Auger, J., *Analyse Factorielle et Evaluation d'Attraction de Sites Recreatifs*, Rapport Technique No. 2, Gouvernement du Quebec, Ministere du Tourisme, de la Chasse et de la Peche, Service de la Recherche, Quebec, Canada (January 1974).

Bargur, J. and A. Arbel, "A Comprehensive Approach to the Planning of the Tourist Industry," Paper presented at the ORSA/TIMS Joint National Meeting, San Juan, Puerto Rico (October 16–18, 1974).

Baron, M. and N. Shechter, "Simultaneous Determination of Visits to a System of Outdoor Recreation Parks With Capacity Limitations," *Regional and Urban Econ.* **3**, No. 4: 327–359 (1973).

Baron R. R., "Seasonality in Tourism—Part 1," *Int. Tourism Quart.*, Special Article No. 6 (1972).

——, "Seasonality in Tourism—Part 2," *Int. Tourism Quart.*, Special Article No. 6 (1973).

Bierman, H., Jr., "Letter to the Editor," *Management Sci.* **14**, No. 6: B281–B282 (1968).

Beaman, J., "Distance and the 'Reaction' to Distance as a Function of Distance," *J. Leisure Res.* **6**, 220–231 (Summer 1974).

——, "Three Methods for Measuring the Attractiveness of a Park—a Comparison," CORD Technical Note, No. 9, Parks Canada, Ottawa, Canada (May 1974).

Bowman, E. H., "Consistency and Optimality in Managerial Decision Making," *Management Sci.* (January 1963).

Burd, O. R. and D. Brewer, "Estimation of Net Social Benefits from Outdoor Recreation," *Econometrica*, **9**, No. 5: 813–827.

Burton, L. and P. A. Noad, *Recreation Research Methods*, Occasional Paper No. 3, Centre for Urban and Regional Studies, University of Birmingham, Birmingham, England (1968).

Canadian Government Travel Bureau, *Canada-Bibliography Tourism Research Studies*, Ottawa, Canada (March 1972).

Carter, W. and R. E. Machol, "Operations Research in Football," *Operations Res.* **19**, No. 2: 541–544 (1971).

Cesario, J., *Final Report on Estimating Park Attractiveness, Population Centre Emissiveness and the Effect of Distance (Location) in Outdoor Recreation Travel*, Cord Technical Note No. 4 (Mimeo), Department of Indian and Northern Affairs, Ottawa, Canada (1973).

——, "Operation Research in Outdoor Recreation," *J. Leisure Res.* **1**, No. 1: 33–51 (Winter 1969).

——, S. E. Goldstone, and J. L. Knetsch, *A Report on Outdoor Recreation Demands and Values to Middle Atlantic Utility Group*, Battelle Memorial Institute, Columbus, Ohio (1969).

Chamber, J. C., S. K. Mullick, and D. D. Smith, "How to Choose the Right Forecasting Technique," *Harvard Bus. Rev.* pp. 57–86 (July-August 1971).

Cheung, H. K., "A Day-Use Park Visitation Model," *J. Leisure Res.* **4**, 139–142 (Spring 1972).

Chubb, M., *Outdoor Recreation Planning in Michigan by a Systems Analysis Approach, Part III—The Practical Application of Program RECSYS and SYMAP*, Technical Report No. 11, Department of Resource Development, Michigan State University, East Lansing, Michigan (1968).

Churchman, C. W. and R. L. Ackoff, "An Approximate Measure of Value," *Operations Res.* **2**, No. 2: 172-187 (1954).

Cicchetti, C. J., C. Fisher, and V. Smith, "Economic Models and Planning Outdoor Recreation," *Operations Res.* **21**, No. 5: 1104-1113 (September-October 1973).

Clarke, R. and A. Trengove, "Are we Creating Super Athletes–Or Monsters?," *Readers Digest*, pp. 141-145 (October 1975).

Clawson, M., "Measuring Outcomes in Terms of Economic Implications for Society" in *Recreation Research*, American Association for Health, Physical Education, and Recreation (1966).

———, and J. L. Knetsch, *Economics of Outdoor Recreation*, The Johns Hopkins Press, Baltimore, Maryland, 1966.

Cline, R. S., "Measuring Travel Volumes and Itineraries and Forecasting Future Travel Growth to Individual Pacific Destinations," Paper presented at the ORSA/TIMS Joint National Meeting, San Juan, Puerto Rico (October 16-18, 1974).

Cohen, E., "Toward a Sociology of International Tourism" *Social Res.* pp. 164-181 (Spring 1972).

Cook, E., *Percentage Baseball*, M.I.T. Press, Cambridge, Massachusetts (1967).

Cotton, W. R., "Intervening Opportunities: Barriers or Stepping Stones?" *Pacific Soc. Rev.* **8**, 75-81 (1965).

Crackwell, B., "Accessibility to the Countryside as a Factor in Planning for Leisure," *Regional Stud.* **1**, 50 (1967).

Crampon, L. J. and K. T., Tan "A Model of Tourism Flow into the Pacific" *Tourist Rev.* pp. 98-104 (July-Sept 1973).

———, "Factors Influencing Travel Flow into and Within the Pacific Basin," Paper presented at the ORSA/TIMS Joint National Meeting, San Juan, Puerto Rico (October 16-18, 1974).

Crevo, C. C., "Characteristics of Summer Week-End Travel," *Highway Res. Record* **44**, 51-60 (1963).

Croft, D. J., "An Application of Two-Phase Discriminant Analysis to Employee Selection," Paper presented at the ORSA/TIMS Joint National Meeting, San Juan, Puerto Rico (October 16-18, 1974).

Davis, D. H., "Potentials for Tourism in Developing Countries," *Finan. and Dev.* **5**, No. 4: 35-39 (December 1968).

Deasy, G. F. and P. R. Gress, "Impact of Tourist Facility on its Hinterland" *Ann. Assoc. Am. Geographers* **56**, No. 2: 250-306 (1966).

Demers, J., "Tourist Flows," Paper presented at the ORSA/TIMS Joint National Meeting, San Juan, Puerto Rico (October 16-18, 1974).

Dubos, R., "The Human Environment," *Ekistics* **178**, 170-3 (1969).

Egan, M., "Interfaces Between Tourism and Outdoor Recreation," Paper presented at the Western Economic Association Annual Conference, San Diego, California (June 25-28, 1975).

El Hodiri, M. and J. Quirk, "An Economic Model of a Professional Sports League, " *J. Pol. Economics*, No. 79: pp. 1302-1319 (November-December 1971).

Ellis, J. B., "Analysis of Socio-Economic Systems by Physical Systems Techniques," unpublished Ph.D. dissertation, Department of Electrical Engineering, Michigan State University, East Lansing, Michigan (1965).

———, and M. D. Milstein, *Michigan Outdoor Recreation Study, Vol. 1, Methods and Models* Technical Report No. 6. Michigan Department of Conservation, Lansing, Michigan (1966).

———, Systems Analysis of Provincial Park Camping–1966 Park User Survey, Parks Branch, Ontario Department of Lands and Forest, Toronto, Ontario, Canada (1968).

——, *A System Model for Recreational Travel in Ontario–Further Results*. Ontario Department of Highways, RR 148, Toronto, Ontario, Canada (July 1969).

Forster, J., "The Sociological Consequences of Tourism," *Int. J. Comparative Sociology* **5**, No. 2: 217–227 (1964).

Freeze, R. A., "An Analysis of Baseball Batting Order by Monte Carlo Simulations," *Operations Res.* **22**, No. 4: 728–735 (1974).

Gaumnitz, J. E., R. L. Swinth, and J. O. Tollefson, "Simulation of Water Recreation User's Decisions," Paper presented at the Tims XX International Meeting, Tel Aviv, Israel (June 26, 1973); to appear in *Land Econ.*

Gearing, C. E., W. W. Swart, and T. Var, "A Decision Structure for Touristic Investment Allocations," *Tourist Rev.* **27**, No. 1: 2–13 (1972).

——, "Determining the Optimal Investment Policy for the Tourism Sector of a Developing Country," *Management Sci.* **20**, No. 4: 487–497 (December 1973) Part I.

——, "Establishing a Measure of Touristic Attractiveness," *J. Travel Res.* **XII**, No. 4: 1–8 (Spring 1974).

——, "A Multi-Period Planning Model for Tourism Development," Paper presented at the TIMS XXII International Meeting, Kyoto, Japan (July 26, 1975).

——, *Planning for Tourism Development: Quantitative Approaches*, Praeger Publishers, New York, New York (1976).

George, S. L., "Optimal Strategy in Tennis–A Simple Probabilistic Model," *Appl. Stat.* **22**, 97–104 (1973).

Goeldner, C. R., C. E. Gearing, W. W. Swart, and T. Var, "Bibliographic Sources for Travel and Tourism Research," *Tourist Rev.* **29**, No. 3: 197, Geneva (1974).

——, "General Information Regarding Organizations Engaged in Tourism and Travel Research Activities" in *Planning for Tourism Development: Quantitative Approaches*, by C. E. Gearing, W. W. Swart and Turgut Var, Praeger Publishers, New York (1976).

Grubb, H. and J. Goodwin, *Economic Evaluation of Water Oriented Recreation in the Preliminary Texas Water Plan*, Report No. 84., Texas Water Development Board, Austin, Texas (1968).

Harmston, F. K., "Differences in Secondary Impact of Through and Recreational Travelers on a Small Western Community." A paper presented to the Western Economic Association, Annual Meeting San Diego, California (June 1975).

Hecock, H. H., "Public Beach Recreational Opportunities and Patterns of Consumption on Cape Cod," Unpublished Ph.D. Dissertation, Department of Geography, Clark University (1966).

Hill, M. and M. Schechter, "Optimal Goal Achievement in the Development of Outdoor Recreation Facilities," in *Urban and Regional Planning*, edited by A. G. Wilson, Pion Ltd., London pp. 110–112 (1971).

Holman, M. A., "A National Time–Budget for Year 2000" *Sciology and Social Res.* **42**, No. 1 (October 1961).

Hsi, B. P. and D. M. Burych, "Games of Two Players," *Appl. Stat.* **20**, 86–92 (1971).

Huska, A. M., "An Experimental Model for the Management of a Major League Soccer Team," Paper presented at the ORSA/TIMS Joint National Meeting, Boston, Mass. (April 22–24, 1974).

Johansson, J. K., A. A. Sunday, and J. L. Simon, "International Advertising and Tourism," Paper presented at the ORSA/TIMS Joint National Meeting, San Juan, Puerto Rico (October 16–18, 1974).

Jud, G. and W. Drause, "Evaluating Tourism in Developing Areas: An Exploratory Inquiry," A paper presented to the Western Economic Association, Annual Meeting, San Diego, California (June 1975).

Kahn, T. D., "Employment in the Texas Tourist Industry." A paper presented to the Western Economic Association, Annual Meeting, San Diego, California (June 1975).

Kain, J. F. and J. R. Meyer, "Computer Simulations, Physio-Economic Systems and Interregional Models," *The American Economic Review, (Papers and Proceedings of the 80th Annual Meeting in Washington, D. C. on December 28-30, 1967)* LVIII, No. 2: 171-181 (May 1968).

Kottas, J. F., "Spectator Seating Preferences as a Determinant in Design and Pricing Decisions," DMG-DRS Journal: Design and Methods (1975).

Ladany, S. P., "Optimal Motel Room Rental Policy," Paper presented at the ORSA/TIMS Joint National Meeting, San Juan, Puerto Rico (October 16-18, 1974).

——, "Optimal Starting Height for Pole Vaulting," *Operations Res.* 23, No. 5: 968-978 (1975).

——, "Optimization of Pentathlon Training Plans," *Management Sci.* 21, No. 10: 1144-1155 (1975).

——, (Editor), *Management Science Applications to Leisure-Time Operations*, North Holland Publishing Co. (1975).

Lentnek, B. et al., "Spatial Behavior in Recreational Boating," *J. Leisure Res.* 1, 103-124 (Spring 1969).

Leopold, L. B., "Esthetics of Landscape," *Natural History Magazine* 78, No. 4: 37-44 (October 1969).

Lilien, G. L., "Optimal Lift Selection: The Weightlifter's Dilemma," Paper presented at the Joint National ORSA/TIMS Meeting, Boston, Masachusetts (April 22-24, 1974).

Lindsey, G. R., "Statistical Data Useful for the Operation of a Baseball Team," *Operations Res.* 7, (1959).

——, "An Investigation of Strategies in Baseball," *Operations Res.* 16, No. 5: 1088-1089 (1963).

——, "Book Review: Percentage Baseball by E. Crook," *Operations Res.* 16, No. 5: 1088-1089 (1968).

Arthur D. Little, Inc., *Tourism and Recreation: A State-of-the Art Study.* U.S. Department of Commerce, Washington, D.C. (1967).

Lucas, R., "Wilderness Perception and Use," *Natural Resources J.* 3, No. 3: 393-411 (January 1964).

Lundberg, D. E., "The Tourist Business," *Institutions/Volume Feeding Magazine*, p. 11 (1972).

Mack, R. P. and S. Myers, "Outdoor Recreation" from *Measuring Benefits From Government Investments*, R. Dorfman (Editor), Brookings Institute, Washington, D.C. (1965).

Machol, R. E., "An Application of the Assignment Problem," *Operations Res.* 18, No. 4: 569-760 (1970).

Maki, D. R. and R. A. D. Beck, "Recreational Programming: A British Columbia Example Working Paper," Department of Economics and Commerce, Simon Fraser University, Burnaby, B.C. No. 75-5-2., p. 1 (1975).

McMahon, J. J., "Tourism Planning and Project Evaluation–The Puerto Rican Case," Paper presented at the ORSA/TIMS Joint National Meeting, San Juan, Puerto Rico (October 16-18 1974).

Means, E. H., "More on Football Strategy," *Management Sci.* 15, No. 2: B-15, B-16 (1968).

Mercer, D., "Discretionary Travel Behavior and the Urban Mental Map," *Australian Geographic Studies* (October 1, 1971).

——, "Urban Recreational Hinterlands," *The Professional Geographer* 22, 77 (March 1970).

Ministere du Tourisme, de la Chasse et de la Peche, Service de la Recherche, Government du Quebec, *Le Flux Touristiques: Project de Recherche et de Development de Mesure de d' Analyse, Part I* (Prepared by Urbatique, Inc. Quebec, Canado, 1973).

Mittchell, L. S., "The Facility Index as a Measure of Attendance at Recreational Sites," *The Professional Geographer* **20**, No. 4: 276–278 (1968).

Mottley, C. M. "The Application of Operations Research Methods to Athletic Games," *Operations Res*. **2**, No. 3: 335–338 (1954).

Nagashima, K., "The Human Environment: Evolution of Social and Leisure Space with Reference to Japan," *Ekistics* **168**, 1461–1468 (1970).

Nijkamp, P., "Environmental Attraction Factors and Regional Tourist Effects," Research Memorandum No. 14, Free University, Amsterdam, The Netherlands (1975).

O.E.C.D. (Organization for Economic Cooperation and Development), *Government Policy in the Development of Tourism*, Paris (1974).

O'Riordan, T., "Planning to Improve Environmental Capacity: A Case Study In Broadland," *Town Plan. Rev*. **40**, No. 1: 39–58 (1969).

Patterson, J. H. and R. A. Wolfe, "An Application of the Assignment Algorithm to Football Player/Position Selection," Paper presented at the 41st National ORSA Meeting, New Orleans, Louisiana (April 1972).

Pollock, S. M., "A Model for the Evaluation of Golf Handicapping," Paper presented at the ORSA/TIMS Joint National Meeting, Boston, Massachusetts (April 1974).

Powers, T. A., "Appraising International Tourism Projects," Papers on Project Analysis No. 1, Inter-American Development Bank, Washington, D.C. (July 1974).

Quandt, R. E. (editor), *The Demand for Travel: Theory and Measurement*. D. C. Heath Company, Lexington, Massachusetts (1970).

Renoux, M., *Rapport Methodologique No. 1 Technique Econometriques de la Demand touristiques et Amorce de leurs Intefractions dans un Systeme Decisionnel*, Government du Quebec Ministere du Tourisme, de la chasse et de la Peche, Service de la Recherche, Quebec, Canada (1972).

——, *Rapport Methodologique No. 3, Vol. 1 Les Modeles de Simulation Appliques au Tourisme et aux Laisirs de Plein Air et leur Integration dans un System Decisionnel*, Government du Quebec, Ministere du Tourisme, de la Chasse et de la Peche, Service de la Recherche, Quebec, Canada (1973).

Ross, J. H., "A Measure of Site Attraction," Occasional Paper No. 2, Environment Canada, Ottawa, Canada (1973).

Saitta, W. W. and I. W. Schedeman, "New Dimensions in Park Management through Linear Programming," *J. Leisure Res*. **4**, No. 4: 333–340 (1972).

Scheid, F., "A Least Squares Family of Cubic Curves with an Application to Golf Handicapping," *SIMA J. Appl. Math*. **22**, No. 1: 77–83 (1972).

Scully, G. W., "Pay and Performance in Major League Baseball," *Am. Econ. Rev*. **LXIV**, No. 6: 915–930 (1974).

Shafer, E. L. R. C. Thompson, "Models that Describe Use of Adirondack Campgrounds," *Forest Service* **14**, 383–391 (December 1968).

Shelley, M., "Competition for Satisfaction Resources between Tourist and the Inhabitant," a paper submitted in the XXth TIMS International Meeting in Tel Aviv (June 25, 1973).

Silverman, D. and B., Schwartz, "How to Win by Losing," *Operations Res*. **21**, No. 2: 639–643 (1973).

Smith, S. L., *An Exegesis of Outdoor Recreation Research*, Special Report, College of Agriculture Texas Agricultural Experiment Station, Texas A.M. University: Department of Recreation and Parks, College Station, Texas (1971).

State of Florida, Department of Natural Resources, Outdoor Recreation in Florida, Tallahassee, Florida, pp. 7 (August 1971).

Stouffer, S. A., "Intervening Opportunities and Competing Migrants," *J. Regional Sci*. **2**, 1–26 (1960).

Swart, W. W., C. E. Gearing, and T. Var, "A Dynamic Programming—Integer Programming Algorithm for Allocating Touristic Investments," *Tourist Rev.* **27**, No. 2: 52–61 (1972).

——, and G. Cann, "Investment Planning For the Development of a National Resource– Linear Programming Based Approaches," *Computers and Operations Res.* **1**, 247–262 (1974).

Taylor, G., "The Canadian Travel Industry Management Improvement Program," Paper presented at the TIMS XX International Meetings Tel-Aviv, Israel (June 26, 1973).

Thompson, M., "On Any Given Sunday: Fair Competitor Orderings with Maximum Likelihood Methods," *J. Amer. Stat. Assoc.* **70**, No. 351: 536–541 (1975).

Tiedman, C. E. and D. Minstein, "Travel Models," Chapter 4 in Volume 1, "Methods and Models," *Michigan Outdoor Recreation Demand Study* (State Resource Planning Program, Michigan Department of Commerce, Lansing, Michigan (1966).

Ullman, E. L., and D. J. Volk, "An Operational Model for Predicting Reservoir Attendance and Benefits," *Papers of the Michigan Academy of Science, Arts and Letters* **47**, 473–484 (1962).

van der Smissen, B., "Effects of Recreation on Individuals and Society," a chapter in *Recreational Research*, National Education Association, Washington, D.C. (1966).

——, and D. Joyce (editors), *Bibliography of Theses and Dissertations in Recreation Parks, Camping and Outdoor Education.* National Recreation and Park Association, Arlington, Virginia (1970).

Van Doren, C. S., *An Interaction Travel Model for Projecting Attendance of Campers at Michigan State Parks: A Study in Recreational Geography.* Unpublished Ph.D. Dissertation, Department of Geography, Michigan State University (1967).

——, and B. Lentnek, "Activity Specialization Among Ohio's Recreation Boaters," *J. Leisure Res.* **1**, 296–315 (Autumn 1969).

Var, T., C. E. Gearing, and W. W. Swart, "O/R and MS in Travel and Tourism," A paper presented at the ORSA/TIMS Joint National Meeting, San Juan, Puerto Rico (October 16–18, 1974).

——, "Outdoor Recreation and Travel Research: Present and Future," Presented at the Travel Research Workshop at the Annual Travel Research Association Conference, San Diego, California (September 10, 1975).

Wagner, H., *Principles of Operations Research*, Prentice Hall, Englewood Cliffs, New Jersey (1969).

Webster's New Twentieth Century Dictionary, 2d Edition, The World Publishing Company, Cleveland, Ohio (1966).

Wennergren, E. G. and D. B. Nielsen, *A Probabilistic Approach to Estimating Demand for Outdoor Recreation*, Bulletin 478, Utah State University, Logan, Utah (December 1968).

Wilkinson, P. F., "The Use Models in Predicting the Consumption of Outdoor Recreation," *J. Leisure Res.* **5**, No. 3 (Summer 1973).

Williams, A. and W. Zelinsky, "On Some Patterns in International Tourist Flows," *Econ. Geography* **46**, No. 4; 549–567 (1970).

Wolfe, R. I., Communications in *J. Leisure Res.* **2**, 85–87 (Winter 1970).

——, "Inertia Model," *J. Leisure Res.* **4**, 73–76 (Winter 1974).

——, "Perspective on Outdoor Recreation–A Bibliographical Survey," *Geographical Rev.* **LIV**, No. 2: 203–235 (April 1964).

——, "Vacation Homes and the Gravity Model," *Ekistics* **174**, 352–363 (1970) and "Communication," *J. Leisure Res.* **2**, No. 1: 85–87 (1970).

AUTHOR INDEX

SUBJECT INDEX